Land Evaluation

Land Evaluation

Papers of a CSIRO Symposium
Organized in Cooperation with UNESCO
26-31 August 1968

Edited by
G. A. Stewart
Division of Land Research CSIRO
Canberra Australia

Macmillan of Australia
1968

THE MACMILLAN COMPANY OF AUSTRALIA PTY LTD
107 Moray Street, South Melbourne, Victoria. 3205

MACMILLAN AND COMPANY LIMITED
Little Essex Street, London WC2
also Bombay, Calcutta, Madras

THE MACMILLAN COMPANY OF CANADA LIMITED
Bond Street, Toronto

MACMILLAN SOUTH AFRICA (PUBLISHERS) PTY LTD
Jorrison Street, Johannesburg

ST. MARTIN'S PRESS INC
Fifth Avenue, New York 10010

Australian National Library
Registry Number AUS 68 — 116

Printed by J. C. Stephens Pty Ltd
Gardenvale, Victoria. 3185
Typesetting by Trade Composition Pty Ltd
68-70 York Street, South Melbourne, 3205

Registered with the G.P.O. for transmission
through the post as a book

Contents

Foreword

G. A. Stewart

Division of Land Research, CSIRO, Canberra, Australia

Land evaluation (terrain evaluation) is the assessment of the suitability of land for man's use in agriculture, forestry, engineering, hydrology, regional planning, recreation, etc.

It was recognized that, while land evaluation in these fields has largely proceeded independently, there was sufficient common ground in their principles and problems to justify bringing together scientists from the many fields of land evaluation. Further recent developments in the basic sciences (e.g., meteorological physics, plant physiology) and technology (e.g., remote sensors, computers) offer prospects for the further development of land evaluation. The Symposium on Land Evaluation in Canberra, 26–31 August 1968, was arranged to meet these needs. This book, published before the Symposium, contains all the papers to be presented at the Symposium.

The objective of the Symposium was to explore the potential of recent advances in science and technology for land evaluation by:

reviewing the present 'state of the art',

examining basic concepts and principles in land evaluation,

assessing the potential use of automatic data processing and interpretation,

discussing some of the land parameters that are pertinent to various forms of land use, and

assessing how new developments in sensing may contribute to the quantification of land parameters.

Seven papers, mostly reviews, were commissioned, and voluntary contributions were sought to complete the programme. Some fifty voluntary contributions were offered but, to ensure that each paper was adequately discussed, only twenty-five were accepted. The organizing committee had the onerous task of selecting those papers most appropriate to the Symposium objective and avoiding repetition.

The Symposium was arranged in collaboration with the Natural Resources Division of UNESCO. It complements the UNESCO Conference held at Toulouse in 1964 on *Aerial Surveys and Integrated Studies* (UNESCO Natural Resources Research Series No. 6, 1968).

I wish to thank Mr C. S. Christian, Member of the Executive of the CSIRO and formerly Chief of the Division of Land Research for his encouragement and support in arranging the Symposium. Thanks are also due to the members of the organizing committee for their cooperation in the definition of the programme and selection of abstracts. Finally, many of my colleagues in the Division of Land Research, in particular Dr T. G. Chapman and Miss M. Mills, have given invaluable assistance in editorial duties, manuscript preparation, and proof reading, and to them I extend my sincere appreciation.

ACKNOWLEDGMENTS

The Symposium Committee acknowledges with appreciation the financial support given by the following institutions and firms.
United Nations Educational, Scientific and Cultural Organization.
Conzinc Riotinto of Australia Ltd.
Wild (Australia) Pty. Ltd.

Symposium Committee

Mr G. A. Stewart — (Chairman)
Mr J. R. M. Wolfe
Mr J. R. McAlpine (Secretaries)
Dr G. D. Aitchison
Mr B. E. Butler
Dr T. G. Chapman
Mr R. G. Downes

Mr. A. I. McCutchan
Professor J. A. Mabbutt
Mr. H. A. Nix
Mr. T. Pearcey
Professor C. C. Renwick
Mr. B. P. Ruxton
Dr. R. O. Slatyer

Mr. J. G. Speight

Erratum

Speight J. G.   P. 241   L.6 from bottom

For   that a land surface with a constant rate-of-change of slope appears as a succession

Read   that a land surface with a constant rate-of-change of slope logarithm appears as a succession

P. 243   L.22 from top
For $L = \pm 0 \cdot 036$ m^{-1} ($\pm 0 \cdot 011$ ft^{-1}).
Read $L = (\pm 0 \cdot 0117G)$ m^{-1} [$(\pm 0 \cdot 0035G)$ft^{-1}], where G is the slope expressed as a tangent.

P.243   L.30 from top
For   1 Notably concave; $L \geqslant 0 \cdot 036$ m^{-1}
Read   1 Notably concave; $L \geqslant 0 \cdot 0117G$ m^{-1}

P. 243   L.31 from top
For   2 Slightly concave to straight; $0 \leqslant L < 0 \cdot 036$ m^{-1}
Read   2 Slightly concave to straight; $0 \leqslant L < 0 \cdot 0117G$ m^{-1}

P. 243   L.32 from top
For   3 Straight to slightly convex; $0 \geqslant L > (-0 \cdot 036)$ m^{-1}
Read   3 Straight to slightly convex; $0 \geqslant L > (-0 \cdot 0117G)$ m^{-1}

P. 243   L.33 from top
For   4 Notably convex; $L \leqslant (-0 \cdot 036)$ m^{-1}
Read   4 Notably convex; $L \leqslant (-0 \cdot 0117G)$ m^{-1}

Land Evaluation

G. A. Stewart

Division of Land Research,
CSIRO, Canberra, Australia

The objective of this paper is to provide continuity to the Symposium programme by reviewing the papers and bringing out the links between the various contributions and between the various parts of the programme.

INTRODUCTION

The term land is used in a comprehensive, integrating sense (see Christian and Stewart 1968) to refer to a wide array of natural resource attributes in a profile from the atmosphere above the surface down to some metres below the land surface. The main natural resource attributes are climate, land form, soil, vegetation, fauna, and water. The term terrain as used by engineers is synonymous with land, and both terms are used in this book.

Some general features of natural resources (Christian and Stewart 1968) are worthy of note. The natural resource attributes are fixed in their location and extent, and in general must be exploited by man at their location, except for water which is naturally mobile and may be transported long distances to meet man's needs. Thus the possible use of water resources calls for different evaluation methods from the other resources. As well as spatial distribution, some natural resource attributes have temporal distribution also, e.g. climate, water, and some aspects of vegetation. Some resources are directly usable (e.g. water for domestic use, natural road-building materials, forests) but others must be combined with other natural resources to produce man's needs (e.g. water and soil in irrigation agriculture). The biological resources, vegetation and fauna, can be self-regenerating under proper management whereas physical resources such as soil and minerals are consumable. These characteristics of the various natural resource attributes influence man's use of land.

Land evaluation is the assessment of man's possible use of land for agriculture, forestry, engineering, recreation, etc. Almost invariably a particular possible use of land by man is dependent, not on a single parameter of a natural resource attribute, but on the interaction of a number of parameters of various attributes, Man's use of land is also very strongly dependent on the human resources: technology, finance, labour. These are not fixed in space, and are time-variable in a manner that is not predictable with great accuracy. Thus land evaluation is not something that can be done once for all time, but must be repeated when significant changes take place in any of the human resources.

In the past, land evaluation was often qualitative, but now the land-use planners require quantitative assessments of inputs and outputs that are amenable to economic appraisal. Economic appraisal is an essential part of land evaluation in order to compare possible alternative forms of land use in one area and/or assess the best use of limiting resources in different areas or forms of land use.

The objectives of the Symposium have been stated in the foreword, and the table of contents sets out the order of presentation of papers under the pro-

gramme headings. The programme was deliberately concentrated on the relationship between natural resource attributes and possible land use in order
that a reasonably comprehensive coverage would be possible in the limited
time of the Symposium.

Some papers make contributions to more than one part of the programme,
and in the following review I have referred to them in the various parts, in an
attempt to provide a link between the various contributions and also between
the various parts of the programme.

PRINCIPLES OF LAND CLASSIFICATION AND EVALUATION

Mabbutt[1] reviews the various approaches to land classification. The genetic
approach leads to large-scale and complex units unsuited to land evaluation.

It has long been realized that, as a result of the processes by which our present
landscapes have formed, areas of land occur that are relatively uniform in a
large proportion of their parameters. Also, it has been recognized that many
landscapes have a recurring pattern of a limited number of distinctive types of
land. These realizations have led land scientists in many countries to develop
similar concepts in land classification by the landscape approach. The relationship of land classification by the landscape approach to various uses is discussed
by Aitcheson and Grant, Dowling, Condon, Robertson et al., Ignatyev,
Renwick, and Bakhtina and Smirnova.

Mabbutt points out that some workers, through dissatisfaction with the
qualitative and subjective results of the landscape approach, have developed the
parametric approach in which attention is concentrated on the quantification
of those land attributes that are considered significant to the particular land use.
This approach lends itself to automated sensing and computation. Examples of
this approach are Benn and Grabau in military engineering for airfield construction effort and cross-country vehicle locomotion, Parry et al. in mobility
studies for military vehicles, and Westby et al. in forest inventory.

In discussing terrain factor classification, Benn and Grabau aim to satisfy
the user need by selecting class intervals that would introduce an acceptably
small error in prediction, provided that the class intervals are not so narrow in
relation to natural variability of the factor that they are unmappable at a scale
appropriate to the form of land use. Accepting the user specification, they show
that appropriate class intervals can be mathematically computed by methods
similar to the Monte Carlo technique.

In his final summing up Mabbutt points out that the three approaches to
classification are not necessarily alternatives and, at the level required for land
evaluation, there would seem to be profitable scope for combinations of the
landscape and parametric approaches.

Mabbutt has referred to the factors that have influenced the development of
our present landscapes, and Ruxton discusses the growth in knowledge of the
processes of landscape evolution, i.e. land dynamics. He examines the application of open systems theory to aspects of land that approach a steady state
of dynamic equilibrium with their environment, and claims that it can contribute
to the understanding of land dynamics. However, owing to inheritance and
multi-complexity of processes, many aspects of land remain in dis-equilibrium
and their dynamics are being interpreted by using an approach similar to that
in geology. These developments in our understanding of land dynamics should

---

[1] Names without dates refer to authors of papers in this Symposium.

not only enable us to understand the relationships of the land that is being classified but should also enable the prediction of the result of man's imposed management on land attributes.

Mathematical and statistical aspects of sampling of land parameters are considered by Goodspeed and Beckett. Goodspeed, considering sampling at the very detailed end of the scale, develops mathematical theory to enable calculation of the sampling interval that will allow complete reconstruction of the variation of the parameter with distance along a transept under certain conditions. The sampling interval can also be computed from the range of values of the parameter and the maximum slope of a plot of the parameter values.

Beckett discusses, from the statistical point of view, mapping precision (variation of parameter values around the mean value for a mapped unit) and accuracy (nearness of the calculated mean to the true mean of parameter values within the mapped unit) in relation to maps produced by the landscape approach to land classification. He points out that, if greater precision of mapped units is required, mapping must be done at a lower level of classification, more samples must be taken, boundaries will be more tortuous, map scale will be increased, and costs per unit area will increase. He compares the accuracy and precision achieved by three types of field sampling and mapping—grid survey, free survey, and physiographic survey. From the limited available information he indicates how an assessment of cost-effectiveness of various methods of survey at various scales should be approached.

The principles involved in the evaluation of the response of land to man's management are discussed by Benn and Grabau for military engineering and by Nix for crop productivity.

In their approach to quantitative evaluation Benn and Grabau use mathematical performance prediction models relating terrain conditions to user needs. The complexity of the models is varied according to the user need. In the airfield construction effort model for use in military strategic planning, high accuracy for individual projects is not needed and the model is relatively simple and the input factors are empirical indices derived from relations between the terrain factors and the various construction activities. The cross-country vehicle locomotion model is a detailed model for tactical planners. It is based partly on classical mechanics and is partly empirical. Various factor maps are combined into terrain factor complex maps. The final step in evaluation is the use of each unique terrain factor complex as inputs to the mathematical model to produce performance predictions which are then substituted on the map for the direct information of the user. This type of approach is still essentially at the research stage. They stress that:

(a) the relationship between the activity and various terrain parameters must be established before the evaluation process can begin,

(b) terrain classification should be carried out only after the model and classification classes have been formulated.

(c) once user requirements have been clarified the terrain evaluator has no freedom of choice in the selection of terrain parameters or in the class limits of each parameter.

Nix describes three approaches to the prediction of crop yield in relation to land. In the mathematical modelling approaches he differentiates between *simulation models* in which the parameters that directly determine crop yield are identified and quantified, and the model should therefore be of universal application for the specific genotype, and *empirical models* based on site factors related to crop yield, which may only have good predictive value for the region in which they were developed. (Chapman, in discussing hydrologic models, refers to deterministic models based on known physical laws or empirical inferences with no randomly varying components, and statistical models expressed in terms of probabilistic or random components and with results expressed in statistical terms. They are similar but not completely equivalent to the two modelling approaches of Nix).

Research on simulation models for biological systems is still in its infancy, and its development is complex due to yield dependence on genotype-environment interactions. Empirical models based on site factors have been widely developed in forestry, but have been little used in agriculture. The approach of Condon to the determination of grazing capacity of arid lands is an example of an empirical site factor approach which, like Benn andGrabau's airfield construction effort model, has input of empirical indices. The third method described by Nix is the *analogue* method, in which input–output relationships from existing commercial or experimental crop production are extrapolated to like areas of land as defined by landscape approach land classification. This method will only have accurate prediction value where the land parameters that determine crop yield covary with parameters used in the definitions of the mapping units. Although simulation models appear to be the desirable long-term objective, much research and development is needed before they will be widely applied to land evaluation. However, as in land classification, the three methods are not incompatible. We can foresee the development and regional application of partial empirical and simulation models in association with analogue methods and a gradual evolution towards complete simulation models.

LAND EVALUATION REVIEWS AND CASE STUDIES

In this part of the programme we examine the present position of land evaluatio in a range of fields, embracing agriculture, engineering, and regional planning. It will be instructive to look at the various approaches to land classification, performance prediction and the potential users.

Robertson *et al.*, in reviewing the assessment of land quality for primary production, specify their user as a development organization, and not the individual farmer, and appear to be primarily concerned with irrigated agriculture. They see a need for three levels of information and assessment.

1. First-stage regional surveys where available information is not sufficient to indicate the possibilities for agriculture, e.g. land system surveys.

2. Second-stage surveys which should provide sufficient data to assess project feasibility, or project priorities where alternatives exist. Apparently landscape approach classification and/or empirical indices, together with analogue yield prediction are acceptable. Social, economic, and national factors must be taken into account in the decisions also.

3. Third-stage or detailed surveys for project plan formulation and cost-benefit assessment. The U.S. Bureau of Reclamation system, which was developed for irrigation assessment, is recommended. It is a parametric land classification. The system includes the estimation of economic inputs and outputs of crop production as well as cost of development of the project.

They emphasise the importance of water resources and climate and suggest that studies in these fields should be carried out first. They stress the need for continuous close contact with the user, and comprehensive documentation of data.

Ignatyev describes the approach to land evaluation for agriculture in the U.S.S.R. The classification of land is carried out by the landscape approach, mainly as integrated land systems, but in some areas as separate soil, vegetation, and physiographic surveys. Various applied maps are prepared by grouping of categories that show similar response to particular types of land use. Crop yields are assessed both by direct measurement and by recorded data from collective and state farms. The prediction of yields appears to be by analogue, but a number of indices are also referred to. Quantitative input–output data at various levels of management are made, and the monetary value of the land is assessed. The author would like, for uniformity, a single basis for assessing land for agriculture and forestry, and recommends one based on basic land properties that separate vegetation types, both natural and cultural.

Condon describes a method of estimating grazing capacity of arid land in Australia by selecting a standard land class of known grazing capacity, and setting up rating scales for the various factors which influence grazing capacity. It is based on landscape approach classification. Numerical rating scales have been developed for soils, topography, tree density (as an inhibitor of pasture growth), palatable trees and shrubs, pastures, condition (as influenced by erosion or growth of weeds), and annual rainfall. The ratings are multiplied together to give estimated grazing capacity in relation to the standard, i.e. the performance prediction is an empirical model. The author admits to the subjectivity of the method, and the possibility of further ratings being necessary. The simple numerical expression of its results allows it to be used by both administrators and individual property managers.

Aitcheson and Grant review the developments in defining terrain for engineering purposes, supplementing the general review by Mabbutt. They put forward an engineering terrain classification by the landscape approach that is virtually identical with the latest developments reviewed by Mabbutt, except for different terminology and that it will be operated entirely by engineers following the establishment of the classification. Turning to performance prediction, they state that 'the military engineer has been unable to define—in engineering terms—his real requirements, while similarly the road engineer has found it difficult to specify the information that he must have in quantitative form'. It is not surprising then that they remain uncommitted on performance prediction, and propose a system of feedback from engineering users and engineering observations in the hope of improving performance prediction.

Dowling has related engineering soil-test data and engineering experience, derived from a number of projects being undertaken as part of a major road development programme by the Northern Nigerian Ministry of Works, to the land systems and land facets that have been defined in the Bauchi and Bornu Provinces in Northern Nigeria. The land classification provides a satisfactory basis for classifying and storing information about engineering features of land. The user, in this case, is the road planning engineer, and examples are given of how the information can be used in planning the most effective effort for the design of new roads.

Parry et al. have studied the potential of large-scale air photographs (1:5000 for the assessment of environmental factors which affect the cross-country mobility of military vehicles. It is not a complete land evaluation system in the sense of Benn and Grabau but an investigation of vehicle-environment interaction that could contribute to the development of a mathematical model for the vehicles concerned. The four land parameters were mapped primarily by air-photo interpretation with a minimum of field work. Subsequent field studies were made to check the validity of the interpretation. The performance of three military vehicles on a range of the terrain types is reported, and the influence of various terrain factors on performance is discussed.

Renwick reports some uses of land evaluation in regional planning in the Hunter region of New South Wales. A land system study has provided a regional inventory of natural resources, and this has been supported by the study of other aspects of land, water resources, and economic structure. An example of the output is the Water Plan, resulting from an integrated study of 34 catchments, recommending two water conservation projects on the basis of the best economic return on the investment in irrigation. A study to determine the optimum allocation of agricultural resources in the project areas is now in progress. Studies are also being made of the regional economic growth in primary, secondary, and tertiary industries as a guide to public and private investment in the region. Some criticisms are made of the suitability of land system surveys for regional planning studies.

Bakhtina and Smirnova report on the assessment of land for urban planning in the U.S.S.R. based on landscape approach land classification. First, at the regional planning level the suitability of various types of land for agriculture, industrial enterprises, and residential purpose is assessed, taking into account economic factors, population growth predictions, and possible migration patterns. Special attention is given to recreation land planning, with emphasis on natural, aesthetic, and functional qualities of land. The second, detailed level involves project planning with considerable attention to architectural-aesthetic qualities.

DATA HANDLING AND INTERPRETATION

Land evaluation involves the collection and interpretation of very large amounts of data. Also, as mentioned in the introduction, land evaluation predictions will change with changes in technology and economic factors. Thus, data concerned with land evaluation must be stored in a way that re-evaluation can readily be made when any or all of those factors change significantly, as techniques improve, and more data become available.

Aerial photographs are virtually in universal use in land evaluation, and it is now recognized that the air photo is a very compact store of land data. Direct measurement of land parameters on air photos, and air-photo interpretation by relating air-photo patterns to non-visible land parameters are both widely used. As carried out at present by humans, air-photo interpretation remains somewhat subjective and dependent on the experience and breadth of knowledge of the interpreter. In recent years, much attention has been given to automated pattern interpretation and this subject is reviewed by Rosenfeld. Goodspeed also discusses the possibility of application of frequency-transform techniques, through optical and other means, to the manipulation of pattern data. To review the mathematical basis of this research is beyond my skill but it appears that research in this field has not yet reached the stage where it could be used in land evaluation, and its mathematical complexity is such that a specialist in this field would be needed to work in close association with land evaluation research workers. Rosenfeld has suggested how man-machine collaboration could be arranged as an intermediate step in the development of fully automated air-photo interpretation.

As a result of the rapid development of computer technology in the last decade, considerable attention is now being given to the application of computers to the storage and processing of land evaluation data.

The most comprehensive computer-based land evaluation system at present is the Canadian geographic information system for regional planning which is described by Tomlinson. Its objective is to store and manipulate land data from the Canada Land Inventory, and eventually will operate in concert with systems for economic and demographic data. The geographic information system is handling five types of pre-classified map data—the present use of land, agricultural land capability, forestry land capability, recreation land capability, and capability for supporting wild life. The methods of storage, up-dating, manipulation, and retrieval of data are explained. Standard request forms and short training programmes for potential users are proposed, but unusual or complex requests for information will need to be handled by specialist programmers.

Parry *et al.* use both maps and computer storage of data on land classification and vehicle mobility, and comment on some of the problems of computer handling of those data.

Grabau describes a possible future system for exploiting quantitative terrain data. It uses the mathematical performance prediction models and parametric land classification described in the earlier paper by Benn and Grabau. To date, most parts of the system have only been carried out by hand on experimental projects. However, some modules appear amenable to automated data processing, and the 'completely integrated and largely mechanical terrain evaluation system for use by engineer and land development agencies can be visualised'.

The system described by Tomlinson is storing pre-classified land data, which may limit its predictive use with future changes in technology and economics. Is computer technology likely to be able to cope with the handling and interpretation of primary data for a continental land evaluation system? Pearcey and Chapman examine the potential needs of an Australian land evaluation system. They conclude that these needs will be within the capacity of computer technology in the next decade, the main technological advances needed being very large rapid access stores and sophisticated input devices.

With the potential for automated data processing, and the probable future developments in remote sensing of land parameters, what is the potential future human contribution to land evaluation? This question is examined by Gibbons *et al.* They point out that the major limitations of humans compared with machines is that they cannot record data quantitatively and that storage (memory) is incomplete. The unique contribution that humans can make is in intuitive interpretation, and development of hypotheses for investigation, and to the definition of purpose. They conclude that humans will, of necessity, maintain the directive role, and leave the routine collection, processing, and storage of data increasingly to machines.

LAND PARAMETERS

The number of land parameters that are likely to be of significance in the full range of land evaluation is very large. In the selection of papers for this session the main criteria were:

(a) Do they contribute to the quantification of land parameters and/or
(b) Do they contribute to knowledge of principles and processes leading to identification of key parameters.

The first three papers, one on land form and two on vegetation, are primarily concerned with quantification. The last four papers are all related to water in various phases, and they all contribute to identification of key parameters.

Speight applies a parametric approach to the description of land-form elements and land systems, each based on four parameters, and shows that synthetic land systems identified on this basis are similar to previously mapped land systems. The advent of automatic photogrammetric machines with digital output is expected to reduce labour involved to a practical level for resource surveys.

Heyligers compares quantification of the structure of lowland tropical vegetation by interpretation of black and white air photos as 1:50,000 scale with ground observations. He shows that forest canopy characteristics can be interpreted more accurately than height. Distinguishing scrub, grassland, and mixed herbaceous vegetation is difficult because, at this scale of photography, interpretation is limited to tone and texture differences.

In contrast, Grabau and Rushing give a very detailed method for describing the structure of vegetation, based on the 'structural cell' concept. The method is computer compatible and can be carried out by relatively non-technical people. The system is planned to be used by foresters, ecologists, and military agencies, and is both open ended and abstractable.

Richards, in reviewing the effect of soil water on soil engineering properties, indicates several areas where recent research is contributing to more meaningful, and less empirical, engineering assessments. From the point of view of this Symposium the most interesting is that the prediction engineering performance of foundations for highways and houses is dependent on two parameters—soil type and sub-surface moisture conditions—that can be inventoried simply by survey techniques.

Woodyer and Fleming report investigations of the feasibility of assessing stream discharge frequency of small (less than 100 sq miles) catchments by reconnaissance methods and conclude that methods based on identification of stream channel benches are the most suitable. The method appears to offer scope for improvement in predictions for engineering needs.

Cowan examines the basic principles of four approaches to the estimation of evaporation from meteorological conditions and concludes that the choice of techniques must be related to the circumstances of the problem being investigated.

Chapman describes the deterministic rainfall-runoff model that will be used for the initial analysis of data from catchments scattered throughout Australia. The objective of the analysis is to obtain greater knowledge of the hydrologic processes in these catchments, as a basis for improved runoff prediction for other catchments.

SENSORS FOR LAND PARAMETERS

Aerial photos are the form of remote sensing that is more or less universally used in land classification and evaluation. Virtually all are black and white photos on panchromatic film, and the most widely used scales are in the range 1:15,000 to 1:50,000. However, not all users realize their full potential and their limitations. Colwell reviews these aspects in relation to photographic film, filter, scale, time of day, and season of year, of both aerial and space photographs taken in the visible part of the electromagnetic spectrum. He also reports on recent research in two new techniques that appear to have a considerable potential use in land evaluation—multiband imagery and multiband sensing.

In contrast to photographic recording of reflected light from an object, where image density is relative to the amount of light reflected by other objects in the viewing area, Romanova has used direct measurement of reflectance to identify sands of different origin and mineral composition in the U.S.S.R. The infrared end of the spectrum gave the most marked separation of different types of sand.

Electromagnetic sensing outside the visible spectrum is not in practical use for land evaluation at present. However, much research is now being carried out in infrared and radar regions, and this is reviewed by Simonett. Both imaging and non-imaging sensors are examined in relation to a range of land evaluation uses.

Rose and Thomas examine the principles involved in measuring land surface temperature by remote sensing in the 8–13 micrometre band of infrared. They conclude that single sensing could be used to extrapolate the degree of vegetative cover and the recognition of wet from dry surface soil, but more sophisticated quantitative estimation, e.g. of water storage, would require sensing several times per day.

Westby et al. describe how a newly developed, accurate, radar altimeter enables the potential of large-scale (1:1000 to 1:1500) aerial photography to be realized. This will add to the quantitative use of aerial photos, and should have many applications in land evaluation.

In contrast with the other papers, which mainly deal with airborne or potentially airborne remote sensors over relatively large areas at a single time or relatively widely spaced time intervals, Molineux describes a sensing system that measures a number of parameters at one remote site at regular time intervals and telemeters the data to monitoring headquarters.

SOME CONCLUDING COMMENTS

A number of authors have referred to users of land evaluation. In order to avoid ambiguity, I suggest the following terminology might be used:

1. Land evaluators include those concerned with land classification, performance prediction, and economic appraisal. These three operations may not always be carried out by one person or by one authority. If one or more of these evaluators use data provided by another they should be termed a *land evaluation user*.

2. *Land planning users* use land evaluation data to plan the use or development of land, e.g. construction planning engineers, military tactical planners, agricultural planners and advisers.

3. *Land users* use land planning data in applying human resources (technology, finance, labour) to land to achieve man's need, e.g. construction contractors, farmers, military transport units.

Land evaluators should provide land planning users with data in a form that they can comprehend, and not all land planning users will have the same capability for using complex data. Some authors have carried their work beyond the stage of the land planning user, e.g. Robertson et al. appear to have acted as both land evaluators and land planners, and Condon has developed a land evaluation that is useful to both land planners and land users.

Contributors vary in their reaction to users from the view that users are always right and must be given what they want to the view that users do not know what they want. Our ability to provide the needs of land planning users depends on the knowledge presently available that is pertinent to the proposed type of land use, and the time and human resources that can be devoted to the evaluation. If the latter are limited, and they usually are, close consultation between the evaluators and the land planning users is essential to obtain the most suitable evaluation from the available effort.

It appears that the greatest problem in land evaluation at the present time is in relating performance to land parameters. Two of the ways available to us for collecting data on this relationship are:

(a) experimental, for example the measurement of performance of military vehicles in relation to a number of combinations of land parameters by Parry *et al.*, in a way parallel to agronomic experiments in agriculture. A problem that then remains is to make allowance for the relatively high level of management skills imposed in experiments compared with the average land user. In agriculture in Australia, Davidson (1962) has shown for a number of crops that average farm yields are close to 2/3 of average experimental yields, and this factor has been used in a prediction of farm crop yield from experimental data.

(b) survey of land user performance, e.g. the survey of wheat yields over a large area in Queensland by Nix. These surveys can only be done where the form of land use is already practised in the region, and the number of users sampled must be relatively large in order to avoid bias due to different levels of management skills in the individual land users.

One of the trends apparent in this Symposium is that toward mathematical models in relating performance to land parameters. One advantage of the deterministic and simulation models is that they should, by exposing areas of inadequate knowledge, stimulate basic research in areas of direct benefit to man's need.

Another area where many further investigations are needed is the definition of the accuracy and precision of parameters of mapped units of land (Beckett), whether mapped by the landscape approach or the parametric approach, and whether mapped by ground sampling or by air-photo interpretation, or by a combined procedure. Such knowledge is essential as a basis for setting up realistic class ranges that are not misleading to the user in their apparent accuracy.

These are only a few of the many points that warrant discussion. As this book is being published before the Symposium it cannot include a summary of discussions. A summary of discussions will be published by UNESCO in *Nature and Resources*.

REFERENCES

CHRISTIAN, C. S., and STEWART, G. A. (1968).—Methodology integrated surveys. In *Aerial Surveys and Integrated Studies*. Proc. Toulouse Conf. 1964, UNESCO, pp. 233–80.

DAVIDSON, B. R. (1962).—Crop yields in experiments and on farms. *Nature*, Lond. **194**, 458–9.

Review of Concepts of Land Classification

J. A. Mabbutt

School of Geography,
University of New South Wales, Australia

'Land' denotes a complex of surface attributes significant to man, and classification involves categorizing land character into units of determinate extent.

Under the genetic approach land is subdivided into natural regions on the basis of environmental factors particularly climate and structure, but the regions are too large and vaguely delimited for land assessment.

The land units of the landscape approach are components with similar land forms, soils, and vegetation; these occur in groups which can be mapped from airphoto pattern.

The parametric approach seeks to establish land types by mapping key attributes in quantitative terms. It will doubtless increasingly replace the landscape approach as improved sensors become available.

INTRODUCTION

The term 'land' denotes a complex of surface and near-surface attributes significant to man. These attributes vary individually and in relation to each other to give local character. Land classification involves identifying and recording this character and establishing its area of occurrence. This review is concerned with the concepts underlying different approaches to land classification.

Whatever his approach, the land classifier faces certain fundamental problems which arise from the nature of land itself.

First are the problems of complexity. From the multitude of land attributes, their variations, and the intricacy of their interrelationships, it might be argued that each spot on the earth surface is in the last degree unique and not to be compared with any other, but the scientific approach to land involves the establishment of principles which enable us to understand the nature of land and to compare it from place to place. A land classification imposes a framework of generalization about land which enables common character to be defined and described, and likes to be related although geographically separate. This is a prerequisite if there is to be any transfer of knowledge about land and any element of expectation in land-use planning.

A second group of problems is associated with extent. Man conceives of and uses land in areas, and land classification is bound up with the delimitation, whether formally cartographic or conceptual only. Difficulties here arise from the differing spatial expression of land attributes. Some, such as land form, are clearly expressed, others, such as substrate material, may not be directly scannable, although new sensors are making inroads in these. Some have clear, sharp limits; others, like the catenary succession of soils, may be gradational. Some properties, slope for instance, tend to be recorded in relation to a facet or sector of land; others, like soil strength, refer to a point only. Any classification system must be capable of defining areas of land at scales realistic to its range of purposes.

Third are the problems of association. The character of land cannot be understood fully in terms of local controls acting in isolation, but is in part determined by relationships with adjoining areas. There is thus an intrinsic advantage in assessing land in terms of interacting units at various scales of grouping.

In this Symposium, emphasis is to be given to reconnaissance land assessment. I take this to mean the following:
1. It will often be preliminary to assessment for specific purposes and must hence be capable of treating the land in general terms.
2. It does not assume prior knowledge of the area, although it can make use of such knowledge.
3. It should be a low cost operation, achieving extensive predictive evaluation on a limited sampling effort.
It is this last characteristic of prediction which particularly distinguishes reconnaissance assessment from procedures involving total sampling. This may be long-range prediction, that a land type known from one region will be found in another of similar setting; or the prediction of similarity between locally recurring elements; or the prediction that an attribute as sampled will hold good across a small land unit.

Each of the triad, environmental controls—areal identity of land—land attributes—offers a distinct approach to the problem of land evaluation. In practice there is some overlap, but in a review of concepts it is appropriate to consider each approach separately.

THE GENETIC APPROACH

Introduction

Attempts to arrive at distinctive land units by repeated subdivision on the basis of causal environmental factors may be grouped as the genetic approach. This has its origins in the development of physical geography in the nineteenth century under the influence of botanists and geologists concerned with the genetic groupings of natural phenomena and the environmental controls of their associations and distributions.

Reconciliation of this outlook with a primary aim of the geographer, namely the recognition of unity in diversity as shown in the distinctive character of portions of the earth's surface, led to the concept of genetically based, 'natural' regions.

Theoretical arguments in support of such a genetic scheme are:
1. It is a logical breakdown, and similarities between widely separated areas* should be predictable where the basic controls are similar.
2. It offers a rational hierachy and should allow further investigation and subdivision within the one framework.
3. It has the promise of universality.

'Natural' and Morphologic Divisions

In the English literature, perhaps the best-known of such schemes is that of Herbertson (1905), which may be regarded as typical. Herbertson's types of natural regions are based on climate, 'since it not merely affects the physical features, but also because it best summarizes the various influences acting on the surface.' The limiting criteria of temperature and amount and distribution of rainfall actually employed have been chosen (like those of later world climatic classifications) for their significance for natural vegetation, this being regarded as an expressive synthesis of the whole complex of climate.

Herbertson claimed that configuration entered in at a lower level in his scheme of subdivision, but although his regional types are defined in climatic terms, closer study of his maps shows that morphology is the overriding criterion used in the actual delimitation of regions, and that climatic boundaries have been adjusted where necessary to avoid conflict. Linton (1951) has pointed out that most so-called natural regions are in fact morphologically delimited. Climatic boundaries are zonal, after all, nor can realistic land units be delimited on criteria which are invisible or hypothetical (as 'natural vegetation' is for an increasingly large part of the earth).

The Davisian interpretation of land forms as a function of structure, process, and stage enabled morphologic subdivision also to proceed on genetic lines, and this is reflected in the division of the United States by Fenneman (1916), in which the physiographic provinces are areas characterized by 'unity or similarity of physiographic history'.

Limitations of the Genetic Approach

When we study Herbertson's types of natural regions or Fenneman's physiographic divisions, provinces, and sections, three points come to mind. First, they are large. Herbertson's types have areas of occurrence of between 10^4 and 10^6 square miles; they rank with Fenneman's divisions and provinces, and the latter's sections are still to be measured in thousands of square miles. The second, as a corollary, is that they are internally complex, despite the genetic bond. Fenneman wrote of his provinces 'the ideal limits . . . are such as to admit of the largest possible number of general statements before details and exceptions are taken up'. Broad, general descriptions of the contents of such areas must suffice instead of precise commitment as to what is where. Third, their boundaries are vague; for instance, Herbertson described his as 'the approximate central lines of transitional areas'.

Clearly these are not regions of such scale and precision as to be manageable land units. This is not because the method has just not been carried far enough; it expresses a fundamental limitation of the approach, namely that breakdown cannot proceed beyond the level of unit appropriate to the genetic bond itself. Linton (1951) has used an apt chemical analogy . . . 'The smallest subdivision of a substance that can exist and still retain the physical and chemical properties of that substance is the molecule. The smallest physiographic subdivision of a land mass for which description is simplified by reference to its morphological evolution is the section. Subdivision of the chemical molecule yields atoms of the constituent elements whose properties are unrelated to each other or either to the compound whole. Subdivision of the physiographic section yields unit areas of the constituent morphological elements, closely related to the subjacent geological formations, but unrelated to each other or to the compound whole'.

It might, then, be argued that the introduction of additional genetically linked criteria of increasing dependence would eventually allow breakdown to realistic scales, but the idea of a sequential and tightly interlocking suite of factors of subdivision proves to be fallacious. The same factor does not appropriately enter in at the same level everywhere: a lithological contrast which in one setting provides an obvious boundary may in another find negligible expression; here it may be soil texture, there height above water level which finally distinguishes the lowest order of land unit called for. Nor are relationships between criteria the same everywhere. Whilst relief may in some areas be held subordinate to climate, in mountain regions it may provide the key to local climatic differentiation. As the range of criteria widens in order to encompass the increasing heterogeneity of the lower units, so the applicability of each factor becomes more localized and its relationships more complex. For each lower level of subdivision there is an increasing number of alternative higher groupings; the arrangement becomes increasingly *ad hoc* and the simple hierarchic structure is lost. Insofar as genetic relationships are still stated, they are a secondary rationalization and no longer the key to division.

To revert at this point to our fundamental requirements from a system of land classification, the genetic approach does not carry definition through to grapple with the complexity of land on a scale realistic for land use; it is deficient in the delimitation of units; it does not bring to light those properties of a land unit which relate to its position, shape, and extent and which arise from its grouping with adjacent units. It has the weakness inherent in a system in which lower units are derived from higher, that generalization is transmitted downwards. Precision is exchanged for the prospect of an overall, rationally based, correlative framework, but the prospect evaporates. The only situations where it promises to be adequate for practical purposes are those in which the dominance of a major attribute is so limiting that further distinguishing properties are not called upon, for instance extreme deserts, areas of perpetual frost, and permanently waterlogged situations.

The genetic approach can, however, be of use in two types of situation in which generalization is acceptable and where there is advantage in a hierarchic arrangement of regions and in the possibility of prediction and correlation on a broad scale. The first of these is in providing a co-ordinating framework, at a high level, for lower-order land units arrived at by an alternative route, for instance an Oxford study group concerned with land classification and data storage (Brink *et al*. 1966) proposed a universal reference mosaic of climatically determined land zones broken into land divisions based on morphostructural units. This was to allow world-wide correlation of land units, at least in generalized, abstracted form, and a degree of prediction of the recurrence of like land units at comparable points within the mosaic. A second, and in principle somewhat similar application is in the first assessment of an area before survey, since the prediction on genetic grounds of the broad pattern of contrasts and similarities should allow a more logical and economic investment of effort in subsequent field sampling.

Herbertson (1905) had claimed merit for his scheme on educational grounds, for the understanding it gave of world patterns, and on the grounds of its usefulness to historians and planners, in that the recognition of similarity of natural endowment in separated areas might provide in some an excuse for the past and in others a hope for the future. But if the genetic approach gives an inadequate, over-generalized picture of the physique of land when studied for its own sake, still less can it provide a realistic basis for discussion of the operation of social geographic factors.

There are two ways in which we can see the relationship between man and his physical environment, each with its appropriate scale. At the broad scale, and following the genetic approach, is the view that the environment has determined or at least limited man's cultural achievements. We may dismiss this as crudely deterministic, for there is no evidence that even the best-defined natural region gives rise to a corresponding cultural unit; in the words of Kimble (1951), 'Nature's curtains are fashioned of more malleable material than iron, and man, with his versatility, has been wont to show little regard for them'. At the other end of the scale, the relationship between man and his physical setting is seen as a functional one, in which land character has expression in the patterns of the cultural landscape. For such analysis we need to study the land with a precision of a different order. Heath (1956) has described how Bowman, in his studies of Andean settlement (Bowman 1916), could use genetically derived physiographic divisions only as a general background; for the study of actual land use, site details were required at the scale of occupance and management. The Michigan Economic Land Survey of 1922, perhaps the earliest systematic attempt at regional land evaluation, also found that detailed definition of land units was required. For this, another approach had to be found.

THE LANDSCAPE APPROACH

Introduction

Tired of fitting boundaries which did not exist around areas which did not matter, regional geographers abandoned the search for the elusive 'natural region' and sought real objects of study in distinctive parts of the observed environment. As a system of regional geography, the method is particularly associated with Unstead (1933), who aimed to show how the small regions so identified could be combined into areas of successively higher order . . . 'to a system of regions developed in this way the term "synthetic" may be applied . . . the process is one, not of division and subdivision of areas, but of combination of the smaller regions in order to arrive at the larger ones. By this means more accuracy is assured . . .'

Unstead's primary units had to be small enough for detailed scientific investigation and at the same time be distinctive geographical entities. He proposed for them the term 'stow', identified by unity of relief, though with characteristic structure, hydrology, plant cover, and land use. Nevertheless he recognized that the stow was made up of yet smaller components or 'features' of the status of minor land forms. His second order unit, the 'tract', consisted of a grouping of types of stow, and its unity might derive from one or all of relief, structure, and soils. Above the tract were levels of regional grouping expressive of characteristic relief type or climate.

At about this time, people concerned with land assessment for such practical purposes as forestry and economic planning also began to analyze terrain patterns at the scale of visual experience. I shall use 'landscape approach' for the path to land classification via the areal identity of land. Methods employed by various groups, although developed somewhat independently of each other, show striking similarity of working concept and of descriptive structure.

Use of Airphoto Interpretation

Since the approach involves analysis of visible features, some portrayal of the landscape on a scale appropriate to locality assessment is called for. Where the relief of the area provides vantage points, the worker may gain this perspective from the ground, as Bowman did in his Andean studies, but such evaluation cannot readily be extended beyond the areas traversed. Again, where relief is strong, a topographic map can provide a picture of land forms, but will probably be deficient in respect of surface cover. Bruhnes long ago compared this study of the anatomy of the landscape with the experience of looking out from a balloon, and in his much-quoted early account of the practical uses of the method, Bourne (1931) stressed the value of air photography as showing 'scenic regions' or characteristic assemblages of landscape features. Airphoto interpretation has since come to distinguish this approach to land classification. This is not the place, in this Symposium, for a review of the potentialities of the airphoto; it is enough to state that tone, texture, pattern, and stereoscopic image combine to offer to the interpreter an expression of land units, both individually and in their groupings, on a scale which is particularly appropriate to this approach, and moreover in a way which facilitates the appreciation of land features as a function of underlying geologic controls and as the expression of geomorphic process.

An Integrated Approach

Unstead (1933) stated as a second reason for applying the term 'synthetic' to the landscape approach . . . 'no one or two characteristics of regions are isolated out for study; as far as possible a general view of the area in question, and the combined effect of the geographical factors, are taken into account'. The land complex as a whole is the object of study, even where a particular attribute may be of prime interest to a land classifier. Such an integrative approach is dictated by the method itself. The differentiation of land is based on landscape character which may be a response to one or more of a group of factors, the relative importance of which can change from place to place. All lines of evidence are admissible, therefore, and no *a priori* assumptions can be made which exclude any part of the land complex. In any case, no land attribute can really be understood in isolation; in a degree it must express the interaction of *all* factors, on ecosystematic lines. Most important of all conceptually, however superficial the criteria chosen to recognize and define the land components, the landscape approach aims at discovering the causes of differentiation. The more fundamental the bases of mapping, the greater the likelihood that the divisions drawn will be significant, not merely for easily read properties, but for those which, like soil microbiological status, cannot as yet be observed with available sensors, and even for those, as yet unknown, which may come into question at a future stage of development. The more fundamental the level at which we seek to understand the land, the more inseparable become the dynamic controls and the more necessary an integrated approach.

    This integrated view of the land complex is particularly appropriate to the assessment of overall land potential, and above all at the reconnaissance stage. In the first place, it is of the essence of reconnaissance investigation that it should be in general terms, for the discovery of profitable lines of specialist endeavour may be an ultimate aim but not generally an initial charter. These lines will not be the same in more than a few areas, and even here it will generally be a matter of relative advantage between alternatives; hence the initial evaluation should not be narrowed. Second, even a single type of enterprise draws on or affects a range of site attributes . . . 'the need for integration arises from the fact that at one site it is rarely one, but more often a number of resource factors which determine what kind of action is best in the interest of development' (Christian and Stewart 1968). Lastly, the development of one resource cannot go forward in isolation, for it will modify and even affect the very survival of others in the same area; in the eastern uplands of New South Wales, for instance, forest development, upland grazing, mineral exploitation, recreational land use, and water supply for power and for urban and farm use are all interlocking. Increasingly, development plans involve consideration of the whole resource complex, and moreover in a framework of land areas, such as the river basin, which constitute natural areas of interplay of land-forming agents.

Components of the Landscape

The landscape approach involves the recognition in the landscape of distinctive components with only a limited range of variation of those attributes important to land use. Some practitioners identify this fundamental component with the 'site' of Bourne (1931), namely 'an area which, for all practical purposes, provides throughout its extent similar conditions as to climate, physiography, geology, soil, and edaphic factors in general'. Most admit of a degree of variation; for instance, the Oxford Working Group on Land Classification (Brink *et al.* 1966) regarded their 'land facet' as being made up of simpler 'land elements', each corresponding to the site of Bourne (1931).

The looseness of definition of the component is noteworthy. This is reflected in guide lines for defining components proposed by the Oxford Working Group, here arranged in order of increasing subjectivity:

It should be capable of delineation on airphotos at scales of between 1:10,000 and 1:80,000.

More than one soil class at family level or higher should not generally occur within it.

There should be a continuous gradation of properties with no definite break (or, as stated earlier by Beckett and Webster (1965), 'facets are defined to be consistent in the kind and degree of their internal variations').

Important differences of operation by land users should not be involved.

Equally instructive are the attempts by Russian landscape analysts to define their corresponding unit, the facies. This is admitted to be a complex, capable of subdivision if required, and is equated with 'a simple relief form'. It corresponds to 'a given rock base, a distinctive microclimate, a single soil type, and a single biocoenesis' (Prokayev 1962). Making the useful point that 'the definition of a landscape unit of any rank must point up to the genuine factor that differentiates it within the superior unit' Prokayev suggests that definition of the facies should be based on the character and thickness of surface deposits, the redistribution of moisture and of heat within it as controlled by local relief, and corresponding properties of soil and vegetation cover and of animal life. In all this geomorphic and hydrologic factors will be paramount. But these are terms impossible of precise definition, and we return to the criterion that 'in determining the degree of complexity . . . within the facies, the investigator can base himself only on practical criteria in the broadest sense' (Prokayev 1962).

Most schemes define the component as a unity in relation to a proposed land use, for instance 'an area where the climate, parent material, topography, soil, and vegetation are uniform within the limits significant for a particular form of land use' (Gibbons and Downes 1964), and 'its physical properties should be sufficiently uniform for a prudent arable farmer to manage the whole extent of one facet in the same way' (Beckett and Webster 1965).

Such pragmatic expressions avoid the commitment of setting firm limits to either end of an acknowledged range of variation. At the lower end of the scale they escape identifying the homogeneous element of landscape—a creature as arbitrary as the class limits which might define it; and at the upper end there is tacit admission that the permissible size and variability of the component are matters of circumstance and judgement. There is saving grace in this flexibility from two points of view; first, it accommodates the complexity and the gradational properties of land, and secondly it admits that land unit divisions are, after all, subjective rather than absolute.

This component may or may not be the basic mapping unit, depending on the scale of the enterprise, but is in most cases the fundamental unit of description.

Patterns in the Landscape

Landscape components recur in distinctive assemblages or patterns, presumably in response to the localizing effect of particular controls. Bourne (1931) applied the term 'region' to this assemblage, but the assemblage itself commonly recurs; other terms used include land unit, land system, and recurrent landscape pattern. As a definition we may use that of Christian and Stewart (1953) for their land system, 'a composite of related units . . . an area, or group of areas, throughout which there is a recurring pattern of topography, soils, and vegetation'. Beyond this area of recurrence we enter other patterns formed from different assemblages of components.

In reconnaissance survey of large areas the pattern rather than the component often becomes the mapping unit and the pattern is commonly the level of first recognition in airphoto interpretation, when the problem becomes the definition and description of components. Since the properties of the assemblage arise from the arrangement as well as from the nature of the components, their interrelationships must be considered and depicted; this is additionally important where the components are not mapped and where their field identification may rest on a diagram and accompanying descriptions.

As with the component, so with the pattern, there appear to be no definite criteria which limit its scale and complexity. It is interesting to note a Russian attempt at precision. The Russian unit equivalent of the land system is the *urochische*—'an association of facies related to individual concavities and convexities in medium-size relief forms or to level interfluve areas with a homogeneous substratum and united by a common direction of drainage, of the transfer of solid material and the migration of chemical elements' (Vinagradov *et al.* 1962). Below this level the *sub-urochischa* consist of 'associations of facies related to a single slope' and above it are the *mestnosti*, loosely defined as made up of genetically and geochemically related *urochischa*. Except for the indication that the *urochische* perhaps corresponds to the simplest Australian land system as known to me, this more elaborate essay does little more than confirm the existence of groupings of components at several levels. Christian (1958) has admitted that most of the land systems mapped by the Division of Land Research are complex or compound, that is combinations of simple land systems based on close relationship or even on mapping convenience.

Practical considerations such as the purpose of the operation and the complexity of the terrain itself are decisive. In general, the pattern is too large and varied to form a unit of land management or to be easily defined in quantitative terms. By those who map at the component scale its usefulness in land classification is seen as providing a convenient arrangement of components—the workable land units—which aids in recognizing and giving reference to them. Christian (1958), as representative of a group mapping at the pattern level, claims a more positive, simplifying role for it since 'it aggregates these units (components) into areas large enough to be mapped at a scale of working, but small enough in number to facilitate regional comprehension and planning'.

It is a matter of debate whether, apart from scale, there is a difference of kind between what I have termed the component, with its own internal complexity, and the pattern of grouped components. The Russian workers deny it and Christian (1958) has also done so, tacitly at least, in suggesting that, with changes in the closeness of investigation or the complexity of land, his land units may be upgraded to land systems and *vice versa*. Many observers would claim that the environment consists of a series of linked patterns at the whole range of scales. However, Beckett and Webster (1962) have differentiated the criteria which distinguish the component and the pattern—physiographic unity in the first and common or related morphogenesis in the second. I would suggest that the test of continuity might be applied, in that the elements of a component should pass into each other in unbroken sequence, as do the slope components of an inter-fluve, whereas distinct breaks may occur between components in a pattern—as between alluvial and colluvial components. For this reason I regard the catenary soils sequence of Milne (1935) as appropriate to the landscape component rather than to the pattern.

Although the scale of grouping may be arbitrary, most practitioners agree that the pattern is nevertheless a 'natural' one, expressive of a real bond . . . 'land-components . . . generally occur in patterns because the independent variables—climate, parent material, topography, are quite few, and one or more is often constant over a broad area with the other features of the environment dependent upon it' (Gibbons and Downes 1964). Christian (1958) states that units grouped together are 'products of a common geomorphological phenomenon' and that they may be differentiated from their environs 'either in parent material, geo-morphological processes, or in the length of period over which these processes have been operating'. More specifically, Beckett and Webster (1965) stress that the unity of the pattern results from the dominance of a single physiographic process or an explicable combination or sequence of two or more such processes. It seems reasonable to insist on the functional relationship between the compo-nents of a pattern, as is implicit in common morphogenesis, in that it might incorporate into the classification an assessment of those properties of land which arise from location and the influence of adjoining units. For this reason, the Oxford Working Group (Brink et al. 1966) endorsed the term 'land system' for 'pattern' because of the connotation of interaction. With this, however, we reach an area of debate as to how far should consideration be given to genesis.

Landscape Genesis and the Landscape Approach

That the observed components and patterns of the land are the logical expression of independent factors, and that land attributes can, in part at least, be under-stood and even anticipated on this basis, is not doubted by those who employ the landscape approach. The expression of this by Christian (1958) is typical of the group . . . 'each part of the land surface is the end product of an evolution governed by parent geological material, geomorphological processes, past and present climates, and time. During this period the land surface has been shaped to existing land forms, each developing in the process its own hydrological features, soil mantle, vegetation communities, animal populations, and range of microenvironments'. Beckett and Webster (1962) have called the landscape approach a physiographic classification, seeing the unity of the component in its physiographic origin and the bond of the pattern as morphogenetic. In fact, the landscape can be analyzed to isolate a particular factor, as by the geologist in airphoto mapping.

This recognition carries advantages, as has been remarked from the geo-morphological viewpoint by Mabbutt and Stewart (1965). It can provide a rationale in extrapolative mapping, for decisions as to grouping into components and patterns are not always obvious, and greater consistency will result where the choice is made with an understanding of why changes of landscape are occurring. An understanding of casual interrelationships within the land complex means that inherent attributes may sometimes be logically anticipated even where not directly recognizable; for instance Christian (1958) describes a distinction between clays of higher and lower phosphate status on the basis of their morphogenetic setting. Further, where genetic controls are understood and seen to be similar, widely separated components and patterns can usefully be compared and experience gained in one area can benefit another. Finally, if we include consideration of chronologic principles here as giving depth to the genetic view, relict features of the landscape, palaeosols for instance, may be understood and their recurrence foreseen.

However, the criticism has been justly levelled that, whilst an understanding of genesis may enrich our understanding of the land complex and usefully guide our classification of it, it remains nevertheless an inferred opinion, and genetic criteria should not be employed to define components and patterns.

Beckett and Webster (1965) have differentiated between the criteria used for the recognition of a land unit and those employed for its definition. Whereas definition attributes should be few, fundamental, invariable, always present, and hence conclusive, recognition features need not be the same everywhere and, whilst obvious, need not have fundamental significance. 'We may define a terrain unit by its water regime, for instance that the water table is usually high and that the terrain is liable to annual floods; we recognize it by noting the ecological and cultural responses to the water regime', and these may differ Locally. Ideally, definitive features should have recognition value. Both recognition and definition criteria, it is agreed, should be features intrinsic to the unit and not inferred properties, such as genesis, and esoteric criteria should be avoided for both purposes. It is for this reason that non-genetic geomorphic criteria are often favoured, since natural vegetation is vulnerable in the face of land development, and the soil character must generally be inferred from associated features rather than read directly.

Recurrent Units and the Problem of Reproducibility

The analysis of landscape has revealed the existence of recurring patterns formed by groupings of similar components, and to express this recurrence, the units of description must be types of land and not regional entities. Since each land unit is in some degree unique, mapping and description in the landscape approach involves a continuous process of generalization, an abstraction of those attributes common to all occurrences of the unit type; this occurs at all levels, from the sample point through the sampled component, between like components in the same assemblage, between like components in recurrences of the same assemblage or pattern, and also between the assemblages themselves.

Beckett and Webster (1965) have used the term 'reproducibility' for the likelihood that a component as defined in one locality will have the same attributes elsewhere. Reliability of classification obviously requires reproducibility . . . 'If any advantage is to result from recognizing types of terrain at a particular site it must be because all examples of that terrain unit are sufficiently similar that one can generalize about them, and infer the properties of an unknown from a known site' (Beckett and Webster 1965). For any component, reproducibility in respect of any attribute will depend in part on the variation of that attribute, but for a given variability we can increase the reliability of predictive assessment 'by subdividing terrain units more finely, by introducing more and more attributes into the definition, and by narrowing the permitted range of each' (Beckett and Webster 1965). To support this trend we must accept a reduction in the area of applicability of our sample information, that is, we must admit the uniqueness of components to a greater degree. And to the extent that we narrow the definition of components we must accept that the difficulty of recognizing their recurrence will increase in proportion and that a more detailed sample base will be called for.

This means a loss of those advantages which one associates with reconnaissance survey, namely that with speed and at low cost it should yield a fair level of knowledge, in fundamental terms and with reasonable reliability, about realistically small units of land, but not in too localized terms. What is held to be fair and reasonable will depend on the resources available, the complexity and potentiality of the land, and the priorities of the would-be user.

However, the investment of effort agreed upon is very relevent to the method of land classification used. The landscape approach is suited to reconnaissance survey in that recognizability is good and extrapolation from a limited sample base is facilitated. Few tests of reproducibility obtained with this approach have been carried out, but Webster (1965) has made a statistical study of consistency between recurrent components in respect of a dozen attributes selected mainly for their relevance to military engineering land use. He reports 'The properties of the soil affecting its potential for engineering purposes were only moderately variable. Coefficients of variation were in general between 20% and 30%. This means, in short, that if the terrain unit is known at a point, the actual value will fall short of the predicted value by more than 25% only once out of 6 predictions and by more than 50% only once out of 40 predictions'. He found that the chemical properties of the soil were generally much more variable, and predictive reliability was accordingly low. It is noted that these statements concern soil properties, which have little recognition value, and that directly observable attributes such as vegetation cover should carry greater reliability.

More detailed evaluation for more intensive land use must eventually require a higher level of reproducibility, presumably exceeding the reasonable limits of reconnaissance appraisal. There are two ways in which this might be achieved within the framework of the landscape approach. One is by the introduction of new sensors which might transfer certain attributes from the inferred to the directly scanned category, and hence achieve a higher level of reproducibility. A second way would be to accept the burden of closer survey, with reduced reliance on recognizability; in this manner, reproducibility could also be raised. Eventually, however, one reaches the limit of the landscape approach, with the generalization implicit in its integrated concept of land. As requirements become more specific and as sensors are developed to fulfil them, limiting values of significant attributes rather than the complex of land as a whole may provide a better basis for the classification of land, and the landscape approach must then be supplanted to some degree by one based on land attributes.

THE PARAMETRIC APPROACH

Introduction

One may define the parametric approach as the division and classification of land on the basis of selected attribute values. For instance, a hypsometric map demonstrates a classification of land based on elevation, with class limits at chosen contours. Employment of the parametric approach ranges from general-purpose surveys considering many attributes, to classification for special purposes and on a narrower basis, and also includes the stiffening of more qualitative systems through the infusion of parametric ingredients.

The tenor of claims made for the parametric approach is that it achieves a more precise definition of land and that it avoids the subjectivity of the landscape method; being quantitative, it allows comparison between and affords greater consistency within land evaluation projects; and it is in terms suited to automatic scanners and computers.

Increasing advocacy of the parametric approach stems partly from dissatisfaction with the results of the landscape method of analysis, with its physiographic and morphogenetic bias, its qualitative framework, and its elements of subjectivity and inference. Not only, it is claimed, is the level of reproducibility, and hence of reliability, low, but the way in which land is defined makes it difficult to measure variance, to formulate rational sampling, or to express probability limits for the findings. But there are more positive reasons also, among them the introduction of new sensors enabling direct scanning of attributes which had formerly to be inferred from associated features. With the advent of these there disappears an important relative advantage of the landscape approach, namely the easy recognition of its land components. Another innovation favouring the parametric approach is electronic data handling, which sets quantitative criteria at a premium and which allows the incorporation of a much greater range of defining attributes. To some degree, also, recent moves towards parametric land classification have resulted from the influence of a new class of practitioners, notably engineers, whose rather specific demands require answers in quantitative form.

Problems inherent in the approach include the choice of attributes and the delimitation of attribute classes; the variance of attributes in space and time, and the translation into terms of land of the areas of occurrence and association of selected parameters.

Choice of Attributes and Attribute Values

Attributes for the parametric approach must be suitable for the operation involved, that is they must be quantifiable and either directly scannable in quantitative terms or capable of being reliably read from their association with other obvious features. Apart from this, the fundamental test remains their relevance for the intended land use, and in this they are unlikely to differ in kind from the attributes used under the landscape approach, although they will generally be more closely defined for a specific purpose.

This is shown in the factors chosen in a study of terrain in Thailand as affecting the mobility of military vehicles (Anon. 1963). They include surface geometry (defined as the relative frequency of slope classes based on good contour maps, and the presence of linear obstacles on the scale of microrelief), surface composition (percentage area of occurrence of four soil trafficability classes based on a rating cone index); vegetation structure (based on the percentage of terrain covered by forests with stand spacing classed in effective vehicle widths, or corresponding obstruction to visibility); and hydrologic geometry (depth, cross profile, and velocity of streams greater than 1 m deep). These correspond broadly with the main categories of form, surface composition, and cover used in combination to define the land complex under the landscape approach; within each category, however, criteria have been selected specifically for their significance to trafficability.

The parameters chosen must establish land units at component and at pattern level. At the component level, form will generally predominate as in the geomorphic parameters of shape, profile, and dimension, but it may be necessary to define arrangements of features below component level, such as microrelief. Reproducibility of components may be measured by the kurtosis and unimodality of frequency distributions of slope, elevation, etc.

At the scale of the pattern there are two types of parameter: those which record the dominant or average content of pattern occurrences in respect of any feature, and those which express the arrangement of components. The first category includes, for instance, characteristic or average relief or slope. Indices employed by Horton (1945) in the study of drainage nets and by Strahler (1958) in the analysis of fluvially dissected land forms are particularly appropriate at the pattern level on account of their morphogenetic significance, in that morphogenesis has been regarded as the bond linking the components of simple terrain patterns. The second type is exemplified by measurements of the grain of relief (dissection) based on the number of changes of slope direction along random traverses (Wood and Snell 1960) and by the schematic plan-profile criteria of van Lopik and Kolb (1959) which combine the percentage of peaked and flat-topped upland forms with expressions of their linearity and parallelism. Fourier series have been applied in the analysis of the cyclic profiles of valleys and uplands and of repetitive microrelief (Stone and Dugundji 1965).

A problem associated with parameters which express a range of values, like that of relief, is determining the extent over which the factors should be measured. Clearly, this must be determined by the character of the land itself. In their quantitative classification of land forms, Wood and Snell (1960) relate this to the grain of the terrain as indicated by inflections on a curve of relief plotted against length of traverse. A nick on the curve denotes characteristic maximum relief and the corresponding distance (grain) is the diameter of the appropriate sample area. Ideally, the curve should yield values corresponding to component and pattern scales.

Under the landscape approach, land unit boundaries express the limits of occurrence of recognition features, for instance the change from forest to grassland. With the numerical criteria of the parametric approach comes the problem of setting limiting values. A simple case is where a threshold value is set by the purpose in hand, for instance by the performance limits of the vehicle in a trafficability analysis of terrain. More difficult is the setting of class limits within an apparently gradational range. For some geomorphic criteria at least the problem may be less than at first appears, in that there are clusterings of values which give rise to 'natural' classes. For example, the mapping of slopes (Savigear 1965) has shown that there exist distinctive facets, each with its range of declivities expressive of a certain dynamic and associated with characteristic colluvial mantles in such a way as to constitute meaningful elements for some types of land use. In the same way, narrow ranges of values of such criteria as relief, drainage density, and maximum slope may be expected to characterize landscape units within which a given dynamic equilibrium prevails. Morpho-metric analyses are needed to establish this and to determine appropriate value classes in a range of physiographic settings, since each should exhibit its own relationships. Morphogenetically bonded land units like the patterns revealed through landscape analysis should respond to such appraisal.

Spatial and Temporal Variation of Attributes

The more closely he attempts the definition of land character in specific and numerical terms, the more necessary it is for the land classifier to grapple with the complex variations of land attributes from place to place. Soils and surface materials, perhaps the most significant features for most forms of land use, exemplify the difficulties very clearly. The soil mantle normally exhibits variable vertical differentiation—the classical basis of soil recognition—as well as horizontal variability; those variations may be abrupt or gradational, for soil character reflects in part the parent material, with its distinct boundaries and also external controls, which have continuity of surface expression; the varying properties most significant to land use are not expressible in simple terms—soil structure, for instance, is not comprehended in the texture of the mineral fraction and the amount and composition of the organic component; the content of soil and its arrangement, unlike the individuals and groupings of vegetation, do not lend themselves to direct expression in terms of levels of association; soil character remains largely hidden from conventional surface scanning.

Under the landscape approach, these complexities are first compounded into soil classes and the key to the distribution of these is sought through the surface pattern of causal factors (parent material and land forms) and through their expression in the vegetation, both of which may be conceived and read *in extenso*. Under the parametric approach, reaction to the same problems may involve a number of courses, such as harnessing new scanning techniques, improving the sample base, narrowed selection, through testing and quantitative mapping, of those more obvious land features most significantly associated with soil properties relevant to the form of land use envisaged, and resolution of the soil complex into measurable component properties known to control or to be diagnostic of the suitability of the soil for the purpose in hand.

From this we may draw some general conclusions about likely trends in the choice of criteria for the definition and classification of land under the parametric approach, namely that the integrated concept of land must give place to its expression in specific and limited terms selected for their readability and for their significance, directly or diagnostically, for a proposed land use. This suggests a detail of investigation and a specificity of purpose beyond those normally associated with reconnaissance investigation.

Where the closer definition of land units under the parametric approach comprises time-dependent parameters, rate of change and periodicity in the landscape can be considered. Lands with changing seasonal aspects and marked climatic rhythms, like northern Australia, call for classification in these terms, as do many shorter-term local variables, for instance the drying cycles of soils. Fortunately, the problem of collecting the necessary data is diminishing. Regular passes of artificial satellites equipped with multispectral scanners should make it possible to record, on a world scale, a host of phenological observations such as flooding, snow cover, and vegetation rhythms. These would make available to the land classifier a sequence of parametric patterns which could be combined to express the seasonal and shorter-term variability of land. Introduction of the fourth dimension, which is certainly facilitated by if not peculiar to the parametric approach, brings into land classification a dynamic concept appropriate to many forms of land use.

The Expression of Attribute Patterns and their Association

The first results of field investigation under the parametric approach will be, for any factor considered, an array of values or qualitative statements for a number of sampling points. With direct scanning of airphotos or maps, and in other cases by interpolative plotting or best-fit mapping, an isarithmic or trend-surface map may be constructed for the parameter in question. These may be used towards defining land units or, placing the emphasis on the attributes, for studying the spatial relationships of one or more attributes. The operation may be cartographic or statistical.

Where the aim is to delimit land units, the procedure can vary with the information available. For instance, maps of supplementary attributes may be superimposed to form a composite mosaic, as in the generalized landscape maps of van Lopik and Kolb (1959) formed from an overlay of maps of the four geometry factors, plan-profile, characteristic slope, characteristic relief, and occurrence of slopes greater than 50%. Characteristic combinations are recognized as landscape complexes and may, for convenience, be related with physiographic types. Again, isarithmic maps of largely independent attributes may be superimposed with the object of outlining areas on the basis of highest common factor content, or by the interpolation or smoothing of approximately coincident boundaries, or by the combination of sectors of complementary isopleths.

Consistent with the parametric approach, however, the land classifier may free himself from the obligation to pursue the establishment of regional identity of the land complex or of its parts, and turn to the analysis of the spatial patterns of attributes, attribute groups, or attribute ratios. Trend-surface mapping is now being widely applied to many forms of land research where the identification of regional trends and the analysis of local anomalies are important (Chorley and Haggett 1965). Possible applications include improved isarithmic mapping, for instance of meteorological data, simplified description and comparison of complex geographical patterns, comparative areal analysis, including trend-surface correlation, and the construction of process-response models.

Expression of contextual influences is possible under the parametric approach, in terms of adjacency where regions are identified or where the best-fit mapping of isarithms takes the network of sample values into account. To this extent the methods simulate the 'intuitive taxonomy' of the mapper of landscape assemblages as patterns. Whether adjacency is a successful measure of the interaction of land-forming factors at the pattern level, or whether the input of chosen attributes is adequate are other matters; the measure of success is the reality of the model for the purpose.

COMPARISONS AND COMBINATIONS

In summary, it is useful to revert to the fundamental requirements of land classification discussed at the outset.

The problem of defining land character along orderly principles so as to categorize and compare land types is answered in three ways. Under the genetic approach a theoretical solution is sought and an attempt made to particularize by degrees, using environmental controls as successive criteria, until a sufficiently narrow definition, in genetic terms, has been reached; however, it appears that no combination of criteria of this sort can yield the precision required for land-use planning. The landscape approach offers a largely empirical solution. The character of land is sought through its appearance as in an aerial view, and it is claimed that with an understanding of the genesis or dynamics of the land we may read the inherent character from the external forms, whereby types of land so defined will be found to be consistent in attributes discovered after closer analysis and experimentation. It is claimed that this ready means of assessing land character as a whole over large areas offers a precision and reliability adequate for moderately intensive land use. Dissatisfied with this last claim, adherents of the parametric approach are prepared to sacrifice comprehensiveness and ease of recognition for the reliability and quantitative output of a definition based on measured properties and note that in any case the picture they offer is becoming increasingly complete and readily obtained with new techniques of scanning and computing.

Since, clearly, what cannot be defined cannot be depicted, the genetic approach fails to deal with the problem of delimiting land types on a scale realistic for land use. The remaining approaches offer different solutions. The landscape approach distinguishes units of land which are invested with an overall character, whilst the parametric approach ascertains patterns of occurrence of selected attributes which may be combined into areal complexes. The landscape units are of realistic size for land-use planning and their delimitation presents little problem; however, a minimal probability that apparent similarity means consistent attributes could require a sampling intensity which might offset this ease of mapping. Areas defined under the parametric approach will be of high reliability, but their mapping may present problems unless scanning of attributes is possible. The more that is known about probable demands on the land, the less are the disadvantages of its narrowly defined land units. An important advantage of the parametric approach is the greater flexibility of spatial concept, with its possibilities of factor analyses of various types.

The problem of depicting the association of land units is answered directly under the landscape approach in that the recognition and demarcation of units is commonly at the level of component groupings which are regarded as being functionally or genetically linked. Somewhat similarly, the object of the genetic approach is to show each unit as grouped in a region of higher order in terms of a genetic factor operative at the larger scale. The isarithmic patterns which form the output of the parametric approach offer an alternative answer in that they indicate the working of areal-process factors at a range of scales, for a number of scanned attributes, and without commitment to any regional framework.

It has been shown that, at the scale of detail required for practical purposes, land can be mapped into landscape units or land-attribute occurrences, and that both methods, in their different ways, answer the requirements of land classification. The two approaches are really not alternatives and can in fact be combined with profit. The relative advantages and hence the degree of emphasis to be placed on one approach or the other are not fixed, but will vary with the circumstances under which they are applied and the technical resources that can be drawn upon. With what is presently regarded as standard equipment, the landscape approach offers the possibility of more rapid survey at low cost. The reliability, although not outstanding, is consistent with reconnaissance investigation as at present conceived, and can be raised, within limits and at a price, by more intensive sampling. Ultimately, there comes a level of investigation at which the greater precision and reliability of the parametric approach are needed and to the extent that improvements in scanning render the method more comprehensive, its inherent advantages of reliability will be exploited, even at the reconnaissance level of investigation.

In practice, the methods are combined to reinforce each other. For instance, past survey procedure of the CSIRO Division of Land Research would be defined as the landscape approach to land classification, but the planning of the operation, including the selection of sampling points, may be guided by a preliminary breakdown of the area on broad physiographic lines, comparable with the genetic approach (Christian, Jennings, and Twidale 1957). Similarly, the test sites of the Waterways Experiment Station may be classified by parametric methods, but for the identification of land in other little-known areas in analogous terms it may be necessary to identify these forms with physiographic components and patterns as under the landscape approach. One can envisage many cases in which the definition and reproducibility of landscape units could be improved by the testing of associated parameters; on the other hand, it may be some time before the parametric approach can provide a sufficiently comprehensive and mappable definition of land for general-purpose classification without some additional support from landscape analysis. It seems inevitable that, with increasing auto-scanning and data handling, as our knowledge of land increases, and as the demands of the land user become more specialized, that parametric analysis will become general practice. But perhaps the ultimate advantage of the approach will be the flexibility of spatial concept that it allows. There seems to be no reason why, at more advanced stages of investigation, the regional concept of convention may not be abandoned completely in favour of measures of functional interdependence such as connectivity, for with progressive development it is the links rather than the breaks in the landscape with which we become increasingly concerned.

REFERENCES

ANON. (1963). WES operation and funding plans for OSD. ARPA mobility-environmental research study (MERS). U.S. Army Corps Engrs, Waterways Exp. Stn, Vicksburg, Miss. Cyclostyled report.

BECKETT, P. H. T., and WEBSTER, R. (1962). *The storage and collation of information on terrain*. Military Engng Exp. Establ., Christchurch, England. Interim report.

BECKETT, P. H. T., and WEBSTER, R. (1965). *A classification system for terrain. Units and principles*. Military Engng Exp. Establ., Christchurch, England. Report 872.

BOURNE, R. (1931). Regional survey and its relation to stocktaking of the agricultural resources of the British Empire. *Ox. For. Mem.* **13**, 16–18.

BOWMAN, I. (1916). *The Andes of Southern Peru*. (Am. Geog. Soc. Publ. 2: New York.)

BRINK, A. B., MABBUTT, J. A., WEBSTER, R., and BECKETT, P. H. T. (1966). Military Engng Exp. Establ., Christchurch, England. Report 940.

CHORLEY, R. J., and HAGGETT, P. (1965). Trend-surface mapping in geographical research. *Trans. Inst. Br. Geogr.* Publ. No. 37, 47–67.

CHRISTIAN, C. S. (1958). The concept of land units and land systems. *Proc. 9th Pacific Sci. Congr.*, 1957. Vol. 20. pp. 74–81.

CHRISTIAN, C. S., JENNINGS, J. N., and TWIDALE, C. R. (1957). Geomorphology. Ch. 5. In *Guide Book to Research Data for Arid Zone Development*. (UNESCO: Paris.)

CHRISTIAN, C. S., and STEWART, G. A. (1953). General report on survey of Katherine–Darwin region, 1946. *CSIRO Aust. Land Res. Ser.* No. 1.

CHRISTIAN, C. S., and STEWART, G. A. (1968). Methodology of integrated surveys. In *Aerial Surveys and Integrated Studies*. Proc. Toulouse Conf. 1964, (UNESCO: Paris.) pp. 233–80.

FENNEMAN, M. N. (1916). Physiographic divisions of the United States. *Ann. Ass. Am. Geogr.* **6**, 19–98.

GIBBONS, F. R., and DOWNES, R. G. (1964). A study of the land in south-western Victoria. *Soil Conserv. Auth. Vict. Tech. Commun.* No. 3.

HAMMOND, E. H. (1954). Small-scale continental landform maps. *Ann. Ass. Am. Geogr.* **44**, 33–42.

HEATH, G. R. (1956). A comparison of two basic theories of land classification and their adaptability to regional photo interpretation key techniques. *Photogramm. Engng* **22**, 144–68.

HERBERTSON, A. J. (1905). The major natural regions: an assay in systematic geography. *Geogrl J.* **20**, 300–12.

HORTON, R. E. (1945). Erosional development of streams and their drainage basins. *Bull. geol. Soc. Am.* **56**, 275–370.

KIMBLE, G. H. T. (1951). The inadequacy of the regional concept. Ch. 9. In *London Essays in Geography*. (Longmans Green: London.)

LINTON, D. L. (1951). The delimitation of morphological regions. Ch. 11. In *London Essays in Geography*. (Longmans Green: London.)

MABBUTT, J. A., and STEWART, G. A. (1965). Application of geomorphology in integrated resources surveys in Australia. *Revue Géomorph. dyn.* **6**, 1–13.

MILNE, G. (1935). Some suggested units of classification and mapping, particularly for east African soils. *Soil Res.* **4**, 183–98.

PROKAYEV, V. I. (1962). The facies as the basic and smallest unit in landscape science·

Soviet Geogr. 3, 21–9.
SAVIGEAR, R. A. G. (1965). A technique of morphological mapping. Ann. Ass. Am. Geogr. 55, 514–38.
STRAHLER, A. N. (1958). Dimensional analysis applied to fluvially eroded landforms. Bull. geol. Soc. Am. 69, 279–300.
STONE, R. O., and DUGUNDJI, J. (1965). A study of microrelief — its mapping, classification and quantification by means of Fourier analysis. Engng Geol. 1, 89–187.
UNSTEAD, J. F. (1933). A system of regional geography. Geog. 18, 185–7.
VAN LOPIK, J. R., and KOLB, C. R. (1959). A technique for preparing desert terrain analogs. U.S. Army Corps Engrs, Waterways Exp. Stn, Vicksburg, Miss. Tech. Rep. 3–506.
VINAGRADOV, B. V., GERENCHUK, K. I., ISACHENKO, A. G., RAMAN, K. G., and TSEL'CHUK, YU. N. (1962). Basic principles of landscape mapping. Soviet Geogr. 3, 15–20.
WEBSTER, R. (1965). Minor statistical studies on terrain evaluation. Military Engng Exp. Establ., Christchurch, England. Report 877.
WOOD, W. F., and SNELL, J. B. (1960). A quantitative system for classifying landforms. Environmental Protection Research Division Tech. Rep. EP-124. Quartermaster Research and Engineering Command, U.S. Army.

Order and Disorder in Land

Bryan P. Ruxton

Division of Land Research, CSIRO, Canberra, Australia

All land tends with time towards a contemporary balance with the forces acting upon it, principally climate and gravity. Some aspects of land rapidly approach a steady state of dynamic equilibrium with their environment and so become ordered, displaying a strong interdependence of attributes, enabling them to be analysed by the open system theory. But other aspects of land respond so slowly to external conditions that they may remain almost indefinitely in disequilibrium. Owing to inheritance and multicomplexity of process many aspects of land appear disordered and most land is made up of natural but unsystematic groupings.

Conventionally integrated land inventories are made by isolating the disordered aspects of land into spatial frameworks and then attempting to relate the areal and temporal dispersion of other attributes to these. The disordered aspects are usually the lithology, structure, and landform assemblages inherited from historical events.

Further progress in land definition requires multi-disciplinary research into land dynamics and land history, and an integration of land dynamics with land inventories, without which extrapolations and predictions from any form of land inventory study will remain severely limited.

INTRODUCTION

Classical land evaluation studies have concentrated mainly on better classification and mapping procedures with a view to perfecting the methods of making land inventories. Sometimes an effort has been made to understand the genesis of the land by taking account of its history, of the forces acting on the component parts and their response to these forces, and of the materials entering and leaving the land. But very few studies have pursued the dynamic processes of land in depth and there has been little attempt to integrate land dynamics with land inventories with the result that much of our information is not of predictive value.

The main reason for this lack of prediction is our failure to understand the importance of what may be termed the 'order and disorder in land' and this paper is intended as a preliminary appraisal of the problems involved.

ORDER IN LAND

The Tendency towards a Steady State

Order in land is here defined as the regular or random distribution of particular attributes of land.

Land formed by whatever sequence of events tends with time to achieve a contemporary balance with the forces of climate and gravity. Provided the internal forces of the earth (volcanic, seismic, and tectonic) are acting very slowly or at a constant rate, land characters approach a steady state of dynamic equilibrium with the forces acting upon them.

Thus, in stable tectonic areas with similar rock, climate, and relief, and well-established drainage systems, there is an essential unity of the landscape with nearly complete interadjustment between all the component parts. There is an areal uniformity of land parameters such as shape, length, and degree of slope; length, width, depth, and gradient of stream channels; discharge, sediment load, and solute load of streams; stream pattern and drainage basin shape; and so on (cf. Howard 1965).

This interdependence and hence intercorrelation of attributes at sites and the orderly recurrence of similar sites or site sequences, such as catenas, forming gross land patterns usually discernable and mappable on aerial photographs, makes such ordered tracts of land ideal simple land systems. Such mutual adjustment of land form assemblages implies a balance between two opposing tendencies; an equipartition of erosional energy and a minimum total rate of work (Langbein and Leopold 1964). In such areas energy, mass, and time can be related by mathematical models based on the empirical analysis of observational data by statistics (Leopold, Wolman, and Miller 1964).

The Relevance of General Systems Theory

The most general model for such coordinated natural tracts of land is the 'open system' (Chorley 1962) wherein the state of balance of the land attributes is maintained by a continuous supply of material to, and removal of material from, the system such that the rate of increase of entropy within the system is zero (Leopold and Langbein 1962). General systems theory can be very valuable in land evaluation because it points to analogies in mechanics and chemistry and so it permits the use of established statistical-mechanical principles and results. Provided the state and organization of such systems can be defined, events in space or time can be predicted using the laws of probability.

Many features and processes of land may be related in terms of dynamic systems and analysed as open systems of complex behaviour (Strahler 1952). The concepts of open system theory have been applied to stream channels and stream patterns (Holmes 1964; Woldenberg 1966); to sediment transport (Tanner 1962a) and beaches (Tanner 1958), and hence to the prediction of heavy mineral occurrences (Tanner 1962b); to fluvially graded ridge and ravine topography (Hack 1960, 1965) and to hill slope profiles (Scheidegger and Langbein 1966); to fans and pediments (Hack 1965; Denny 1967); to weathering systems affecting solute denudation (Miller 1961); and to soil formation (Nikiforoff 1959).

Other features and processes of land may display oscillatory, cyclic, or decay type behaviour; for example, in the classical geomorphic cycle it was assumed that the rapid tectonic uplift of land was followed by a long period of still-stand while the land was gradually worn down to a peneplain; further uplift then initiated another geomorphic cycle. Thus, the classic type of geomorphic cycle displays decay type behaviour and is partly analogous with a closed system–a special case of an open system with no transfer of energy or materials across its boundaries. The sequence of landscapes developed in a classic geomorphic cycle are such that their state at any one time is dependent on the initial system conditions and the elapsed time, or in geomorphic terms on structure, process, and stage.

Open System Theory and Land Evaluation

Several powerful concepts, fundamental to land definition, have emerged from the application of open system theory to land.

Le Chatelier's Principle—Owing to gross climatic changes, slow earth move-ments and vertical inhomogeneities in lithology and structure, open systems are subject to changes in time, but such changes are in accordance with Le Chatelier's principle and tend to be self-regulating, that is any response in the system to an external change is such as to minimise the disturbance. Moreover, upon dis-turbance, the initial rate of change back towards equilibrium is proportional to the degree of disequilibrium induced, and thereafter it decreases exponentially.

For example, a small landslide may lead to the formation of a bar in a river channel, but the steepening of the river gradient over the bar increases the water velocity causing a tendency to erode the obstruction (cf. Langbein and Leopold 1964).

Constancy of Geometric Patterns—Over certain areas of land a steady state may be recognized, in the sense that some statistical parameters, such as relative frequency and periodicity of components (land form, soil, vegetation, etc.) are constant, even though the locations of individual occurrences are changing (Nikiforoff 1959). For example, in piedmont regions the size of fans is an exponential function of the size of the source area and piracy of piedmont streams causes changes in the location of areas of pediments but not in their relative proportion of the total area (Denny 1967). Similarly, despite the fact that each stream has its own unique combination of characteristics with its own rate of response to external variables (Holmes 1964) many river patterns have constant differential growth ratios, that is, they grow allometrically according to the requirements of open system theory (Woldenberg 1966).

In these circumstances some of the basic patterns of land attributes can be rigorously defined and organized into valid abstract land facets or systems (Brink *et al.* 1966), the term 'abstract' indicating that the facet or land system has a universal application and is not restricted to a particular region or location.

Time Averages Replaceable by Space Averages—Some land characteristics which respond rapidly to external variables can be explained in terms of current processes by a study of the distribution of the characteristics in space. In these circumstances the deviations in the dimension of time approximate, and can be replaced by, the deviations currently observed in space (Langbein and Leopold 1964). Replacement of time averages by space averages is applicable to stochastic processes–random phenomena that arise through processes which are developing in time in a manner controlled by probabilistic laws (Agterberg 1967)–in systems close to the steady state. This concept is analogous with the ergodic principle in statistical mechanics (Scheidegger and Langbein 1966).

Thresholds and Metastable States—'In certain cases the response of a system to a change of external variable may involve a *threshold*, or discontinuity, which separates two rather different system economies . . . Changes of external factors which require system parameters to cross a threshold may allow a metastable disequilibrium state to continue because of the great change required to initiate an equilibrium regime' (Howard 1965, p. 308). In some instances a small change in one factor may make a critical change in many others. Realisation of a threshold being involved can bring order to an otherwise apparently disordered landscape.

For example, the tendency for granites with similar texture and mineralogy to form both sand plains and bold mountains during the denudation of a region is probably governed by a critical threshold value in the balance between the rate of surface erosion and the rate of subsurface chemical weathering (Thomas 1966, p. 187).

Limitations of Open System Theory

Some aspects of land (e.g., river channel characteristics) rapidly approach a steady state of dynamic equilibrium with their environment and so become ordered, displaying a strong interdependence of attributes, enabling them to be analysed by open system theory. But other aspects of land (e.g., mature weathering profiles) respond so slowly to changed external conditions that they may remain for long periods, or almost indefinitely, in a state of disequilibrium. Thus, as will be discussed in the next section, many aspects of land appear disordered and most land is made up of natural but unsystematic groupings, and so open system theory can only be applied rigorously to specific systems, in certain areas, over limited spans of time.

A major problem then is the need to recognize in what circumstances or in what areas of land can an approach to equilibrium be assumed. Not only should there be a uniform pattern of components but also the components must be mutually adjusted. In many instances equilibria can only be validated statistically. Thus 'a group of apparently similar forms in nature vary among themselves and only as their averages define a general or usual condition' (Langbein and Leopold 1964, p. 793). It is also essential to recognize disequilibrium and to attempt to define degrees of departure from equilibrium.

In the analysis of open systems in a steady state we are concerned with frequency analyses and areal distributions not with actual series of events or with particular geographic locations. The statistical methods and concepts involved in analysing open systems generally involve the divorce of each observation from its three-dimensional spatial location and from its sequence in time so losing vital geographic and sequential data. Thus, predictions from open system analyses are given in terms of probable space or time frequencies and do not allow prediction at both a moment in time and a point in space. In some recent studies, however, it has proved possible to retain data on both location and orientation in regional analysis (Latham 1963; Whitten 1966).

DISORDER IN LAND

Disorder the Natural State of Land

The term disorder is used here to describe those aspects of an area of land in which no regularity or randomness, spatial or temporal, can be discerned, either in individual occurrences of components or in any of their statistical parameters. Disorder therefore refers to non-regular, non-random systems which cannot be resolved into regular and random parts. To some extent the degree of disorder in land depends on our lack of understanding of it and to this extent this disorder is not an intrinsic property of the landscape.

Very few natural landscape systems approach closely enough to the equilibrium state for the irregularities to be ignored. Most land is in various degrees of disequilibrium, or has too high a degree of irregularity to be ignored, and so is disordered. A corollary of disorder in land is that each area of land is unique and this fact has long been recognized by geographers and earth scientists.

That disorder in land is the normal and natural state of the earth's surface is evident from the failure of a century of effort by geographers to discover regions (Kimble 1951; James 1952; McDonald 1966). Thus, it is usual not to find interdependence and hence intercorrelation of all the attributes at a site. Most areally distributed geologic data is non-random (Cadigan 1962) but in many cases any regularity in the pattern of areal variability is yet to be discovered. Similarly, a subarea homogeneous with respect to one attribute is commonly heterogeneous with respect to most other attributes measured for the same population of objects (Whitten 1966).

For example, it is normally assumed that chemical weathering is controlled by the movement of subsurface water and the level of the water-table, both of which are usually adjusted to the levels of stream channels and the pattern of stream lines. But in practice, as many engineering excavations have shown, it has to date proved impossible to predict the nature or depth of weathering from surface conditions and hydrologic data. The problem appears to be most difficult in massive apparently uniform crystalline rocks (Thomas 1966).

The Cause of Disorder in Land

Disorder in land is the result of two main factors, the multicomplexity of process and inheritance.

Multicomplexity of Process—Perhaps the most obvious reason for disorder in land is that the earth's surface is the result of two entirely different groups of processes: the land building forces of the earth's interior expressed in earth movement, seismicity and volcanicity; and the land modification forces of subaerial denudation dependent largely on solar energy and gravity. There has always been a tendency in geography and land evaluation studies to simplify the effects of the land building forces by either assuming them constant or by assuming a periodicity of action (as in geomorphic cycles) or, particularly in stable regions, of even ignoring them. In the past this was partly due to the lack of quantitative data, but rapid advances in the last two decades indicate that even in the apparently most 'stable' parts of the continents earth movements are not constant and should not be ignored.

Even within the group of external earth forces there are many sets of opposing forces or tendencies. Each process is extremely complex involving both the interplay of a multitude of variables, the simultaneous variation of all or most of them, and the feedback mechanisms operating amongst them (cf. Whitten 1964). Moreover, each component of land is the result of a special group of processes, each process proceeds at a different rate, and 'each kind of process results in a different kind of area differentiation' (James 1952). The result is a variegated pattern of land with natural but unsystematic groupings, though some of the chaos is due to land being viewed in man's scale of space and time and may not be a reflection of basic disorder. As has been pointed out by Haggett (1965), data which are apparently disordered at one scale may appear ordered at another.

An example of apparent disorder due to complexity of process is the presence of thresholds in a geomorphic system. Thus, the incredibly varied fluvial and aeolian regimes evident in the riverine plains of south-eastern Australia over the past few tens of thousands of years (Pels 1966; Bowler 1967) are at least partly due to the closeness of the system and the external variables to several critical geomorphic thresholds. One of these, the proximity of saline groundwater to the ground surface, governs salting of the land which then leads to loss of vegetative cover and consequently allows greatly increased aeolian activity causing formation of deflation hollows, lakes, and lunettes.

Inheritance—The major cause of disorder in land is the inheritance of both a heterogeneous lithology and structure and the overprint of weathering profiles, superficial deposits, soils, and various land form assemblages of different ages.

We may agree with Melton (1958) that 'The variability in any natural environment is the product of the happenings in many geological periods . . . (and) to argue that this variability could ever be entirely explained is absurd.' Indeed inheritance in land has been stressed in every geomorphology chapter in our Land Research Series publications and has been especially highlighted in separate publications on the western Macdonnell Ranges (Mabbutt 1966) and on the Daly River basin (Wright 1966).

Land is the result of innumerable events over a long period of time. Some of these events can be reconstructed from traces left in the materials or land forms by these events using a set of temporal ordering principles, disciplined imagination, deductive reasoning by analogy, and multiple working hypotheses. These methods, as used by historians, archaeologists, geomorphologists, and geologists give good retrodiction but until recently they have proved of little predictive value. Retrodiction has greatly improved in recent years where isotope ratios and radiometric dating has allowed independent verification (and the addition of an absolute time scale) of stratigraphic sequences and events based on temporal ordering principles and fossil dating. Sufficient quantitative data are becoming available to construct process-response models, and it appears that prediction will be possible. Such process-response models will only be approximations as only a few of the variables can ever be quantified but the models can be designed in such a way that their validity can be tested.

Inheritance, then, is the principle cause of the infinite variety of land and it is very much more difficult to investigate than is the apparent disorder due to multicomplexity of process.

DISCUSSION

Order and Disorder in Land Definition

Nearly all attempts at regionalization, and of mapping land for management or development purposes, have of necessity been a compromise between the scale and purpose of mapping on the one hand and the actual land attributes on the other. Conventionally, land is grouped into areas relatively homogeneous in structure, lithology, and land form so that the areal and temporal dispersion of other features can be related to these. By this means the disordered aspects of land, largely inherited features and unsystematic groupings, are isolated into component parts in a geographic framework. In general, each component (land system or region) mapped will have undergone a unique geologic and geomorphic history and will be subject to an equally unique combination of processes.

In a few instances, such as in stable areas with homogeneous structure, lithology, and relief, the component areas may approach a steady state of dynamic equilibrium with climate and are sufficiently ordered to be mapped objectively either with sharp clear boundaries at discontinuities or at arbitrary values of regional trends. In such a land the geographical region, apart from man and his influence, would be reality. Elsewhere, the drawing of boundaries is nearly always an arbitrary matter and the patterns that are mapped and described merely act as a foundation for further systematic investigations or as a framework for further discussion.

Land definition can never be strictly a contemporary study because area differences have to be explained in terms of cause and effect, and so land definition may be resolved into land inventories and land dynamics. To achieve an integrated view of land needs not only a multi-disciplinary approach but also a linkage or correlation between the various dynamic systems and land inventories. Thus, it is envisaged that for each mapped component of land with limited variability of its attributes, a particular set of constants and coupling functions will be necessary to apply the various models of dynamic processes to it. Because of the disorder in land many of these constants and coupling functions will be unique for each land facet.

Land definition then can never be just a matter of making better and more complete land inventories. To be of predictive value and, for example, to foretell the effect of the various practices of man on land it is necessary to understand a whole panoply of processes and their interplay.

Land Dynamics

As we have seen, part of the disorder in land is apparent, being due to the complexity of process, and may be turned into order by land dynamic studies leading to better models or more sophisticated statistical analyses, and hence to better prediction.

Figure 1 is constructed to illustrate the absolute time scale (on an exponential basis) over which it is necessary to measure data to construct adequate frequency series for different earth processes. For catastrophic events the figure only shows their time duration. In other processes the order of time indicated also approximates the response times of the various 'earth systems'. Four arbitrary groups of dynamic systems are recognized: very rapid catastrophic changes, rapidly varying systems where the data necessary to construct reliable frequency series can be collected in less than 100 years, slowly varying systems where data collection is relevant up to several hundred thousand years, and systems changing so slowly that they may be assumed constant for the purposes of land evaluation. *Very Rapid Catastrophic Changes*—Volcanic eruptions, earthquakes, major landslides, great bush fires, and meteorite impacts are catastrophic events occurring in a short time period and each such event causes great changes to some or all of the land features involved. Sometimes, new forms or deposits are produced which are independent of the normal land processes.

Many such events are unpredictable in time and space though for earthquakes and volcanicity it has been possible to define regions on the basis of frequency of recurrence and (for earthquakes) to forecast in a statistical way the risk involved in particular areas.

Some effects of volcanism are a major cause of disorder in land, for example, in New Guinea ash-fall layers may blanket a whole range of land types in which there had previously been good intercorrelation between rock, land form, soil, and vegetation.

Rapidly Varying Dynamic Systems—The dynamic systems of contemporary climate (including global atmospheric circulation), fluvial channels, beaches, seral vegetation, and so on have frequency series such that they can be measured directly in man's scale of space and time. Knowledge of these systems is advancing so rapidly that conceptual models are being rapidly replaced by deterministic models in which all the relevant response characteristics are incorporated in a unifying differential equation that can be used for accurate description and prediction (Whitten 1964; Smagorinsky 1965; Weyl 1966).

In practice actual measurements of these rapidly varying systems have only been made over a few decades and there is still a scarcity of information on rare events of great magnitude (Wolman and Miller 1960). Many such events, great floods, storm surges, typhoons, etc., are like the very rapid catastrophic changes, still unpredictable in time and space, and are another cause of disorder in land. *Slowly Varying Dynamic Systems*—To obtain the necessary frequency analyses to construct models for the formation of soils, weathering and lateritic profiles, slopes, and for gross changes of climate and vegetation it is necessary to resort to geological methods of reconstruction using a set of temporal ordering principles and historic and radiometric dating techniques. Thus, it is now

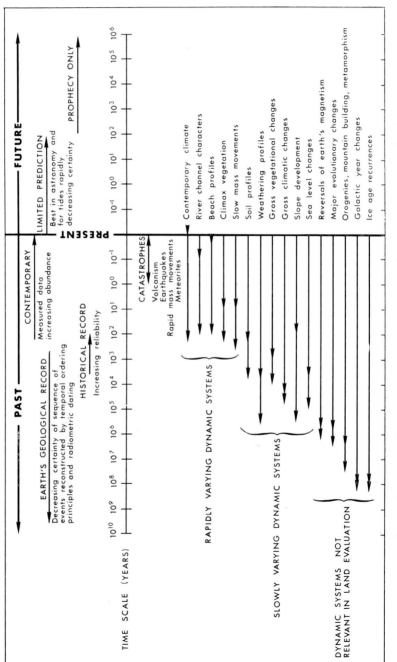

Fig. 1. Time scales of major changes in various dynamic systems relevant to land definition.

possible to identify, and measure, gross climatic and vegetational changes for several tens of thousands of years (Dury 1967; Tsukada 1967). On larger time scales, models have been constructed, using simulation techniques, to imitate geological processes acting over periods of several million years (Harbaugh 1966).

Many such reconstructions and models are indicating a periodicity or cyclicity of many earth processes. Thus, over the last several hundred thousand years the gross climate is now believed to have oscillated from cold to warm to cold many times with a period of 40,000 years. Complementary changes took place in vegetation and soils.

Systems Assumed Constant—Changes requiring many millions of years to effect, such as mountain building and destruction, Milky Way galactic year changes, major ice age recurrences, and so on are so far removed from man's scale of space and time that they can probably be ignored in land definition.

CONCLUSION

The land system concept, based on partial interdependence and hence inter-correlation of several attributes at a site and the recurrence of similar sites or site sequences (such as catenas) forming gross land patterns or systems, quali-tatively applied by many survey organizations since 1946 has been partly quantified independently by geomorphologists who have applied the principles of systems theory to many land characteristics. Further progress requires both multidisciplinary research into land dynamics and inheritance, and coupling of land dynamics to land inventories.

Both the land system concept and open systems theory have proved most useful in regions with homogeneous rock, climate, and relief where a steady state of dynamic equilibrium is approached. Here, there is almost complete interdependence and intercorrelation of attributes and all components of the land are mutually adjusted. Definition of the state and organization of such a land system allows predictions to be made according to the laws of probability; however it is necessary to recognize and study metastable states, thresholds, and rare events of great magnitude. Some land characters may be time dependent and treatment by closed system theory is more appropriate as, for example serial stages in the denudation of a volcano.

Owing principally to inheritance and the multicomplexity of process, most land is disordered, being made up of natural but unsystematic groupings whose attributes are not inter-adjusted. Thus, it becomes essential to recognize disequilibrium, to define degrees of departure from equilibrium, and to appreci-ate the decreasing reliability of extrapolations and predictions as systems depart further from the steady state.

REFERENCES

AGTERBERG, F. P. (1967). Computer techniques in geology. *Earth-Sci. Rev.* **3**, 47–77.

BOWLER, J. M. (1967). Quaternary chronology of Goulburn valley sediments and their correlation in south-eastern Australia. *J. geol. Soc. Aust.* **14**, 287–92.

BRINK, A. B., MABBUTT, J. A., WEBSTER, R., and BECKETT, P. H. T. (1966). *Report of the working group on land classification and data storage.* MEXE No. 940. Military Engineering Experimental Establishment Oxford.

CADIGAN, R. A. (1962). A method for determining the randomness of regionally distri-buted quantitative geologic data. *J. Sedim. Petrol.* **32**, 813–18.

CHORLEY, R. J. (1962). Geomorphology and general systems theory. *U.S. Geol. Surv. Prof. Paper* 500-B.

DENNY, C. S. (1967). Fans and pediments. *Am. J. Sci.* **265**, 81–105.

DURY, G. H. (1967). Climatic change as a geographical backdrop. *Aust. Geog.* **10**, 231–42.

HACK, J. T. (1960) Interpretation of erosional topography in humid temperate regions. *Am. J. Sci.* **258-A**, 80–97.

HACK, J. T. (1965). Geomorphology of the Shenandoah Valley Virginia and origin of the residual ore deposits. *U.S. Geol. Surv. Prof. Paper* 484.

HAGGETT, P. (1965). Scale components in geographical problems. Chapter 9. In *Frontiers in Geographical Teaching.* (Ed. R. J. Chorley and P. Haggett.) (Methuen: London.)

HARBAUGH, J. W. (1966). Mathematical simulation of marine sedimentation with IBM 7090/7094 computers. *Kansas geol. Survey Computer Contr.* 1.

HOLMES, C. D. (1964). Equilibrium in humid-climate physiographic processes. *Am. J. Sci.* **262**, 436–45.

HOWARD, A. D. (1965). Geomorphological systems — equilibrium and dynamics. *Am. J. Sci.* **263**, 302–12.

JAMES, P. E. (1952). Toward a further understanding of the regional concept. *Ann. Ass. Am. Geogr.* **52**, 195–222.

KIMBLE, G. H. T. (1951). The inadequacy of the regional concept. In *London Essays in Geography.* (Ed. L. D. Stamp and S. W. Wooldridge.) (Longman and Green:London.)

LANGBEIN, W. B., and LEOPOLD, L. B. (1964). Quasi-equilibrium states in channel morphology. *Am. J. Sci.* **262**, 782–94.

LATHAM, J. P. (1963). Methodology for an instrumented geographic analysis. *Ann. Ass. Am. Geogr.* **53**, 194–209.

LEOPOLD, L. B., and LANGBEIN, W. B. (1962). The concept of entropy in landscape evolution. *U.S. Geol. Surv. Prof. Paper* 500-A.

LEOPOLD, L. B., WOLMAN, M. G., and MILLER, J. P. (1964). *Fluvial processes in geomorphology.* (Freeman: London.)

MABBUTT, J. A. (1966). Landforms of the western Macdonnell Ranges. In *Essays in Geomorphology.* (Ed. G. H. Dury.) (Heinemann: London.) 83–119.

MCDONALD, J. R. (1966). The region: its conception, design, and limitations. *Ann. Ass. Am. Geogr.* **56**, 516–28.

MELTON, M. A. (1958). Correlation structure of morphometric properties of drainage systems and their controlling agents. *J. Geol.* **66**, 442–60.

MILLER, J. P. (1961). Solutes in small streams draining single rock types, Sangre de Cristo Range, New Mexico. *U.S. Geol. Surv. Prof. Paper* 1535-F.

NIKIFOROFF, C. C. (1959). Reappraisal of the soil. *Science, N.Y.* **129**, 186–96.

PELS, S. (1966). Late Quaternary chronology of the riverine plain of south-eastern Australia. *J. geol. Soc. Aust.* **13**, 27–40.

SCHEIDEGGER, A. E., and LANGBEIN, W. B. (1966). Probability concepts in geomorphology. *U.S. Geol. Surv. Prof. Paper* 500-C.

SMAGORINSKY, J. (1965). Implications of dynamical modelling of the general circulation in long-range forecasting. *W.M.O. Tech. Note.* **66**, 131–7.

STRAHLER, A. N. (1952). Dynamic basis of geomorphology. *Bull. geol. Soc. Am.* **63**, 923–38.

TANNER, W. F. (1958). The equilibrium beach. *Trans. Am. geophys. Un.* **39**, 889–96.

TANNER, W. F. (1962a). Geomorphology and the sediment transport system. *SEast. Geol.* **4**, 113–26.

TANNER, W. F. (1962b). The use of equilibrium concepts in the search for heavy minerals. *Trans. Amer. Soc. Mining Engineers* **223**, 395–9.

THOMAS, M. F. (1966). Some geomorphological implications of deep weathering patterns in crystalline rocks in Nigeria. *Trans. Inst. Br. Geog.* No. 40.

TSUKADA, M. (1967). Vegetation in subtropical Formosa during the Pleistocene glaciations and the Holocene. *Palaeogeogr., Palaeoclim., Palaeoecol.* **3**, 49–64.

WEYL, P. K. (1966). Environmental stability of the earth's surface — chemical considerations. *Geochim. cosmochim. Acta* **37**, 663–79.

WHITTEN, E. H. T. (1964). Process-response models in geology. *Bull. geol. Soc. Am.* **75**, 455–64.

WHITTEN, E. H. T. (1966). Sequential multivariate regression methods and scalars in the study of fold-geometry variability. *J. Geol.* **74**, 744–63.

WOLDENBERG, M. J. (1966). Horton's laws justified in terms of allometric growth and steady state in open systems. *Bull. geol. Soc. Am.* **77**, 431–4.

WOLMAN, M. G., and MILLER, J. P. (1960). Magnitude and frequency of forces in geomorphic processes. *J. Geol.* **68**, 54–74.

WRIGHT, R. L. (1966). Landform inheritance and regional contrasts in the Daly River basin, Northern Australia. In *Geography as Human Ecology.* (Ed. S. R. Eyre and G. R. Jones.) (Edward Arnold: London.) 122-46.

Sampling Considerations in Land Evaluation

M. J. Goodspeed

Division of Land Research, CSIRO, Canberra, Australia

In the evaluation of land characteristics we proceed from measurement of properties at a finite number of points to endeavour to assess these properties everywhere in a defined area. Consideration is needed of the sampling density to be aimed at, in order to avoid loss of important information resulting from too sparse sampling and wasted effort in collecting data in unnecessary detail.

In this paper an examination is made of the extent to which such problems may be profitably considered through frequency-transform techniques.

The sampling theorem and its extension to the case of more than one independent variable are briefly presented. Implications for measurements of field variables (soil type, depth, etc.) are considered.

The possibilities for manipulating data from aerial photographs in the transform domain, by optical and other means, are then considered.

It is concluded that such considerations can offer useful guidance in the planning of field surveys and that direct application of the techniques in photo-manipulation may well be profitable.

INTRODUCTION

In the evaluation of those properties of an area of land which can be quantified, we generally proceed from their measurement at a finite number of points to endeavour to assess their value everywhere in a defined area. In performing this interpolation we are often guided by the identification of recognizable patterns on aerial photographs of the area in question. For example, we may, on the basis of past experience, be satisfied that a certain identifiable pattern on the aerial photographs represents an area of uniform soil pH value. We may measure soil pH at a number of points, check the assumption of uniformity, and then assert that this value applies over all the defined area.

Conditions are rarely as simple as in the above trivial example. our interpolation may, in other cases, be based on the postulation of a uniform trend in a definite direction, or of a cyclically-repeating pattern in a definite direction. Here again we are guided by the recognition of a pattern on the aerial photographs.

Viewed in this way, two different sorts of questions arise in the evaluation of land areas, typically:

1. What sampling density on the ground is needed to adequately define the variations of a selected parameter?

2. What patterns exist on the aerial photographs with which measurable parameters may tentatively be correlated?

The answers to both sorts of questions may be approached using techniques of frequency-transform analysis which have been developed to handle analogous problems in mathematical physics and communications engineering. In this paper we first examine the relevance of these techniques to questions of ground sampling density problems. Recognizing the impracticability of carrying out long and involved calculation during the actual course of field work, we endeavour merely to outline the relevant theory and suggest how it may be used to provide guidance during the planning stage of field surveys.

In the second part of this paper the use of frequency-transform methods, either optically or by digital computer, in the detection and manipulation of certain types of patterns on aerial photographs is examined.

FIELD SAMPLING

Most of the parameters we wish to measure will be functions of position on the ground only, that is, they may be considered as determined by two co-ordinates. Examples are altitude, slope and all other topographic parameters, vegetation density, etc. Although we may on occasions wish to consider parameters as functions of position and altitude (e.g., annual precipitation) or depth below the surface (e.g., soil parameters) we will not consider such cases here beyond remarking that the principles remain unchanged.

Sampling in One Dimension

We shall first consider the variations of a parameter p as a function of x, distance along a straight line. Figure 1 shows a continuous plot of the 'true' values of p along a transept, with samples taken at regular intervals Δx apart. We assume that the samples are measured without error. It is evident that the smaller the sampling interval Δx, the more accurately we can reconstruct the complete curve relating p to x, but it is also clear that, as we continue to decrease the sampling interval, the improvement in precision per sample becomes progressively smaller. This suggests that an optimum sampling interval may exist. We now show that, subject to certain restrictions on the form of the relationship between p and x, such an optimum sampling interval can be defined.

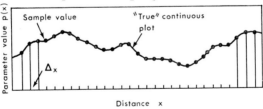

Fig. 1. Continuous parameter sampled at regular intervals.

The sampling theorem (Whitakker 1935; Shannon 1949) states that, if p(x), the 'true' relation between p and x, is 'band-limited' with upper frequency limit W, then p(x) can be *completely* reconstructed if samples are taken $1/2W$ apart. The process of reconstruction is rather complex (see Appendix 1) but need not be considered in detail here.

The term 'band-limited' relates to the process whereby the continuous plot of Figure 1 is approximated by adding together a large number of sine waves of varying amplitude, wave-length, and phase. It can be shown that any relationship which can be plotted as in Figure 1 can be represented as precisely as desired in this way; in general an infinite number of components is required to reproduce the original plot in every detail. Plotting the amplitude of these components against frequency (Fig. 2) we obtain the 'amplitude spectrum' of p(x); if amplitude is negligible above a certain frequency W then p(x) is said to be band-limited with limiting frequency W. These concepts are defined more precisely in Appendix 1.

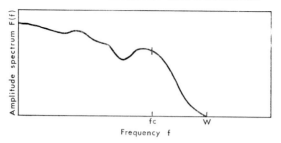

Fig. 2. Amplitude spectrum of p(x).

In terms of the sampling theorem, the band-limited character of a function only becomes useful in allowing us to increase the interval between samples when the limiting frequency is low, i.e. no higher than about 10–20 times the highest dominant frequency (fc in Fig. 2) present in the spectrum.

The mechanisms tending to lower the limiting frequency are as varied as the quantities we can represent as in Figure 1. We note that any discontinuities or sharp changes in slope of the graph produce high-frequency components in the frequency domain (see, for example, Lee 1960), tending to extend the limiting frequency W to very high values; degradational and erosional processes tend to remove these sharp discontinuities and thus produce useful band-limiting. For example, one would expect initial sharp discontinuities in the values of many soil parameters to become more diffuse as solute transport and weathering processes proceed. Similarly, erosional processes generally operate to smooth out sharp topographic features in a landscape. Thus, the shape of a cross section through the peak of the Great Pyramid of Cheops has gradually lost its initial high frequency components as natural and man-accelerated erosion has proceeded.

There are also, however, processes which operate in the opposite direction. Tectonic activity such as orogenesis and movement along fault planes, volcanism, wave-action at a coastline, and the incisive action of streams tend to regenerate sharp discontinuities in topography and many other quantifiable parameters. In any particular area, therefore, the extent to which this approach may be useful tends to be determined by the relative dominance of regenerative and degradational processes in recent geological times.

If we wish to approach the sampling problem from this viewpoint our principal difficulty is to assess the limiting frequency W in any particular situation. In Appendix 1 it is shown that, if we know M, the range of values which a parameter may assume, and also S, the maximum possible slope of a plot of the parameter values against distance, then W can be readily computed. The assessment of M and S in any particular situation is of course a matter for the specialist in the relevant field.

Consequences of Inadequate Sampling

If the sampling interval used is too large then, from the viewpoint advocated here, this amounts to an underestimation of W. Calling this underestimated frequency W_a the effect is that components between W_a and W are added to the high-frequency end of the resulting spectrum, falsifying amplitudes over all frequencies as far below W_a as W is above W_a. This effect is called 'aliasing' in the literature, the implication being that high-frequency components are 'falsely identified' with a lower frequency (Lee 1960). As the sampling interval is increased the distortion progressively affects lower-frequency parts of the spectrum. Thus, if the sampling interval is only slightly larger than $1/2W$ then we are distorting only the very highest parts of the spectrum where amplitude is in any case low; we introduce relatively small errors in our interpolations but our interpretation of broad trends is unaffected. However, if we continue to increase the sampling interval, the distortion passes to lower parts of the spectrum where amplitude is high; our interpolations now contain significant errors and no longer reproduce correctly even the broad trends.

Smoothing of Data

In many cases where we can make a reliable estimate of W before commencing sampling we may decide that we are not interested in the finer detail produced by high-frequency components; our purposes would be served by reliable measures of broad trends in the data. We cannot validly proceed by ignoring the presence of components of higher frequency than those we are interested in since, as outlined in the previous subsection, those components will thereby be aliased into regions in which we are interested and may lead to serious errors in interpolation.

We can, however, adopt procedures which have the effect of reducing the amplitude of redundant high-frequency components. In Figure 3 is shown a plot of a band-limited parameter $p(x)$ which has been sampled at $1/2W$. If we replace the original sample values by running means over three samples then we have reduced the amplitude of components in the upper half of the spectrum to less than 10% of their initial values (Hamming 1962). This is an example of a simple numerical filter; other more efficient (and more elaborate) filters can be formulated (e.g., Rader and Gold 1967).

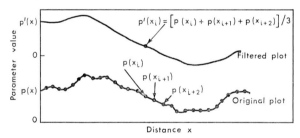

Fig. 3. Original and filtered plot of parameter (px) ('running mean' filtering).

To use such a numerical filter we still require, in principle, to know the parameter values at intervals determined by $1/2W$. The number of sample values to be collected has not been reduced. However, the effective limiting frequency of the derived data has been considerably reduced (by a factor of about 2 in the above example) and this leads us to expect relatively minor aliasing errors to result from sampling the *derived* data at an interval rather greater than $1/2W_d$ (where W_d is the limiting frequency of the derived data). This is the justification for the commonly used procedure of averaging a number of sample values in the vicinity of a 'sample point' and repeating the procedure at other sample points some distance away; the procedure is examined in some detail in Appendix 2. It is shown there that in fact a reduction of the total number of samples is not often to be expected. However, accessibility considerations may make the procedure profitable.

Sampling in Two Dimensions

All of the above considerations apply also in the case of sampling over an area.

Basically, a grid should be laid over the area such that the intervals between the points of intersection are adequately spaced in each direction relative to the limiting frequency along that direction. Samples taken at the points of intersection then provide a satisfactory basis for interpolation (Fig. 4).

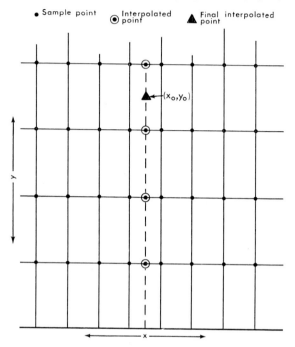

Fig. 4. Area sampling with rectangular grid, indicating interpolation procedure.

It should be noted that the grid lines need not be straight. In fact, if the two-dimensional spectrum (see below) were known, it would be possible to specify a grid to minimise the total number of samples, and such a grid would, in general, depart considerably from a regular, rectangular grid. These questions are briefly discussed in Appendix 3.

If we have no knowledge of the spatial frequency distribution of a particular parameter then we can do no better than to lay out a regular rectangular grid. However, if the parameter can be correlated with another of which we have some knowledge, say topography, or tonal patterns on the aerial photograph, then we are justified in altering the grid accordingly.

Conclusions on Field Sampling

We have approached the problem by considering the sampling interval needed for *complete* definition of the parameter. We have shown that this interval can be related to the limiting frequency of the spectrum of the parameter and have given one method by which this might be estimated. We have indicated that valid procedures exist by which unnecessary detail may be removed.

All these procedures depend, in varying degree, on knowledge of the spectral composition of the parameter in question. Some work has been done on this in the case of microrelief (Stone and Dugundji 1965) and geological parameters (see Agterberg 1967) but much would be learnt from further work on these and other parameters.

It is recognized that practical considerations of accessibility and cost will generally limit the number of samples to considerably less than that needed for complete definition. However, benefit may be obtained from consideration of the concepts discussed, in ensuring reasonably productive use of the resources available.

It is concluded that these considerations are useful in the sampling of band-limited parameters. However, they are of no direct assistance in the study of those rapidly varying or discontinuous parameters which cannot be considered band-limited. In fact, it appears that the only satisfactory basis on which to define an adequate sampling procedure for such parameters is by correlation with others which are band-limited. If we have established that a specific crop cannot be grown where soil salinity exceeds a certain level, then adequate sampling of salinity enables us to map completely the discontinuous parameter representing suitability for crop establishment (in respect of soil salinity). Again, we can map areas subject to flooding for any given water level on a topographic map because of the near-perfect correlation between topography and water level. In other cases where sufficiently high correlation with a single band-limited parameter cannot be established it may be profitable to use multiple correlation against a number of such parameters. It may be expected that many of these will be correlated, to some extent, with tonal patterns on the aerial photograph.

FREQUENCY DECOMPOSITION OF AERIAL PHOTOGRAPHS

Principles of the Technique

It is well known (see, for example, Maréchal 1963) that the two-dimensional Fourier spectrum of an object can be formed in the focal plane of a lens placed in front of the object (Fig. 5). In normal photographic practice this transformed

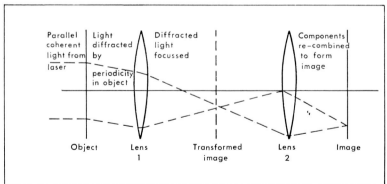

Fig. 5. Formation of two-dimensional spectrum through a lens.

image is then re-transformed and recorded. However, by means of a suitably designed optical system, access to the transformed image is possible. This transformed image may be recorded photographically, in which case a record of the two-dimensional periodicities present in the object, and their respective intensities and directions, is obtained. Alternatively, the transformed image may be manipulated by the masking out of unwanted components ('spatial filtering') and then re-transformed to produce a modified photographic image. This modified image may, for example, show the result of removing all high-frequency components from the photograph; or it may accentuate periodicities in a particular direction.

This technique, which has been used for several years in various fields (e.g. Dobrin, Ingalls, and Long 1965), is a powerful tool in the assessment of spatial periodicities. However, a specialized high-quality optical system, using a laser as light source, is needed for its effective use and severe practical difficulties arise if one wishes to do more than merely remove entirely certain parts of the spectrum. In particular, manipulation of phase is severely limited by the fact that a different physical filter must be made for each different manipulation one might wish to use.

The purpose of this section is to point out that, because of developments in computer hardware and in numerical analysis, it is now becoming possible to consider the use of the digital computer to perform these operations. The capacity for almost unlimited flexibility in manipulation is thereby presented.

Devices are now becoming available (e.g. Ledley 1964) which enable pictorial information to be read into the core-store of a computer entirely automatically and extremely rapidly. The information content of an aerial photograph is very high and only the largest machines would have sufficient capacity to hold the information content of even one photograph in rapid-access storage at one time. However, concurrent developments in high-capacity, high-transfer rate backing stores have the potential to overcome these problems (Pearcey and Chapman 1968).

Once the digital 'image' of an aerial photograph is available to the computer, its two-dimensional Fourier spectrum (McCowan 1966) can be computed. However, classical methods of performing the required calculations have been so extremely time consuming as to be entirely impracticable. For example, on a CDC 3600 machine transformation of a photograph resolved on a 1000×1000 raster would take approximately 60 hours by these methods.

Recently Cooley and Tukey (1965) have developed a much improved algorithm for the performance of these calculations. Their procedure is very much faster than earlier methods. Further, the speed ratio increases with increasing number of sample points and thus the method is particularly advantageous when large amounts of data are to be processed, as in the present application. The execution time for the above example is reduced to approximately 30 minutes.

At the present time no pictorial input device is available at the CSIRO computer and therefore it is not possible to present actual examples of this

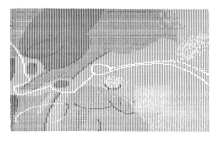
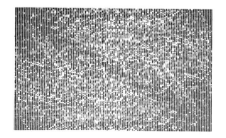

Fig. 6   Fig. 7

Fig. 6. Synthetic 'aerial photograph'.
Fig. 7. Two-dimensional power spectrum of Fig. 6 (Zero frequency in centre, higher frequencies towards the edges).

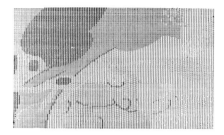 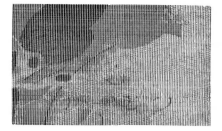

Fig. 8   Fig. 9

Fig. 8. Synthetic 'aerial photograph' after spatial filtering — lower 10% of spectrum removed, all directions.

Fig. 9. Synthetic 'aerial photograph' after spatial filtering — lower 30% of spectrum removed, all directions.

approach to spatial filtering. However, in order to demonstrate its feasibility a 'synthetic aerial photograph' (Fig. 6) was generated in the computer store, its two-dimensional spectrum obtained (Fig. 7), and the results of two types of simple spatial filtering produced (Figs. 8 and 9). Because of the simplicity of the original data these achieve little more than to show that a perceptible modification has been produced. It is, however, suggested that they indicate the existence of a worthwhile field of investigation to be followed when input facilities become available. It is hoped that more informative examples may be available by the time this paper is presented.

Potential Applications

Applications of the techniques fall into two classes, depending on whether the two-dimensional spectrum itself, or its recomposition into a modified picture after spatial filtering, is regarded as the final product.

Applications of the Two-dimensional Spectrum—This may be used as a basis for the characterization of land patterns, since it presents in a clearly understandable manner important elements, spatial periodicities and their variation with direction, of the original landscape.

It also provides a firm basis for the establishment of an adequate sampling grid for those field parameters which may be tentatively correlated with photographic tone, as discussed earlier in this paper.

Applications of the 'Spatially Filtered' Photograph—The principal application here is likely to be the removal from the photograph of those periodic components which are masking others of greater importance for a particular purpose. As an example, we may wish to remove a regular pattern of sand dunes in order to study other unrelated features on the photograph. Again, if the sand dunes themselves are the object of study then other disturbing features might be removed.

Conclusions on Frequency Decomposition of Aerial Photographs

The technique, using optical methods, is well established in geophysics and other fields; there are doubtless many potential applications in land evaluation also. However, it is suggested that the greater flexibility and convenience of the use of the digital computer warrants further investigation when the necessary input facilities become available.

D. J. Mclean, Division of Radiophysics, CSIRO, developed the routine FOURIOUS (an implementation of the Cooley-Tukey algorithm) used in the spectral analysis. Figures 6 to 9 were produced using HALFTONE, a routine developed by A. K. Head, Division of Tribophysics, CSIRO.

APPENDIX 1

Fourier Transform of a Parameter as a Function of Distance

The process outlined in the text whereby the function $p(x)$ is analysed into sinusoidal components is in fact that of evaluating the Fourier transform of $p(x)$.

$$F(\omega) = \frac{1}{\sqrt{2\pi}} \int_{\infty}^{\infty} p(x)e^{-i\omega x}\, dx,$$

where ω is the 'angular frequency', related to the frequency f (as we have used in the text) by

$$\omega = 2\pi f.$$

$F(\omega)$ is in general a complex function of ω. The 'amplitude spectrum' is given by

$$A(\omega) = |F(\omega)|$$

and the 'power spectrum' by

$$P(\omega) = (A(\omega))^2.$$

Band-limited Functions

The function $p(x)$ is said to be band-limited with limiting frequency W if

$$F(\omega) = 0 \qquad \text{for } |\omega| > 2\pi W.$$

Sampling Theorem

It can be shown (e.g. Shannon 1949) that if $p(x)$ is band-limited with limiting frequency W then its value, for *any* x, is expressible in terms of its value at sample points spaced $1/2W$ apart by the equation

$$p(x) = \sum p\left[\frac{n}{2W}\right] \frac{\sin(2\pi Wx - n\pi)}{2\pi Wx - n\pi}. \tag{1}$$

Equation (1) may be interpreted as follows: to find the value of $p(x)$ at a point x_0 (in general *not* one of the sample points) we compute a weighted sum of *all* the sample values. The weight m to be assigned to each of the sample points is determined from its distance d from x_0 by

$$m = \frac{\sin 2\pi Wd}{2\pi Wd}.$$

In practice this procedure is rarely used in interpolation from sample values because of its complexity. The crucial point is that if samples are taken at an interval of $1/2W$ or less then all the available information has been obtained. We may then use simpler interpolation procedures if we wish, aware of the inaccuracies thereby introduced; but these interpolations are securely based on adequate control data.

Maximum Possible Slope of a Band-limited, Amplitude-limited Function

A relation is here derived which permits the computation of W from estimates of M, the total range of $p(x)$ and S, the maximum possible slope of $p(x)$.

Without loss of generality we can assume that $p(x)$ is confined to the range $-M/2$ to $M/2$.

Accordingly, we assume a function $p(x)$ restricted in the following two respects:

$$| p(x) | \leqslant M/2 \quad \text{for all } x$$
$$(M \text{ is a positive constant}) \tag{2}$$

$$F(\omega) = \frac{1}{\sqrt{2\pi}} \int_{-\infty}^{\infty} p(x)e^{-i\omega x}\, dx$$
$$= 0 \quad \text{for } | \omega | > 2\pi W. \tag{3}$$

Differentiating (1), we obtain

$$\frac{dp}{dx} = 2W \sum p \left(\frac{n}{2W}\right) \left[\frac{(2Wx-n)\pi\cos(2\pi Wx-n\pi) - \sin(2\pi Wx-n\pi)}{(2Wx-n)^2\pi}\right] \tag{4}$$

If we can find the maximum value of dp/dx for any particular value of x (say x_0) then we can argue that this is the maximum possible value for *any* x, since x can be brought to x_0 by a change of origin, which does not, of course, run counter to restrictions (2) and (3).

Thus, setting $x = 1/4$ in (4), we obtain

$$\left(\frac{dp}{dx}\right)_{x=1/4 w} = \frac{2W}{\pi} \sum p \left(\frac{n}{2W}\right)\frac{(-1)^{n+1}}{(n-1/2)^2}$$

which is maximised, subject to condition (2), by setting

$$p\left(\frac{n}{2W}\right) = (-1)^n\, M/2. \tag{5}$$

One function which would give sample values as in (5) is

$$\varphi(x) = \frac{M}{2} \sin (2\pi Wx - k/2W) \tag{6}$$

(a sine-wave at the maximum frequency of the pass band defined by (3)). Since the sample values completely define any function within the pass band, $\varphi(x)$ is the only function which maximises $\left[\frac{dp}{dx}\right]_{x=1/4w}$. Therefore

$$S = \frac{d\varphi}{dx} = WM.$$

$$\text{or } W = \frac{S}{\pi M.} \tag{7}$$

Sampling Interval in Terms of S and M
From (7)

$$\Delta x = 1/2W$$
$$= \pi M/2S. \tag{8}$$

APPENDIX 2

Bandwidth Compression by Averaging of Adjacent Samples

It is appropriate to examine this question in terms of the power spectrum (Appendix 1) rather than the amplitude spectrum of $p(x)$ since, at the stage of survey planning, we have no knowledge of phase as a function of frequency.

It can be shown (e.g. Hamming 1962) that if each sample value is replaced by the mean of m adjacent values then the power spectrum of $p(x)$ is multiplied by a factor $g(f)$ given by

$$g(f) = [\sin m\pi f/(m \sin\pi f)]^2 \tag{9}$$

Thus function, which is well known in physical optics and other fields, is plotted for several values of m in Figure 10. It is seen to be characterized by a peak of unit magnitude at frequency zero and a number of smaller peaks at higher frequencies. With increasing m the number of these secondary peaks increases but the magnitude of each decreases.

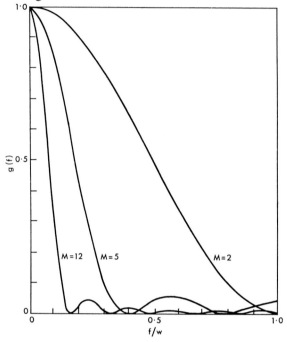

Fig. 10. Characteristics of 'running mean' filter for indicated values of m.

The value of this bandwidth compression can only be assessed if we have an estimate of the spectrum of p(x). As an example, in Figure 11 is shown a typical

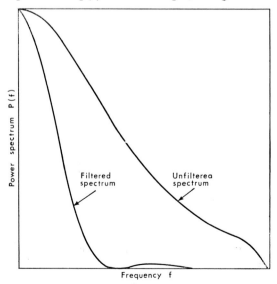

Fig. 11. Parameter spectrum before and after filtering (m = 5).

spectrum together with a plot of the filtered spectrum obtained with m equal to 5. The drastic reduction in high-frequency components is apparent. If we are prepared to tolerate the distortion resulting from aliasing of, say, 5% of the total power, we can derive a much reduced value for W and a correspondingly increased value for the interval between sample groups.

Table 1 presents, for the above example, values for the factor by which the sampling interval can be increased corresponding to given values for the acceptable distortion level. However, no precise statements of this nature can be made in any particular situation without a knowledge of the spectral characteristics of the parameter in question. It should also be noted that the averaging process distorts the relative amplitudes of those parts of the spectrum retained. Strictly, account should be taken of this in any interpolation.

TABLE 1

Factors by which sampling interval may be increased for several levels of aliased power (spectrum shown in Fig. 11)

Aliased Power (%)	Sample Interval (Single samples)	Sample Interval (Mean of 5 subsamples)
0	1·0	1·0
5	1·3	3·7
10	1·5	4·6
15	1·7	5·0
25	2·2	6·2
40	3·1	9·1
50	4·0	11·1

APPENDIX 3

Parameter Sampling in Two Dimensions

Figure 4 shows a rectangular grid of sample points at which measurements are to be made with the object of complete reconstruction of the parameter value everywhere in the area covered. Clearly, spectral characteristics in the x and y directions are independent, and we have assumed limiting frequencies such that the permissible sampling interval in the y direction is the greater. Interpolation at a point (x_0, y_0) proceeds as follows:
1. Interpolate for $p(x_0, n/2W_y)$ for all n, i.e. along each profile parallel to the x axis,
2. Interpolate along these values for $p(x_0, y_0)$.

At each stage equation (1) should strictly be used. The required sampling density is clearly $4W_xW_y$ samples per unit area.

More General Sampling Grids

The above example, in which we have applied a rectangular grid, enabled sample density to be reduced because of the recognition of differences in spectral composition between two directions which applied all over the map. Such a grid would be appropriate, for example, in sampling topography over the lateral slopes of a ridge when variability down the slope is less than that parallel to the ridge.

In other circumstances other grids may be more appropriate. For example, in sampling topography around an isolated peak, curved grid lines (as in

Fig. 12) may be needed to minimise sampling density. Interpolation in such cases proceeds exactly as for the earlier example.

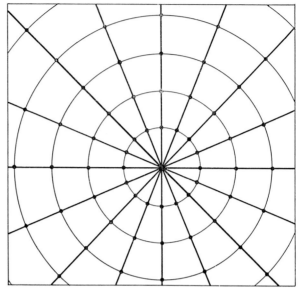

Fig. 12. Minimum-density grid for sampling topography around an isloated peak.

No general procedure, other than successive approximation, appears to exist for the specification of minimum-density grids, since such specification depends on knowledge of the spectral characteristics which can only be obtained by performing sampling. However, if variations in the parameter can be reasonably correlated with ground patterns visible on aerial photographs then a basis for the layout of an efficient grid is available.

REFERENCES

AGTERBERG, F. P. (1967). Computer techniques in geology. *Earth-Sci. Rev.* **3**, 47.

COOLEY, J. W., and TUKEY, J. W. (1965). An algorithm for the machine computation of complex Fourier series. *Maths Comput.* **19**, 297.

DOBRIN, M. B., INGALLS, A. L., and LONG, J. A. (1965). Velocity and frequency filtering of seismic data using laser light. *Geophysics* **30**, 1144.

HAMMING, R. W. (1962). *Numerical Methods for Scientists and Engineers.* (McGraw-Hill: New York.)

LEDLEY, R. S. (1964). The high-speed automatic analysis of biomedical pictures. *Science, N.Y.* **146**, 216.

LEE, Y. K. (1960). *Statistical Theory of Communication.* (Wiley: New York.)

MARÉCHAL, A. (1963) Optical filtering by double diffraction. In *Optical Processing of Information.* p. 20. (Spartan Books: Baltimore.)

MCCOWAN, D. W. (1966). Finite Fourier transform theory and its application to the computation of convolutions, correlations and spectra. Unpublished Tech. Mem. p.8–66, Teledyne Industries Inc., Alexandria, Virginia.

PEARCEY, T., and CHAPMAN, T. G. (1968). Aspects of a computer-based land evaluation system. In *Land Evaluation.* (Ed. G. A. Stewart.) (Macmillan: Melbourne.)

RADER, C. M., and GOLD, B. (1967). Digital filter design techniques in the frequency domain. *Proc. IEEE* **55**, 149.

SHANNON, C. E. (1949). A mathematical theory of communication. *Bell Syst. tech. J.* **27**, 379.

STONE, R. O., and DUGUNDJI, J. (1965). A study of microrelief — its mapping, classification and quantification by means of a Fourier analysis. *Engng Geol.* **1**, 89.

WHITAKKER, J. M. (1935). *Interpolatory Function Theory.* (Cambridge University Press: Cambridge.)

Method and Scale of Land Resource Surveys, in Relation to Precision and Cost

P. H. T. Beckett

Soil Science Laboratory, Department of Agriculture, Oxford

The paper draws attention to some criteria by which the quality of maps of land resources may be judged. It indicates briefly how the scale of mapping is related to the intensity of land use, how the cost of mapping depends upon the scale, and how the choice of mapping procedure affects the cost. It presents some hypothetical extrapolations from the small amount of information available in order to indicate the nature of the choice between different mapping procedures, and to draw attention to the data necessary for this decision.

INTRODUCTION

The world is now being covered by a patchwork of maps of land resources, good and bad, at many scales and by a multitude of procedures. The maps vary widely in the quality of their execution, and in their appropriateness to the problems they were meant to solve. This paper presents some preliminary thoughts on one stage in a continuing study (e.g., Beckett 1967; Beckett, Burrough, and Webster 1968) to develop criteria for quality and cost-effectiveness in land resource surveys. It is based partly upon field work in Britain (e.g., Beckett and Webster 1965; Webster 1965; P. A. Burrough unpublished) and partly upon an as yet unfinished study (Beckett and Bie, unpublished) of the use made of soil and land resource maps in Australia.

CRITERIA OF A GOOD MAP

If we map the natural resources of a region (soils, vegetation, land capability, etc.) we do so *in order to be able to make more precise statements about the mapped subdivisions of the region than we can about the region as a whole.*
The immediate purpose of such maps may be to distinguish areas suitable for development, i.e., to resolve a region into areas of approximately equal land-use potential. It may be to indicate the limits of the area to which the conclusions of a particular agricultural research station may be applied, or the aim may be to resolve a region into a conceptual framework of terrain classes to facilitate the acquisition and organization of miscellaneous information of agricultural or engineering import (e.g. Brink *et al.* 1965). But whatever the exact purpose, it will be achieved only if the map enables us to make more precise statements about the mapped parts than was previously possible for the region as a whole. In other words, the classes distinguished must be more uniform in some or all of their properties pertinent to various kinds of land use than was the landscape at large.
Natural resource maps at large[1] scales, and particularly, soil maps, are also

---

[1] A map at 1 : 1,000,000 is at a smaller scale than one at 1 : 1000.

used in the design of field trials (of crops, fertilizers, grazing management, cultivation, etc.) to ensure that the effects of the treatments are not confounded by differences in, for example, soil. Here too, if the residual variance of trials stratified according to soil classes is to be effectively reduced, the intra-class variability of the mapped soil classes must be small.

In all these instances, the landscape is resolved into a number of subdivisions, each defined as accurately as the available information allows and as precisely as the mapping procedure justifies (see below). It is usually assumed that subdivisions defined on one set of properties can serve as vehicles for other kinds of information too—i.e., that the correlation between the definitive and other properties of all or some of the mapped subdivisions is close enough to allow us to make reasonably precise, and therefore useful, statements about the latter properties too. The assumption is frequently but not always true.

In the simplest or 'one-stage' maps, the boundaries shown are those of the defined subdivisions. The utility of the maps thus depends on the precision of the definitions of the mapped units, and the skill with which their boundaries have been located and recorded.

Commonly, and more particularly in areas of intricate terrain or on maps at small scale, it is not the defined subdivisions which are mapped but groups or complexes of them. Such 'two-stage' maps portray, for example, soil associations made up of defined soil series (cf. publications of CSIRO Division of Soils) or land systems made up of defined land units (cf. publications of CSIRO Division of Land Research). Statements of a general character can be made about the complex second-stage units which are mapped, but the detailed information must inevitably be linked to the defined first-stage units. To draw upon the detailed information, the user of the map must first identify the constituent first-stage units within the mapped complexes. To this end, the map legend and/or the memoir to a two-stage map usually attempts to indicate, by means of block diagrams, sections, and annotated air photographs, how the unmapped first-stage units are to be distinguished.

The utility of two-stage maps thus depends not only on the precision of the definition of the first-stage units, and the accuracy of the mapping of the second-stage units, but also on the ability of their presumed user (lacking special skills or sophisticated equipment) to identify the limits of the first-stage units within the area with which he is concerned. This point was first raised by Brink *et al.* (1965) and has largely escaped study. It must not be forgotten that the presumed user of the map turns to it for information in the expectation that he can thereby obtain the information with less effort than if he went out into the field to collect it himself. He will expect to be able to identify the limits of the defined first-stage units in the field with less trouble than by mapping them himself *ab initio*.

'Three-stage' maps (e.g., Coaldrake 1961) exist. They are of little value for presenting or storing detailed information about first-stage units: the identification of the latter is too complicated.

In the extreme case there is no map but only a key to the identification of the constituent parts of the landscape. Northcote's (1965) 'Factual Key' to Australian soils is an example of this. For many purposes, such a key provides an adequate index to recorded information about land resources. For a given amount of research effort, a key commonly provides a finer subdivision of the landscape than a map, and with fewer anomalies.

Soil Maps

t will be convenient to continue this discussion in terms only of soil maps.

Soil is by no means the only feature of an area to determine its pattern of development. In some areas, the cost of clearing the natural vegetation is the major part of the investment. Relief, climate, and economic factors are all important, and in some cases, of over-riding importance. But there is a wider range of soil maps for examination than there are maps of any of the other factors, and spatial changes are significant at more levels of development in soils than are spatial changes in some of the other land parameters.

Precision and Accuracy

A soil map is a good one if we can make both precise and accurate statements about the properties of the mapped soil units. Precision and accuracy are not the same. The statements will be *precise* only when the intra-unit variability is low – if the measured values of properties, a, b, . . . , etc., of a number of randomly selected samples from within any mapped unit show only a small scatter about the mean (μ_a) for each property. When this is so, there is only a small chance that the value of a for any single sample will differ greatly from μ_a, on which the unit should have been defined. Precise statements can be made about the mapped units, and the predicted properties of samples from previously unvisited sites will usually be close to the properties actually found.

The variance $_A\sigma_a^2$, is the most useful measure of the intra-unit variability of property a, in unit A. It is calculated from the measured values of property a for an effectively infinite number of samples from unit A. $_AS_a^2$ is calculated from the values for a finite number of samples and provides an unbiased estimation of $_A\sigma_a^2$, of which the accuracy increases with the number of samples. In both cases the values of the property will have been normalized if necessary. Precision increases as σ_a^2 decreases. The aim of the soil surveyor is to map soil units with as small values of σ^2 in as many properties as possible. Thus, in terms of any one property, a, the quality of a soil map might be assessed by the extent to which the variances of a, within all the mapped soil units, are less than the variance of the same values of a about the mean value of a for the whole area mapped.

An earlier paper (Beckett 1967) presented the ratio Q as a qualitative measure of the quality (effectiveness) of a soil map:

$$Q = \frac{(\Sigma A_A) \times \sigma_a}{\Sigma(A_A \times {_A\sigma_a})} \tag{1}$$

A_A, . . . are the areas covered by soil units A, . . . , etc.; $_A\sigma_a$ and σ_a are the standard deviations of property a within, respectively, unit A or the whole area mapped. Q tends to unity when the map has brought about no increase in precision and to infinity when the map is perfect.[1]

In fact, $Q = 1/(1 - \rho)$, where ρ is the intra-class correlation coefficient.

The possibilities of assessing the quality of a soil map in terms of more than one soil property have been indicated elsewhere (Beckett, Burrough, and Webster 1968). The assessment of a soil map in terms of qualitative properties

---

[1]This over-simplifies the problem, since the surveyor will not have attempted to define soil units lacking all intra-unit variability, but only to define units of a small, manageable variability. Also, for the same reason, the distribution of values of a about μ_a will not be normal.

of the mapped soil units is less easy. A measure of the degree of association between properties and classes is probably the simplest. Webster (1965) has indicated some treatments of this problem.

Accuracy

Statements made about mapped soil units are commonly based upon the mean or mode of only a small number (n) of measurements. It will frequently happen that the mean (m_a) of the measured properties of a small number of samples from a mapped unit differs from the mean (μ_a) for all possible samples for the unit. The difference is given by:

$$\left| \mu_a - m_a \right| \leqslant \frac{t.\sigma_a}{\sqrt{n-1}} \qquad (2)$$

The value of t, ascertainable from tables, decreases with n, rapidly for small values of n and slowly when n > 20, and increases with the confidence of the statements we wish to make. Thus, for a given confidence, the accuracy of statements about the properties of mapped soil units decreases with increasing σ_a^2 and increases with $\sqrt{n-1}$. When the precision of a mapped soil unit is low (or unknown) we will need a large number of samples to define it accurately, and *vice versa*.

Increasingly fine subdivision of the mapped units (and larger map scales) usually increases the precision of the statements that can be made about each of them. But the accuracy of the statements may even be decreased unless the number of observations or samples to each subdivision is decreased proportionately less than the ratio of the variances of the divided to the undivided units. This is particularly a problem in physiographic mapping (see below) in which there is a proper tendency to define a soil or land unit for every distinguishable difference in the air-photo pattern. Such refinement may prove to be of dubious value when the logistic effort available allows only one or no ground observations of each unit thus defined.

MAP SCALE

The precision of statements that can be made, other things being equal, about mapped (or keyed) soil classes increases with the degree of subdivision of the classes (e.g., great soil group – family – series – type – phase). Each stage of subdivision should produce soil classes more narrowly defined than in the stage above.

But with increasingly fine subdivision, the average areas of ground occupied by the individual occurrences of each subclass becomes smaller. Also the boundaries to be mapped must become more tortuous if the variability within the mapped subclasses is to be as small as their definitions allow. Buringh, Steur, and Vink (1962) and Johnson (1962) have emphasized how the scale of a map increases as the size of the minimum areas to be mapped decreases. In addition, for grid and free surveys (see below) the number of soil observations per unit area mapped will have to increase with the tortuosity of the boundaries to be mapped and the scale of the map should increase with the number of observations (Buringh, Steur, and Vink 1962). Thus, for all kinds of surveys the map scale should increase with the degree of subdivision of the mapped soil units.

Provided therefore, that the map scale is properly adjusted to the frequency of the soil boundaries to be mapped, there should be a simple relation between the precision of the statements that can be made about the soil units mapped, and the scale at which they are mapped.

A previous study (Beckett 1967) on the lateral changes in soil variability drew attention to the different ways in which the variance of soil properties within a square sample plot might vary with the size of the plot. The form of the relation between variance and plot size is both a consequence of the natural intricacy of the landscape sampled, and a good way of describing it. It was shown how the intricacy of the landscape, and the magnitude of the variance which the user of the map will accept within each mapped soil unit, together decide the average spacing of boundaries on a soil map. The required spacing controls the map scale. Several illustrations were given.

With increasing intensity of land use, the sensitivity of farmers' responses to soil changes tends to increase. Fertilizer applications, management, drainage, crops, etc., tend to be more closely adjusted to soil differences. Finer soil differences are recognized. The recommendations of extension officers are more closely tied to specific soil properties and/or to more narrowly defined soil classes.

In short, the acceptable variability within mapped soil classes tends to decrease with increasing intensity of land use. So the degree of subdivision of soil classes and the required scale for soil maps both increase with increasing intensity of land use (e.g., U.S. Department of Agriculture 1951; Lewis 1952; Buringh and Kadry 1956; Duchaufour 1960; Steur 1961; Johnson 1962; Taylor and Pohlen 1962; Vink and Gibbs 1962; Edelman 1963).

SURVEY PROCEDURES

We may distinguish three main groups of soil survey procedures. They differ mainly in the extent to which the mapped boundaries are based on field observations of the soil by auger, or on observations of the external or associated properties of the soil. Since all combinations of the three occur, the division is to some extent, artificial. It serves to sharpen the comparisons which follow.

Grid Mapping

Grid mapping or 'base-line survey' (Steur 1961) is the simplest and also the most laborious procedure. It requires the least skill. Blackburn and Baker (1958) provide a good example.

By this procedure, observations of the visible or tangible soil properties apparent on an auger sample are made, or soil samples are collected, along regularly spaced traverse lines. In the extreme and purest form of grid survey, the observations are at regular intervals. Commonly, the spacing of observations is varied according to visible changes in the soil surface or soil environment. Soil boundaries are drawn across the grid of point observations to separate soil classes defined on soil morphology or on analyses. Beckett, Burrough, and Webster (1968) have discussed the relative advantages of mapping soils on a large number of cheaply determined properties not directly related to the soil's agronomic potential or on a smaller number of expensive analyses of properties directly affecting plant growth. If the boundaries between grid points are interpolated in the field as the survey proceeds, then the interpolation will inevitably be guided by visible changes in vegetation, land form, etc. To this extent, the procedure shares some features with free survey, next described.

Grid mapping is the only procedure of the three in which all parts of every map unit have an approximately equal chance of being recognized. A grid layout is not random, but the values of $_A m_a$ for each mapped soil unit calculated from grid samples offers a reasonably unbiased estimate of $_A \mu_a$. Values of $_A S_a^2$ calculated from grid samples offer rather less satisfactory estimates of $_A \sigma_a^2$.

As the intricacy of the landscape increases, or when the permitted intra-unit variability decreases, the spacing of the grid points must be reduced, and the scale of the map increased. There seems to be no *a priori* limit to the precision of increasingly finely subdivided soil units mapped out with decreasing grid spacings.

But at smaller scales (wider grid) the precision of soil units mapped only by grid survey (i.e., minimum use of external properties or air photographs in interpolating soil boundaries) falls off more sharply with scale than by other procedures. So grid surveys are not used for small-scale maps.

It is, however, rather frequently overlooked that, if the aim is to estimate the *proportions* of different soils in an area rather than their distribution, this can be more cheaply estimated from a relatively small number of samples on an organized grid of random origin, than by mapping out all the different soils by free or physiographic survey (see below). This is particularly so in the common situation where the intricacy of the land, or the map scale, requires a 'two-stage' map anyway, from which estimates of the proportions of the unmapped 'first-stage' units are notoriously subject to bias, unless estimated from an organized grid – in which case the map has been superfluous.

Free Survey

Free survey is Steur's (1961) term for the mapping of soils by their boundaries. It is the procedure generally employed for detailed soil mapping in Europe and North America (e.g., U.S. Department of Agriculture 1951). In this case, the surveyor makes a preliminary examination of the landscape to determine the mean or modal properties of the units to be mapped and to define their precision. The accuracy of the mean values specified increases with the number of preliminary observations.

Having established the map legend, the surveyor locates one or a few soil boundaries and follows them around on their association with their external properties, such as land form, vegetation, land use, etc., as seen on the ground or on air photos, making the minimum number of soil observations necessary to confirm the association and to verify the position of the boundary. The same procedure is repeated for each boundary in turn.

Free survey, as described, thus provides a map with accurately located soil boundaries mapped all along their course. It may overlook small inliers of one soil in another, to a greater extent than grid survey. After the preliminary examination, all the observations will have been near the soil boundaries, so free survey does not estimate m_a or σ_a^2 with much greater accuracy than physiographic survey, though the value of σ_a^2 is likely to be less because of the better boundaries.

In free survey, the soils to be differentiated must have some external expression in the landscape, though the association between soil and external characters need be neither of the same kind, nor of the same degree, along the whole length of even one boundary. The experienced surveyor carries in his head a number of partial and *ad hoc* associations between soils and landscape features and he uses whichever is appropriate to a particular length of boundary. He uses the auger mainly to confirm that the soil boundary lies where he has predicted. Necessarily, the soil classes can be defined only on properties discernible on an auger sample.

As long as the soil classes to be mapped do have some external expression, albeit variable, they can be mapped with fewer observations than by grid survey, or to higher precision with the same number of observations. But with increasing map scale, subdivision of soil units eventually reaches a stage beyond which some, or most, of the soil differences that have now become the most significant, have no external expression. Free mapping at scales larger than this will not increase the precision of the mapped soil units. Gethin-Jones (1954) quotes an interesting example from a soil survey at 1 : 25,000 of mixed forest and thorn in East Africa, where traverses identified 13 soil classes but only 8 classes had sufficiently distinctive external expression (on air photographs) for boundaries to be interpolated. At larger scales than this, grid mapping will give higher precision.

Conversely, as the map scale is decreased, the location of soil boundaries depends increasingly on unchecked interpolation. The resulting map is unlikely to be of higher accuracy than by physiographic mapping (curves A and B on Figure 2 are hypothetical), and the latter procedure will usually be preferred. Hubble and Thompson (1953) present an interesting example of a soil map prepared by interpolation between widely spaced grid traverses, a procedure transitional between free and physiographic mapping.

Physiographic Mapping

In physiographic mapping, boundaries are drawn with little or no ground check, on the external properties of soil or landscape, as perceived on air photographs or by special sensors working on narrow wavebands in or out of a visible range. In this procedure, field observations are primarily intended not to locate boundaries, but to identify (or describe) the soils of the areas within the boundaries thus drawn. The number of observations per unit area mapped is small and not sufficient to verify that the same change in air-photo tone or pattern always represents the same soil change, nor that all occurrences of one air-photo pattern represent the same soil unit. By this procedure, soils can only be mapped if they not only possess some external expression visible on air photographs but also if the association between soil and external expression is constant. This is likely to be the case for the relatively drastic soil differences that will be mapped at small scale. It is unlikely that the smaller soil differences to be distinguished on maps of intermediate scale will show such constant external expression even in areas of undisturbed natural vegetation. In many parts of the world, human interference has so modified 'the natural vegetation that any one soil family carries a wide range of vegetation types (subclimax or deflected climax) of different photo pattern. Many of these also occur on adjacent soil families. So in the precision of the soil units mapped, physiographic survey may be equivalent to, or superior than, free mapping at small map scales, and is likely to require fewer observations to achieve this. But, as the map scale increases, the precision of physiographically mapped soil units is unlikely to increase beyond a certain point unless the sampling density is increased to such an extent that the procedure is no cheaper than free survey.

COST EFFECTIVENESS

Costs

The variable cost, per unit area mapped, of making a soil map for a particular region, can be resolved into field costs and laboratory costs. The latter cover mainly the time and effort of air-photograph interpretation and the rendering of field data into the standard format of the fair copy manuscript map. Carto-graphic and clerical costs are approximately constant per unit area of map, and thus decrease in proportion to the square of the map scale when expressed as costs per unit area mapped. They are not considered here.

For any one area and mapping procedure, field costs tend to be proportional to the number of soil observations made and the number of observations per unit area mapped is proportional to the square of the map scale. Vink's (1963) and Krupsky's (1962) figures have already been quoted (Beckett 1967). Steur (1961) suggests that observations at the rate of 4–20/ha, 2–8/ha, and $\frac{1}{3}$–1/ha are appropriate to map scales respectively of scales greater than 1 : 10,000, of 1 : 10,000, and of 1 : 25,000, while Edelman (1963) reports five observations per hectare for map scales of 1 : 5000 or greater in Germany. Johnson (1962) suggests mapping of 80, 60–120, and 800 hectares per man day at scales of respectively, more than 1 : 15,640, of 1 : 15,640, and of less than 1 : 15,640. J. R. D. Wall (private communication) estimates costs of £1–1·4, £4, £120, and £1040 per square kilometre surveyed in Sarawak at scales of 1 : 100,000, 1 : 25,000, 1 : 12,000 and 1 : 2400 respectively.

In general, the figures available tend to confirm that, other things being equal, field costs are approximately proportional to the square of the map scale. At map scales where both procedures are possible, the field costs per unit area mapped are less for physiographic mapping, which has fewer ground observations, than for free survey. Free survey costs less than grid survey. Effort and costs increase with the intricacy of the terrain (Krupsky 1962).

Air-photograph interpretation admittedly makes a higher contribution to physiographic survey than to free survey and much higher than to grid survey, and contributes correspondingly more to the laboratory costs per unit area of map. But it is not clear that the laboratory costs are so enormously different when re-calculated per unit area of ground mapped. Such as they are, the laboratory costs are likely to increase with map scale. The relation between map scale and the cost of physiographic survey is probably still parabolic.

Figure 1 attempts to represent all this for different survey procedures, in the one area and at all map scales. It extrapolates the cost of free and grid survey over all map scales from the range of scales over which they are usually employed. It assumes a parabolic relation for the variable costs of physiographic survey. It guesses at the relative costs of the three surveys at each scale. The relative positions of the inflections of Figure 3 depend on the relative costs of the three survey procedures.

Precision versus Scale

Similarly, Figure 2 attempts to suggest what seem likely to be the relative levels of precision achieved on mapping the soils of one area by all three procedures and at a range of map scales. In view of the very large number of soil and land surveys that have been executed, there has been surprisingly little attempt to assess the relative or absolute precision of their results. So Figure 2 rests mainly on qualitative impressions. Its crucial parts are the ceilings to the precision attainable by each procedure. The existence of the ceilings has been suggested

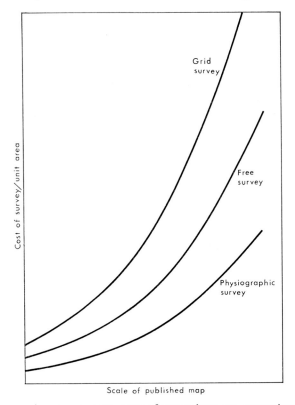

Fig. 1. In any given survey area, costs of survey increase, approximately, with map scale[2]).

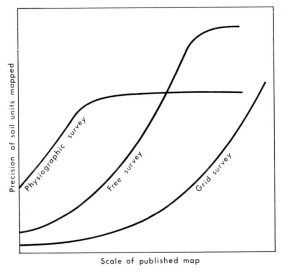

Fig. 2. In a given survey area, the precision of the mapped soil or land units increases with map scale, probably up to a ceiling in the case of free and physiographic survey.

above, and the reasons for them. The map scales at the points of inflection, and the heights of the ceilings, will depend on the intricacy of the terrain. Their existence is crucial to the form of Figure 3.

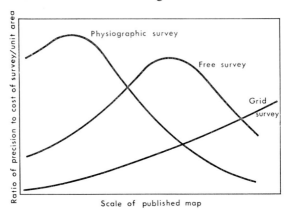

Fig. 3. In a given survey area, cost-effectiveness, assessed by precision/cost per unit area mapped, depends on map scale and survey procedure.

Cost Effectiveness

Figure 3 is obtained by plotting the ratio of precision (Fig. 2) to cost of mapping per unit area mapped (Fig. 1), against map scale. It indicates how the relative cost-effectiveness of different procedures may vary with map scale. If for each procedure there is a ceiling precision, then there are likely, as in Figure 3, to be ranges of map scales between which one mapping procedure gives a greater increase in precision (assessed by Q or ρ) than others. Figure 3 is hypothetical. It shows the possibility that, by collecting the data only guessed at in Figures 1 and 2, it may be possible to make a more rational discrimination between alternative survey procedures.

Thanks are due to the Division of Land Research, CSIRO, for facilities and support, and to Mr G. A. Stewart for criticizing an earlier draft of this paper: to Dr J. R. D. Wall and the Director of Agriculture, Sarawak, for permission to quote figures from Dr Wall's thesis: to Dr R. Webster, Mr P. A. Burrough, and Mr S. W. Bie for discussions and for their collaboration on the continuing study referred to in the introduction to this paper.

REFERENCES

BECKETT, P. H. T. (1967). Lateral changes in soil variability. *J. Aust. Inst. agric. Sci.* **33**, 172.

BECKETT, P. H. T., and WEBSTER, R. (1965). *A classification system for terrain.* Military Engng Exp. Establ., Christchurch, England. Report 872.

BECKETT, P. H. T., BURROUGH, P. A., and WEBSTER, R. (1968). The cost of soil surveys in relation to the classification criteria employed. *Ind. J. Soil Sci.* (in press).

BLACKBURN, G., and BAKER, R. M. (1958). A soil survey of part of Brunei, British Borneo. *CSIRO Aust. Soil and Land Use Ser.* Publ. No. 25.

BRINK, A. B. A., MABBUTT, J. A., WEBSTER, R., and BECKETT, P. H. T. (1965). *Report of the Working Group on land classification and data storage.* Military Engng Exp. Establ., Christchurch, England. Report 940.

BURINGH, P., and KADRY, L. T. (1956). Soil survey and classification in Iraq. *Trans. 6th Int. Congr. Soil Sci.* **5**, 83.

BURINGH, P., STEUR, G. G. L., and VINK, A. P. A. (1962). Some techniques and methods of soil survey in the Netherlands. *Neth. J. agric. Sci.* **10**, 157.

COALDRAKE, J. E. (1961). The ecosystem of the coastal lowlands of southern Queensland. *CSIRO Aust. Bull.* No. 283.

DUCHAUFOUR, P. (1960). *Précis de Pédologie.* (Masson: Paris.)

EDELMAN, C. H. (1963). Application of soil survey in land development in Europe. *Int. Inst. Land Reclamation and Improvement, Netherlands.* Publ. No. 12.

GETHIN-JONES, G. H. (1954). The value and limitations of soil survey. *Proc. 2nd Inter-African Soils Conference, Leopoldville,* p. 201.

HUBBLE, G. D., and THOMPSON, C. H. (1953). The soils and land use potential of the lower Burdekin valley, north Queensland. *CSIRO Aust. Soil and Land Use Ser.* Publ. No. 10.

JOHNSON, W. M. (1962). Principles of soil classification and mapping in the United States. *Trans. Comm. V and VI, Int. Soc. Soil Sci. New Zealand.* p. 522.

KRUPSKY, N. K. (1962). Large-scale soil survey in the Ukraine. *Trans. Comm. V and VI, Int. Soc. Soil Sci. New Zealand.* p. 540.

LEWIS, A. B. (1952). *Land classification for agricultural development.* FAO Development Publ. No. 18.

NORTHCOTE, K. H. (1965). A factual key for the recognition of Australian soils. *CSIRO Div. Soils divl Rept.* 2/65.

STEUR, G. G. L. (1961). Methods of soil surveys in use at the Netherlands Soil Survey Institute. *Boor Spade* **11**, 59.

TAYLOR, N. H., and POHLEN, I. J. (1962). Soil survey method. *Bull. Soil Bur. N.Z.* No. 25.

UNITED STATES DEPARTMENT OF AGRICULTURE (1951). Soil survey manual. *U.S.D.A. agric. Handb.* No. 18.

VINK, A. P. A., and GIBBS, H. G. (1962). National and international soil resources maps. *Trans. Comm. V and VI. Int. Soc. Soil Sci. New Zealand.* p. 876.

VINK, A. P. A. (1963). Planning of soil surveys in land development. *Int. Inst. of Land Reclamation and Improvement, Netherlands.* Publ. No. 10.

WEBSTER, R. (1965). *Minor statistical studies in terrain evaluation.* Military Engng Exp. Establ., Christchurch, England. Report No. 877.

Terrain Evaluation as a Function of User Requirements

Bob O. Benn and Warren E. Grabau

U.S. Army Engineer Waterways Experiment Station, Vicksburg, Miss., U.S.A.

Terrain evaluation is useless unless it satisfies the requirements of a user, and the users must specify an acceptable accuracy for the performance prediction that is the objective of the evaluation. Terrain evaluation consists of three steps: development of mathematical performance prediction models, mapping of terrain factors in terms of model requirements, and construction of performance prediction displays. Ideal factor classes can be established by numerical analysis. Terrain factors, mapped independently, can be compiled into factor complex maps which can be converted to appropriate performance prediction maps. Terrain analysts have little freedom in the choice of either factors or classes.

INTRODUCTION

The function of terrain evaluation is to provide military planners, civil engineers, foresters, and other users with a reliable estimate of the effect of the terrain on their activities or machines. In order to meet modern requirements, such estimates must be quantitative and accurate within acceptable limits; qualitative estimates (i.e., 'construction is easy in the broad valleys' or 'vehicle locomotion is impractical on the steep mountain slopes') are not sufficiently definitive. In addition, the process from statement of requirement by the user to the presentation of the end product must require only a very short time.

The achievement of a terrain evaluation process that requires only a relatively short time, and yet yields an accurate prediction of the effect of the terrain on the activity or machine, requires the solution of a number of technical problems. These problems fall into three general classes:

1 Development of mathematical or analytical performance prediction models relating terrain conditions to the activities or machines specified by the user.

2 Mapping the terrain factors required by the mathematical models, at a scale (i.e., degree of detail) commensurate with the user's requirements.

3 Construction of a display of the performance predictions over the area of interest, and in a form that is easy to interpret.

It must be emphasized that in this view, terrain evaluation is achieved only at the end of the third step: completion of the construction of the performance prediction display. It is *not* achieved by a display showing only the attributes of the terrain which presumably affect the user's machines or activities; such a display is at best only a terrain description.

DEVELOPMENT OF ANALYTICAL MODELS

Since the user demands objective and reliable predictions of performance, it seems obvious that the fundamental requirement is for a set of mathematical models relating each specified activity to the terrain environment in such a way that the performance of the activity or machine in any segment of the terrain can be quickly calculated. Among the several difficulties is the fact that users come in a variety of types.[1] At one end of the spectrum is the strategic planner; his demand is for predictions of a general nature covering large geographic regions. For example, one of his problems might be the determination of the number of engineer construction battalions which would be needed in a given time period in a theater of operations. Such an estimate requires prior knowledge of, among other things, the number of airfields required and the amount of time required to build them. It matters little whether the estimate with respect to any individual field be absolutely accurate, but it matters a great deal that the total estimate be reasonably accurate. Obviously the mathematical 'airfield construction effort' model for this purpose can be quite generalized.

At the other end of the spectrum there is the tactician who must select a specific route across a very small piece of terrain, and estimate within minutes how long it will take his vehicles to negotiate the selected path. It is apparent that the tactical user can be satisfied only by a terrain evaluation which takes into account almost every tree and ditch. This means very great detail in the terrain description, the great sophistication in the 'cross-country performance prediction' model.

From this, it is clear that user requirements dictate the nature of the mathematical model, as well as the scale and degree of generalization of the terrain description and evaluation. Both general and specific models have been developed for military purposes.

Airfield Construction Effort Model (ACE Model)

The existing model for predicting the construction effort (Dept. of the Army 1965) (in battalion-days) required to build a military airfield of specified type in any terrain context (other than in very cold environments) is intended for use by strategic planners, and is thus very generalized. It was developed jointly by scientists conversant with the definition, characterization, and delineation of terrain attributes, and by engineers familiar with current airfield design and construction methods. The relations between terrain factors and construction activities, on which the model is based, are entirely empirical. However, experience over the past four years has demonstrated that the predictions are accurate enough to be extremely useful for planning purposes.

The model is based on the assumption that airfield construction effort is primarily influenced by five variables related to the environment: volume of grading; relative difficulty of grading; relative rock volume; relative difficulty of providing adequate drainage; and relative difficulty of clearing vegetation.

The model is expressed by the equation:

$$C_e = \left\{ k_g \left[\frac{D_s I_v (100 - V_i)}{100} + \frac{D_r I_v V_i}{100} \right] + k_d d + k_c C \right\} F$$

where:

C_e = construction effort (in battalion-days),
D_s = relative difficulty of moving soil (Fig. 1b).

---

[1] The users usually served by the Waterways Experiment Station are military planners, with interests ranging from tactical to strategic.

I_V = relative volume of grading (Fig. 1a)[1],
V_i = relative rock volume (Fig. 1c),

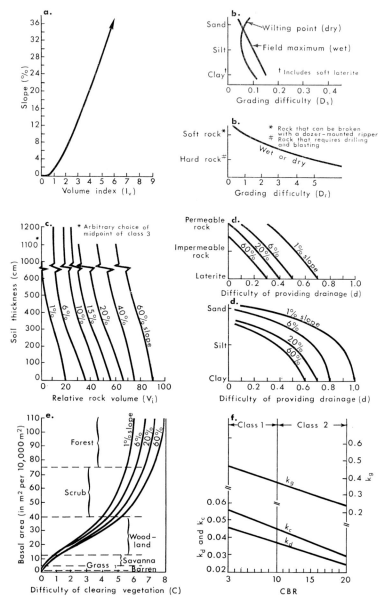

Fig. 1. Terrain factor/activity relations used in connection with ACE model.
a, volume of grading; b, grading difficulty index; c, relative rock volume
index; d, relative difficulty of providing drainage; e, relative difficulty of
clearing vegetation; f, constants (k_d, k_c, k_g) for a light lift aircraft in the
battle area.

---

[1] Graphs shown in Figure 1 are modified from those used as the source statements
from which the tables of input data presented in Dept. of the Army TM 5-366 1965
were derived. Minor changes have been made in the light of experience obtained since
the publication of TM5-366.

D_r = relative difficulty of moving rock (Fig. 1b),
d = relative difficulty of providing adequate drainage (Fig. 1d),
C = relative difficulty of clearing vegetation (Fig. 1e),
k_g, k_d, k_c = constants depending on airfield capacity, aircraft tire pressure, and
        runway length, respectively (Fig. 1f),
F = factor depending upon type of construction battalion.

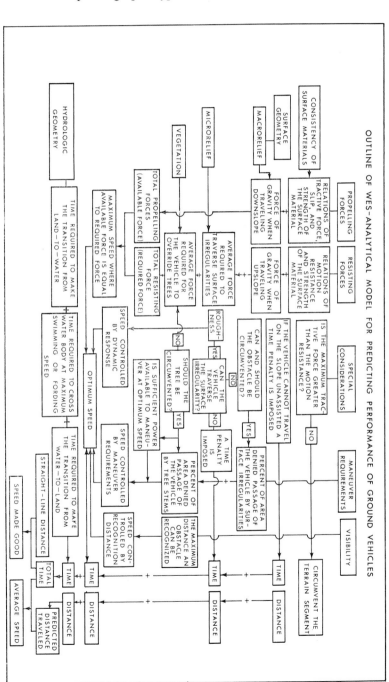

Fig. 2. Generalized schematic of WES cross-country vehicle locomotion model.

It should be noted (see Fig. 1) that while the input factors to the model are index numbers, those indices are derived from relations between terrain factors and the various constructions activities which must be conducted to build an airfield. The actual terrain factors required are: slope (Figs. 1a, 1c, 1d, 1e), soil (and rock) class (Figs. 1b, 1d), soil thickness (Fig. 1c), plant stem basal area (Fig. 1e), soil shear strength (CBR) (Fig. 1f), and soil moisture (Fig. 1b).

Cross-country Vehicle Locomotion Model (CCL Model)

The WES model for predicting the cross-country speed of ground-contact vehicles is intended to provide information primarily for battlefield planners, both tactical and logistical, and is therefore very detailed. It is intended to predict with relatively good reliability the actual average speed of a specific vehicle over a chosen piece of terrain. It is based on an energy concept within the framework of classical mechanics, and employs both theoretically and empirically derived terrain factor/vehicle relations to compute the principal forces propelling and resisting the vehicle. If the force propelling the vehicle is greater than the resisting force, the difference is related to the maximum speed attainable. The model first determines for a terrain that speed a given vehicle can attain in a straight-line path on level smooth surfaces; it next calculates the effects that slope, microgeometry, vegetation, and visibility have on speed, and the lowest average speed is determined. If the vehicle encounters a portion of the terrain that it cannot negotiate or circumvent, the model predicts 'no go'.

A generalized schematic of the analytical procedures is given in Figure 2. Two types of input are required for the model: terrain data and vehicle data. The terrain factors required are listed in Figure 3. Table 1 lists the vehicle parameters and performance data required as input. As many as possible of the terrain factor/vehicle relations have been verified by field tests. For example, the work required to override a tree of a given stem diameter has been obtained by extensive field testing. The relation, which is one of many incorporated in the model, is:

$$Wb = 56 \cdot 0 \, d^3$$

where:

$$Wb = \text{work per tree, lb-ft}$$
$$d = \text{stem diameter, in.}$$

TABLE 1
Vehicle parameters and performance data required as input
by the cross-country locomotion model
Vehicle Performance

Fuel economy versus road speed
Hard surface motion resistance versus speed
Rotational speed of the wheel or track versus tractive force
Turning rate (deg/sec)
Water speed (mph)

Vehicle Parameters

Vehicle weight (lb)	Fording depth (in.)
Wheel base (in.)	Depth below water line
Track width (in.)	when loaded (in.)
Track length (in.)	Drawbar pull in water (lb)
Overall length (in.)	Tire size
Cargo capacity (tons)	Tire ply rating (in.)
Vehicle width (in.)	Tire overall diameter (in.)
Turning radius (ft)	Tire width (in.)
(wall to wall)	Inflation pressure for 25%
Max. steering angle (deg)	tire deflection (psi)
Undercarriage clearance (in.)	Tire deflection (%)
Approach angle (deg)	Maximum force leading edge
Departure angle (deg)	will withstand (lb)

TERRAIN FACTOR	DEFINITION
Soil mass strength	Cone index values
Soil surface strength	Shear stress–normal stress relations
Stem spacing	Spacing of stems ≤ 5, 13, 23, and 127 cm in diam. Spacing of stems ≥ 2.5, 7.5, 15, and 25 cm in diam.

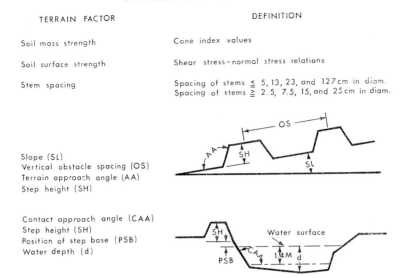

Slope (SL)
Vertical obstacle spacing (OS)
Terrain approach angle (AA)
Step height (SH)

Contact approach angle (CAA)
Step height (SH)
Position of step base (PSB)
Water depth (d)

Fig. 3. Terrain data required by the CCL model.

MAPPING THE TERRAIN FACTORS

Establishing the Terrain Factor Classification

The mathematical models are formulations of the relation of an activity to the terrain factors that affect that activity. That the model states only the relevant factors needed for the evaluation is implicit. It is obvious then that the model isolates the terrain factors to be used and that it can accept only specific terrain values as inputs. This imposes the problem of establishing the optimum terrain factor value classes to be used in mapping the areal distributions of the individual factor values. It may seem at first glance that the concern over classes is unnecessary, especially in view of the fact that the analytical models will only accept discrete values. However, the concern is entirely justified, because the only known way of mapping the distribution of factor values is to subdivide the total range of values exhibited by the factor into convenient classes and map those classes. It is impractical to map in terms of absolute values, since an infinite number of points would be required to specify the factor value at every possible location.

Since classification is a necessary appurtenance of the mapping process, it is apropos to consider the nature of an ideal classification system. There is one overwhelming requirement: the class intervals should be such that any point selected between class limits would introduce only an acceptably small error in prediction. That is, and assuming that all other factor values are held constant, the difference in prediction which would result from accepting a point taken near the upper end of the class range, as opposed to another taken near the lower end of the class range, would be small enough to be acceptable by the user. The problem is thus to select class ranges for all terrain factor variables in such a way as to minimize the effect of the stratification. This ideal must, of course, be tempered by practicality; class intervals too small to be identified by any practical interpretation or mapping process must be avoided.

In the past, the classifications used as the basis for mapping were derived largely on the basis of intuition. The process was, first, to select class intervals that were realistic in terms of the model. Second, and almost equally important, classes were selected such that they were recognizable or at least interpretable from air photographs *using existing interpretation procedures*, because the only practical method of extrapolating data to large unsampled areas was by means of photo interpretation. The balance between these presumed constraints was made on purely subjective grounds. This has long been known to be unsatisfactory. Accordingly, an effort was made to formalize an objective method of deriving a classification for the various terrain factors needed as input for any given model.

A procedure which can be used to classify factor values for complex multivariable models is as follows. One of the terrain factors is selected as the point of departure. For example, in the ACE model it might be I_V (volume index; an indicator of the amount of earth to be moved). (Parenthetically, the ACE model is by no means an ideal example of the use of this technique for classifying terrain factors, because the model does *not* accept terrain factor values directly. Instead (and see Fig. 1), it accepts indices which are only *related* to terrain factors. To use the model, the terrain factors describing an area are fitted to the graphs of Figure 1, and the appropriate index values (of which I_V is one) are determined.) Despite this indirect utilization of the terrain factors, the procedure described above can still be used to derive 'ideal' classifications of terrain factors for the ACE model.

A value for I_V is arbitrarily selected near the lower end of its value range

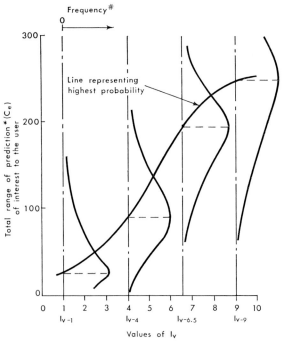

* Total range of prediction of interest to the user: the total range of possible values which all combinations of input values of all variables will produce, within the range of interest specified by the user.

Frequency: the number of times that a given predicted value of C_e will occur in any large sample of prediction computations, assuming the factor values other than I_V are allowed to vary randomly.

Fig. 4. Construction of highest probability curve.

(Fig. 1a), such as '1', and placed on the abscissa of a coordinate system as illustrated in Figure 4. The abscissa of the diagram in Figure 4 defines the total range of variation of I_v (or according to Fig. 1a, 0–10). The ordinate of the diagram in Figure 4 is the total possible range of products of the prediction model. (In the case of the ACE model, the range of interest is approximately 0–300 days.)

Then, holding I_v constant at the chosen value, all other terrain factor values are varied randomly, and the solution is iterated several scores (or perhaps hundreds) of times. If the products are plotted as a frequency distribution curve to the right of the line fixed by the chosen I_v value, the result will look rather as illustrated in Figure 4. The curve thus generated is a statement concerning the probability of occurrence of specific C_e values when I_v is held at the specified constant value. As drawn, it indicates that the most common value for C_e when $I_v = 1$ is about 20 days.

As an example (Fig. 5), let it be assumed that the user wants an area mapped in terms of airfield construction effort (C_e), and that he specifies that the product classes (i.e., classes of C_e) be in 10-day increments from 0 to 50 days with an

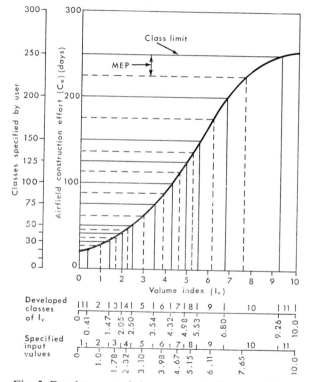

Fig. 5. Development of classes on an index term (I_v).

MEP[1] of less than 6 days; 25-day increments to 150 days with an MEP of less than 13 days; and 50-day increments beyond this point with an MEP of less than 27 days. The approximate developed classes for I_v are then 0–0·41, 0·41–1·47, etc., as indicated in Figure 5.

---

[1] Maximum error of prediction is the absolute value of the largest difference between the predicted value computed from a single point representing a factor class and the predicted values using the class limits as defining the factor class envelope.

This is not yet, however, a classification of a terrain factor; it is at this stage only a classification of an *index* derived from a terrain factor. However, since I_v is related to the terrain factor *slope* (Fig. 1a), the subdivisions of the abscissa in Figure 5, derived from the specified classes of C_e, can be transferred directly to the abscissa of Figure 1a, and the 'specified input' value for each class thus identified can be readily determined.

In theory, the classes of the various terrain factors thus derived are the most useful that can be erected, since the use of their 'specified input values' as inputs to the ACE model will *on the average* yield the smallest MEP's possible within the classes of C_e specified for the final terrain evaluation product. If different output classes (i.e., in this case a different stratification of the C_e values) are desired, then a new 'best' classification of the various terrain factors must be generated.

The process described above can, of course, be repeated for each of the terrain factors used as model input. It is apparent that the procedure described above for classification of terrain factor values is completely mechanical; the only subjective decision in the chain is the one which prescribes the output classes. Since that decision is made by the user, the terrain analyst has virtually no freedom of choice insofar as the terrain description and classification systems are concerned. Both the factors to be evaluated and the stratification of the factor values are dictated by the requirements of the user.

It is, of course, true that the terrain factor value classes must be mappable. In general, this means that photointerpreters (or interpreters of other kinds of imagery) must be able to recognize them on their imagery. However, the proper procedure is not to tailor the classes for ease of interpretation, but rather to learn to interpret for the specified (and required) classes. There is at least one historical precedent for this process. The use of the *Unified Soil Classification System* (WES 1960) by civil engineers presented photointerpreters with a new requirement for soils information. After some hesitation, they accepted the challenge, and now produce maps of USCS soil types as a matter of course.

Mapping the Terrain Factor Classes

The determination of the areal extent of the terrain factor value classes is primarily accomplished by air-photo interpretation procedures. The procedures vary considerably depending on the amount of ground truth data available, and there are of course variations of detail among the factor families, because each factor requires examination of somewhat different attributes of the air photos. However, many of the procedural steps are in common.

Before the air photos are studied, a mosaic is constructed on which all available ground truth sample points for each factor family are located. The factor values in terms of class ranges (as determined in the previous section of this paper) are assigned to each site location. With this as a starting point, the various patterns on the photographs are identified according to tone, texture, and geometry. Where the sample points occur within a pattern, the class range for that pattern is extrapolated to similar patterns. For patterns without ground data, the terrain characteristics are assigned through associations of land forms, topographic position, and the interpreter's knowledge of the area. When all the identified patterns have been outlined and assigned a number or map unit symbol representing a factor class range, the outlines are transferred to the mosaics and from there to a base sheet of appropriate scale.

For example, Figure 6a is a portion of a map, compiled in the manner described, of the slope factor value classes selected for use with the CCL model.

here are four terrain factors in the surface geometry factor family; thus there are four basic maps: slope, vertical obstacle spacing, terrain approach angle, and step height.

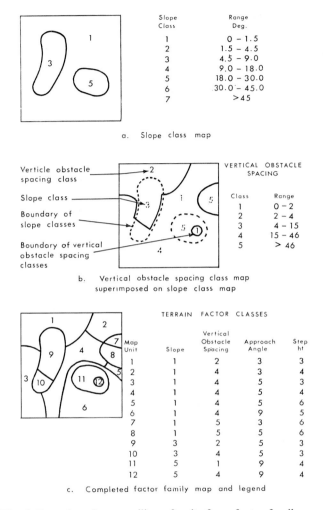

Slope Class	Range Deg.
1	0 – 1.5
2	1.5 – 4.5
3	4.5 – 9.0
4	9.0 – 18.0
5	18.0 – 30.0
6	30.0 – 45.0
7	>45

a. Slope class map

VERTICAL OBSTACLE SPACING

Class	Range
1	0 – 2
2	2 – 4
3	4 – 15
4	15 – 46
5	> 46

Verticle obstacle spacing class

Slope class

Boundary of slope classes

Boundary of vertical obstacle spacing classes

b. Vertical obstacle spacing class map superimposed on slope class map

TERRAIN FACTOR CLASSES

Map Unit	Slope	Vertical Obstacle Spacing	Approach Angle	Step ht
1	1	2	3	3
2	1	4	3	4
3	1	4	5	3
4	1	4	5	4
5	1	4	5	6
6	1	4	9	5
7	1	5	3	6
8	1	5	5	6
9	3	2	5	3
10	3	4	5	3
11	5	1	9	4
12	5	4	9	4

c. Completed factor family map and legend

Fig. 6. Procedure for compiling of units for a factor family map.

Presentation of separate maps for each of the surface geometry factors results in unnecessarily complex display, which imposes problems in evaluating surface geometry characteristics in each specific area of interest. To eliminate these problems, it is often feasible and desirable to synthesize all of the factors into a single map. This synthesis is simply a process involving sequential superimposition of the four factor maps. For example, Figure 6b shows the vertical obstacle spacing map superimposed on the slope class map.

This process is repeated as many times as there are factor maps in the set and each map unit is now identified by an array of four numbers (for example, 1, 2, 3, 3,) representing the map classes of slope, spacing of vertical obstacles, terrain approach angle, and step height, in that order from left to right.

This tabulation is the basis for the legend for a combined map, which is called a 'factor family' map. The factor family map derived from the example is presented in Figure 6c. Each discrete combination of factor value classes is assigned a single code number (map unit) as indicated in the legend of the sample map. The code numbers are used as symbols to identify areas on the map.

Construction of Terrain Complex Maps

Terrain factor complex maps represent the final synthesis of the factors of the four families which describe terrain. The compilation process is analogous to that used in the compilation of the factor family maps, as described previously and illustrated in Figure 6. Figure 7 diagrammatically shows the various factors of both areal and linear terrain factor complexes and the sequence in which

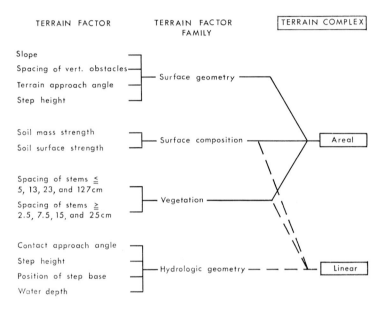

Fig. 7. Construction of terrain factor complex maps.

they are combined. Because of mapping scale, features on the hydrologic geometry factor family maps are almost entirely portrayed as a simple line which indicates the planimetric position of the hydrologic feature (e.g., a segment of stream or canal, or the shore of a lake), and the factors characterizing that feature are annotated in a symbol beside it. On the other hand, the surface geometry, surface composition, and vegetation factors can almost always be portrayed as areas. Therefore, to avoid the cartographic confusion that would result from mixing areal and linear designations on the same map, two different terrain factor complex maps are compiled. Areal factor complex maps are composed of surface geometry, vegetation, and surface composition factor combinations, and linear factor complexes are composed of hydrologic geometry, vegetation, and surface composition factor combinations which occur in zones too narrow to delineate as areas.

The areal and linear terrain factor complex maps produced by this method comprise a detailed description of the terrain in quantitative terms, *but* that description is valid *only* for the purposes of cross-country locomotion analysis. Since the factors and factor value classes as exhibited on the factor maps have been selected on the basis of their utility as input to the CCL model, the maps contain, in terms acceptable by the model, all of the terrain data required to evaluate vehicle performance in the areas mapped.

PREDICTION OF PERFORMANCE

The final step in the terrain evaluation process is predicting the performance (i.e., speed, fuel consumption, etc.) of the vehicle using each unique array of factor value classes (terrain factor complex) as inputs to the model. Each performance parameter of interest is then substituted for the terrain factor complex map unit and a performance map is constructed. For example, an areal complex map is shown in Figure 8a; Figure 8b shows the predicted speeds for two vehicles, Vehicle 1 and 2, for each factor complex shown

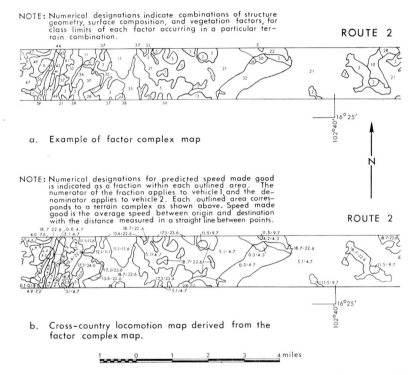

NOTE: Numerical designations indicate combinations of structure geometry, surface composition, and vegetation factors, for class limits of each factor occurring in a particular terrain combination.

ROUTE 2

a. Example of factor complex map

NOTE: Numerical designations for predicted speed made good is indicated as a fraction within each outlined area. The numerator of the fraction applies to vehicle 1, and the denominator applies to vehicle 2. Each outlined area corresponds to a terrain complex as shown above. Speed made good is the average speed between origin and destination with the distance measured in a straight line between points.

ROUTE 2

b. Cross-country locomotion map derived from the factor complex map.

Fig. 8. Example of a factor complex and cross-country locomotion map. Strip maps are from plates 2 and 4 from U.S. Army Engineer Waterways Experiment Station (1965).

in Figure 8a. This does not necessarily mean that each terrain factor complex will impose a different cross-country speed or fuel consumption on each vehicle; it is likely that a number of quite different terrain factor complexes will produce the same performance parameter as an end product. However, it may safely be assumed that each terrain factor complex will affect any one vehicle in a different way. For example, extreme surface geometry might result in a vehicle speed of 3 km/hr across a factor complex, because of limitations imposed by vertical accelerations on driver or cargo. Another factor complex might be characterized by soft soil, which would also impose a limiting speed of 3 km/hr. Thus, while the limiting speeds are identical the *reasons* for the limits are quite different.

Nevertheless, in general, the user ultimately desires a prediction of performance in the most straightforward manner possible. The performance maps have the advantage of displaying the desired values directly, without being encumbered with the factors underlying the prediction. It is obvious, however, that if the maps are to be used in the field it would be necessary to overprint the prediction display on a photomosaic or a map showing sufficient cultural or natural features to allow the user to associate the predictions with the terrain.

DISCUSSION

The concepts presented for terrain evaluation have been found to be useful in fulfilling military operational needs. For the most part, the procedures described above have been used only in research programs, where time and effort are not necessarily critical. For example, extensive ground data were collected to augment the photo interpretation for mapping the terrain factor classes during the development of the CCL model (Shamburger and Grabau 1968). Considerable development work is needed in model formulation, objective terrain factor value classification, air photo or remote sensing interpretation, and in automating the compilation of the factor maps before terrain evaluation can be done as rapidly and accurately as needed. Nevertheless it is felt that, if the objectives of terrain evaluation are to be reached, the user requirements must be considered to be the dictum.

To summarize, there appear to be three basic principles that govern the objective evaluation of terrain: (1) the relationship between the activity and terrain must be mathematically stated before the evaluation process can begin; (2) terrain classification can be accomplished only after the model has been formulated; and (3) the terrain analyst has virtually no freedom of choice in either the selection of the terrain factors or in the classification of those values once the user has stated his requirement.

REFERENCES

DEPARTMENT OF THE ARMY (1965). *Planning and design for rapid airfield construction in the theater of operations.* Headquarters, Department of the Army, Washington, D.C. Technical Manual 5–366.

SHAMBURGER, J. H., and GRABAU, W. E. (1968). *Mobility environmental research study. A quantitative method for describing terrain for ground mobility.* U.S. Army Engineer Waterways Experiment Station, CE. Vicksburg, Miss.

U.S. ARMY ENGINEER WATERWAYS EXPERIMENT STATION (1960, repr. 1967). *The unified soil classification system.* U.S. Army Engineer Waterways Experiment Station, CE. Vicksburg, Miss.

U.S. ARMY ENGINEER WATERWAYS EXPERIMENT STATION (1965). *A plan for a quantitative evaluation of the cross-country performance of prototype vehicles.* U.S. Army Engineer Waterways Experiment Station, CE. Vicksburg, Miss.

The Assessment of Biological Productivity

H. A. Nix

Division of Land Research, CSIRO, Canberra, Australia

Land evaluation involves translation of primary land data into a quantitative expression of site quality for the stated purpose. Such an expression must include a productivity or performance term.

Three different approaches to the problem of assessing biological productivity are recognized. The traditional analogue *approach is based upon general, multi-attribute soil and land classification systems. The* site factor *approach seeks to identify key attributes which may then be used to generate special classifications for a specific purpose.* Systems analysis and simulation *methods hold prospects of predicting biological productivity of a stated genotype at any location.*

INTRODUCTION

Land is a limited resource. Increasing population pressure upon this limited resource means that all forms of land use become more competitive. Any given area of land can have a multitude of potential uses and many, or indeed all, of these may require consideration in the management policy for a land resource.

The problems confronting engineers, agriculturalists, foresters, and others involved in land evaluation are, in many respects similar. All require a quantitative expression of site quality for the stated purpose, which in turn demands:
(a) Identification of key parameters which specify the multidimensional systems involved.
(b) Delineation of the spatial and temporal distributions of these key parameters.
(c) A methodology for translating these data into accurate predictions of performance or production.
The predictive value of a given land classification and associated evaluation system, for a specified form of land use, will depend on the degree to which these conditions have been satisfied.

Land evaluation simply means assigning a value to a specified unit area of land. In practice, the final expression of this value will be in economic terms. Technically, it is possible to modify any given site to satisfy a particular need or requirement. However, the extent to which this occurs, in practice, is a function of the inherent characteristics of the site and the cost of modifying them in relation to the value of desired product. Thus, any quantitative expression of site quality should have a physical input/output form suitable for economic analysis at any subsequent period.

Existing methods of land classification for biological production may permit acceptable predictions of physical inputs necessary for site reclamation and management, but prediction of physical output (i.e., crop yields) is generally unsatisfactory. This is a serious deficiency, since clearly, any quantitative expression of site quality must include a performance or production term.

The biological response (growth, development, reproduction, survival) at a given site is primarily a function of genotype and environment, both of which can be manipulated by man for optimum results. Agriculture, in the widest sense, is concerned with the manipulation of this biological response in both space and time. Prediction of biological productivity therefore involves both spatial and temporal extrapolation.

LAND EVALUATION FOR BIOLOGICAL PRODUCTION

In an absolute sense, biological productivity is expressed in terms of dry matter/ unit area/unit time. Biological production may be divided into primary (dry matter production by plants), secondary (heterotrophs feeding on plants), and tertiary (decomposers, etc.) forms. This paper will be concerned, for the most part, with the evaluation of land for primary forms of biological production (pastures, crops, forests).

In practice, biological production at a specified site is normally expressed in terms of economic yield, i.e. that part of total biological yield harvested by man. The ratio of economic yield to biological yield has been termed harvest index (Donald 1962). For many commonly grown crops this ranges between 20 and 50%. In attempting to understand biological production processes and their relationship to site parameters, it is important to recognize that economic yield represents part only of total biological yield.

Any quantitative expression of site quality for biological production should include an output term in the form of expected economic yield of the specified crop. The prediction of temporal and spatial variations in yield is a first pre-requisite in the attainment of this objective. Three different, but not mutually exclusive, approaches to this problem are recognized. It is suggested that the methods described represent different stages in evolution with respect to understanding of functional relationships between site parameters and biological production systems.

Analogue Methods

Most of the current land classification and associated land evaluation systems are firmly based upon concepts of transfer by analogy. Thus, the physical input/output data necessary for evaluation are extrapolated from experimental sites or from farm experience to analogous areas defined by land or soil classification.

Such methods do not require any *a priori* knowledge of functional relation-ships between site parameters and the specified form of biological production, although such criteria may be incorporated. The base land resource, either total complex (e.g. land system – land unit) or separate major component (e.g., land form, soil, vegetation, climate) is classified on the basis of a number of observed and measurable characteristics.

Subsequent land evaluation is based on the hypothesis that all occurrences of a physically defined and characterized land or soil class will respond in a similar way to management for any specified form of use. This hypothesis has been questioned by a number of research workers on the grounds that correla-tions between land or soil classes and crop yields are generally poor (Visser 1950; Gibbons 1961; Avery 1962; Butler 1964).

The utility of such general, multi-attribute classifications will depend to a very large extent upon the relevance of the observed and measured attributes used. Restrictions of time and space not only limit the range of attributes selected but commonly lead to subjective methods of selection. Ideally, if the attributes measured are significant for all possible uses and all such attributes are measured, then multi-attribute systems of classification may satisfy the conditions necessary for predictions of site productivity.

In the past, general land and soil classifications have imposed conceptual limits on associated methods of land evaluation. Too often, the designated land or soil class is accepted as an indivisible entity and evaluation is conducted within this imposed framework. Statistical methods are designed specifically to overcome problems of variation within the so-called uniform site and are principally concerned with treatment/yield interactions.

Butler (1964) has suggested that most field experiments and agronomic trials are designed to particularize treatment/yield interactions. Such trials must be repeated over a number of years in order to attain any measure of temporal predictive value and can be repeated indefinitely in both time and space without in any way uncovering the functional relationships between the treatment, site parameters (including weather parameters), and the resultant yield.

In situations where the land resource is already intensively used, management (input) and yield (output) data for the soil or land class can be obtained from survey data, farm records, or small experimental plots (Odell 1950, 1958; Rust and Odell 1957). Not the least of the problems involved is that of data acquisition. From analysis of results obtained in a soil productivity study in Illinois, Odell (1958) estimated that at least 50 separate observations on each soil type under defined management, repeated for at least 10 years in humid climates and at least 20 years in semi-arid climates were necessary to arrive at a reliable estimate of productivity.

A major defect of such studies is that they accept the inevitable restrictions imposed by working within arbitrarily defined soil or land classes. In addition, they are based upon existing land use and may or may not provide a basis for prediction of productivity at different levels of management or of other forms of land use.

Most general land and soil classifications are not structured to give very precise information on the climatic environment. Thus, Riecken (1962) quotes an example of a soil series (and phase) having a corn production potential ranging from 60 to 90 bushels depending on geographic location. Perhaps because of the strong emphasis upon the directly observed and measurable morphological characteristics in land and soil classification, associated methods of land evaluation have sought to measure biological productivity in terms of these characteristics as modified by weather. A more appropriate method might be to measure biological response to weather as modified at the land surface.

Land evaluation by analogue methods can be effective, particularly where attributes known to be relevant are included in the general classification. However, predictions made are essentially location specific and can have no general validity.

Site Factor Methods

Site factor methods seek to relate key parameters to biological productivity within a given environment. In principle such methods are based upon paired measurements of biological productivity and selected site factors over a wide range of sites. These data are analysed and parameters related to yield are identified. The yield at a site within the region studied is described by a multiple regression equation of form

$$Y_g = a + b_1 X_1 + b_2 X_2 \ldots b_n X_n,$$

where Y_g = predicted yield of specified genotype, $b_1, b_2, \ldots, b_n$ are the partial regression coefficients, and $X_1, X_2, \ldots, X_n$ are the observed values of independent site parameters.

By far the greatest development of such methods in land evaluation has taken place in forest management. The very extensive literature on site-factor-forest productivity relationships attests to this (Coile 1952; Duffy 1965; Pegg 1967). An apparent advantage in using tree growth at an index age as a measure of productivity is that the tree has integrated weather through time such that a simple index (e.g., annual rainfall) may suffice as a measure of forest climate. This advantage may be more apparent than real, since differential weather effects on young trees may greatly influence resultant growth.

The use of site factor methods in studies of agricultural productivity is much less evident, but has been advocated by Visser (1950), Avery (1962), and Butler (1964). Most of the studies reported in the literature have been concerned with a rather limited range of soil properties and management factors. This contrasts with the forestry studies which usually incorporate a wide range of site factors such as lithology, land form, slope class, slope aspect, depth to least permeable horizon, soil physical and chemical characteristics, climate, and management.

Butler (1964) has suggested the use of 'edaphic' trials in agricultural research. These would impose standardized treatments upon a range of selected sites, the aim being to particularize the yield/site factor interaction for a given treatment. When key site factors have been identified these may then be used to generate a special classification for the stated form of land use.

Whatever the technique adopted in site factor studies the fact remains that they are essentially location specific and use specific. The statistical equations developed are static representations of dynamic systems and are valid only within the range of site properties and for the form of biological product studied. Nevertheless, within the stated region such equations can have predictive value and serve as a basis for delineating areas of land with the appropriate combination of site factors.

Systems Analysis and Simulation Methods

The need for a holistic approach to problems of measurement, analysis, and management of biological systems has long been recognized. However, the great complexity of such systems and the computational effort required to solve the differential and simultaneous equations describing functional pathways and interactions proved a major limitation. The advent of the digital computer, coupled with a rapidly increasing understanding of biological production processes, now makes such an approach feasible.

Systems analysis is concerned with resolution of a complex system into a large number of simple component processes and subsequent synthesis into a symbolic representation or mathematical model of the whole system. When a model is developed which accurately describes the behaviour of a complex system it can be generated through time in simulation studies and used to show how the system can be manipulated for optimum results.

The application of systems analysis and simulation methods to complex biological systems is still in its infancy, but a few large-scale simulation studies have been reported, such as the study of forest insect pest management (Watt 1964) and the management analysis for a salmon fishery (Paulik and Greenough 1966).

In applying these techniques to land evaluation for biological production, the primary objective should be to develop realistic working models of crop ecosystems (using the term crop in the widest sense of harvested product). The identification of key biological and physical parameters is a corollary to such model development. Following from this, the inventory of land resources should be directed toward the development of methods for measurement or estimation of the spatial and temporal variation of these key parameters. Such an inventory, coupled with an appropriate model, can then be used to predict output or yield (expressed as a probability) of any crop under a defined system of management at any location.

MODELLING BIOLOGICAL PRODUCTION SYSTEMS

Primary biological production is the result of dynamic interactions between genotype and physical environment. Though knowledge of the precise nature of these interactions is still limited, enough is known to permit construction of simple working models. At this point a distinction should be made between analytical models which examine basic concepts and computational models which apply these concepts to real world situations. In applying systems analysis and simulation techniques to real crop ecosystems, we are largely concerned with computational models. Ideally, such models should be firmly based upon known functional relationships.

Development of the Model Structure

The output of a crop ecosystem, in terms of biological and economic yield is determined by the flow of matter and energy between biological and physical systems. Biological yield may be regarded as the integrated result of energy, water, nutrient, gas, and associated biotic regimes during the course of growth and development of the crop. This can be stated simply, thus:

$$Y_g(T) = \int_0^T y_g(R_e, R_w, R_n, R_g, R_b)dt,$$

where Y_g is biological yield of genotype g at time T, y_g is the rate of change of Y_g which is a function of R_e, R_w, R_n, R_g, R_b (energy, water, nutrient, gas, and biotic regimes) all in turn functions of time t.

Practical considerations necessitate approximation of the integration by summation of Y_g over finite time periods. The general availability of meteorological data inputs will normally set a lower limit of one day for this time period. A daily period has some advantages in that it facilitates accounting of diurnal rhythms in physiological processes. Where longer periods must be used, integration should be carried out within discrete phenological periods, because of differential effects of various regimes at successive development stages.

Specification of genotype is essential, since it will be necessary to take account of specific thresholds, limits, and rates for growth and development, in relation to component regimes. For intensively managed crop ecosystems this specification should be at cultivar level, though it may be possible to group cultivars and even species whose growth and development responses are similar.

In addition to the major component regimes in the stated equation, which determine the general course of growth and development, it is necessary to consider such episodic hazards as cyclonic winds, hail, floods, unseasonal frosts, and other factors. Where records are available, the frequency, duration, and timing of such hazards in relation to specific crop development phases can be included in the simulation model and used to determine optimum avoidance strategies at the given location.

The core of a simulation model for a biological production system will be concerned with functional relationships between the stated regimes and the processes of growth, development, and dry matter production. Management of a given system involves manipulation of one or more terms in the biological yield equation and should be considered from this viewpoint.

Though models of crop ecosystems which take all component regimes and their interactions into account have not, as yet, been developed, a number of partial models have been developed for specific crop ecosystems in specific locations. This is due, in part, to the natural preoccupation of agricultural research workers with location-specific problems and also to the fact that it is rarely necessary to consider all the component regimes to make realistic yield predictions at a given location. Thus, over vast tracts of the world's crop lands the energy regime (both light and heat) is the major yield limiting factor. In other areas of the world, equally vast, water regime is paramount. In such situations, relatively simple partial models may have excellent predictive value.

In the short term, partial models of the complete genotype/environment interaction will continue to be developed and used. Existing models are based, for the most part, on direct empirical functions relating yield (biological and/or economic) to some measure of the energy, water, or nutrient regimes integrated throughout the growth cycle or over some specified 'critical' phase of the growth cycle. Ultimately, for an ecosystem model to have complete generality, i.e. applicable to any combination of genotype and environment, it must operate at the level of basic physiological processes such as photosynthesis, respiration, transpiration, and dry matter accumulation.

Parameters, Inputs, and Partial Models

Key parameters are patently those which will permit a realistic simulation of energy, water, nutrient, gas, and biotic regimes within a crop ecosystem during the course of growth and development. As a first approximation it may be convenient to consider energy, water, and nutrient regimes alone, in relation to crop response. In practice, in the field, the gas regime (specifically carbon dioxide) is not limiting at existing yield levels, although carbon dioxide enrichment is practiced in glasshouses in parts of Europe. The biotic regime (e.g. pests, diseases) associated with a given genotype in a crop ecosystem can be simulated as a sub-model.

In developing simulation models for general application to wide regions, the fundamental restrictions imposed by the availability of data must be appreciated. In particular, with meteorological data inputs, such restrictions apply in both time and space. Thus, in addition to limitations imposed by inadequate measurements, there are further restrictions imposed by the density of the recording network and length of record.

The Energy Regime of Crop Ecosystems—The energy regime is here taken to include consideration of all components in the energy balance at a given location, with particular reference to the incident light energy available for photosynthesis. The thermal regime, as measured by soil and air temperatures, and the effects of photoperiod are included.

The only data inputs currently available at widespread locations throughout the world are duration of sunshine hours and daily maximum and minimum temperature. More developed networks may have records of daily global radiation (and less often, net radiation) and continuous records of air temperatures and water vapour in the air. Soil temperatures are generally recorded at a very limited number of stations. Where data are totally lacking, estimates of global radiation may be obtained by calculation (e.g. Black 1956).

Fortunately, at a given location the components of the energy regime exhibit a considerably lower degree of seasonal variability than other meteorological parameters, particularly when periods of one week or more are used as unit time periods. Thus, direct measurement over relatively short time sequences (e.g. 5 years) may provide reasonable estimates at a specific location. In addition to this, the use of remote sensing methods may allow direct mapping of surface temperature differences at local scale (Rose and Thomas 1968).

Despite the limitations in the data available, a number of working models of crop response to incident light energy (all other factors non-limiting) have been developed. Crop response involves two separate but interrelated processes, i.e. *growth* which is simply increase in matter and *development* which is the sequence of phases throughout the crop cycle which relate to changes in form and structure.

Growth is a direct result of carbon fixation by photosynthesis less total respiration. The photosynthetic rate of a leaf canopy is the result of a complex interaction between plant structure and other physiological properties and the physical properties of the incident light. De Wit (1959, 1965) has developed analytical models for examination of functional interrelationships between key plant-and-light parameters in photosynthesis. From these he has developed a computational model which can be used to calculate canopy photosynthesis for any combination of leaf and canopy characteristics and meteorological data. This model assumes no limitations to photosynthesis through water or nutrient stress and does not consider respiration. Saeki (1960) and Loomis and Williams (1963) have proposed formulae for calculation of dry matter production based solely upon energy considerations. Such approximations can prove useful in estimating the limits to biological productivity at a given location.

An excellent example of the application of foregoing concepts to a real crop ecosystem is that of Tanaka, Kwano, and Yamaguchi (1966) in the studies on rice at Los Banos in the Philippines. Grain yield was related to the balance between photosynthesis and respiration as influenced by plant structure and physiological activity, incident light energy, temperature, and nitrogen status throughout the course of growth and development. The extension of such studies to dryland situations, where further restrictions are imposed by water stress, would prove extremely valuable in the development of general crop ecosystem models.

Simulation of crop development through time may require considerations of photoperiod, threshold temperatures, accumulation of heat units or radiation receipts above certain thresholds and even such factors as physiological delay due to reduced plant water status, as in grain sorghum. The simulation of development phases is extremely important as the timing of particular development phases (e.g. flowering, fruiting) in relation to the prevailing weather factors may significantly influence yield.

Simulation of Water Regime in Crop Ecosystems—The water regime of a crop ecosystem is here taken to include considerations of both soil water regime *and* plant water regime. Such a distinction is necessary, since the physiological processes involved in growth and yield are functions of plant water status which is only partly determined by soil water status.

The development of water balance concepts has greatly facilitated the study of soil and plant water regimes in real situations. Simulation of soil water-regimes has found wide application in irrigation, hydrological, and general climatic studies. Consideration of the various terms in the water balance equation (for a hydrological application) is given in the paper by Chapman (1968) in this Symposium.

The primary data inputs to a water balance model are unit time sequences of precipitation and evaporation data. Daily rainfall totals are available over a very wide network of recording stations throughout the world on a short-term basis (<10 years). Such short-term records may prove adequate in humid regions with low rainfall variability, but in most simulation studies of water regimes in crop ecosystems, long-term records (>20 years) are essential. Not many recording stations satisfy this requirement.

Tank or pan evaporation data are available from a restricted network of recording stations and generally cover shorter periods of record than rainfall data. Empirical formulae (Thornthwaite 1948; Penman 1948, 1956) may be used to estimate potential evaporation where sufficient data are available. Penman's method is generally more accurate, but requires more data. An empirical method based on maximum and minimum temperature and vapour pressure data has been shown to give close agreement with tank evaporation at widely spaced locations on the Australian continent (Fitzpatrick 1963).

The water regime of crop ecosystems is the result of dynamic interactions between weather, soil, and plant parameters. As understanding of these complex processes has developed, sophisticated analytical models of water transport in the soil-plant-atmosphere system have been formulated (e.g. Cowan 1965) and more generalized computational models have been developed for application to specific crop ecosystems (Holmes and Robertson 1959; Shaw 1964; Baier and Robertson 1966).

These generalized water balance models are primarily concerned with simulation of soil-water regime under a given crop or pasture and operate over a daily time interval. It has been shown that such models can provide realistic predictions of soil-water status on a daily basis. The utility of these models for widespread applications is limited to the extent that reliable daily evaporation data are available. However, water balance models which use an accounting unit period of 5–7 days and equivalent estimates of potential evaporation may prove of value where data are limiting.

In real situations it is generally necessary to simulate soil-water regime through complete cropping sequences or rotations, as the preceding crop or treatment may greatly influence the amount of soil-water available to a succeeding crop. Thus, in an alternating fallow-crop system it will be necessary to simulate soil-water regime under a bare soil phase and under crop (and sometimes stubble) in a continuous sequence. Such a model has been developed and tested (Fitzpatrick and Nix, unpublished 1968).

From the soil-water regime of the crop ecosystem it is necessary to proceed to a consideration of plant water regime. The plant water status of the crop canopy is very largely a joint function of soil-water regime and the prevailing evaporative demand. The effects of reduced plant water status on such basic physiological processes as photosynthesis, transpiration, and growth are well documented (Gates 1964) and known relationships between water stress and the economic yield of a wide range of crops have been reviewed by Fischer and Hagan (1965).

The few studies of crop ecosystems which have attempted to simulate plant water status (in addition to soil-water regime) have shown encouraging results. Thus, Dale and Shaw (1965) using a water balance model of a maize crop ecosystem were able to account for 83% of the variation in yield over a 30-year period at Ames, Iowa. These workers used the concept of 'turgor-loss point' developed by Denmead and Shaw (1962) as a measure of water stress during a critical period of crop development.

In a study of wheat and grain sorghum yields at Biloela, Queensland, the use of alternating fallow-crop models, coupled with an index of crop water stress at the critical flowering and grain development phases, accounted for between 65 and 83% of the yield variation in long-term variety trials (Nix and Fitzpatrick, unpublished 1968). Application of these techniques to wheat yields at widely spaced locations between 22° and 28°S in Queensland accounted for between 60 and 73% of yield variation at individual locations, and a combined regression equation accounted for 66% of the total variation in wheat yields over the entire range of sites.

As water-balance models of crop ecosystems are refined and developed it seems likely that they will find wide application in field experimentation and in evaluation of cropping strategies for dryland situations.

Simulation of Nutrient Regime in Crop Ecosystems—The nutrient regime is here taken to include the chemical and biological activity of those mineral elements known to be essential for plant growth and production. It may also be extended to considerations of the ionic balance within the plant and the effects of both nutrient and other mineral elements in toxic quantities.

The relative ease with which nutrient deficiencies can be corrected may appear to simplify the problem of developing crop ecosystem models. Certainly, the productivity of the site in terms of energy and water regime with nutrient regime non limiting would be an important reference level. However, prediction of response to added nutrients is extremely important in terms of input to a crop ecosystem and subsequent economic analysis.

Basic inputs to a model of nutrient regime would include some measure or test of the level and state of major and minor essential mineral elements in the system. Because understanding of nutrient element transformations in the soil and uptake by plants is still very limited, such measures will be restricted to the simple diagnostic chemical tests for specific elements which are currently available.

Because of the paramount influence of energy and water regimes on crop growth, development, and dry matter production it is difficult to conceive of an effective model of nutrient regime and plant response which would not be based upon a consideration of these other regimes. Thus the availability of nutrients to and uptake by plant roots are conditioned by dynamic interactions between plants, soil, micro-organisms and weather.

Though analytical models have been developed and used to test concepts about the uptake of ions at a plant root (e.g., Passioura and Frere 1967) and concepts of cationic-anionic balance in the plant system (De Wit, Dijksoorn, and Noggle 1963) computational models which apply such concepts to problems of nutrient response in crop ecosystems have not, as yet, been developed.

CONCLUSIONS

Analogue methods of assessing biological productivity, based on general land and soil classifications are still dominant. As understanding of functional relationships between site parameters and biological productivity grows it is conceivable that analogue methods could be greatly improved through the use of key parameters in constructing general classifications. However, the need to classify sets of several continuous variables into a system of fixed classes has lessened with the advent of computer techniques for storage and retrieval of location specific data.

Site factor methods have undoubted utility within restricted environments and further development of such methods to include more direct indices of the major limiting factors should lead to further improvements in predictive value. However, such methods afford static mathematical representation of dynamic systems and thus have distinct limitations in terms of temporal and spatial extrapolation.

Systems analysis and simulation methods have not, as yet found application in methods of land evaluation for biological production. As more comprehensive models of whole crop ecosystems are developed and key parameters are identified it becomes feasible, in concept, to predict the performance of a stated crop genotype at any location, given specified data on land characteristics and a historical record of weather.

REFERENCES

AVERY, B. W. (1962). Soil type and crop performance. *Soils Fertil.* **25**, 341–4.

BAIER, W., and ROBERTSON, G. W. (1966). A new versatile soil moisture budget. *Can. J. Pl. Sci.* **46**, 299–315.

BLACK, J. N. (1956). The distribution of solar radiation over the earth's surface. *Arch. Met. Geophys. Bioklim.* **7**, 165.

BUTLER, B. E. (1964). Assessing the soil factor in agricultural production. *J. Aust. Inst. agric. Sci.* **30**, 232–40.

CHAPMAN, T. G. (1968). Catchment parameters for a deterministic rainfall-runoff model. In *Land Evaluation.* (Ed. G. A. Stewart) (Macmillan: Melbourne.)

COILE, T. S. (1952). Soil and growth of forests. *Adv. Agron.* **4**, 329–98. Academic Press Inc.; New York.

COWAN, I. R. (1965). Transport of water in the soil–plant–atmosphere system. *J. appl. Ecol.* **2**, 221–39.

DALE, R. F., and SHAW, R. H. (1965). Effect on corn yields of moisture stress and stand at two fertility levels. *Agron. J.* **57**, 475–79.

DENMEAD, O. T., and SHAW, R. H. (1962). Availability of soil-water to plants as affected by soil moisture content and meteorological conditions. *Agron. J.* **45**, 385–90.

DONALD, C. M. (1962). In search of yield. *J. Aust. Inst. agric. Sci.* **28**, 171–8.

DUFFY, P. J. B. (1965). Relationships between site factors and growth of lodgpole pine (*Pinus contorta* Dough. var *latifolia* Engelm.) in the foothills section of Alberta. *Dept. For. Publ.* No. 1065. Ottawa.

FISCHER, R. A., and HAGAN, R. M. (1965). Plant water relations, irrigation management and crop yield. *Expl Agric.* **1**, 161–77.

FITZPATRICK, E. A. (1963). Estimates of pan evaporation from mean maximum temperature and vapor pressure. *J. appl. Met.* **2**, 780–92.

GATES, C. T. (1964). The effects of water stress on plant growth. *J. Aust. Inst. agric. Sci.* **30**, 3–33.

GIBBONS, F. R. (1961). Some misconceptions about what soil surveys do. *J. Soil Sci.* **12**, 96–100.

HOLMES, R. M., and ROBERTSON, G. W. (1959). A modulated soil moisture budget. *Mon. Weath. Rev. U.S. Dep. Agric.* **87**, 101–6.

LOOMIS, R. S., and WILLIAMS, W. A. (1963). Maximum crop productivity: An estimate. *Crop Sci.* **3**, 67–72.

ODELL, R. T. (1950). Study of sampling methods used in determining productivity of Illinois soils. *Agron. J.* **42**, 328–35.

ODELL, R. T. (1958). Soil survey interpretation and yield prediction. *Proc. Soil Sci. Soc. Am.* **22**, 157–60.

PASSIOURA, J. B., and FRERE, M. H. (1967). Numerical analysis of the convection and diffusion of solutes to roots. *Aust. J. agric. Res.* **5**, 149–59.

PAULIK, G. J., and GREENOUGH, W. (1966). Management analysis for a salmon resource system. In *Systems Analysis in Ecology.* (Ed. K. E. F. Watt) (Academic Press: New York.) 215–52.

PEGG, R. E. (1967). Relation of slash pine index to soil, vegetation and climate in southeast Queensland. *Qd Dep. Forestry Bull.* No. 19.

PENMAN, H. L. (1948). Natural evaporation from open water, bare soil and grass. *Proc. R. Soc.* **193** A, 120–45.

PENMAN, H. L. (1956). Evaporation: an introductory survey. *Neth. J. agric. Sci.* **4**, 9–29.

RIECKEN, F. F. (1963). Some aspects of soil classification in farming. *Soil Sci.* **96**, 49–61.

ROSE, C. W., and THOMAS, D. A. (1968). Remote sensing of land surface temperature and some applications in land evaluation. In *Land Evaluation*. (Ed. G. A. Stewart) (Macmillan: Melbourne.)

RUST, R. H., and ODELL, R. T. (1957). Methods used in evaluating of soil productivity. *Proc. 4th Int. Cong. Soil Sci. Amsterdam* 1, 373–7.

SAEKI, T. (1960). Interrelationship between leaf amount, light distribution and total photosynthesis in a plant community. *Bot. Mag., Tokyo* 73, 55–63.

SHAW, R. H. (1964). Prediction of soil moisture under meadow. *Agron. J.* 56, 320–4.

TANAKA, A., KWANO, K., and YAMAGUCHI, J. (1966). Photosynthesis, respiration and plant type of the tropical rice plant. *Tech. Bull. int. Rice Res. Inst.* 7, 1–46.

THORNTHWAITE, C. W. (1948). An approach toward a rational classification of climate. *Geogrl Rev.* 38, 55–94.

VINK, A. P. A. (1956). Application of soil surveys in the Netherlands. II. Agriculture. *Trans. 6th Int. Cong. Soil Sci. Paris* E, 639–44.

VISSER, W. C. (1950). Quantitative basis of evaluating of soil productivity. *Trans. 4th Int. Cong. Soil Sci. Amsterdam* 1, 373–7.

WATT, K. E. F. (1964). The use of mathematics and computers to determine optimal strategy and tactics for a given insect pest control problem. *Can. Ent.* 96, 202–20.

WIT, C. T. DE (1959). Potential photosynthesis of crop surface. *Neth. J. agric. Sci* 7, 141–49.

WIT, C. T. DE, DIJKSHOORN, W., and NOGGLE, J. C. (1963). Ionic balance and growth of plants. *Versl. Landbouwk. Onderz. Ned.* 69, 15.

WIT, C. T. DE (1965). Photosynthesis of leaf canopies. Institute for Biol. and Chem. Res. on Field Crops and Herbage, Wageningen. *Agric. Res. Rep.* 663.

The Assessment of Land Quality
For Primary Production

V. C. Robertson, T. N. Jewitt, A. P. S. Forbes and R. Law

Hunting Technical Services Limited, Boreham Wood, Herts., England

Land quality assessment is discussed with particular reference to the needs of the user, who in this context is taken to be a development organization, either public or private, rather than the individual farmer.

An examination of existing systems of land classification in the light of the needs of different stages in development planning is made and for detailed surveys the system evolved by the United States Bureau of Reclamation is preferred.

A systematic procedure for land evaluation is outlined and the initial importance of water in land resource appraisal in the stage of land development planning is stressed. At the second stage, when priorities are assessed and projects identified, formal land classification on the lines developed by the United States Department of Agriculture is advocated as a guide to land quality. Finally at the project level, the most critical assessments of productivity from the land are made and all social and economic factors are weighed in order to project potential production and production increases with time.

INTRODUCTION

For the purposes of this review we have assumed that 'primary production' is concerned with production from plants (i.e. agricultural field or tree crops, pastures for livestock, or forest tree crops) rather than from minerals. There are, of course, examples, such as opencast mining of tin, bauxite, coal, iron, etc., where such mining could be termed primary production from the land and where, in fact, there may be serious clashes of priority. This problem, in relation to tin, is recognized in the Malaysian system of land classification, and the mining of bauxite in Jamaica raises similar issues. We have also, in this review, adopted the definition of land used by Christian (1958, 1963). This concept of land within its overall physical environment (though Christian refers to a 'vertical profile', which has implications in respect of, for example, water which are raised at the end of this review) is, we consider, vital in any assessment of land quality which is to be of real value to the user. The 'user', in the present context, is intended to be the government, government of international agencies, government, international, or private financing agencies, or large-scale private developers. We are not here primarily concerned with the needs of the individual farmer as the 'user'.

A number of methods of approach to land classification have been developed and used, some of them quite widely. Most of them are concerned primarily with analysis or classification of the physical bases of production and the extent to which they define or determine comparative levels of production is limited. Only one system (the United States Bureau of Reclamation's land classification system – directed mainly towards irrigation development) can be used to assess the different productivity potential of land units in any degree of detail, taking into account socio-economic as well as physical factors.

It is the effect of these last factors that makes the step between assessment of fairly broad differences in potential and detailed (and realistic) productivity assessment so difficult in practice. The user – the developer – is faced with regional priorities, with project priorities within a region, and with location and types of development within projects. Any system which simply evaluates production in terms of physical factors can go only so far towards such decisions, though it should be made clear that a proper assessment of physical resources is a vital step in getting priorities right. Even though final decisions may be made on socio-economic grounds, a proper assessment of physical potential is critical – not only in prevention of totally wrong decisions but in assessing the costs involved in allowing social considerations, for example, to override others.

Where assessment of actual productivity – in crop yields for example – can be built into land capability systems, the productivity rating is almost inevitably concerned with what one may term 'ultimate potential'. This concept assumes all necessary inputs and a high order of management. What the developer needs to know is not only what this ultimate production level may be, but how soon he may expect to reach it. This sort of assessment, which is extremely important when capital for investment is short or has to be attracted (and this means demonstrating a reasonable rate of return on investment), involves predictions which are outside the range of physical land resource assessment. The U.S.B.R. system referred to earlier does attempt a detailed productivity rating, including such items as farmer capacity, distance from markets, etc., but this does not incorporate the crucial time factor and, moreover, it has been developed in a specific and well-documented socio-economic environment. For this last reason the U.S.B.R. system requires extensive modification if it is to be used elsewhere to the full, and in practice it is rarely used outside the United States beyond a fairly crude level of detail. We have no final answers to this problem to offer, which may be as important to the user as the initial physical assessment. In most developing countries there is probably no short answer, especially where one is involved not only with supply over time of physical inputs such as water or fertilizer, but with growth of effective extension and agricultural education and removal of such brakes on production and incentive as obsolete or harmful land tenure and taxation practices. Our own approach to these problems has been through close observation of representative village, farm, or watercourse units over periods of at least a year (and preferably, of course, much longer), in order to identify and evaluate both constraints and potential breakthrough points. Often such factors, of course, have a general application and cannot be related to different physical land units.

This discussion also introduces our view as to the primary importance of water in land quality assessment, and advances our opinion that much development expenditure can be wasted, especially in the early stages of exploration or planning, if examination of water resources – whatever their nature – is not given equal or higher priority to investigation of other physical resources.

TYPES OF SURVEYS

The methodology for measuring land quality is very varied. It depends on the purpose for which the survey is being carried out, the scale at which it is done, the time available for its completion, and the amount and nature of prior knowledge available. This latter factor is of considerable importance, since it will dictate the amount of work necessary to provide information for a specific purpose and the scales at which the research has to be carried out. Ideally, land quality surveys should first concentrate on the integrated collection of information on all factors involved in characterizing the nature of a particular unit of land, followed by a systematic assessment of these factors both individually and as a natural complex to determine their potential for a variety of uses or for a specific use. If the resource inventory is conducted carefully and systematically, it should provide the basis for assessment of land quality not only for the requirements of the present but should also be capable of re-evaluation in the light of future requirements.

First-stage Regional Surveys

In countries where knowledge of the natural resources is insufficient to indicate the possibilities for agricultural production, the initial requirement is for rapid general surveys to give some idea of the range of possibilities and where more detailed investigations are likely to be most rewarding. Such rapid surveys can provide sufficient information for a government to base its future planning of agricultural production in the sense of choosing where initial development should be carried out. This kind of general survey will not usually provide sufficient detail to indicate the potential of such development, or the costs that are likely to be involved in the development. All it really provides is a framework on which to base further research, and to show where such research is likely to prove worthwhile. If a fair amount of local knowledge is available, this very general stage may not be necessary, and research may be carried out profitably and efficiently at some more detailed level.

A first-stage survey should indicate what resources there are that could be developed. It should indicate the general nature of the climate, even if this is possible only in a zonal sense. Some general information is necessary on the availability or otherwise of water in areas of inadequate rainfall or where it is suspected that rain may be unreliable for commercial crop production. Some indication of the nature of the soils can also be given even if only at fairly high categorical levels. Such information can often, even at general levels, supply a lot of valuable information. Much the same applies to rapid estimates of the nature of the natural vegetation, especially as regards grassland and forestry. Cognisance must also be taken of the natural hazards that may limit development. This is especially true of slope and other characteristics of the land form, and some general land form analysis is essential at this stage. This should recognize where erosion is active and where the land resource is being diminished in value.

It is obvious that first-stage surveys do not provide many answers, but they should indicate where the answers should most profitably be sought. If they can be conducted rapidly and at small cost, they are justifiable. To achieve this, actual field work must be kept to a minimum, while at the same time sufficient information must be obtained to provide for succeeding stages. Careful and systematic use of aerial photography has been found to be the answer to this, and most reconnaissance types of surveys rely heavily on aerial photo-interpretations.

This has resulted in methodologies being devised in which photo-interpretation plays a major role, and which allows some division of land into units that will provide necessary information with a minimum of actual field checking. However, it must be emphasised that field work is necessary, and that photo-interpretation can be over-emphasised. Such a methodology has been devised and used by the Division of Land Research of CSIRO in Australia over the last 20 years or so in a wide range of conditions (Christian 1952, 1958; Christian and Stewart 1953, 1968; Haantjens 1965). It is known as 'land systems' survey, and is important in that it is designed not only to provide a maximum of basic information from a minimum of field data, but also to provide a method which allows the integrated study of the many factors involved. The basic unit of study is the land system, which is defined as a complex unit made up of recurring land units which are associated in such a way that they produce a characteristic pattern on aerial photographs. At the most general scale, the land units themselves may not be individually mappable but their characteristics will be noted since the nature of a particular land system depends on the characteristics of its component land units. In more detail, a land unit is con-sidered to be an assemblage of characteristic facets, so that the whole land system is built up of a succession of natural units. Land form and particularly geomorphology is the basic factor used in defining and delineating both the land system and its subsidiary components. Land systems themselves can be grouped into larger units of study. This is important in order to emphasise the natural interaction between one system and another, especially in relation to a large drainage basin that will contain several land systems from source to final outlet. Within each system, information on a large range of resources is sought, the system itself serving to show the natural unity of which these resources are component parts. The whole methodology depends on the fact that visible differences in land form and geomorophology will reflect, in general, differences in the associated resources. In relation to soil, the land form and soil relationship has always been an important feature of soil mapping as, e.g., associations and catenas. In much the same way, so has vegetation. The land system approach has the advantage that it is flexible and the whole complex of resources or a single resource can be expressed within its framework.

As used by the Division of Land Research of CSIRO, very large areas have been covered very rapidly. The land system approach has also been adopted by the Directorate of Overseas Surveys in London (Brunt 1967; Bawden 1967). The land system technique has also been applied in terrain analysis by the British Military Engineering Experimental Establishment. Its use in this instance is obviously more specialized, but the general discipline is similar. In similar vein, an attempt has been made to divide the hot deserts of the world into a finite number of land systems (Mitchell and Perrin 1967). In this approach, only land systems and facets were used. In the U.S.S.R., a whole new school of thought appears to have arisen in geography based on landscape science, although there appears to be some argument as to whether landscape geography is fundamentally different from regional geography. The approach to landscape divisions in the U.S.S.R. is very similar in general to that of the Division of Land Research of CSIRO, but there are important differences in detail. In the U.S.S.R., the number of named subdivisions of landscape is greater than in Australia. Soviet geographers recognize, in ascending scale of complexity, facies, sub-urochishche, urochishche, and mesnost (Solntsev 1961). In con-nection with landscape geography, Soviet geographers accept a definite series of influence as regards the interaction of the components of landscape. In their view, in this series, the earth's crust occupies the 'strongest' position followed by the atmosphere, water, soils, vegetation, and animal life in descending order of importance (Solntsev 1961).

Ideally, first-stage regional surveys provide sufficient information to allow the identification of development requirements or possibilities. Normally, the information is insufficient for project identification. A second more detailed stage would be required to do this. However, the first-stage survey should also point out where further information is necessary. This is especially important for climate and water resources, where longer-term measurements are necessary to provide essential additional information.

Second-stage Surveys

Having identified a development area, or a group of project areas, as a result of the initial reconnaissance work, it is necessary then to make an evaluation of the various possibilities. This will require that sufficient information is sought to indicate whether specific projects are in fact feasible, both from the physical point of view, and from a general cost/benefit aspect. This will provide the user with an indication of the value of each particular project which is considered feasible, but will also provide the information in which to base the choice between alternative projects where the question of priority is an important one, as is usually the case. This means that the scale of the work has to be enlarged to provide fairly detailed information on the various resources involved. Soil surveys at some suitable scale must be carried out, and vegetation must be quantified – in terms of volumes of exploitable timber, for example, or in the carrying capacity of any existing rangeland. Storage sites for surface water must be identified and groundwater supplies measured and tested for quality in the cases where a possible project involves irrigation. Present land use will be an important consideration at this stage since it can supply information on present yields, and can be projected to allow potential yields to be assessed in relation to specific improvements which can be carried out.

The methodology for expressing this stage of evaluation is fairly diverse. Fundamentally, all are interpretations of the basic data of climate, water, soils, vegetation, and land form. A system which has been widely used is the land capability classification of the Soil Conservation Service, United States Department of Agriculture (Klingebiel and Montgomery 1961). In this system land is grouped according to its potentialities and limitations for sustained production. The classification is divided into arable and non-arable sections, each with four classes, giving a class range of from I (for land with no limitations, or only slight limitations to sustained production) to VIII (for land with the highest degree of limitations that render it unsuitable for any use other than recreation, wildlife cover, and water supply).

The main classes give a measure of the degree of inherent limitation involved, and four subclasses show the general nature of the limitation. A further subdivision into units allows more precise statements to be made concerning (a) the kind of crops which can be grown, (b) the degree of conservation and management required, and (c) the potential productivity. Each unit should have sufficiently uniform characteristics to make it possible that (a), (b), and (c) will be similar within any one unit.

This classification is based on the permanent qualities of land that cannot easily be changed. The presence of scrub, trees, low fertility, etc., factors that can be remedied fairly easily, are not considered to be permanent characteristics and are not used in the evaluation. The aims of this classification are best summarized by the assumptions on which it is based. Briefly, these are that the class is a measure of the degree of hazard or limitation, but does not necessarily indicate the kind of management necessary. Management requirements may differ widely within a class. Valid generalizations about suitable kinds of crops cannot be made at the class level. A favourable input/output ratio is one of the criteria used in class designation, but it is not a productivity rating for specific crops. The presence of excess water, lack of water, stoniness, toxicity, alkalinity, or flood risk are not considered as permanent soil characteristics if the removal of these is considered feasible within present day economic possibility. In such cases, the land is classified according to existing permanent limitations after the removal of the non-permanent hazards. Research data, recorded observations, and experience are used as the basis of placing land in the capability units, sub-classes, and classes. In areas where local information is lacking in detail, the classification is achieved by making use of information on similar soil and land characteristics, described elsewhere. Throughout the system, classification is based on the assumption that moderately high levels of management will be operated.

This classification is capable of being used both for general and specific purposes, but it is not designed for use in the case of crops, like rice, with highly specific requirements. Special groupings in such cases must be made in areas where they are significant. This classification system meets the requirements of land evaluation at the intermediate, semi-detailed stage. It has been adopted and adapted for use in many parts of the world, in a wide range of conditions. In New Zealand, capability groups have been related to genetic soil types, using a range of only five classes (Cutler 1964). The groupings are based on the degree and number of limitations to land use. Each class is subdivided according to the kind of limitation and each subclass is divided according to the soil moisture regime. In Jamaica, capability classification has been used, in this case with a seven-class system with subclasses as in the American system, but with capability units based on significant slope classes (Steel, Vernon, and Hewitt 1950). A seven-class capability system is also used in Canada, and a similar system has been proposed for Britain (D. Mackney 1967 private communication).

The other main evaluation system in operation is the soil capability rating devised by Storie (1933, 1948). This is defined as 'a numerical expression of the degree to which a particular soil presents conditions favourable for plant growth and crop production under good environmental conditions'. It 'is based on soil characteristics that govern the land's potential utilization and pro-ductive capacity. It is independent of other physical or economic factors that might determine the desirability of growing certain crops in a given location'. The system is expressed by scoring the soils, on a 1 to 100 scale separately for Factor A – soil profile characteristics, primarily depth of soil and permeability of the profile; Factor B – texture of the surface soil; Factor C – slope of the land; and Factor X – miscellaneous factors that can be modified by manage-ment, such as drainage, alkali, nutrient level, aridity, erosion, microrelief. The final soil rating is arrived at by multiplying the ratings of these individual factors. The soil rating system has had world-wide application, and has been much used in the evaluation of land for irrigation. Examples of this usage are found in Canada (Bowser and Moss 1950). In this instance particular attention is paid to genetic soil type, and to the geological nature of the parent material, since this is considered to influence the lateral movement of water. Vertical movement is considered in relation to profile type and soil texture. In India, in rating soils for irrigation, the Storie system has been slightly modified. Six profile characteristics have been considered, and the final soil rating is arrived at by addition of the marks assigned to each individual characteristic. The value for each characteristic is arrived at by dividing the profile into three zones, and scoring each individually. A capability rating system has been proposed for use in the Philippines (Hernandez 1955). This consists of applying a standard rating to land capability classes, of which nine are recognized in the Philippines

(Alicante and Mamisao 1948). The rating is done on a percentage basis, allowing a maximum of 50% for the soil factor, divided into various characteristics, 25% for the slope factor, and 25% for an erosion factor. Soil rating has also been applied in New Zealand (Leamy 1964), modified to include a new factor of moisture availability.

Fundamentally, both systems are largely similar, since they are based on the same measurable and observable characteristics. They are different forms of expression, but the end results of applying either will be similar. Most weight is given in both to the permanent, largely unchangeable characteristics of land.

Apart from attempts to evaluate land in general terms, it is often required that evaluation be made for specific purpose. Examples of this are woodland suitability, range potential, suitability for special crops, etc. In such cases, a narrower range of characteristics is likely to be involved, and will not necessarily coincide with general evaluation.

The end product of this second-stage evaluation is a reasonably detailed evaluation of the natural resources, and the identification of likely projects. At this stage, various other factors must be included. The question of the sequence in which a range of possible projects is to be developed may be decided by social and political considerations, and not simply in order of potential worth. The constitution of a government may demand that development be spread as far as possible so that all sections of the community and as much of the country as possible should benefit. This may result in attention having to be given to poorer-quality areas as well as to areas of higher potential. Further, the evaluation of the long-term potential of land as described above, cannot include a measure of the costs of initial development. This is a factor which must also be considered in deciding the priority of development, if capital for development is limited. For example, a potentially high-quality soil may require prior removal of trees and other vegetation cover, while a lower-quality soil may not require this. With a limited fixed amount of capital, there may exist a choice between limited development of the high-quality land and much larger-scale development of the lower-quality land. Distance from markets or export facilities may also materially affect priorities, as will the local and world demand for the products whose production is physically feasible.

Third-stage or Detailed Surveys

Detailed consideration of an area is necessary to formulate a specific project plan, and to show in detail the cost/benefit ratios of the activities considered. At this stage, some re-evaluation of the predictions made as a result of the second investigation stage may be necessary, especially where there is considerable complexity in the natural resource factors to be developed. The third-stage investigation should be able to concentrate on the final details of what is to be produced, what the necessary management practices will be, the exact costs of carrying out the development, and the likely yields to be obtained from the enterprise. If the whole development has to be undertaken quickly, then it may not be possible to start pilot projects to investigate experimentally the optimum management practices, or the yields to be expected. If this is the case, careful predictions must be based on the sum of all the knowledge available, both locally and from elsewhere, and allowance made for amendments in the light of future experience. Ideally, some sort of pilot project investigation should be carried out as soon as sufficient information is available from the semi-detailed investigation. Pilot experiments may even be necessary to determine the choice of enterprise, if little local knowledge is available on crop perfomance.

A great deal of detailed investigations have been carried out throughout the world for irrigation projects. Because of the normally high initial costs of development, very careful assessments are necessary and detailed investigations are normally essential. There are exceptions to this in some cases where development is considered in areas where there is a high degree of uniformity of the natural resources to be considered. An example of this is the proposed large-scale extension of irrigation enterprises in the central clay plains of the Sudan. Here, the high degree of uniformity in soils, vegetation, climate, and land form over large areas, made possible the drawing up of development plans based on only semi-detailed investigation of the above-mentioned resources. This was further supported by the long existence of the Gezira irrigation scheme in similar conditions.

A system which has had world-wide use in the assessment of land for irrigation projects is that of the United States Bureau of Reclamation. This is a system which is best used in conjunction with a detailed investigation, since considerable detail is necessary properly to fulfil the requirements of its classification. The system is one that considers not only the physical factors of land, but factors of productive capacity, costs of production, and the costs of initial development. It is intended to give a measure of the repayment capacity of land. In practice, the distinction between classes is arrived at by consideration of the physical factors soil, topography, and drainage, and relating these to direct economic factors. As formally set out, this system depends rather more on single criteria than do other systems: for example, failure to meet a depth requirement places land in a lower class regardless of its other properties, which may be all near optimum. In the Bureau of Reclamation system, four basic classes are used to identify arable lands according to their suitability for irrigation agriculture. The first three classes represent lands with progressively less repayment capacity. Class IV is used to indicate land of use for special purpose or crops with a highly variable repayment capacity. Class V is used for lands which must be considered as non-arable under existing conditions, but which may have some potential if and when large-scale improvements become feasible. It is a class of land which requires special investigation to allow its final worth to be estimated. Class VI is reserved for lands which do not have, under any circumstances, sufficient payment capacity to warrant consideration for irrigation.

The end result of the detailed investigation should be a development plan showing what crops can be grown, how they should be managed, and what the cost/benefit ratios of the enterprise will be as a whole, and the ability of the operators to pay for the costs of development. It should be realized that project profitability is not necessarily the same as repayment capacity. The difference arises basically because the first charge on the production from a project must frequently be assigned to the farmer and is not available for repayment of project costs.

A SYSTEMATIC PROCEDURE FOR LAND EVALUATION

In the initial or exploratory stages of land quality assessment, we have cited in particular the land systems approach developed by CSIRO in Australia. This approach provides important information on physical resources, by a method which allows large areas to be covered rapidly at comparatively low cost. These are important considerations. It is however necessary, we feel, to point out that certain key resources, those of climate, soil, and – particularly – water, are not tied at all closely to land systems. It is at least arguable that it might be better to study these aspects first and to consider how best to exploit them.

The Importance of the Water Resources

For example, an assured rainfall in an area is a good reason for seeking to exploit it. A groundwater resource is a fit object for study and so, of course, is a river basin. A country with a wide range of sunshine hours could well direct its enquiries first to areas with the better radiation figures. From an investment point of view, the user is interested in the difference between present production and potential production, with due regard to the growth pattern between the two and the associated cost flows. Although it may be valuable—and academically satisfactory—to have a systematic coverage of a country by regional first-stage surveys, time and funds are in practice usually both in short supply. There is usually information available about climate and the water resource (though often very little in connection with groundwater) so that it is possible to direct first-stage land resource surveys to regions where the water resource shows some promise.

When climate is unsuitable, in particular where there is no reliable rain and where there are no river and other water resources, it does not matter how good the soil is or how industrious the people or how attractive the landscape— pending some breakthrough on the technological front such as effective desalinization process.

If one seeks primary production, therefore, one should ask first are there water resources. An affirmative answer justifies the next stage of investigation, which is to find out whether there are good soils and what mixture of crops will grow best there. If this investigation shows that there are good soils which will give good crops, it is time to ask how much will it cost and what will be the value of increased production. If the investigation shows no good soil and the water is rainfall, the proper course of events may be to leave the natural vegetation or replace it by a better one. If the water resource is a river, consideration should be given to seeing whether the water can be taken elsewhere. The question of river resources is linked with power generation and one must remember that most countries have an industrial sector of their economy, as well as an agricultural sector. Happily, the same water can usually be used for both power and irrigation, but the releases for power and irrigation rarely have the same optimum pattern.

The concentration on water as the prime natural resource carries with it the clear implication that the resource should be conserved. The preservation of the resource requires that catchments should have a special use, which may not be its most immediately profitable one. This is one point on which governments may not properly conduct their affairs on a discounted basis, though such an exercise may be illuminating.

A government, as the user, is of course not solely concerned with the cost/ benefit aspect of development: it has to consider social and political aspects. As noted earlier, some constitutions have explicitly written in to them the need to give all citizens approximately equal opportunities, and in most, the need to spread development funds is implicit. Nor is a government so interested in the present worth of projects as an individual might be. The present worth of not having a revolution in 20 years time is difficult to assess, but it is a thing for governments to take into account if their vision extends beyond the next elections. Such considerations suggest that the population of a region is an important resource and this resource, under-employed or poor, is of a different seriousness than say the waters of a river pouring into the sea past land which could use it.

Water has been considered as an exploitable resource. There is, of course, the situation where water is in excess locally and regionally, in which case the investment to be considered is drainage, in one of its several forms, and protection of land against erosion.

The main purpose of this review is to indicate our view that it is easy to spend too much time and resources on far-flung reconnaissance surveys and classification. The policy-making part of government needs to know the resources of its lands, but it needs to know even more their potentialities. The basic resource, water, is the one for investigating, and where this is rain or river flow it is usually already known. The potentialities of groundwater may go much longer unrealized and, in our view, appraisal of this particular resource is one of the first tasks. There are not many situations in which a groundwater survey has no purpose.

First-stage Regional Appraisals

A first-stage assessment of the potentialities of a region or country implies to us that it should be carried to a stage when the government can be made aware of an order of priority for development and investment. Since, by general knowledge, the most important resource of an area—water—is usually known in advance, the amount of detailed attention given to other resources must be carefully considered if the survey is to advance significantly the process of choice. It is here we feel that something needs to be added to the CSIRO land system approach if the user is to be given the basis for priority or choice of development at the first stage of survey. These additions are in the fields of crude production potentialities and similarly crude cost estimates for say, major engineering works.

The combination of agricultural information with that on soils is basic to the evaluation of the potentialities of land – it yields projections of potential crop production. Local information is clearly most valuable but, in general, the application of knowledge from other areas plays a large part. The process is the changing of a soil map to a land capability map in its more positive aspects. The rather more negative aspects of the danger of erosion and waterlogging are other factors, but basically, one needs to know what production may be when the best practices are applied to control erosion and other limitations – and how long it takes to get there. This process has been made somewhat easier in modern times by the reasonable assumption that specific fertility limitations can be controlled by fertilizers. Few major producing areas at present subsist on native soils without amendments.

It is one of the purposes of broad land classification to assess the possibilities of changes in the basic known natural resources of an area, and this first-stage process is not really finished until this is done within the limits of known technology. This broadens the scope of first-stage surveys and, looking a little ahead, leaves them with the task of seeing what the next generation of technologists will be offering—it may be desalinisation of water for agricultural use.

The costs of control of erosion and drainage installations and costs of operation are the obverse of the potential production picture and without them the land quality for agricultural production cannot be assessed. The net production value of land is the real measure of its value. How far this has to be expressed in monetary terms depends on the stage of planning, in choosing whether or not to make an investment this process of using financial terms is essential, and needs to be as precise as is possible in this changing world. In choosing areas for investigation, clearly the need is not so urgent and most systems of classification at this stage will give only generalized description of potentialities, indicating only the kind of problem and their generalized solution. In some circumstances, however, something better is needed by the user—in this situation probably the government—and indeed it may be imperative that first estimates of development costs are given early: a government needs to know at least the relative costs of two possible development regions. If one involves a major dam, the cost of which could not be provided within national financial projection, the government needs to know this, so that it may choose for investigation an area with a smaller prospective investment. To meet this kind of need, it is necessary to include some engineering capability at an early stage. The estimates given for such works as dams, barrages, land clearance, erosion control, flood control, need only be rough and at the pre-feasibility level.

Integration of Regional Surveys with Regional Planning

We suggest that regional first-stage level surveys have the function of identifying promising areas for second-stage surveys, whose aim is project identification. Regional surveys should be far sighted, and not under pressure: they should foresee developments in the far future, and more immediate problems. At some stage they direct second-stage surveys to parts of their areas: these surveys, in much greater detail, identify project areas. Our understanding is that a regional survey would not provide the level of detail that would lead to project evaluation —where this happened we would feel it was losing its regional (or more probably national) attributes of long-term appraisal and its function of over-seeing the integration of the use of natural resources, in the sense that it should be able to detect the exploitation of a resource which would preclude a wider plan being operated.

We believe that regional surveys should be controlled by a planning group responsible for seeing that development activities were forming part of a general plan. For example, we should expect this group to see that not too much development of, say, tobacco was being planned in relation to forecast demands, that a project using irrigation water was not proceeded with until the project planners could show that alternative areas had been investigated. Again, it may be necessary to safeguard urban water supplies from agricultural exploitation. All this really means is that the regional survey should be integrated with a national planning group which has more than survey functions. For this concept of a planning group to be effective we would consider that its composition should include those who understand physical resource assessment and utilization as well as economists. In the absence of a planning group of this kind we recognize that desire to see development of resources might well lead to a superficial piecemeal development with unhealthy competition for funds by sectional interests.

Outside the field of development such a group would have the responsibility for guiding changes in the existing use of land which in most economies would involve the use of taxation, price supports, and such like instruments. Changes in existing use should be made with knowledge of the physical environments so that government-induced changes in land use are directed to the most suitable areas, and so that the reasons for them are fully known to those directing new development.

In our concept of a regional survey indicating the order and scope of second-stage surveys, we see the national planning group as the continuing recipient and guardian of the new information yielded by second- (and later) stage surveys. As we see it, however, this information, sought with development in mind, will not always be of the form or nature that central planning needs. For

example, a second-stage survey might justifiably abandon groundwater search
when convinced that that resource could not be used. From a broader view of,
say, large-scale movement of groundwater this information might be of use
and a national survey might require its collection. There would, therefore, be
aspects of regional survey that would continue along with accretion of more
detailed survey results from second-stage surveys.

Second-stage Surveys

The authors of this paper have been more actively concerned with the second
stage in the process of investigation that leads to development and investment.
We accept as a basis that a broad regional survey should be done and that a
choice of areas for investigation can be made as a result. With our acceptance
of water (and climate) as the resource of prime importance, we would ourselves
base a regional survey primarily on it, emphasising the study of climatic zones,
and river valleys and catchments.

The second stage of investigation of a promising region should involve a
whole range of disciplines. The aim should be to identify investment opportunities and make precise measurements of the resources that have been indicated by the prior survey in general terms. Now, for example, the natural
vegetation is expressed in numerical terms – the existing forest resources are
quantified and the carrying capacity of range land estimated. Groundwater
information is extended by drilling and well testing. Storage sites for surface
water are identified and stream flow records are analysed for feasibility-level
assessments of storage possibilities. Where there are existing crops, they are
studied, more particularly in attempts to relate yields to site characteristics and
at the same time a soil survey is made of potentially useful areas.

In a second-stage survey of, say, a land system or other region such as a river
basin, the aim is still the general development, but as the survey proceeds
project identification should become possible. For example, it might become
evident that rainfed areas could support an animal enterprise, a marsh area
might be used for rice, and alluvial soils existed which could be irrigated for
citrus or other fruit. Such findings could be left at the project-identified stage
until the area plan was complete, the scale and scope of the survey continuing
as originally planned. In practice, it is likely that the second-stage survey would
modify itself to test, for example, whether irrigation should rest on a river
structure or pumps involving the contour surveys that would not have formed
part of the original survey plan. It would also be wise to institute market
research on the three enterprises suggested. We believe that a second-stage
survey, once it had shown development possibilities, should institute certain
serial observations such as expanded river gauging, meteorological stations,
groundwater observation points, and ecological control areas (as by fencing).

The end product of a secondary survey would be an inventory of the present
resources, likely projects identified, and a projection of what will happen in the
region with or without the projects. Certain basic estimates must have been
made, the most important of which is the potential crop yields. Here, there is
perhaps less need for pessimism than is generally accepted. This arises from
technological advances in the last few decades, advances typified by the acceptance of fertilizers, the ability to estimate crop water requirements from
climatological data, the appreciation of the water-holding capacity of soils, a
greatly advanced knowledge of drain design and drainage requirements, the
expansion of agricultural research in general and by international organizations
such as the International Rice Research Institute. All this together with a general

awareness in all countries of the merits of patient collection of basic climatological data, stream flows, and the like so that the long-term basic requirements
of planning are becoming increasingly available.

We have suggested how broad regional surveys have the end point of a choice
of investigational effort, with the feeling that even here some broad assessment
of costs and productivity is needed in order to direct this choice. A second-stage
survey in much more detail is intended to identify possible projects or modes of
development. Full project-feasibility studies in detail are not yet advisable, for
the reason that before these are necessary a government policy decision is often
required. In the hypothetical case erected above government plans may negate
any further interest in rice growing. Nevertheless, the second-stage survey
should be able to sketch out its identified projects with some degree of costing.
This is necessary because, there being numerous possible projects offered to the
government, it must make a choice at this stage. As we have stressed earlier
the choice is not decided solely in cost/benefit and capital requirement considerations, but by social, political, and what we may term macro-economic thinking.

The third-stage survey is project evaluation and design. At this stage there
is no doubt that cost/benefit analysis largely decides the question whether to
implement the development or not. Some of the political and social factors will
already have been taken into account.

It will be noticed that in this discussion we have not in fact, found it necessary
to evaluate in detail the quality of the land. In identifying projects we have,
in fact, done so implicitly because non-project lands have been discarded on
the grounds of their low productivity or because they must be preserved to
protect another land or water resource, or because rough assessments have
shown their development to be uneconomic. It will be noticed that cost/benefit
considerations are applied intuitively to the first and third category. Land held
back for exploitation because it protects a watershed is in a somewhat different
category.

As part of the second-stage survey one should, in fact, do a formal land
classification, in most environments on some system allied with U.S.D.A.
method. This system groups land according to its capabilities after the application of reasonable measures to mitigate its disabilities. This is one useful and
valid way of assessing land but if the aim is to develop, it is clearly necessary
to decide at an early stage what control measures are justified in the near
future. To take a single example, the U.S.D.A. system indicates the ranking
of the land close to and flooded by a river as if the river were controlled. Now,
the cost of doing this may vary enormously, from a simple embankment to
regional river control, and in our second-stage survey we would feel compelled
to take account of these very different costs.

It will be appreciated that the second-stage survey aim is to decide what
should best be done with specific parts of the region and not merely to describe
and enumerate and classify. Lines would be drawn on a map, not to say what is
there, but what should be done: not to give various degrees of excellence, but
to list the order and nature of action. The survey would, of course, include
other maps such as soils and contours, present land use and some formalised
land classification, and these would be the material which would enable the
development map to be modified with changing markets and changing technology. What the user really wants is a development map indicating the projects
on which he can base choice of investments.

A Consultants' Association, involving the authors' firm, has recently, in
West Pakistan, completed a second-stage survey that led to a map of the description outlined above. With a constrained surface water supply we sought to

maximise the returns, and identify the stages of development within the region (the southern part of the country), prescribing the crops to be grown in each climatic region and the uses of groundwater according to its salinity. The projects were given a profitability raiing, each sub-area carrying its share of certain protective projects such as regional drainage works. The investigation has only limited analogies with most regional surveys in that the area has an existing irrigation system upon which drainage and groundwater supplies were to be imposed, but nevertheless there were many different possibilities of development.

The user received a very wide range of maps showing climate, physical resources, present production, etc., together with all the detailed observations made during the survey, which in some disciplines provide most of the information required for project planning. He also received an action programme summarized in a development map. This survey went further towards establishing the feasibility of its projects than would usually be the case: indeed one project was carried through to the stage of implementation while the survey proceeded and two others have since been brought to the design stage. There is, perhaps, some general significance in this, in that second-stage surveys should be flexible and vary their scale of investigations when promising situations become apparent.

Land Classification at Project Level

We have written most of the above with a sense of the urgency of development planning, with the feeling that the 'user' is a government in a hurry to improve and expand primary production. We have therefore stressed the need for identifying areas where action should be taken, to the extent perhaps of short-circuiting some resistances which the perfectly logical and safest approaches seem to offer to this process. Examples of this are to be found in our insistence that water is the prime productive resource and should be so pursued, in our urging that even in large-scale regional surveys costs of development should sometimes be taken into account, and thirdly in suggesting that a second-stage survey should be flexible in its scale and detail and should be influenced by the priorities of developments.

We are aware that this urgency could lead to error and waste of resources, particularly where it leads to single purpose one crop development. It seems to us, however, that this is guarded against at the project planning stage. Here, the degree of risk is stated clearly and evaluated as far as possible. The risks arise in two ways: firstly from a miscalculation of either or both of the productivity of the single crop and the associated costs; and secondly from changes in market prices or demand arising probably from technological change—such as, for instance, those brought about by synthetic substitutes. Clearly, these errors are much more serious with a project that can *only* succeed with a single crop or single enterprise. For example, a misjudgment of a system supplying stock water is more serious than one with a project to supply infrastructure to an already producing area with a mixed economy. This single use or multiple use finds its expression in many systems of land classification—such for example as 'adapted to a wide range of climatically suitable crops' in the definition of Class I irrigable land in the U.S.B.R. system.

Clearly, a project is safer if its lands have at least viable alternative uses. What the user needs, apart from a project plan, is an alternative or contingency plan. If the project is definitely only viable for a single enterprise, this should be made clear by the land classification, or the land classification should indicate how much of the area is in this category. The economic expression of the risks is perhaps outside land classification, but the flexibility of land use is within the user requirements of land classification.

Those who are concerned with land classification naturally would like a unified world system and on a purely physical descriptive basis there is no reason why they should not have one. The present progress in defining and describing basic land form units such as the 'facet' indicates that this can be done; as development-minded pragmatists we are not quite clear as to how all this helps development. If all development planning had to be done on the basis of aerial photographs, it would clearly be of advantage if one country's situation could be identified with that of others, but this is not in fact the way in which development is done. Development is done within the limits set by a set of resources of which land form is only one subsidiary component. The aims of development are themselves sharply influenced by national considerations and national financial resources, and even if all the physical attributes of land and climate are the same in two countries, the development is not likely to be identical, and the evaluation of land quality will differ. Since, in our view, a land classification should reflect potential production, it would seem that the units in such a classification cannot freely be applied in different parts of the world if the units are to reflect the net value of production rather than the physical volume. It has to be remembered that agricultural investment is governed by the profitability of alternative forms of investment in a free economy or by governmental decision on the division of investment between the different sectors of the economy.

As stated earlier, the U.S.D.A. system of land capability classification implies a uniform high order of management. The impact of management on productivity – and hence in effect on land quality – is of the utmost importance in development planning, but this impact varies sharply with environment. In the Highlands of Scotland, for example, the physical environment (especially climate) may dominate or override the effects of management at any conceivably economic level, whereas in the humid tropics effective management may be much more important than physical land quality. A similar situation can arise in irrigated areas. None of the current land classification systems takes this factor into account, and indeed it is not possible for them to do so. It is, however, a factor that needs to be considered at project-feasibility (third-stage) level, and can indeed affect the choice of project priorities.

All this strengthens our view that the evaluation of land for primary production in *general* terms is of comparatively little value. The general nation-wide appraisal is of value in deciding the general direction and for long-term guidance but, from our point of view, both the absolute and relative values of land are really only possible in the context of their actual and potential use. The precision of the analysis increases as we go to greater detail of survey, so that in the project plan stage we estimate both physical production and economic worth.

CONCLUSION

Throughout this discussion we have been concerned principally with what the user, very often the government, needs to know at different stages. We have put forward the idea of the dominance of the water resource in the initial stage, probably allied with land resource assessment or a land systems model. At the second stage, when priorities are assessed and projects identified (but not evaluated fully), formal land classification on U.S.D.A. lines is advocated as a guide to land quality. Finally, at project level, the most critical assessments of productivity from the land are made, at this stage building in fully all social and economic and financial factors in order to project potential production and production increases with time.

REFERENCES

ALICANTE, M. M., and MAMISAO, J. P. (1948). Methods of conservation farming. 1. Land-use planning. *Dept. Agric. and Nat. Res. Tech. Bull.* 17.
BAWDEN, M. G. (1967). Application of aerial photography in land systems mapping. *Photogramm. Rec.* 5, 461–4.
BOWSER, W. E., and MOSS, H. C. (1950). Soil rating and classification for irrigation land in Western Canada. *Scient. Agric.* 30, 165–71.
BRUNT, M. (1967). The methods employed by the Directorate of Overseas Surveys in the assessment of land resources. *Trans. Second Int. Symp. Photo-Interpretation,* Paris, 1966, pp. 1–10.
CHRISTIAN, C. S. (1952). Regional land surveys. *J. Aust. Inst. agric. Sci.* 18, 140–6.
CHRISTIAN, C. S. (1958). The concept of land units and land systems. *Proc. 9th Pacif. Sci. Congr.,* 1957. Vol. 20. pp. 74–81.
CHRISTIAN, C. S. (1963). The use and abuse of land and water. In *The Population Crisis and the Use of World Resources.* Vol. 2. (World Academy of Art and Science: The Hague.)
CHRISTIAN, C. S., and STEWART, G. A. (1953). General report on survey of the Katherine–Darwin region, 1946. *CSIRO Aust. Land Res. Ser.* No. 1.
CHRISTIAN, C. S., and STEWART, G. A. (1968). Methodology of integrated surveys. In *Aerial Surveys and Integrated Studies.* Proc. Toulouse Conf. 1964, UNESCO. pp. 233–80.
CUTLER, E. J. B. (1964). Soil capability classification based on the genetic soil map. *Trans. Joint Meeting of Commissions IV and V, Internat. Society of Soil Science,* 1962. pp. 743–54.
HAANTJENS, H. A. (1965). Practical aspects of land system surveys in New Guinea. *J. trop. Geogr.* 21, 12–20.
HERNANDEZ, S. C. (1955). A proposed score card for rating land-use capability. *J. Soil Sci. Philipp.,* No. 7.
KLINGEBIEL, A. H., and MONTGOMERY, P. H. (1961). Land capability classification. *U.S.D.A. Soil Conserv. Agric. Handb.* No. 210.
LEAMY, M. L. (1964). The correlation of soil classification and soil capability in the Upper Clutha Valley, Otago, New Zealand. *Trans. Joint Meeting of Commission IV and V, Internat. Society of Soil Science,* 1962. pp. 749–54.
MITCHELL, C. W., and PERRIN, R. M. S. (1967). Subdivision of the hot deserts of the world into physiographic units. *Trans. Second Int. Symp. Photo-Interpretation,* Paris, 1966, pp. 89–106.
SOLNTSEV, N. A. (1961). Basic problems in Soviet landscape science. *Izvestiya Vseso-yuznogo Geografichoskogo Obsalichestua* No. 1, 3–14.
STEELE, J. G., VERNON, K. C., and HEWITT, C. W. (1950). A capability grouping of the soils of Jamaica. *Trans. Fourth Internat. Cong. Soil Sci.,* Amsterdam No. 3.
STORIE, R. E. (1933). An index for rating of agricultural value of soils. *Univ. Calif. Agr. Exp. St. Bull. 556.*
STORIE, R. E. (1948). Revision of soil rating chart. *Univ. Calif. Agr. Exp. St. Bull.*

Classification of Cultural and Natural Vegetation Sites as a Basis for Land Evaluation

G. M. Ignatyev

Faculty of Geography,
Moscow State University, U.S.S.R.

In land evaluation for agriculture or forestry the main factors to be considered are those that affect biological productivity. Such evaluation should be applicable to both developed and undeveloped areas, and should, if possible, take the monetary value of the land into account. Land evaluation surveys in the Soviet Union derive their data both from field observation and from questionnaires and farm production records. Presentation of this data may be in the form of maps of individual components or, more commonly, a single landscape map showing natural territorial complexes equivalent to land systems. It is suggested that land classification should be based on those land properties that separate vegetation sites. These are primarily soil moisture and soil nutrient availability, which act independently except in extreme moisture conditions. Quantitative indices of soil moisture and of biological productivity include indirect indices referring to experience of yields and problems of management, and direct indices taken from soil analyses. Other relevant properties of vegetation sites include aspects of climate and relief.

INTRODUCTION

Research in the field of land evaluation in the Soviet Union is being carried out for various purposes: for industrial, civic, and urban construction projects, for agriculture and for forestry and, on a wider scale, for regional planning. Research work relating to the requirements of agriculture and forestry differs essentially from work connected with construction in that the central focus is on the biological productivity of the land, whereas for construction projects the main factors bearing on the total economic productivity may not be those of biological significance. It is very difficult to generalize about these factors because of their great variety and the variation in importance of individual factors from place to place. For this reason our attention will be concentrated mainly on those factors referred to in land classifications that exert an influence on biological productivity.

In the study of the Soviet Union's land resources two types of classification are used: basic and applied. Basic classifications are drawn up with reference to the main natural properties that distinguish a given territory. Applied classifications result from a grouping of categories of the basic classification to form categories related directly to particular types of land use. Their specific characteristics depend on concrete requirements which are in turn determined by the type of land use envisaged.

The main subjects of evaluation research in the U.S.S.R. are agricultural (arable and pasture) and woodland areas. Part of such land has not long been under cultivation and its original properties have as yet been only slightly modified by man. Other land (first and foremost in the European part of the U.S.S.R.) has already been cultivated by man for many centuries, and its properties, including its biological productivity, depend to a large extent on the methods and type of cultivation employed both at the present time and in the past. The evaluation of land such as this plays a role as important as the evaluation of newly cultivated territories, for its reliable evaluation contributes towards the improvement of existing methods of cultivation employed on this type of land, towards the modification of such methods in keeping with the natural properties and in particular the productivity of the given land. In order to make this evaluation more effective it is believed to be advisable that this operation should also include an estimate of the land's value (present and prospective if possible) in monetary terms, bearing in mind existing methods of cultivation and specific economic conditions (distance from markets, etc.). In this context, land classification according to basic natural properties, such as soils, rocks, and land forms, that are stable in time is of extreme importance for it should provide the main instrument in attempts to define the features of land to be evaluated.

What kind of material should be taken into account in land classification? The correct answer to this question is one of the tasks confronting the many expeditions working on the territory of the Soviet Union and in particular the expeditions of the Geographical Faculty of Moscow University. Similar studies are also being conducted by the geographical faculties of Leningrad, Lvov, Riga, and Voronezh Universities, and by several planning institutes and laboratories. Problems connected with the classification and evaluation of agricultural land have frequently been brought up at specialist conferences and there exists extensive reference material in this field.

LAND EVALUATION SURVEYS

The experience of teams who have been commissioned to carry out studies of this type by agricultural organizations serves to demonstrate that the material essential for land classification and evaluation is not confined to a single map or textual description based on a field survey. A wide variety of material furnished by the expeditions from Moscow University can be divided into two main groups according to the type of source from which it was obtained: material collected in the field, and material collected with the help of questionnaires or statistical data.

Material collected on the spot includes all basic types of information with relation to the natural properties of the land, such as details as to the land form, soil profiles, botanical sites, the results obtained from field and short-term stationary observations of the soil's hydrophysical properties, and calculation of fallow land productivity by weighing the hay harvested from sample sites. This type of material also includes laboratory analyses of samples which provide the research team with information as to the chemical composition of the soil and the plants' ash content.

The second group of material includes data about the crop yield of the collective or state farm fields and the achieved productivity of the fallow land and pastures, information with regard to the natural 'defects' of the fields and also all the special features of land use in the given area (crop rotation, the extent to which natural or chemical fertilizers are used, measures undertaken to counteract land erosion, etc.). In order to draw up an evaluation of the land in monetary terms it is essential to draw up data with regard to the labour expenditure and money spent on cultivating the various different crops. All this material can be collected from the annual accounts of agricultural enterprises and also via local questionnaires in the given district.

The quantity of data recorded at production farms taken all in all is very comprehensive and this creates certain difficulties as far as its summary is concerned. For classification purposes it is essential to record these data territorially by charting them on a map. When correlations between various phenomena in the territory in question are observed this facilitates such a task considerably. Two basic tendencies in large-scale mapping have been adopted in Soviet land evaluation: (1) field maps are drawn up for each component feature of the territory, such as the form of the relief, the soil, and the vegetation which all serve to complement each other, and (2) one multi-purpose map and a series of subsidiary maps or diagrams are drawn up.

Both types of mapping have their advantages and drawbacks. In the first method the assessment of the correlations between the different components is a lot more objective and provides a more precise exposition, which excludes any risk of interpreting desired results as actual results. However, this first method is extremely time consuming and is comparatively rarely employed in large-scale mapping.

In the second case the main task is the drawing up of one multi-purpose map, which is sometimes referred to as a landscape map. On it are charted the border of the given landscape and its component natural territorial complexes. The term landscape in research of this kind probably corresponds almost exactly to the concept 'land system' to be found in the work of Australian scientists, while the natural territorial complexes within a landscape (Soviet geographers divide these up into units of varying taxonomical importance) are 'recurring pattern(s) of topography, soils, and vegetation' (Christian and Stewart 1953, p. 21). Theoretical analyses of the properties of landscapes and their morphological components have been carried out by Solntsev (1949), Isachenko (1965), and others.

In some types of multi-purpose maps in addition to basic natural properties of the territory in question specific features which come into being in conjunction with its exploitation also have to be taken into account. For example, during the study of the land of the collective farms of the Dniepropetrovsk region of the U.S.S.R., maps were drawn up in which the area division was based on the following features: land-use unit (fallow, pasture, etc.); vegetation association; the agrotechnical condition of the land (the condition of the crop and the percentage of weeds, etc.); the relief; the angle of the slope; the soil; the mechanical composition of the soil; the character and degree of erosion; and soil-forming rock.

Very frequently the basic features of the natural properties of a given territory have been charted on a soil map, which should in that case contain a large quantity of information referring not merely to the soil but also to the soil-forming rocks, surface contours, signs of erosion, etc. However, in the study of fallow and pasture land it is also essential to have geobotanical maps as well. Thus this type of study is in its nature a variety of the first type of mapping mentioned above.

Land evaluation requires that the territory under examination be divided up into special units equal as regards productivity and which require identical land management. When land evaluation maps are being drawn up on a scale of 1:10,000 or 1:25,000 these units as a rule are between 100 and 150 hectares in size. When defining these units the research team, basing their decisions merely on the natural factors which they are studying, cannot always be sure that that particular combination of land properties is of prime importance and that all the factors which influence land productivity have been taken into account in sufficient detail. For this very reason analysis of land use is of inestimable importance and so is information obtained from questionnaires distributed among the local population. Only by comparing physico-geographical and economic geographical data is it possible to maintain that the features of the land to be classified and evaluated have been shown precisely enough[1].

So far this paper has concentrated on the setting up of territorial units for classification and evaluation purposes. A great deal of attention was focussed on this aspect because even carefully elaborated territorial classification serves no useful purpose if units that are to be classified are not sufficiently uniform. However, at the same time it is important that the approach to this question should not be too pedantic. Clients who receive material from research associations complain frequently that the maps are too detailed even at their final stage, and the mapping units must still be grouped together to meet their practical demands. The key to finding the optimal solution lies, in the opinion of the author of this paper, in the co-ordination of all the research into the natural and economic features of the given territory. At the same time research teams should always bear in mind the simple fact that, if it actually comes to the point, it is always easier to join a number of units together than to split up one of them into parts.

CLASSIFICATION OF VEGETATION SITES

Material obtained by field research opens various approaches to the subsequent grouping of the units of a given territory. In the U.S.S.R. there is no universally accepted method for the classification of natural types of land; this can be traced back to the enormous variety of natural conditions and the diversity of land use requirements in different parts of the country. Nevertheless many research scientists consider that for the practical aims of the use of agricultural and forest land a single classification should be set up, and the most expedient type of local classification would be one based on the basic land properties that separate vegetation sites—both of the natural and cultural varieties. These properties are first and foremost, although not exclusively, properties of the soil.

The properties of the soil not only exert a direct influence on the fertility of a given territory but also reflect the overall combination of external factors of the natural environment and man's economic activity in the given area. The basic features of the soil which influence its biological productivity can be expressed in concrete terms by means of two groups of indices: the supply of available nutrition for the vegetation and the supply of soil moisture (the water regimes of the soil). It is not difficult to realize that these indices have a complex character showing the totality of local conditions, for they vary widely according to the type of relief, climate, and the types of land use. These two indices are frequently used as a basis for the classification of cultural or natural vegetation sites. It is interesting to note that classifications based on references to these two groups of indices were first used in the U.S.S.R. (independently of each other) in the study of forest vegetation (Sukachov 1931; Pogrebnyak 1955), pasture land (Ramensky 1938), and arable land (Zvorykin *et al.* 1958).

---

[1] In practical field work it is accepted practice for economic geographical research to precede the charting of natural features; material obtained in this kind of research leads to the concentration of field research on phenomena and factors which require special attention.

The essence of these classifications consists in the fact that, with the exception of extreme moisture conditions, the quantity of available means of nutrition and the quantity of moisture in the soil influence vegetation independently of each other, and in optimal types of land there is usually to be found a series of land types, similar as far as productivity level is concerned but differing one from another with regard to the composition of biological production and requiring different forms of land improvement measures. The classification of types of sites is usually drawn up in the form of a graph along the abscissa axis of which are set out the various degrees of biological productivity, while along the other axis soil moisture is plotted. The classification categories plotted on the diagram constitute a figure in the shape of an ellipse, the large axis of which slopes down and to the right in areas of surplus moisture and down and to the left in areas with a dry climate (Fig. 1). In areas with excessive or insufficient moisture, where the land's productivity is directly dependent on the amount of

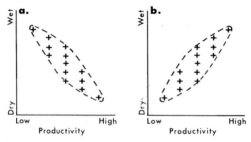

Fig. 1. Local classifications of lands in areas with a, abundant, and b, insufficient moisture (hypothetical figures). Each cross represents a type of land.

moisture the small axis of the ellipse is shorter and the figure tends to resemble a line. In areas of adequate moisture, the form of ellipsis is distorted. By way of example, let us examine the classification of cultural vegetation sites (arable lands) in a region with a normal moisture level, situated in the wooded steppe zone of the Ryazan region (Fig. 2). This is an area for which the figure plotting the complex of sites is as elongated as possible and the number of site variations on both axes of the graph is large.

This classification shows only a most general regularity of relationships existing in nature, and in no way lays claim to being their mathematical model. However, the development of precise methods of research promises good prospects in this respect too.

To a pedologist who classifies soils only by their inherent properties, such classification would seem insufficiently grounded. But in this case, the investigators had at their disposal not only data on soil intrinsic properties, but also direct information on soil productivity, as well as on other features noticed by farmers. It was the comparison of these materials that made it possible to fix the order shown in Figure 2.

Indeed, each group of symbols in the diagram (each type of land) has additional characteristics that include a list of cultivated crops and their yields. After the processing of economic data, it became possible to determine as well the profitability of each type of land with certain levels of management. Thus, the investigators had a good number of comparable quantitative indices to enable them to check on the correctness of positions of the classified units in the diagram.

The most difficult question is which quantitative indices should be taken into account in the allocation of land categories to this or that class of land.

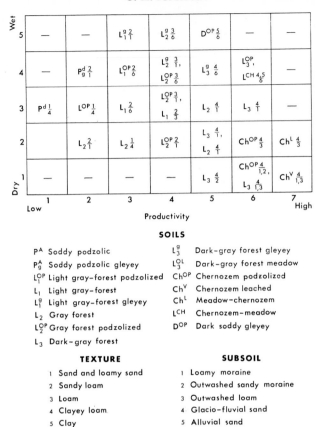

Fig. 2. General classification of arable land of the Sapozhkovsky region, Ryazan province (after Zvorykin *et al.* 1958). Soil type symbols are followed by a numerator indicating texture, and a denominator indicating subsoil.

The difficulty is not that there are only a few quantitative indices of productivity and soil moisture but rather that there are too many. They can all belong to two categories: indirect or direct. The first category includes data extracted mostly from statistical accounts which characterize productivity, such as bio-masses, their annual growth, site classes, and crop capacity. The degree of moisture is indicated by the proportion of hydromorphic and xeromorphic plants in the given vegetation associations or the length of the plants' vegetative phases. In the extensive plains of the U.S.S.R. the surface of the earth is covered with snow in winter. After it melts the supply of water in the fallow land is very uneven. The time at which individual sections of these areas are ready for spring ploughing and sowing after the ground has dried again to a sufficient extent represents another important indirect factor relevant to the plotting of moisture levels.

Direct data are taken straight from the results of analyses of the chemical and hydrophysical properties of soil. Although in isolated cases it is possible to trace a direct correlation between the crop capacity and one particular property of the soil, for example the percent of humus contained in it or the thickness of the humus layer, all the numerous and diverse indices of soil properties act on the vegetation simultaneously and as one. For this reason the results of such analyses should be estimated in their totality. This at least makes it possible to define whether one type of soil is better than another but it does not enable us to determine how many times one type of soil is better than another. For this reason it is deemed expedient to make use not only of direct indices but of indirect ones. In the example mentioned earlier, in addition to the properties of the actual soils, the crop capacity for the main crops and the dates by which the soil was ready for spring ploughing were already taken into account.

The classification of land by natural and cultural vegetation sites should not be regarded merely as a specific type of soil classification. It is possible to cite a wide range of examples in which factors which exert a strong influence on vegetation are reflected only to a very slight degree in soil properties; for example, frosts during plants' growing period or the freezing over of the soil in cases of dislodgement of the snow cover during winter. The exposure of slopes and other micro-climatic features are not always clearly reflected in soil properties. A marked dissection of the surface of fields by ravines or river valleys sometimes makes it necessary to assess separately small sections of farm land distinguished by configurations of an awkward type for cultivation. Labour productivity, even if crop capacity is identical, is usually lower in such areas. All this points to the fact that factors of climate and relief can and must be taken directly into account in the definition of land categories and the system of their classification.

Classifications of vegetation sites are important on an intra-regional scale. They are drawn up for specific territories throughout which one and the same combination of factors obtain. It is very difficult and very unlikely to be worthwhile to combine in one system land from different geographical zones. The author of this paper was commissioned to study the properties of the woodland in the Carpathian Mountains. Comparison of data relating to the composition and productivity of these woods with the properties of the soil in this area indicated that it was worthwhile first of all to single out the high-altitude belts and then, in the confines of each of these, to assess the different types of soils in relation to their particular productivity and moisture content.

In research devoted to the evaluation of agricultural land, classification which takes into account the properties that distinguish cultural vegetation sites can turn out to be the best basic type of classification. Its categories, known as land types, are sufficiently uniform for the distribution of identical crop rotations, cultivation methods, for the calculation of ideal norms for fertilization and land improvement measures. This type of classification does not exclude or replace the need for the creation of other types of applied classification, for instance, with regard to the degree of erosion hazards or the broader classification of land capabilities generally accepted in the U.S.A. and various other countries. However, it represents the most convenient form of classification since it clearly reflects the main qualitative distinctions between various types of agricultural land. In a number of surveys its categories were subject to evaluation in cost indices based on yields and expenditure of labour, materials, and the amortization of agricultural equipment. The results of such work are valuable with respect to the creation of land cadasters of the agricultural territory in question.

There is still a great deal of work to be carried out in the study of the influence on land productivity of individual factors both separately and in totality. It is also essential to link up more closely work being carried out on land classification techniques for different purposes. Further, it is essential to ensure co-ordination between the findings of research teams with regard to different types of natural conditions. International co-operation on the part of specialists working in this field has a vital role to play in this respect, likewise exchange of information and experience between scientists of different countries.

REFERENCES

CHRISTIAN, C. S., and STEWART, G. A. (1953). General report on survey of Katherine-Darwin region, 1946. *CSIRO Aust. Land Res. Ser.* No. 1.

ISACHENKO, A. G. (1965). *The Foundations of Landscape Science and Physico-Geographical Regionalization.* (Vysshaya Shkola Publishing House: Moscow.)

POGREBNYAK, P. S. (1955). *The Foundations of Forest Typology.* (Acad. Sci. Ukra. S.S.R.: Kiev.)

RAMENSKY, L. G. (1938). *Introduction to Synthetic Soil-Geobotanical Land Research.* (Selkhozgis Publishing House: Moscow.)

SOLNTSEV, N. A. (1949). On the morphology of natural geographical landscapes. *Questions of Geography* **16**, 61–86.

SUKACHEV, V. N. (1931). *Guide to the Study of Forest Types.* (Selkhozgis Publishing House: Moscow.)

ZVORYKIN, K. V., PERTSEVA, A. A., TSEDELER, E. E., LEBEDEV, N. G., and VIDINA, A. A. (1958). Conclusions drawn from research experience in the field of typological and qualitative evaluation of arable land. *Questions of Geography* **43**, 86–114.

Estimation of Grazing Capacity on Arid Grazing Lands

R. W. Condon

Soil Conservation Service of N.S.W.

A method of estimating grazing capacity of arid lands is described. This requires the selection of a standard land class for which the grazing capacity is known, or can be determined with reasonable accuracy; and the establishment of rating scales for the various factors which influence grazing capacity. The most important of these rating scales is average annual rainfall.

INTRODUCTION

The settlement of arid and semi-arid lands for grazing has, in Australia and many other countries of the world, been accompanied by excessive optimism as to the carrying capacity of the pastures. This optimism no doubt derives from the amazing response to good rains which is characteristic of desert environments, and from the fact that desert environments, in the pristine state, will carry stock at a very high rate while seasons are good. However, the arrival of the inevitable prolonged run of bad seasons is accompanied by a serious decline in the condition of soils and pastures as excessive stock numbers graze out the pastures and browse plants, and trample the soil into a condition highly vulnerable to erosion. This may leave the land open to serious erosion from which recovery is very slow or impossible, or to invasion of depleted pastures by weed species of little or no forage value.

These sequences of events occurred in western New South Wales at the turn of the century. Sheep numbers on the 80,000,000 acres (32,000,000 hectares) of the Western Division, with average annual rainfall ranging from 6 to 16 in. (152 to 405 mm) were reduced from 15,000,000 to 4,000,000 following the 1901–02 drought. Subsequently, sheep numbers have rarely exceeded 8,000,000 until the late 1950's.

In evidence to a Royal Commission in 1901, landowners in western N.S.W. reported widespread erosion and the complete disappearance from extensive areas of valuable shrub species such as saltbush (*Atriplex*) and bluebush (*Kochia*). In other areas, noxious scrub species had increased to a point where it became impossible to muster livestock in country which, 20 years before, it had been possible to see sheep half a mile away.

Similar sequences of events have occurred in the arid grazing country of South Australia in the late 1920's (Ratcliffe 1936), and in Western Australia in the late 1930's. A further example took place in central Australia in the late 1950's and early 1960's as cattle numbers, built up to excessive proportions during a run of good seasons, were decimated by a long run of increasingly bad seasons (Anon. 1964).

Much of the damage to the soils and pastures in Australia's arid interior has resulted from ignorance of what was a reasonable level of stocking, and ignorance of the effects of excessive stocking. There have also been many instances of deliberate destruction of valuable shrub pastures, with a high drought-grazing capacity, with the object of producing an apparently high-yielding pasture of annual herbage.

The holders of leasehold land, and the administrators of that land, have a responsibility to the nation to maintain that land in good condition. Owners of freehold lands have a similar responsibility. The most important factor in maintaining grazing land in good condition is an accurate knowledge of the grazing capacity of the pastures and browse species.

Also important is the knowledge that different types of country may vary considerably in grazing capacity, and in reaction to excessive grazing pressure. Some soils are highly productive but also highly erodible, and excessive grazing will cause rapid deterioration to a condition from which recovery is impossible (Condon 1961). Other country of moderate productivity may not be greatly affected by excessive grazing and will appear to recover completely within two or three years of good seasons. In such instance, although recovery may be complete, the number of times that this can happen will be limited.

When the N.S.W. Soil Conservation Service agreed to advise the Northern Territory Administration (Anon. 1967) on the deterioration of soils and pastures as a result of the prolonged drought in central Australia, it was considered that some means of accurately determining grazing capacity was essential. The survey of land resources previously carried out by CSIRO (Perry et al. 1962) provided an inventory of most of those factors having an important influence on grazing capacity, viz., soils, topography, timber, pastures, and rainfall.

It was possible to establish rating scales for each of the factors that influence grazing capacity so that aspects that increased grazing capacity were given a bonus rating, while those aspects that had an adverse effect on grazing capacity were given a penalty rating. To apply the rating scales it was necessary to establish a standard, being a particular class of country (in this case at the land system level), preferably widespread, for which the grazing capacity at a particular rainfall level is either known, or can be determined with reasonable accuracy.

This technique was used successfully in determining grazing capacities in central Australia, using the rating scales to establish a standard grazing capacity for each land system, as mapped by CSIRO Division of Land Research (Perry et al. 1962). To this was subsequently applied a rainfall factor according to location and a 'condition' factor (while values for other factors were varied if necessary) to determine the grazing capacity of a land system on a particular pastoral lease. Grazing capacities were determined in this way for 86 leases totalling 110,000 sq miles (285,500 sq km) in area. This technique is readily adaptable to determining the number of stock that can be carried on a particular watering point, or within a particular paddock.

Although the land system has been used as the basic unit in central Australia, the technique is more readily and more accurately applicable to the land unit. This is the basis on which it is being applied to leasehold lands in the Western Division of N.S.W. where the average lease is much smaller (20–200 sq miles, 50–500 sq km) than in central Australia (200–2000 sq miles, 500–5000 sq km).

The detailed knowledge available on the soils, pastures, tree species, and erosional behaviour had made it possible to develop very precise rating scales for the many factors that influence grazing capacity, and to reduce very considerably the degree of subjectivity in assessing these factors.

The determination of grazing capacity of arid lands in the manner described below can be used for several different purposes. It can be used as a means of evaluating the potential of undeveloped land for pastoral purposes. It can be used by the land administrators who need to know the grazing capacity for the purpose of making land available to settlers on an equitable basis and who need to determine a fair rental based on productivity. The land administrators also need to exercise some control after settlement to avoid the abuses that have occurred in the past due to excessive optimism or the desire for a quick fortune.

It can be used by the soil conservationist whose responsibility it is to advise the land administrators and landholders on satisfactory levels of grazing in conjunction with the most suitable methods of land management to avoid damage to soils and pastures.

It can be used by the landholder in the day-to-day management of his land and livestock, to determine how many stock he can safely carry on a particular watering point or paddock. It will aid him in planning the development of his holding because he can be shown the relative productivity of various types of country.

Used in conjunction with a knowledge of the reaction of various classes of country to grazing pressure, and especially the erosional behaviour of soils, the technique offers a means of ensuring the safe utilization of arid grazing country and avoiding the serious damage to soils and pastures that has been responsible for lowering the productivity of arid grazing lands in the past.

The areas of Australia to which this technique of estimating grazing capacity has been applied, or is being applied, are shown in Figure 1.

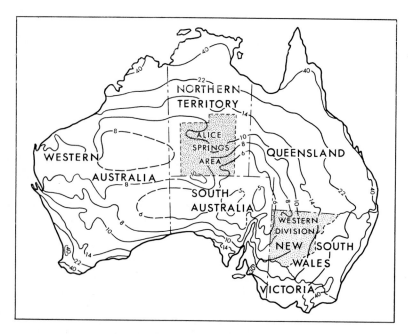

Fig. 1. Map of Australia showing average annual rainfall (in.) for all years of record until 1957 and areas to which grazing capacity determinations are being applied (After Bureau of Meteorology 1960).

The application of this system of estimating grazing capacity requires a survey to determine and map land classes, together with an inventory of those factors within each land class for which rating scales are used. This paper describes briefly how each rating scale has been developed.

The factors for which rating scales have been developed in western N.S.W. are soils, topography, tree density (as an inhibitor of pasture growth), trees and palatable shrubs (as suppliers of drought forage), pastures, condition (as influenced by erosion or growth of noxious weeds or scrub), and rainfall.

BASE VALUE

As the values from the rating scales are used as multipliers, it is necessary to have a base or standard from which all other grazing capacities are determined. This should be an area of known and proven grazing capacity, preferably widespread, and intermediate in most of the factors concerned. For example, soils should preferably be intermediate in productivity between sand and clay. Topography should be relatively level so that there is no pronounced run-off or run-on. Tree density should preferably be insufficient to provide competition against pastures. Rainfall should be somewhere near the centre of the range for the area being considered. Desirably the land class chosen should not be highly susceptible to erosion. If no reliable information is available on grazing capacity, it needs to be a unit that can reasonably be compared with a unit of known grazing capacity in another region.

The unit chosen as a base in western N.S.W. was a red sandy loam brown acid soil, of level to slightly undulating topography, carrying open mulga scrub with woolly butt (*Eragrostis eriopoda*) or corkscrew grass (*Stipa variabilis*) pastures of moderate to good palatability. Long-term stocking records show this class of country to have a grazing capacity of 8·0 dry sheep per 100 acres (1 sheep per 12½ acres) at an average annual rainfall of 10 in. (254 mm).

To establish rating scales for the various factors having an influence on grazing capacity, par (1·0) values were allotted to the particular aspect of each factor characteristic of this class of country. Thus, a value of 1·0 was allotted to red sandy loam brown acid soils and all other soils likely to be encountered in the Western Division were rated in relation to this standard. Similarly, level to slightly undulating topography was rated at 1·0, and other aspects of topography, dependent on its influence on run-on, rated in relation to this value.

The grazing capacity of any area depends upon availability of potable water. To determine the number of stock that may be carried on any area of land, the grazing capacity determined by the rating scales is applied to areas within a radius of 3 miles of water in the case of sheep and 5 miles from water in the case of cattle.

SOILS

Ratings for soils need to take account of three main aspects:
(a) *Inherent Fertility.*—Heavy clays have a high fertility and are rated generally in the range 1·2 to 1·4. Loams and sandy loams are moderate in fertility and are rated 1·0. Deep sands are low in fertility with ratings down to 0·75. Solonized brown soils, with a high lime content, are rated generally 0·15 higher than brown acid soils of equivalent texture because of their greater productivity.
(b) *Moisture Relationships*—The response to rains of varying amount is a most important determinant of grazing capacity. For example, heavy, grey self-mulching clay soils, which are very highly productive under good rains, are rated lower than gilgai types or other firmer clays which respond to light falls

because of run-off from small areas of poorly permeable soils on to nearby (1–3 m) absorptive soils. For the same reason, 'hard red' loams and sandy loams are rated 0·1 higher than 'soft red' loams and sandy loams.

(c) *Erodibility*—Soils with a high susceptibility to erosion are rated 0·1 to 0·2 lower than other soils of equal productivity. Soils with a loose sandy surface are rated lower because of higher erodibility and because young pastures are frequently buried by sand during bouts of strong wind. Soils carrying sand dunes are penalised depending on the proportion of land occupied by dunes.

The rating allotted for soil type does not purport to give a measure of the total productivity of a particular soil in relation to the standard. It is rather an estimate of the relative amount of forage that is available to grazing animals from the particular soils. Heavy clay soils may conceivably produce up to 2–3 times more plant matter than a sandy loam under equivalent climatic conditions, but only portion of this additional forage is available to the grazing animal before it decomposes or is blown away. The relative values for soils have been established by comparing known grazing capacity of different soils under equivalent climatic conditions.

TOPOGRAPHY

Ratings for topography endeavour to assess the relative influence of loss of moisture from the land unit as run-off, or gain of moisture as run-on.

Two rating scales are used. One scale gives penalties for varying degrees of steepness of slope, values ranging from 0·95 for slopes of 2 to 5% to 0·60 for slopes in excess of 30%.

The other scale shows bonus values applicable to various run-on situations. The productivity of run-on areas depends upon frequency of run-on and the width of the run-on area, the latter normally being a function of grade or slope of the watercourse. Narrow watercourses are generally steeply graded and run-on has less chance of being absorbed as it passes over the surface. However, flows are frequent. Broad run-on areas, being flatter in grade, are more likely to receive a good flooding but flows are usually infrequent.

Rating values range up to 1·5 for the situation where a broad run-on area received two flows per year. Because of the inverse relationship between run-on frequency and width of run-on area, values in practice are most frequently in the range 1·3 to 1·4. Often run-off and run-on areas are mixed in a complex pattern. If it is possible to determine the relative proportions of each, the grazing capacity of each unit is determined and the grazing capacity of the whole determined on the basis of relative proportion.

TREE DENSITY

To determine appropriate ratings for varying degrees of tree density it was necessary to make allowance for the many different types of tree and shrub species encountered in the area. These range from large eucalypts having a marked influence on pasture growth over a diameter of some 15–20 m, to mulga (*Acacia aneura*) having a slight influence over a diameter of 4–6 m.

Although some data were available from other States on the amount of pasture available under mulga of varying density, it was considered that the best means of obtaining relative values was to establish curves denoting the proportion of area occupied by circles of varying diameter and varying spacing;

to fit species to these curves in accordance with their relative effect on pasture growth; and to adjust the curves following observations in the field.

In this way four curves were established, representing rating values for different spacings of four groups of tree and shrub species. At a spacing of 5 m these values ranged from 0·1 for mallee and bimble box (*Eucalyptus populifolia*), species with a diameter of influence of 15–20 m, to 0·5 for mulga. At a spacing of 20 m these values ranged from 0·6 to 0·95.

In Figure 2 are shown the mathematically determined curves showing the proportion of land not 'occupied' by trees having a diameter of influence of 5 m and 15 m, in relation to average spacing. Also shown are the curves established for the four groups of species after adjustments following field inspections.

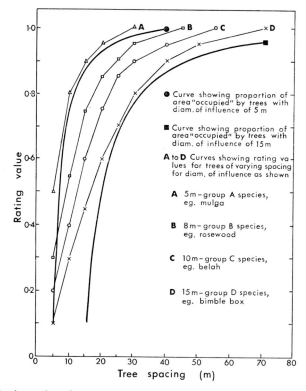

Fig. 2. Rating values for tree density in Western Division of N.S.W.

The rating values for the four groups of tree species, and for shrub species with a diameter of influence of 2–3 yards, are given in Table 1.

Trees are not always distributed uniformly but may be frequently arranged in clumps separated by varying widths of treeless country. To cater for distribution in clumps, rating tables were prepared for each of the four groups of tree and shrub species, showing rating values for percentage of country occupied by clumps with trees at various average spacings. In Table 2 the rating table for group C species (diameter of influence 10 m) is shown for clumps of trees at various average spacings. These values for 100% clumps (bottom line) are the same values for the rating scale for uniformly distributed trees in group C (see Table 1).

Abbreviated recording is important for field mapping, note taking, and internal reporting. The symbols C40, T15 indicate that 40% of an area is occupied by clumps of trees at an average spacing of 15 m. Two-letter symbols are used to denote particular species.

TABLE 1

Rating scales for tree density for tree stands with uniform density

Spacing (yd or m)	Species Group (and approx. diam. of influence)				Small Shrubs (2–3 m influence)	
	A (5m)	B (8m)	C (10m)	D (15m)	Spacing	Factor
T5	0·50	0·30	0·20	0·10	S1	0·10
T10	0·80	0·55	0·40	0·30	S2	0·20
T15	0·90	0·75	0·60	0·45	S3	0·40
T20	0·95	0·85	0·75	0·60	S4	0·60
T25	1·00	0·90	0·85	0·70	S5	0·75
T30		0·95	0·90	0·80	S7	0·85
T40		1·00	0·95	0·90	S10	0·90
T50			1·00	0·95	S15	0·95
T60				1·00	S20	1·00

The symbol T10 indicates trees at a spacing of 10 metres

The symbol S2 indicates shrubs at a spacing of 2 metres

TABLE 2

Rating scales for tree density for tree stands with "clumpy distribution" (Group C trees)

Percent Clumps*	Spacing within Clumps							
	T5	T10	T15	T20	T25	T30	T40	T50
C10	0·95	1·00						
C20	0·90	0·95	1·00					
C30	0·85	0·90	0·95	1·00				
C40	0·80	0·85	0·90	0·95	1·00			
C50	0·70	0·80	0·85	0·90	0·95	1·00		
C60	0·60	0·75	0·80	0·85	0·95	1·00	1·00	
C70	0·50	0·70	0·75	0·80	0·90	0·95	1·00	1·00
C80	0·40	0·60	0·70	0·80	0·90	0·95	1·00	1·0
C90	0·30	0·50	0·65	0·75	0·85	0·90	0·95	1·0
C100	0·20	0·40	0·60	0·75	0·85	0·90	0·95	1·0

* Percentage of area occupied by clumps of trees at average spacings shown.

DROUGHT FORAGE

In arid grazing country, the ability of country to carry livestock through short- and medium-term droughts is a most important attribute, and needs to be catered for in a rating scale. In central Australia, where cattle are able to utilize mulga and other topfeed species to an almost unlimited extent by breaking down large branches off the trees, it was possible to establish a separate drought grazing capacity in accordance with the frequency of topfeed species. This gave an estimate of the grazing capacity of the land after three years of continuous drought conditions, with a sliding scale down to this figure for the first and second years of drought.

In the case of sheep, the animals are not able to break down branches from trees. Once a stand of forage trees has been browsed heavily the sheep have access only to leaves that grow within reach, or that fall from the trees. The amount of forage available from this source is therefore limited. For this and other reasons, it is not possible to establish a drought grazing capacity for sheep in the same way as can be done for cattle.

The grazing capacity established for sheep assumes that pastures with a reasonable component of palatable perennial grasses and herbs will carry sheep for 12 months into a drought at the rate specified. Ground pastures composed almost solely of ephemeral grasses and herbage are downgraded to 0·8 on the pasture rating scale. Country with a reasonable frequency of accessible fodder trees and palatable shrubs is upgraded to a maximum of 1·2 on the drought forage rating scale.

Thus, country which may be penalised for heavy tree density gets a compensating bonus for drought forage if the tree storey contains species that will provide drought forage for sheep.

PASTURES

Ratings for pastures were not used in the central Australian survey because pasture type is very uniform throughout most of this country, being composed of short grasses and forbs, with long-lived perennials very much in the minority. The exception to this is country dominated by spinifex (*Triodia*) which is of very low palatability and for which a special rating scale was devised. Some account was also taken of pasture quality in the condition ratings so that pastures dominated by *Salsola*, or other useless annuals, were rated low in condition.

In western New South Wales there is a considerable range of pasture communities dominated by perennial species. Early attempts at rating country without using any pasture rating produced anomalies that were removed when appropriate pasture ratings were used.

The ratings for pastures depend on their palatability and usefulness as forage, and their perenniality. The rating scale for pastures adopted a value of 1·0 for corkscrew grass and woollybutt, these being the dominant grasses on the standard or base land unit. Some pastures dominated by species of higher productivity and acceptibility to livestock and of equal perenniality, are rated at 1·1. Penalty ratings are as low as 0·8 for pastures carrying only annual herbage. Special scales have been prepared for species such as spinifex, canegrass, lignum (*Muehlenbeckia cunninghamii*), and other small shrub species that occupy much space but provide little forage.

CONDITION

Condition is a word used to describe the 'health' of the range. Normally, it purports to assess the health of a pasture community by recognizing the influence on grazing, of types of species making up the pasture. It also needs to take account of deterioration by erosion.

In the scheme being applied in western N.S.W. ratings have been established for pastures (see above) that are, in effect, a measure of pasture condition. The condition rating scale thus takes no account of pastures, giving only a measure of the effect of erosion on productivity.

Different scales have been developed for different forms of erosion. The scale for wind sheeting, which has a permeable surface more likely to regenerate naturally, is not as severe as that for scalding or water sheeting.

Condition ratings are not directly proportional to the amount of bare space, allowance being made for the fact that water that runs off the eroded country is normally retained nearby and offers some benefit, as run-on, to vegetation in limited areas. Special scales of values can be prepared to suit particular circumstances, such as country where sandhills alternate with scalded claypans.

It is also possible to establish condition rating scales for thick stands of noxious scrub or weeds, providing a reasonable estimate can be made of the proportion of country occupied and of its effect on pasture productivity. Some samples of condition ratings are given in Table 3.

TABLE 3

Condition ratings for various forms of erosion in relation to proportion of country "occupied" by bare space

Bare Space (%)	Wind-Sheeting (1)	Water-Sheeting (2)	Water Sheeting with Gullying (2)	Scalding	Noxious Weeds or Scrubs (3)
10	0·95	0·90	0·90	0·90	0·90
20	0·90	0·85	0·85	0·85	0·85
30	0·85	0·80	0·80	0·80	0·80
40	0·80	0·75	0·70	0·75	0·70
50	0·75	0·70	0·60	0·70	0·60
60	0·70	0·65	0·50	0·65	0·50
70	0·65	0·60	0·40	0·60	0·40
80	0·60	0·50	0·30	0·50	0·30
90	0·50	0·40	0·20	0·40	0·20
100	0·40	0·30	0·10	0·30	0·10

Notes

(1) Much more permeable and more easily regenerated than most eroded surfaces.

(2) Ratings would depend on the condition of drainage lines. If the latter are badly gullied so that run-off is carried off to other land units instead of promoting growth in localized run-on areas, ratings given in the third column should be adjusted to those shown in the fourth column.

(3) Ratings would be varied according to the amount of forage "allowed" by the noxious species at 100% cover.

RAINFALL

The most important factor influencing grazing capacity is rainfall. To establish a relationship between rainfall and grazing capacity, detailed analysis was made of livestock statistics of the 46 counties comprising the Western Division of N.S.W. (made available by the Western Lands Commission of N.S.W.). The average grazing capacity for each county (with areas averaging about 3000 sq miles, 7700 sq km) was plotted against average annual rainfall. The curve so obtained was a parabola which fitted the expression

$$y = 0·05x^2 + 0·38x$$

for the range from 0 to 10 in., and

$$y = 0·2x^2 - 2·7x + 15·5$$

for the range from 11 to 18 in. average annual rainfall.

In the above expression y is grazing capacity in sheep per 100 acres (40·5 hectares), x is average rainfall in in. per annum (1 in. = 254 mm). To establish a rating scale for rainfall, the values for each $\frac{1}{2}$ in. of average annual rainfall were all related to a value of 1·0 for 10 in. per annum. The curve of grazing capacity in relation to average annual rainfall and the rating values for each inch of average annual rainfall are given in Figure 3.

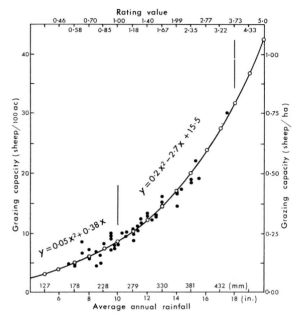

Fig. 3. Grazing capacity in relation to average annual rainfall in Western Division of N.S.W.

In the early phases of developing the overall rating scheme, consideration had been given to allotting bonus values for those areas that received a more pronounced winter or summer rainfall. It was decided to allot bonus values up to 1·15 for areas receiving 40% excess winter rainfall. It was considered that the effects of excess summer rain would be negated by higher evapotranspiration during that period and it was decided initially not to allot bonus values for pronounced summer rainfall.

Because anomalous results were being obtained from trial ratings in the pronounced summer rainfall area, an attempt was made to isolate this factor by drawing isopleths of grazing capacity on Beadle's (1948) vegetation map by applying rating values already established for soils, topography, tree density, pastures, condition, and rainfall. Isopleths of carrying capacity generally parallel to isohyets were drawn for all vegetation communities throughout Beadle's map. The expected grazing capacity of each county was then estimated according to the proportion of various types of country represented, and the values so obtained compared with actual figures.

It was immediately obvious that those counties along the northern and southern borders of the State were carrying more stock than would be expected, while areas throughout the centre (on each side of the line of uniform summer and winter rainfall) were generally carrying less than would be expected. This appeared to be a summer and winter rainfall effect. To ascertain if this was so, the differences between actual and expected grazing capacity for each county were plotted against per cent excess summer and winter rainfall.

Although there were some anomalies, this plotting gave a curve (Fig. 4) which gave a strong linear relationship for increasing proportion of summer

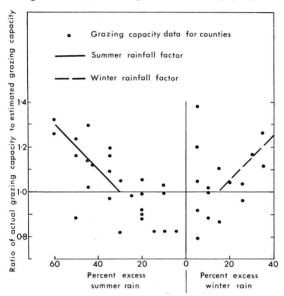

Fig. 4. Summer and winter rainfall factors in Western Division of N.S.W.

rainfall and a similar relationship for increasing proportion of winter rainfall (in spite of values having already been allotted for excess winter rainfall). As a result it was decided to adopt a summer rainfall rating scale for areas with more than 30% excess summer rain and a winter rainfall rating scale for areas with more than 15% excess winter rain. Thus, there are two rating scales for rainfall for determining grazing capacities in western N.S.W.– one for average annual rainfall and one for excess summer or winter rainfall.

It is also probable that rainfall variability would have an influence on grazing capacity. In western N.S.W. and central Australia the lines of equal variability are closely parallel to the rainfall isohyets. The improvement in rainfall reliability with increasing average annual rainfall probably accounts, to some extent, for the exponential nature of the rainfall against grazing capacity curve.

BARREN AREAS

Two classes of country fall within this category—salt lakes and hills and mountains which may be too rocky and stony or be inaccessible to animals. Other areas may be pastorally barren or nearly so, because of dense scrub cover, or because of overwhelming predominance of a pastorally useless species. In most cases barrenness is rarely complete—there are some areas scattered throughout salt lakes or hills or dense scrub which are usable. If the distribution is complex the relative proportions of barren and usable country can be estimated and a grazing capacity for the usable country determined. This would be qualified by a factor appropriate to the proportion of usable country.

In the case of country studded with salt lakes this factor would be inversely proportional to the area occupied by salt lakes. In the case of hilly areas the factors used would not be directly in inverse proportion to the area occupied by unusable hills, but would make allowance for the fact that the hills would run much water to usable valley areas and to adjoining country during storms.

The values used in the central Australian survey for unusable hills and salt lakes are shown in Table 4.

TABLE 4

Rating values for unusable hills and salt lakes (As applied in central Australian survey)

Unusable Area (%)	Rating Values	
	Hills	Salt Lakes
10	1·00	0·90
20	0·95	0·80
30	0·90	0·70
40	0·80	0·60
50	0·70	0·50
60	0·60	0·40
70	0·50	0·30
80	0·40	0·20
90	0·30	0·10
100	0·20	0·00

In cases where hilly country is usable, as with sheep grazing, the hills are penalised heavily for steep topography, and may be also penalised appropriately for rockiness, or difficulty of access.

CONCLUSION

The objective in determining grazing capacities in central Australia and western N.S.W. has been to minimise soil erosion and pasture degeneration, and to maintain productivity of country which is very susceptible to deterioration with excessive stocking. Any determination of grazing capacity must be backed by adequate legislative authority and administrative procedures.

The technique described involves some element of subjective judgement, and the assessor requires experience of the area concerned. No doubt, adjustments will be made to existing rating scales with accumulating experience. Future experience will also bring to light circumstances that are not covered by existing rating scales. Analysis of their influence on grazing capacity will enable a special rating scale to be devised. Rainfall variability is one such factor which has already been discussed.

As the method has been derived by paying close attention to stocking rates which are known to be effective in preventing soil erosion and pasture degeneration in western N.S.W. it has shown reasonable agreement with previous official assessments for lands in good condition. In several cases, especially where pastures are degenerate or condition is poor, it has given a result much lower than the previous official assessment, but almost exactly coincident with the landholders experience.

The adaptability of the technique enables it to be applied rather broadly on a land system basis, on a land unit basis, or, if necessary, at the soil type level. Refinements can be made as information becomes available, or as experience dictates.

REFERENCES

ANON. (1964). Central Australia drought. Evidence to Land Board Enquiry, July 1964. Unpublished Report, Northern Territory Administration.

ANON. (1947). Report on soil erosion and pasture deterioration in central Australia and necessary remedial measures. Unpublished report from Soil Conservation Service of N.S.W. to Northern Territory Administration.

BEADLE, N. C. W. (1948). *The Vegetation and Pastures of Western N.S.W. — with special Reference to Erosion*. (Govt. Printer: Sydney.)

BUREAU OF METEOROLOGY (1960). Maps of average annual rainfall, Australia. (Govt. Printer: Melbourne.)

CONDON, R. W. (1961). Erosion and management problems in western N.S.W. *J. Soil Conserv. Serv. N.S.W.* **17**, 86–102.

PERRY, R. A., *et al.* (1962). Lands of the Alice Springs area, Northern Territory, 1957. *CSIRO Aust. Land Res. Ser.* No. 6.

RATCLIFFE, F. N. (1936). Soil drift in the arid pastoral areas of South Australia. *CSIRO Aust. Pamph.* No. 64.

Terrain Evaluation for Engineering

G. D. Aitchison and K. Grant

Division of Soil Mechanics,
CSIRO, Syndal, Victoria, Australia

The history of terrain evaluation as developed in the United States of America, England, South Africa, and Australia as a means of communicating engineering knowledge and experience is reviewed and commented upon. The philosophical relationship of terrain evaluation to engineering problems is discussed. It is noted that no system of terrain evaluation, irrespective of its origin, has been adequately tested in relation to engineering land use.

Some forms of terrain classification may be adequate for a first appraisal of engineering problems in a given area but may not be adequate for all engineering purposes in all areas.

The further development of terrain evaluation for engineering may result in the emergence of specialist terrain engineers who will quantify terrain in terms of its engineering potential.

INTRODUCTION

Engineers, both military and civil, have been accustomed, for so long, to the appraisal of terrain for the specific purposes of their projects, that there cannot now be any element of novelty in the basic concept of terrain evaluation for engineering.

The road engineer, in designing and constructing mile upon mile of major and minor highways, has become aware of the repetitive nature – often the monotonous repetition – of his problems; problems of earthmoving, of subgrade properties, of river crossings, or of material resources; and he must have noted frequently that the recurring pattern of his problems has been linked with the recurrences of recognizable features of the terrain.

The water supply engineer, seeking sites for dams and for distribution channels, has been keenly consious of at least two attributes of the terrain: firstly, the physiographic features of the landscape and, secondly, the nature of the earthen materials on which his construction must proceed.

The military engineer, if concerned with 'going' conditions for the transport medium of the day, has also been acutely aware of a similar pair of basic terrain attributes – the physiographic features and the firmness or otherwise of the surface soil or rock. In his alternate capacity as constructor of roads and airfields, dams and canals, tunnels and bridges, the military engineer has paralleled the experiences of his civilian counterpart, but with a heightened appreciation of terrain arising often from enforced experiences on unfavourable terrain.

Examples of this type of awareness of an interaction between an engineering operation and the nature of terrain are limitless throughout the history of engineering – from the early Roman roads to modern hydro-electric schemes: in any properly managed engineering project or operation, it has become axiomatic that the characteristics of terrain, in so far as they are (or were) definable and in so far as they are (or were) known to impinge in a particular manner on the task in hand, should be taken into consideration: and yet the principles of terrain evaluation for engineering are still largely unstated.

In part, at least, the lack of an established discipline of terrain evaluation for engineering is purely a problem of communication: for it is not always a simple matter to define the characteristics of a particular terrain; and it is often even more difficult to express whatever existing knowledge there may be of the engineering experiences encountered on a specific terrain.

There are many aspects to this problem of communication of knowledge pertinent to the engineering evaluation of terrain: firstly, there is the obvious need for a method of communication of recognition criteria, so that an engineer at one place and time may appreciate the similarity or otherwise of his terrain to that described elsewhere, possibly by another engineer at another time: secondly, there is the need for a logical language for expressing and communicating engineering knowledge (including data and experience) concerning terrain: thirdly, there is the need for an orderly system of recording and transmitting the vast fund of information which must necessarily arise from the preceding developments: and finally, there is the overriding requirement that each of these stages must be compatible – in language, in detail, and in breadth.

Most of the work on terrain evaluation which has been undertaken so far by engineers or for engineers has been concerned with the first of the above aspects of the problem of communication, i.e. the task of communicating the means by which terrain can be described for recognition by others, so that (presumed) similarities of engineering characteristics can be recognized; thereby permitting the transfer of engineering knowledge.

Mabbutt (1968) has reviewed the general field of terrain classification and therefore, in this paper, attention is first given to a review of the pattern of progress in achieving the present status of definition of terrain as a means of communicating engineering knowledge. As a complement to this factual review an attempt is made in the second portion of the paper to present a critical review of the adequacy of current approaches to terrain evaluation for engineering, leading to a commentary on potential and/or desirable developments in the near future.

REVIEW OF PROGRESS IN TERRAIN DESCRIPTION AS A BACKGROUND TO ENGINEERING EVALUATION

The key to modern methods of description of terrain and to the communication of some of the concepts of description lies in the availability of aerial photographs. This review deals, in the main, with those developments which have arisen from the use of airphotos (even though it is recognized that a significant volume of current engineering evaluation of terrain is proceeding without the use of airphotos (Anon. 1966b)).

Terrain Studies as a Background to Civil Engineering in U.S.A.

Early work on engineering terrain studies can mostly be attributed to Belcher and co-workers at Purdue University. Belcher (1942a) noted that, in Indiana, related groups of soils occurred in large, definite areas and postulated that parent material and topography were the principal factors governing these occurrences. He stated:

'Assuming a reasonable similarity of climate, it is possible to expect the same soil types to occur on like parent material in similar topographic positions, regardless of geographic location.'

Subsequently, Belcher (1942b) suggested that the soil, land form, parent material relationship was significant in the definition of engineering properties.

'. . . soils developed under the same conditions of climate, topography, and parent-material are related and will have similar engineering properties' and

'. . . similar soils will be found on similar slopes and in similar positions.'

Belcher et al. (1943), in a comprehensive treatise dealing with the engineering properties of the rocks and soils of Indiana and the types of problems and failures encountered in their use, advocated the making of a complete inventory of the engineering materials of the State, and discussed the application of aerial photography to their identification. In the treatise, the land forms of the State were grouped in terms of slope classes, and the soils were classified at the series level with typical profiles for each presented diagrammatically, each diagram being fully annotated with a description and typical location for the soil and an account of the problems (together with possible solutions) likely to be encountered in the use of the soil. A map of the State of Indiana at a scale of approximately 1 : 730,000 showing the location of soil parent materials was included. This treatise can be regarded as probably the first general terrain assessment for engineering purposes.

Shortly afterwards, Belcher (1943) extended his basic concepts further into the engineering field in the following tenets:

'Regardless of geographic distribution, soils developed from similar parent materials under the same conditions of climate and relief are related and will have similar engineering properties which in comparable positions will present common constructional problems . . .' and

'Because of their individual properties, these parent materials produce a soil pattern that is related to their texture, slope, ground water conditions, and origin. This can be termed "the principle of the recurring profile" which becomes significant not only in engineering soil survey but in standardizing highway or airport pavement design and construction methods. When a soil profile recurs, as it does in comparable positions within a parent material area, the soil pattern will also recur. This is the link between soil pattern in the air photos, the soil profile and the related problems. Thus, by proper sampling of a given soil area the results may be used to determine soil characteristics in other areas having a similar pattern in the airphoto without respect to distance.' Belcher defined the pattern as seen on aerial photographs in terms of elements:

'The elements that make up the soil pattern are visible features that are directly or indirectly influenced by the physical properties of the soil profile. These elements form patterns of their own; among them are the land form, soil color, erosion, surface drainage, vegetative cover, slope, land use and others such as biological evidence, micro-relief, and farm practices.'

Thus Belcher stressed the concept of 'the principle of the recurrent pattern' with its implication not only of recurrent soil pattern but also of recurrent land form or terrain pattern, coupled with the suggestion that the recurrent pattern, once recognized, could be extended by aerial photograph interpretation to other occurrences of the same pattern, each of which could be expected to possess predictable engineering properties.

The position of aerial photograph interpretation with respect to the engineering properties of natural materials and the mapping of these materials was surveyed by Jenkins et al. (1946). The soils and their parent materials, land forms, slopes, drainage patterns, and vegetation of the United States of America were considered in detail, particularly in relation to aerial photograph pattern. An engineering soils map of the United States of America at a scale of approximately 1 : 4,000,000 was appended.

Belcher (1942b and 1948) made claims about the amount of soil data which could be extracted or inferred from aerial photographs. He maintained that soil texture, soil moisture and ground water conditions, lithology, approximate depth of soil cover, and vegetative cover could be directly determined. Also, he held that these data could be converted to estimate soil properties including Atterberg limits and compaction properties; equipment requirements for excavation or fill in soil or rock; the influence of weather on construction; location problems such as avoiding unstable soils, landslide susceptible zones and potential wash-out areas; drainage requirements, e.g. number of culverts and routing of ditches; source of borrow material for subgrade, embankments, and dams.

Hittle (1949) reviewed the application of aerial photograph interpretation to engineering problems and drew attention to the limits of the technique, particularly in relation to attempts to interpret below the soil surface.

The possible use of a contoured geological map as a basic engineering map was advocated by Eckel (1951). He considered that going conditions, the supply of construction materials, foundation and excavation conditions, water supply (both surface and ground), and soil conditions could be inferred from such a map.

Thornburn (1951) referred to the preparation of county soil maps in Illinois. He proposed a system of mapping based upon soil plasticity and parent materials. At the same time, Greenman (1951) discussed the effective application of a combination of various methods for soil surveys for engineering purposes. Among methods included were agricultural soil mapping, geological mapping, aerial photograph interpretation, and geophysical testing. He gave an example of a comprehensive table of the engineering properties of some soils classified at the soil series level. Also, Miles (1951) described methods for preparing limited engineering soil maps by aerial photograph interpretation combined with a compilation of existing data available for the area concerned and Lueder (1951) discussed the use of aerial photographs not as a reconnaissance aid, but as a major tool for use in the preparation of an engineering soil map for the State of New Jersey.

Methods for materials survey using aerial photograph interpretation, agricultural soil maps, topographic maps, and literature survey were comprehensively reviewed by Mintzer and Frost (1952). In conclusion, they tested and recommended an approach using all methods in combination.

In a Highway Research Board Bulletin (1961) dealing with methods and applications of soil mapping, with an accent on engineering materials, a number of authors considered aerial photograph interpretation, field survey, and engineering assessment. The general conclusions indicated that an integrated approach was preferable. Later, Miles (1962) again reviewed the field of aerial photograph interpretation in relation to engineering material classification and mapping and discussed land form, parent material, and soil classification for mapping purposes.

As a result of the early work of Belcher and succeeding developments, there have been many practical examples of engineering terrain appreciation, both on a limited and regional basis, in a number of States of the United States of America.

The principal area of application has been in road planning and construction. Hofmann and Fleckenstein (1960) used a terrain study technique to investigate the relative merits of two alternative routes on which to build a major highway in New York State. Of the two possible routes, one traversed rough, rocky mountainous terrain, while the other traversed lowlands along a river and lake valley. After appraisal of the geology, earthworks, and material resources of both routes, it was decided that the upland route was the more desirable from both location and cost viewpoint.

On the regional scale, Helmer (1959) applied terrain evaluation principles in Oklahoma. In a comprehensive manner, he discussed the soils (classified at the series level) and related the soil associations to parent materials. The engineering classification of the soils and other road-building materials were treated in detail and their engineering properties listed, some in a quantitative form. Accompanying the report were a geological map of the State, a soil association map of one county (as an example), and a complete set of block diagrams depicting typical land forms with soil associations indicated in appropriate position for each type of terrain occurring in Oklahoma.

Johnstone *et al.* (1962) dealt similarly with the soils of eastern Colorado. The geology, physiography, and soils classified at the series level, occurring in the region, were described and profile diagrams were included for each soil mentioned. Engineering problems associated with soil properties were discussed. A large coloured soil map at a scale of 1 : 500,000 is a feature of the work.

Terrain evaluation and survey has also been found useful in forms of engineering other than road building. The Federal Housing Administration (1962) used similar methods for assessing the potential for urban development, being concerned mostly with the permeability of soils for the sanitary disposal of household wastes. Olsen (1964) also discussed the application of soil survey to problems encountered in urban development and demonstrated the relationship of soil properties to sanitation, health, and general urban engineering.

Comment on Developments of Terrain Appreciation for Civil Engineering Purposes in U.S.A.

Many other such examples are available to define the pattern of progress of terrain appreciation for engineering purposes — specifically in the United States of America. By way of commentary on this apparent progress it is useful to compare the state of engineering appreciation of terrain in, say, 1964 with the principles expounded by Belcher more than 20 years ealier.

Belcher's stated principles remained uncontested, even if often untested. The great volume of new material gathered in the many studies of the various engineering authorities may well have proved valuable at project or regional level, but there was little or no contribution to the science of terrain evaluation. Most, if not all of the information was aimed, intrinsically, at those utilizing the art of terrain appraisal for engineering – in an extension of the age-old procedure of the 'practising' engineer.

The promise, implicit in Belcher's early work, that there could be a wholly logical series of relationships between land form, soil, airphoto, and engineering characteristics, remained unfulfilled – not disproven, yet neither quantified nor justified.

The difficulty lay not so much, if at all, in the validity of the principles enunciated by Belcher and his colleagues, but in the absence of a language and of a methodology for expressing and for communicating the characteristics of terrain. This shortcoming which led to a degree of stultification in the purely engineering environment was of course an object of study in other areas (see section on terrain studies in U.K.).

Terrain Studies for Military Engineering Purposes in U.S.A.

This review is naturally restricted to those aspects of military engineering study which are generally available. It is appreciated that a great volume of classified or unpublished material, which may be of considerable significance, is inaccessible to most readers.

The U.S. Corps of Engineers (1963) have recognized that all factors which influence military operations must be measured and have devised a classificatory scheme dealing with such factors and combinations of factors and relating them to terrain. At the lowest level is the *environmental factor* defined as:

'A specific attribute of the environment (which can be defined either quantitatively or in semi-quantitative or qualitative fashion) that forms an exclusive category. Environmental factors include all terrain factors, as well as relating to climate and weather.'

A defined range of variation within an environmental factor produces a *factor class*:

'A specific category within an environmental factor which has been defined as having a specific range of size, configuration, strength or other property.'

Moving into the field of terrain, a *terrain factor* is defined as

'An environmental factor describing an attribute of the landscape. Terrain factors include all attributes relating to soils, rocks, surface water, geometric configuration of the surface, and vegetation'

and *landscape* as

'A region throughout which a specific assemblage of environmental factor classes occur, and throughout which those factor classes are related to each other in a similar way.'

They also recognize that factor classes and landscapes have relationships with individual land forms within a terrain and develop a concept of *land form units*, within each one of which all factor classes will be in common, and of *land form components* which are composed of similar land form units arranged in the same way with respect to one another i.e., assemblages of recurrent land form units. To complete the circle, assemblages of recurrent land form components form a landscape.

'The repetitive occurrence of these land form components, within some established limit of variance, would identify a landscape.'

Speaking of the relationship of environmental factors to vehicular mobility when assessing the results of trials in Thailand, the Corps of Engineers state:

'The total number of environmental factors which are either known or hypothesized to affect ground mobility is very large. Many, such as slope, directly affect the performance of a vehicle. Others, such as soil moisture, operate only subtly, and in concert with other factors, to produce a measurable effect. While such factors tend to escape immediate notice, they are no less important, because it is the sum of all effects from all factors acting in concert that controls the resultant vehicle performance.'

The Corps of Engineers also noted that certain types of effects on vehicle mobility tended to be imposed by a limited array of environmental factors acting in concert and it seemed logical to divide the total array of environmental factors into families of factors which tend to operate in concert in accordance with the following criteria.

'First, the factors should, either alone or in concert, impose a specific type or set of types of effects on vehicles; and second, they should maintain at least a portion of the natural unities which are present in the environment as a whole.'

As a result of this process, five *factor families* affecting vehicular mobility have been recognized, viz., surface composition, surface geometry, vegetation, hydrologic geometry, and weather and climate. Within each factor family, all measurable aspects having any bearing on the configuration of the family are measured in as quantitative a manner as possible, e.g. taking surface composition as an example, measurements are made on the soil to determine organic matter content, grain size, Atterberg limits, specific gravity, soil classification (Unified Soil Classification and U.S. Department of Agriculture systems), soil moisture content, soil density, percentage saturation, and soil strength (in terms of a cone penetrometer rating both on the undisturbed soil *in situ* and on remoulded specimens of the same soil): the results are interpreted in conjunction with considerations of topographic position, slope, vegetation, and surface and ground-water characteristics at the test site.

The designation of limits for classes of environmental factors, i.e. factor classes, has caused some difficulty. The Corps of Engineers point out that, while some environmental factors fall naturally into groups and some can be related to vehicle characteristics, others, at the state of present knowledge can be subdivided only on an arbitrary basis. It is admitted that this three-fold method of grouping and, in particular, the arbitrary basis are not altogether satisfactory.

Overall, the approach of the Corps of Engineers is based upon the principle that the properties of terrain can only be properly understood and evaluated when all significant terrain variables can be measured in a completely quantitative form, i.e. when all significant terrain parameters are available; hence, the method of working is known as the parametric approach. Grabau (1963) has summarized some of the principles of the approach when comparing the results and uses of quantitative and qualitative terrain evaluations.

However, Tyson (1964) predicted that the number of parameters to be evaluated might be too large for convenience. Also, with progress in military design, the critical parameters may be constantly changing involving continuous re-measurement. Tyson advocated amending the method so that analyses should be made of the effects of environmental causes on particular military operations at particular times. He pointed out that, although there are an unfortunately large number of environmental characteristics, there are relatively few possible effects upon military operations. Once the relationship between cause and effect is known, parameters critical to the operation may then be determined to guide the choice of the best method for operational success.

Comment on Developments of Terrain Appreciation for Military Engineering Purposes in U.S.A.

From a logical point of view there is a great deal to commend the approach expounded by Grabau. If all of the terrain factors affecting a particular engineering operation can be defined and quantified, and if the manner in which each of these factors (separately or in concert) affect the operation can also be defined and quantified, then the possibility exists for a wholly scientific method of performance prediction—in relation to the specific operation.

This idealistic situation has many drawbacks—most of which are so obvious as to invite strong criticism. It is evident that the terrain factors of importance may change drastically for any change in the nature of the engineering operation So too will the quantified relationship between terrain factors (individually or in concert) and the engineering operation. Thus, if these principles are to be followed the effort required for prediction of a multiplicity of types of engineering performance could be immense.

Nevertheless the fact remains that work is proceeding and some success has been achieved in a project which is a wholly scientific example of terrain evaluation for engineering.

Terrain Studies for Highway Engineering in South Africa

The initial approach to terrain studies in South Africa was simply a pragmatic expression of the requirements of the highway engineer. Jennings and Brink (1961) initiated engineering soil mapping by recommending the properties of soils which should be noted or measured as a basis for mapping. Brink (1962) investigated aerial photograph interpretation in relation to soil engineering mapping; and Kantey and Williams (1962) advocated the preparation of soil engineering maps and analysed their use. The approach adopted in both cases involved the mapping of an area a few miles wide along the length of a pre-determined line of road. It was realized that regional assessment was in some ways preferable, but this could not be considered with the limited resources available. The method of working as described by Brink (1962) was to determine the properties of mapping units in the field by investigation of geology and soil; and then to determine their extent and to map them by aerial photograph interpretation. Such photographic features as land form, drainage pattern, grey tone, surface texture, and vegetation patterns were used in the extrapolation.

Based upon the method outlined, a number of recent road projects have been constructed after geotechnical maps with accompanying reports for the approximate line of route had been prepared. The geotechnical map, in these cases, was basically a coloured geological map with soil types indicated by the symbols proposed by Jennings and Brink (1961). Block diagrams illustrating terrain relationships were included for some areas, and the properties of the natural materials in relation to road building were indicated.

The status of the work in South Africa was summarized by Brink and Williams (1964), at which time it was indicated that increasing emphasis was being placed upon preliminary aerial photograph interpretative methods of mapping. Shortly thereafter, arising from international studies a developing interest in terrain classification became apparent, leading to the expression of the classificatory concepts of Brink *et al.* (1966).

By way of comment it is suggested that the pattern of development of terrain evaluation in South Africa is particularly important. Within a time interval of the order of five years, studies have ranged in nature from the wholly pragmatic approach to the almost purely philosophical, yet most, if not all, studies have been oriented ostensibly towards engineering requirements. The conclusions to be derived from these parallel studies are discussed later.

Terrain Studies as a Background to Civil and Military Engineering in U.K.

The work of engineering terrain assessment in England can be traced back to the methods proposed by Bourne (1931) for the assessment of forestry resources. Bourne was not only one of the pioneers of aerial photograph interpretation, but recognized the recurrent nature of terrain, particularly at the land form level. He noted that a change in land form association implied a distinct change in terrain. In order to describe the recurrent land forms, he conceived an entity which he called a *site*; and for each distinctive association of land forms, another entity which he called a *region*.

While Bourne's work had no direct engineering significance or necessarily influenced the concepts of terrain classification evolved by later workers, he must be regarded as the originator of terrain classification on the recurrent land form basis. Later workers have mostly tended to classify terrain on this basis and their concepts show a marked similarity to the site and region concepts of Bourne.

It was not for another twenty years that the next step in engineering terrain appreciation was taken in England when the Road Research Laboratory, Department of Scientific and Industrial Research used the method for investigating the location and properties of road-building natural materials in tropical areas of Africa, British Borneo, and the Caribbean.

Clare and Beavan (1962) discussed the use of regional surveys in locating and determining the engineering properties of soil and other road-building material in Northern Borneo. Schofield (1957a) described work involving the use of aerial photograph interpretation in the determination of the road-building properties of the soils in Nyasaland (now Malawi). He also noted the recurrence of typical land forms within the bounds of distinct regions. Later in the same year, Schofield (1957b) discussed the laterites of Nyasaland and their appearance in patterns on aerial photographs. Ackroyd (1959) assessed, on a regional basis, the engineering characteristics of road-building materials, with particular reference to laterite in western Nigeria. Clare (1960) similarly dealt fully with British Borneo, and Clare and Newill (1963), Beavan (1964), and Carroll (1964) with certain Caribbean islands. Generally, the geology and the properties of soils and other road-building materials were discussed. Aerial photograph interpretation was an important tool in the work and in some cases block diagrams were used to depict terrain relationships. Dowling (1963) investigated the use of aerial photograph interpretation for evaluating the engineering soil properties in an area in northern Nigeria. He concluded that an understanding of the regional geology, geomorphology, pedology, and vegetation characteristics was necessary for a satisfactory assessment of the features shown in aerial photographs. He also noted that care had to be exercised in interpreting land use as a guide to soil properties. He advocated a system of terrain classification as an extension of the work. Later, the same author (Dowling 1964) concluded that aerial photograph interpretation alone could be used to locate various lateritic formations.

Dowling and Williams (1964) attempted to predict the engineering properties of natural materials in certain areas in Nigeria. From their observations, they state:

'Each particular landscape is typified by such things as the shape and slope of the ground, the drainage pattern, the nature of the soils, vegetation, land usage, and other similar characteristics. All these natural features or elements show a characteristic relationship to each other and collectively form a pattern of landscape which at its simplest level reflects the geological and climatic history of the area and is dissimilar to other areas where geology and climate are different.'

Among their conclusions they found that, while aerial photograph interpretation was useful for mapping and locating soils, the prediction of the properties of natural materials could be made with greater accuracy when the influence of geology and climate was also known; for locating gravels, knowledge of recent erosional and depositional history was useful. Also when the control of geology and climate on terrain was taken into consideration, recurrent landscape patterns and facets as defined by Beckett and Webster (1962) appeared to be a reasonably sound basis for recording terrain data.

In the field of terrain classification, Beckett and Webster (1962), interested in the prediction of terrain properties for military engineering purposes in inaccessible areas, experimentally devised a system based upon the principle of terrain analogues. The principle pre-supposed that for any given terrain, there are always analogues available in some other area. As a background to the recognition of terrain analogues, Beckett and Webster proposed a system of terrain classification of a type reminiscent of Bourne (1931). The system was based upon the recurrent land form pattern principle using the term facet for the land form unit and recurrent landscape pattern (RLP) for the regional unit.

In describing the method of working, Barrie and Beckett (1964) have taken the concepts further and have recognized that because no two pieces of terrain will be exactly alike, but can be to all intents and purposes similar, for comparative purposes, facets and RLP's must be idealized; the entity investigated in the field may differ from this ideal in various, but minor, ways. Thus they allowed facet variants which arise from minor differences in the physiographic processes which formed them, e.g. in the gravel content or thickness of two terraces in the same valley, or in the depth of alluvial material in two outwash fans. Also, they admitted local form facets which they describe as equivalent to local varieties and races of a species in biological terminology.

Beckett and Webster (1965) illustrated the working of the scheme by describing a small area around Oxford, England. They established the terrain classification and demonstrated relationships between physical properties of the terrain and the classificatory units. A further example was provided in a publication from the Military Engineering Experimental Establishment (Anon. 1965b) in which a 'terrain brief' for military engineering purposes was described for a small area in Nigeria.

Terrain Study in Australia

Workers in fields other than engineering have contributed significantly to concepts of terrain classification which may be made applicable to engineering requirements.

Australia, interested in assessing the resources of its undeveloped northern regions, in 1946 established the Northern Australia Regional Survey (now the Division of Land Research) within the framework of the Council for Scientific and Industrial Research (now the Commonwealth Scientific and Industrial Research Organization).

The survey unit undertook reconnaissance type surveys intended to assess terrain for potential agricultural and pastoral development. The approach used was an integrated one, studying broadly all of the factors of consequence to this type of land use.

It was immediately recognized that, in order to make an assessment of resources within a continually varying medium such as terrain, some form of terrain classification, rather than the separate delineation of each resource, was essential. To this end a classificatory system at two levels of generalisation was devised, using the term land unit for the lower unit and land system for the upper mapping unit (Christian and Stewart 1953). Subsequently (Christian and Stewart 1968) the term site was defined as the lowest, most uniform classification unit and the land unit was related to a particular land form. Land systems may be simple, compound, or complex, depending on scale of working and complexity of the terrain pattern.

In the same paper, Christian and Stewart (1968) stressed that the use of their concepts allowed a broad scale assessment of terrain in the first instance, followed by detailed investigation of particular localities for diverse required purposes, including engineering.

The apparent success of this method of terrain classification for agricultural and pastoral purposes led to an attempt by the soil Mechanics Section (now the Division of Soil Mechanics) of CSIRO to evaluate the method and to apply its principles for engineering terrain assessment. As a background to the series of studies which commenced in 1962, it is worthy of note that extensive plans were being made in the northern parts of Australia for the construction of a network of development roads. Little or no scientific information was available to the engineers concerned with the design and construction of these roads, although some studies of the Division of Land Research had been made or were about to be made in the areas of interest.

It was stated, bluntly, by the senior engineer responsible for the greater part of this complete network that the land system–land unit basis of terrain description was inadequate for engineering purposes. In his opinion some engineering interpretation was required prior to use in any such project.

An attempt was made by Soil Mechanics Section, operating in collaboration with the Division of Land Research, to make interpretations for this purpose. In a three-pronged study the Section
(a) examined a large area (the Leichhardt–Gilbert region) which had been classified without specific regard to engineering requirements,
(b) cooperated in the survey of a smaller area (the Isaac–Comet region) with a view to defining the engineering requirement so that cognizance could be taken in establishing the terrain classification, and
(c) undertook a survey of a small area (the Mt. Isa–Dajarra region) in which a highway was being planned—to observe the compatibility of terrain classification with the requirements of highway engineers.

In each case it was concluded that engineering significance could be attributed only to simple, but not to complex or compound land systems. The flexibility inherent in the definition of a land system tended to cause confusion—with the biassed requirements for one form of land use, e.g. pastoral purposes, often conflicting with the biassed requirements for engineering land use. A similar conclusion was found for the land unit category.

The small area in north-western Queensland chosen for the separate survey had previously been evaluated by the Division of Land Research (Christian et al. 1954). The complex and compound land systems originally mapped by the Division of Land Research were subdivided, for engineering purposes, into a number of simple land systems with correspondingly simple land units (Grant 1965). Such engineering factors as topographic suitability for road location, quantities of earthworks, and bridging frequencies, were associated with these simple land systems. The trafficability of the natural surface, the location of resources for embankment or pavement construction, and the method of use of local materials were associated with the corresponding land unit. Some relevant terrain parameters such as stream frequencies, depth of stream incision, widths of interfluves and slopes, which were regarded as important from the engineering viewpoint, were determined for each simple land system. An engineering terrain map at a scale of 1:100,000 was appended to the report.

Comment on the Developing Compatibility of Terrain Studies in U.K., South Africa, and Australia

By 1964 it was readily apparent that the concept of terrain evaluation for engineering held considerable promise, even if the direction of development was not clear.

The practical value of all of the attributes of terrain as a guide to the solution of road problems had been suggested through the pragmatic approach of the early work of Kantey and colleagues in South Africa and Beavan, Williams, Clare, Dowling, and colleagues in U.K. However, this work lacked a language of communication and consequently it was difficult to extrapolate across the barriers of location, time, and experience.

Terrain classification as expounded in U.K. by Beckett and Webster, and in Australia by Christian and Stewart, had achieved the coordination of terrain attributes into terrain classifications but the approach developed in U.K. for military engineering purposes differed from that developed in Australia for non-engineering purposes, and still further from the modified terrain classification which was seen as a requirement following preliminary engineering studies in Australia.

No fundamental incompatibilities were observed to exist at that time between all of the work which has been discussed above. And yet it was evident that there was not in existence any definition of a systematic procedure of terrain evaluation to serve the purposes of engineering.

In an endeavour to achieve some uniformity of approach towards an agreed form of engineering terrain classification (as a prerequisite to a system of terrain evaluation for engineering), the Soil Mechanics Section, CSIRO, convened a mobile field conference (Anon. 1965a), to which delegates from U.S.A., England, South Africa, and Australia were invited. The conference assembled in Darwin (N.T.) and, while moving to Cairns (Queensland), examined the terrain along the line of route. Much of this terrain had already been evaluated by the Division of Land Research, CSIRO.

Extensive discussion during the course of the conference confirmed the view that no serious incompatibilities existed in basic philosophies of terrain classification, but highlighted the requirement for modifications to existing systems in order to achieve a completely satisfactory system for engineering purposes.

Following this conference, new proposals were outlined independently by Brink et al. (1966) and by the Soil Mechanics Section (Anon. 1966a).

Brink, Mabbutt, Webster, and Beckett (Brink et al. 1966), meeting as a working group at Oxford, England, attempted a synthesis of the English and Australian approaches as expounded by Beckett and Webster (1962) and Christian and Stewart (1968) respectively. The working group proposed a multi-level system of terrain classification with the lowest level, which was termed a *land element*, equivalent to the *site* of Bourne (1931). Other levels in ascending order were termed *land facet*, *land system*, *land region*, *land province*, *land division*, and *land zone*.

The working group recognized, as did Beckett and Webster (1962), that land facets and land systems tend to recur locally in forms that differ in minor ways; these variants were designated local forms, and abstract land facets and land systems were erected to cover the general cases. A set of eight rules was laid down to cover the erection of these abstract forms.

Coupled to the terrain classification scheme is an envisaged data storage system in which data relevant to each level in the classification is stored on punched and annotated cards. It is intended that this data store should consist of three libraries.

1. *The type index*—This will contain the definitions and descriptions of all abstract land units defined for local forms in the terrain index.
2. *The terrain index*—This will contain the definitions and recognition characters of all land system local forms so far described.
3. *The data store*—This will contain useful information about particular land units—land systems, facets, or elements listed in the terrain index.

Military Engineering Experimental Establishment has produced descriptions of some land systems (Anon. 1965b) in terms of land facets and has detailed a possible mechanism for the punched and annotated data store (Anon. 1967). Brink and Partridge (1967) have applied the system in describing an area in South Africa.

An important conclusion arising from the mobile field conference was that there could be no acceptance of the validity or otherwise of any postulated terrain classification for engineering purposes unless each stage in the classification had been proven by engineering experiment (in contrast to the engineering or other opinion which formed the bulk of the preceding 'justification' for the various classifications). With this purpose of providing an opportunity for engineering testing, and at the same time with the intention of reporting the logical outcome of the discussions of the mobile field conference, the Soil Mechanics Section prepared a tentative form of an engineering classification of terrain, coupled with proposals for appropriate testing (Anon. 1966a). The proposed engineering trials have not eventuated but the system of terrain classification has been adopted for studies in Australia (Grant 1968a).

The Australian scheme for factual engineering terrain classification based entirely on recognition characteristics was elaborated by Aitchison and Grant (1967). The scheme adopted the principle that any terrain classification scheme for engineering must ultimately be operated by engineers who could not be expected to possess specialist skills in the earth sciences (as geomorphology); therefore, such a scheme should be erected and expressed in terms of manifestations of terrain normally available to engineers; no abstractions should be attributed to any level. The scheme was planned to operate at four levels of generalization, viz. *terrain component, terrain unit, terrain pattern*, and *province*. Of these four levels of generalization (in classification) only three were considered as vehicles for the expression and transfer of engineering information. These were the terrain *pattern*, terrain *unit*, and the terrain *component* to each of which could be attached engineering significance appropriate to the level of generalization (Grant 1968a). The method of systematic coupling of these three levels of terrain classification to the relevant evaluated engineering behaviour was designated the P.U.C.E. program of terrain evaluation for engineering (pattern, unit, component, evaluation).

The key entity in the system was defined as the readily recognizable terrain unit 'an area occupied by a single physiographic feature formed of a characteristic association of earthen materials with a characteristic vegetative cover'.

The relationships of terrain pattern, terrain unit, and terrain component are depicted in Table 1 and Table 2. Grant (1968a) has discussed the principles of the scheme and has further elaborated the description, as well as demonstrating its application in a large area of Queensland (Grant 1968b).

It is not surprising that there is a great deal in common between the classificatory schemes presented by Brink *et al.* and by Aitchison and Grant, since all of the principals in the preparation of both schemes were participants in the discussions of the mobile field conference.

Differences between the systems are largely associated with the intended mode of use—for it was made apparent during discussions in the IVth African Regional Soil Mechanics Conference that the South African–U.K. system envisages the participation of a specialist (geologist and/or geomorphologist), as well as an engineer, at all stages of the establishment and operation of the classification, whereas the Australian proposal envisages the virtual independence of the engineer following the establishment of the classification (Grant 1968c).

TABLE 1

Establishment and expression of the terrain classification

Source of Non-contact Information	Intermediate Stage in Classification		Supplementary Source of Information	Stage in Terrain Classification		
	Relevant Factor in Classification	Title		Relevant Factor in Classification	Title	Mode of Expression
Geological maps or aerial photographs[1] (scale of order 1:10⁶)	—	—	—	Areas of constant geology at the group level; areas of similar airphoto pattern[2]	Province	Map 1:250,000
Aerial photographs[1] (scale of order 1:10⁴)	Areas of similar airphoto pattern	Airphoto pattern	Ground study of geomorphology and association of terrain units	Areas of similar airphoto pattern[2]; and constant geomorphology; and constant association of terrain units	Terrain pattern	Map 1:250,000 Statement (and block diagram) of association of terrain units
Photogrammetric studies of airphotos (scale of order 1:10⁴)	Single physiographic feature	Landform unit	Ground study for recognition and assessment of dimensions of physiographic features (where not obtained from airphoto studies); or ground study of association of earthen materials and vegetative cover; or studies of association of terrain components	Areas occupied by single physiographic feature with characteristic association of earthen materials and vegetation; areas with similar associations of terrain components	Terrain unit	Map 1:50,000 Statement of characteristic combination of topography, and associations of vegetation and earthen materials; and of relative dominance within terrain pattern
—	—	—	Ground studies for recognition of specific slopes, soil, surface cover, and vegetation associations	Areas of constant rate of change of slope; consistent soil at primary profile level; consistent vegetation associations	Terrain component	Not usually mapped Statement of characteristic combination of slopes, vegetation and soil; and of relative dominance within terrain unit

[1] Or equivalent presentations of data from remote sensors.
[2] Or similar patterns defined by other sensing devices on an appropriate scale.

TABLE 2

Description and quantification associated with terrain classification

Stage in Terrain Classification	Terrain Factors Suitable for Descriptive Expression	Terrain Factors Suitable for Quantitative Expression		Mode of Entry (By an Observer in the Field) To Recorded Descriptions and Data
		Factors	Methodology of Quantification	
Terrain pattern	Geomorphology; basic characteristics of soil, rock, vegetation common among constituent terrain units; drainage pattern	Relief amplitudes, stream frequencies	Airphoto or ground study; airphoto study	Via terrain pattern map and legend
Terrain unit	Physiographic unit; principal characteristics of soil, rock, vegetation	Dimensions of physiographic unit (relief amplitude, length, width)	Airphoto or ground study	Via terrain pattern map and legend of constituent units, and recognition of physiographic characteristics of terrain unit; or by direct recognition of physiographic and associated characteristics of terrain unit[1]
Terrain component	Physiographic component, lithology, soil type, vegetation association	Dimensions of physiographic component (relief amplitude, length, width, slopes)	Measured in situ	Via recognition of terrain unit by either method as above, and recognition of physiographic and associated features of terrain component
		Dimensions of vegetation (height, diameter, spacing)	Measured in situ	
		Dimensions of surface obstacles including rock outcrops and termitaria	Measured in situ	
		Properties of earthen materials throughout profile (depth, particle size gradation, consistence, strength, permeability, suction, mineralogy)	Measured in the field where practicable; otherwise in standard laboratory procedures	
		Quantities of earthen materials	Measured or estimated in situ	

[1] The direct recognition of a terrain unit is not difficult from appropriate description as in last column in Table 1 but recognition is facilitated by prior knowledge of the terrain patterns under consideration.

THE ADEQUACY OF PRESENT APPROACHES TO TERRAIN EVALUATION FOR ENGINEERING

Despite the evidence of a continually improving compatibility between all systems of terrain description and evaluation as developed by, or for engineers, or as adopted in engineering studies, it does not follow that any of these systems is necessarily adequate for engineering purposes in general, or for any individual engineering purpose that may be specified.

It is a surprising fact that, although much of the impetus for terrain evaluation has come from engineering, yet still the engineering requirements *from* terrain studies remain unstated. The military engineer has been unable to define—in engineering terms—his real requirements, while similarly the road engineer has found it difficult to specify the information which he must have in a quantitative form.

Almost as a matter of course, the workers involved in the establishment of a terrain classification have presumed that the engineering requirement of any particular operation could be stated—in terms appropriate to a level of generalization within the classification. This is rarely the case, and indeed almost all of the studies to date have been limited to the attachment of data indicative of generalized engineering properties to other data indicative of the nature of the terrain.

Two serious fallacies must be avoided in the various aspects of terrain studies. It must not be assumed that, because a terrain classification exists as an apparently logical subdivision in nature, it must necessarily have any significance to an engineer—or if it is of value to one field of engineering, it necessarily has significance in any other field of engineering. Similarly, it must not be assumed that, because engineering achievements exist, there is necessarily a formula, or an explanation defining all of the processes responsible for the success attained in the project.

The inexactitudes of engineering, as well as of terrain description, suggest that any process of development of a logical system of terrain evaluation for engineering, must involve a great deal of feed-back, so that at every stage in the developmental process there may be an opportunity for correction based upon new evidence.

An attempt to outline some of the interactions in any such process is presented in Figure 1. This diagram relates specifically to the feed-back mechanisms which may operate in connection with the P.U.C.E. system as defined in Tables 1 and 2, but it may apply in principle to any comparable terrain evaluation system. It should be noted here that the P.U.C.E. system was specifically established with an attempted engineering bias in order to facilitate its examination in engineering trials. No other claim for any particular advantage of the P.U.C.E. system is made by the authors.

Figure 1 suggests two important conclusions. The first is that, although the prime purpose of any terrain evaluation system is to service an information storage and retrieval system, the actual operation of any such data processing system must necessarily present a major problem; for there can be no independent variables. Every item of information, every interpretation, and indeed every aspect of the classification, must be subject to revision on the basis of accumulated evidence. The second conclusion arising from the complexity of Figure 1 is that it is totally unrealistic to expect to find that—for any originally postulated terrain classification—the requirements for amendment arising from any one form of engineering operation (e.g., road construction) will necessarily be similar to those arising from other forms of engineering (e.g., construction of electric power transmission routes, or transportation on the natural surface).

Thus, the concept arises that, at the present state of knowledge, it may well be essential to consider, not only a generalized form of terrain evaluation for engineering—which can be regarded as a working hypothesis for examination— but also a number of specialized terrain evaluation procedures for specific

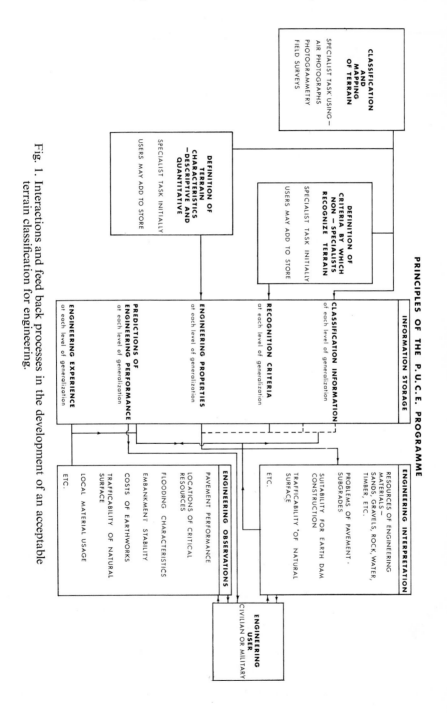

Fig. 1. Interactions and feed back processes in the development of an acceptable terrain classification for engineering.

engineering purposes. Some of the interactions involved in this process are depicted in Figure 2. It should be stressed, in relation to Figure 2, that any deficiencies in a postulated terrain classification for engineering can rise with equal ease from lack of appreciation of engineering problems and processes, as from inadequate definition of terrain.

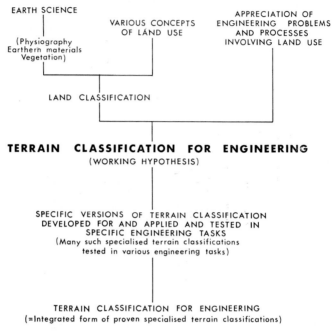

Fig. 2. Stages in the development of a possible generalized terrain classification for engineering.

In circumstances where a reasonably competent understanding of the engineering process exists, it may well be economic to proceed with the pattern of examination of a proposed terrain classification in order to develop a scientifically based terrain evaluation system for the specific engineering purpose. At this stage there may well be some compatibility between such a specialized terrain evaluation system and that derived following the parametric approach outlined by the Corps of Engineers.

A wholly logical system of terrain evaluation for engineering in a wider sense can only emerge from the integration of proven specialist terrain classifications each with their relevant quantification. This would represent a task of mammoth proportions and one which may be totally unrealistic in relation to the economic return.

Thus, the present position of terrain evaluation for engineering may be assessed in two rather conflicting ways. It is evident that a terrain classification of a form similar to that presented in Tables 1 and 2 may be considered as entirely adequate for a first appraisal of specific engineering characteristics and specific problems in a given area. Present knowledge does not however lead to any confidence in the total adequacy of any system of terrain evaluation for all engineering purposes.

CONCLUSIONS

As a summary of the extensive and almost amorphous mass of material which describes the development of engineering interest in terrain evaluation to date, several useful conclusions may be drawn:

1. The *attributes of terrain* have been adequately recognized in terms of physiography, earthen materials, and vegetation. Present concepts of these attributes do not differ significantly from those noted in the early work of Bourne and Belcher.

2. The *logic of terrain classification* as an integrated expression of the several terrain attributes appears to be well established. This logic does not differ significantly from that stated in the early work of Christian and Stewart.

3. The statement of a *terrain classification for engineering* appears feasible as a framework within which to record specific engineering data and experience.

4. No real attempts have been made to test the validity of a complete terrain classification for engineering.

5. Apparent correlations have been demonstrated between some quantitative data of (descriptive) engineering significance and some terrain attributes and/or some categories in a terrain classification. Some such correlations appear to be obvious. Nevertheless few, if any, of these correlations have been based on adequate tests.

6. In the absence of experimental proof of the validity (either for general or specialised engineering purposes) of any terrain classification, there is little point in attempting to refine present concepts of classification. A system such as that described in Tables 1 and 2 will serve as a first working hypothesis.

7. Until the process of scientific examination of the proposed system of terrain evaluation is completed, it must be accepted that terrain classification can contribute very little to engineering science, although it may make a major contribution to the art of engineering.

8. As a corollary to conclusion 7, it follows that the engineer in developing the engineering art of terrain evaluation, may face a choice between remaining subservient to an arbitrary terrain classification, or attaining a mastery of the essential background to terrain classification, so that the whole procedure may be moulded to his purposes. This paper is written in the expectation that the engineer will be both capable and willing to tailor his thinking to the potential which he may be able to see within the present horizons of terrain classification.

9. The logical outcome of this process is the probable emergence of a specialist branch of engineering—terrain engineering. Just as the discipline of soil mechanics and the field of soil engineering arose from the recognized necessity to quantify engineering geology as it existed 50 years ago, so the field of terrain engineering must develop through the necessity to quantify—in rational engineering terms—the present and potential approaches to terrain classification.

REFERENCES

ACKROYD, L. W. (1959). The engineering classification of some western Nigerian soils and their qualities in road building. *Overseas Bulletin* No. 10, Road Research Laboratory, D.S.I.R., Harmondsworth.

AITCHISON, G. D., and GRANT, K. (1967). The PUCE programme of terrain description evaluation and interpretation for engineering purposes. *Proc. 4th Reg. Conf. Africa Soil Mech. Fdn Engng* **1**, 1.

ANON. (1965a). *Report on the Mobile Field Conference on Terrain Evaluation—Darwin–Mt. Isa–Cairns.* August 5th–23rd. Soil Mechanics Section, CSIRO, Melbourne.

ANON. (1965b). *A terrain brief.* Military Engng Exp. Establ., Christchurch, England. Report 931.

ANON. (1965c). *A classification system for terrain—description of a land system.* Military Engng Exp. Establ., Christchurch, England. Report 955.

ANON. (1966a). *Scheme for factual engineering terrain classification (1st approximation)*. Presented to A.B.C.A. Planning Conference, Vicksburg. Internal Report, Soil Mechanics Section, CSIRO, Melbourne.

ANON. (1966b). *Terrain evaluation by a new technique*. Terrain Evaluation Cell, Directorate of Engineering Research and Development Organization, New Delhi.

ANON. (1967). *Terrain evaluation data storage*. Military Engng Exp. Establ., Christchurch, England. Technical Note No. 5/67.

BARRIE, A. O., and BECKETT, P. H. T. (1964). *Terrain classification, units and principles, an interim report*. Military Engng Exp. Establ., Christchurch, England.

BEAVAN, P. J. (1964). Roadmaking materials in the Caribbean. II, Trinidad. *Lab. Note* No. LN/518, Road Research Board, D.S.I.R., Harmondsworth.

BECKETT, P. H. T., and WEBSTER, R. (1962). *The storage and collation of information on terrain—an interim report*. Military Engng Exp. Establ., Christchurch, England.

BECKETT, P. H. T., and WEBSTER, R. (1965). *A classification system for terrain*. Military Engng Exp. Establ., Christchurch, England. Report 872.

BELCHER, D. J. (1942a). The use of soil maps in highway engineering. *Proc. 28th Am. Road School, Engineering Bulletin* 26, 64. Engineering Extension Department, Purdue University.

BELCHER, D. J. (1942b). Use of aerial photographs in war time engineering. *Rds Str.* 85, No. 7, 35.

BELCHER, D. J. (1943). The engineering significance of soil patterns. *Proc. 23rd Ann. Meeting, Highway Research Board*, 23, 569.

BELCHER, D. J. (1948). Determinations of soil conditions from aerial photographs. *Photogramm. Engng* 14, 482.

BELCHER, D. J., GREGG, L. S., and WOODS, K.B. (1943). The formation, distribution and engineering characteristics of soils. *Highway Research Bulletin* No. 10, *Research Series*, No. 87. Joint Highway Research Project, Engineering Experiment Station, Purdue University.

BOURNE, R. (1931). Regional survey and its relation to stocktaking of agricultural and forest resources of the British Empire. *Ox. For. Mem.* 13.

BRINK, A. B. A. (1962). Airphoto interpretation applied to soil engineering mapping in South Africa. In *Transactions of the Symposium on Photo Interpretation*. pp. 498–506. (International Society for Photogrammetry: Delft.).

BRINK, A. B. A., MABBUTT, J. A., WEBSTER, R., and BECKETT, P. H. T. (1966). *Report of the Working Group on Land Classification and Data Storage*. Military Engng Exp. Establ., Christchurch, England. Report 940.

BRINK, A. B. A., and PARTRIDGE, T. C. (1967). Kyalami land system: An example of physiographic classification for the storage of terrain data. *Proc. 4th Reg. Conf. Africa Soil Mech. Fdn Engng* 1, 9.

BRINK, A. B. A., and WILLIAMS, A. A. B. (1964). Soil engineering mapping for roads in South Africa. *National Institute for Road Research, Bulletin* No. 6, C.S.I.R., Pretoria.

CARROLL, D. M. (1964). Roadmaking materials in the Caribbean. IV, Barbados. *Lab. Note* No. LN/534, Road Research Board, D.S.I.R., Harmondsworth.

CHRISTIAN, C. S., NOAKES, L. C., PERRY, R. A., SLATYER, R. O., STEWART, G. A., and TRAVES, D. M. (1954). Survey of the Barkly region, Northern Territory and Queensland 1947–48. *CSIRO Aust. Land Res. Ser.* No. 3.

CHRISTIAN, C. S., and STEWART, G. A. (1953). General report on survey of the Katherine–Darwin region, 1946. *CSIRO Aust. Land Res. Ser.* No. 1.

CHRISTIAN, C. S., and STEWART, G. A. (1968). Methodology of integrated surveys. In *Aerial Surveys and Integrated Studies*. Proc. Toulouse Conf. 1964. (UNESCO: Paris.) pp. 233–80.

CLARE, K. E. (1960). Roadmaking gravels and soils in central Africa. *Overseas Bulletin* No. 12, Road Research Laboratory, D.S.I.R., Harmondsworth.

CLARE, K. E., and BEAVAN, P. J. (1962). Roadmaking materials in British Borneo; I. Geology, roadstone and soil classification. *Lab. Note* No. LN/86. II. Properties of soils. *Lab. Note* No. LN/87. III. Soil location and stabilization, general conclusions. *Lab. Note* No. LN/88. Road Research Laboratory, D.S.I.R., Harmondsworth.

CLARKE, K. E., and NEWILL, D. (1963). Roadmaking materials in the Caribbean. I, Jamaica. *Lab. Note* No. LN/318, Road Research Laboratory, D.S.I.R., Harmondsworth.

CORPS OF ENGINEERS (1963). *Environmental factors affecting ground mobility in Thailand*. U.S. Army Engineer Waterways Experiment Station, Vicksburg.

DOWLING, J. W. F. (1963). The use of aerial photography in evaluating engineering soil conditions in a selected area of northern Nigeria. *Lab. Note* LN/379, Road Research Laboratory, D.S.I.R., Harmondsworth.

DOWLING, J. W. F. (1964). The use of aerial photographs and land form analysis in the location of laterites. *Lab. Note* LN/523, Road Research Laboratory, D.S.I.R., Harmondsworth.

DOWLING, J. W. F., and WILLIAMS, F. H. P. (1964). The use of aerial photographs in materials surveys and classification of land forms. *Conf. on Civil Engineering Problems Overseas.* Institution of Civil Engineers, London.

ECKEL, E. B. (1951). Interpreting geologic maps for engineers. *Symp. on Surface and Subsurface Reconnaissance.* ASTM STP **122**, p. 5, Am. Soc. Testing Mats.

FEDERAL HOUSING ADMINISTRATION (1962). *Evaluation of soils and use of soil survey for engineering purposes in urban development.* Washington.

GRABAU, W. E. (1963). *A comparison of quantitative versus qualitative descriptive systems for mobility analysis.* U.S. Army Engineer Waterways Experiment Station, Vicksburg.

GRANT, K. (1965). Terrain features of the Mt. Isa–Dajarra region in north-western Queensland and an assessment of their significance in relation to potential engineering land use. *CSIRO Aust. Soil Mechanics Section, Tech. Pap.* No. 1.

GRANT, K. (1968a). A terrain evaluation system for engineering. *CSIRO Aust. Division of Soil Mechanics, Tech. Pap.* No. 2.

GRANT, K. (1968b). Terrain classification for engineering purposes of the Rolling Downs Province. *CSIRO Aust. Division of Soil Mechanics, Tech. Pap.* No. 3.

GRANT, K. (1968c). Reply to discussion on terrain evaluation by M. J. Mountain and G. J. Floyd. *Proc. 4th Reg. Conf. Africa Soil Mech. Fdn Engng* **2** (in press).

GREENMAN, R. L. (1951). The engineer looks at pedology. *Symp. on Surface and Subsurface Reconnaissance.* ASTM STP **122**, p. 46, Am. Soc. Testing Mats.

HELMER, R. A. (1959). *Soil Manual.* Research Section, Dept. of Highways, Oklahoma City.

HIGHWAY RESEARCH BOARD (1961). Soil mapping: methods and applications. *Nat. Acad. Sci., Nat. Res. Council, Washington. Bull.* 299.

HITTLE, JEAN E. (1949). Airphoto interpretation of engineering sites and materials *Photogramm. Engng* **15**, 589.

HOFFMAN, W. P., and FLECKENSTEIN, J. B. (1960). Comparison of general routes by terrain appraisal methods in New York State. *Proc. Highw. Res. Bd* **39**, 640.

JENKINS, D. S., BELCHER, D. J., GREGG, L. E., and WOODS, K. B. (1946). *The origin, distribution and airphoto identification of United States soils.* U.S. Dept. of Commerce, Civil Aeronautics Administration, Washington.

JENNINGS, J. E., and BRINK, A. B. A. (1961). A guide to soil profiling for civil engineering purposes in South Africa. *Trans. S. Afr. Instn civ. Engrs* **3**, No. 8, 1.

JOHNSTONE, J. G., RAMARATHNAM, S., and RICHARDS, D. B. (1962). *The soils of Eastern Colorado, their origin, distribution and engineering characteristics.* Colorado School of Mines, Golden, Colorado.

KANTEY, B. A., and WILLIAMS, A. A. B. (1962). The use of soil engineering maps for road projects. *Civ. Engr S. Afr.* **4**, 149 and **5**, 41.

LUEDER, D. R. (1951). The preparation of an engineering soil map of New Jersey. *Symp. on Surface and Subsurface Reconnaissance.* ASTM STP **122**, p. 73, Am. Soc. Testing Mats.

MABBUTT, J. A. (1968). Review of concepts of land classification. In *Land Evaluation.* (Ed. G. A. Stewart) (Macmillan: Melbourne.)

MILES, R. D. (1951). Application of aerial photographs to preliminary engineering soil surveys. *Symp. on Surface and Subsurface Reconnaissance.* ASTM STP **122**, p. 57, Am. Soc. Testing Mats.

MILES, R. D. (1962). A concept of land forms, parent materials and soils in airphoto interpretation studies for engineering purposes. In *Transactions of the Symposium on Photo Interpretation.* pp. 462–76. (International Society for Photogrammetry: Delft.)

MINTZER, O. W., and FROST, R. E. (1952). How to use air-photos and maps for material survey. *Highway Res. Bd Bulletin* No. 62, p. 1, Nat. Acad. Sci. Nat. Res. Council, Washington.

NORTHCOTE, K. H. (1965). A factual key for the recognition of Australian soils (2nd ed.). *Division of Soils, CSIRO Aust. Divisional Report* 2/65.

OLSEN, G. W. (1964). Application of soil survey to problems of health, sanitation and engineering. *Memoir* 387, Cornell University Agricultural Experiment Station, Ithaca.

SCHOFIELD, A. N. (1957a). The use of aerial photographs in road construction in Nyasaland. *Overseas Bulletin* No. 4, Road Res. Laboratory, D.S.I.R., Harmondsworth.

SCHOFIELD, A. N. (1957b). Nyasaland laterites and their indications on aerial photographs. *Overseas Bulletin* No. 5, Road Res. Laboratory, D.S.I.R., Harmondsworth.

THORNBURN, T. N. (1951). Preparation of county engineering soil maps for Illinois. *Symp. on Surface and Subsurface Reconnaissance.* ASTM STP **122**, p.4, Am. Soc. Testing Mats.

TYSON, P. J. (1964). The physical environment: A study of characteristics and effects. *Technical Paper* No. 64–1, Dept. of Geography, University of Denver, Denver.

Land Evaluation for Engineering Purposes in Northern Nigeria

James W. F. Dowling

*Road Research Laboratory, Ministry of Transport,
United Kingdom*

*Engineering soil-test data and engineering experience, derived from a number
of projects being undertaken as part of a major road development programme by
the Northern Nigerian Ministry of Works, have been related to the land systems
and land facets that have been defined in the Bauchi and Bornu Provinces of
Northern Nigeria.*

*It is shown that the land classification provides a satisfactory basis for classifying
and storing information about the engineering features of land. Examples are
given of how such information can be used in planning the most effective effort
for the design of new roads.*

*A land classification system that can be applied to the evaluation of both
agricultural land use potential and road engineering needs is of particular value
in underdeveloped countries where there is relatively little recorded information
on the nature of land and its potential uses.*

INTRODUCTION

In a series of reports dealing with the road-making materials of Central Africa,
Nigeria, Northern Borneo, and the Commonwealth countries of the Caribbean,
the Road Research Laboratory has drawn attention to the relationship that
exists between methods of road construction and the physical environment of
each territory expressed in terms of its geology, soils, and climate. For the first
time in these countries, geological and soils mapping units have been employed
to indicate the location, extent, and engineering properties of naturally occurring
earth materials. For two of the territories, namely Guyana and Northern
Borneo, maps have been produced at scales of 1 : 250,000 and 1 : 1,000,000
showing the regional distribution of road-making materials and road-building
problems (Clare and Beaven 1965).

Whilst regional surveys of this kind can provide a valuable inventory of
engineering experience – experience that would otherwise have gone unrecorded
– they are often limited in their application. One reason is that only small
quantities of relevant engineering data can be classified on a regional basis
because the amount of completed geological and pedological mapping is small
in most developing countries. Another reason is that the mapping units employed
in geological and soil surveying are not always best suited to the presentation
of engineering information: geologists are concerned with demonstrating the
extent and structure of broad lithological divisions and largely neglect the
unconsolidated mantle; soil scientists on the other hand, are mainly interested
in the chemical and textural character of the upper layers of the soil profile.
Again, in neither case can it be expected that the rate of mapping will appreciably
increase in the immediate future so as to provide the coverage that is necessary
for storage purposes.

The regional surveys of the kind so far produced have more application in the early stages of regional road planning when routes are being selected and alternative road-making processes are being reviewed: they are less useful to the engineer engaged on specific road projects. Here the engineer's main concern is with identifying such ground features as small but significant variations in the bearing capacity of soil subgrades, the location of road-building materials, and the nature and extent of earthworks. Of equal importance is the early recognition of problem situations such as erosion and the instability of slopes and seasonal flooding which, if overlooked in the pre-design surveys, could subsequently lead to costly failure.

It is evident, from the many road projects that have run into difficulties, that inadequate site investigation is largely responsible for the failures that have occurred. The reason for this is that engineers sometimes experience difficulty in appreciating the nature and extent of the materials they will have to use and the problems that are associated with them.

It is commonplace, in current road-design practice, for site investigations to bear little relationship to the complexity of the terrain as far as the frequency of sampling is concerned. Thus, the amount of soil sampling and laboratory testing that is carried out is frequently of the same order for difficult ground as for ground that offers few problems. Again, regardless of the length of the road or the variability of the ground conditions, it is a constant feature of most new roads that there are relatively few changes in pavement design, and even the materials selected for use in the construction are invariably restricted to a limited number of borrow areas.

The absence of any rationale in most site investigations is largely attributable to a general lack of knowledge about the way in which engineering materials occur and are distributed over the earth's surface. In the past, this has been further aggravated by the lack of any method for systematically recording relevant geotechnical information once it has been obtained.

In spite of the increasing attention that is being paid to new surveying techniques such as aerial photography and geophysical methods of sub-surface exploration, a very real need still exists to make terrain information more readily avaiable to engineers in the pre-design stages of roadworks.

Following an investigation undertaken by the Road Research Laboratory in Northern Nigeria to find out how aerial photography could be used to locate engineering materials (Dowling and Williams 1964), it was appreciated that methods of land classification offered a desirable contribution to the problem of storing engineering experience. Land classification, which involves the classification of ground into distinctive and recurring patterns using evidence obtained both from the field and from aerial photography, is used in a number of countries to assess quickly the potential use of agricultural land for the purpose of establishing priorities for agricultural development. It has been previously shown in parts of Oxfordshire, England, that a physiographically based land-classification system has many advantages over geological and pedological mapping as far as recording engineering intelligence is concerned (Beckett and Webster 1965). Moreover, the wide application of land classification surveys provides a means of simultaneously recording information about both agricultural and engineering forms of land use – a potentially valuable contribution in many developing countries where communications play a vital part in the exploitation of natural resources.

Brink et al. (1966) have proposed rationalisations of terminology in land classification that now appear to be widely accepted, and Mabbutt (1968) has reviewed concepts in land classification. For the purpose of this paper it is sufficient to state that the land of a region is conceived as a series of land systems, each of which contains typical land facets which have similar features wherever they occur and which can be readily identified on aerial photographs. Each land facet may contain a number of distinctive land elements, which are the smallest units of landscape. If land elements within a land facet are distinctly different, engineering land use will be related to individual land elements rather than land facets. However, in the investigations reported below, the land facets were mostly sufficiently uniform to provide a suitable basis for engineering appraisal.

LAND CLASSIFICATION IN NORTHERN NIGERIA

In an area of roughly 30,000 sq miles in Bauchi and Bornu Provinces, Northern Nigeria (Fig. 1), some 20 land systems have been defined and mapped. The survey procedures of Beckett and Webster (1965) were used, including pattern recognition on print laydowns (photomosaics), and detailed air-photo interpretation. Existing geological information (Carter, Barber, and Tait 1963), agricultural reconnaissance soil maps (Klinkenberg *et al.* 1963), information collected on a number of ground engineering surveys, and provisional information from an extension of a survey by the Land Resources Division of the Directorate of Overseas Survey, U.K. (Bawden and Tuley 1966), were used to check and revise the results of the air-photo study.

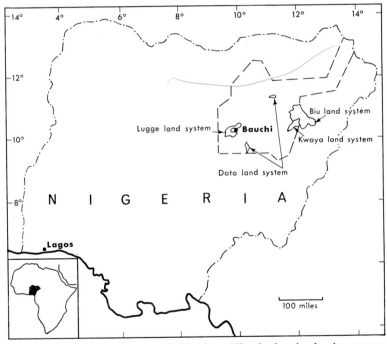

Fig. 1. The limits of the study area in Northern Nigeria showing land systems used as examples.

The climate of the study area is characterized by a brief rainy season in the summer months and a long dry season in the winter. The whole of the area investigated falls within the West African svanna zone and the vegetation has been ascribed to the Sudan and Sub-Sudan zones (Clayton 1957).

The present paper describes some of the results obtained from the investigations of the relationship between engineering soil-test data and engineering experience, derived from a number of road projects being undertaken as part of a major road development programme by the Northern Nigerian Ministry of Works, and the land systems that had been identified and mapped.

THE ENGINEERING APPLICATION OF LAND CLASSIFICATION

The engineering data comprised the results obtained from a range of tests commonly employed in road-design surveys to determine both the bearing capacity of soil subgrades and the suitability of soils for use as materials for building the road pavement. These included measurements of the particle-size distribution; of plasticity characteristics, including Atterberg limits and linear shrinkages; of maximum dry densities at different levels of compaction; and the soil strength at optimum moisture content expressed in terms of the California bearing ratio. Most results were obtained from soil samples that had been taken at fixed intervals along the centre lines of roads in accordance with conventional site-survey practice.

The complete investigation covered an extensive range of engineering soil types derived from a wide variety of geological parent materials representing most of the geological formations that occur in north-east Nigeria. They included Basement Complex granites and migmatites, Cretaceous sandstones and shales, Tertiary sandstones, and more recent aeolian, lacustrine, and alluvial sediments. In addition lateritic ironstones were also encountered.

A striking example of the variation in engineering character of two adjacent land systems (see Fig. 1) is shown in Figure 2. Biu land system is developed over a series of Tertiary basalt lavas which form the Biu Plateau. Kwaya land system is formed from a predominantly granitic parent rock which forms part of the Pre-Cambrian Basement Complex. Figure 2 shows the variation of two engineering properties, linear shrinkage and maximum dry density, along a road line which crosses both land systems. For the first 18 miles where the line traverses Biu land system large linear shrinkage values predominate, while corresponding values for maximum dry density are low. The soils are weak

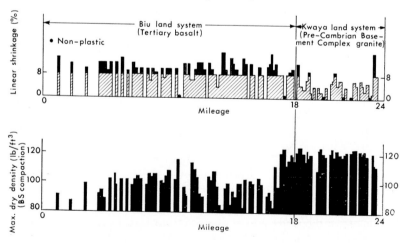

Fig. 2. Variation in two engineering properties along a road line crossing two land systems in Northern Nigeria.

expansive clays and clayey gravels derived from the weathering of the basalt lavas: dark red-brown in colour, they possess low strengths.

Beyond mile 18 there is an appreciable decrease in the values of linear shrinkage with a corresponding increase in the recorded dry densities. Here, the soils are derived from the weathering of Basement Complex granite gneisses and comprise coarsely graded gravelly sands with small amounts of clay. It is worth noting that, adjacent to the basalt, the granite soils display high linear-shrinkage values. This is accounted for by the presence within the granite soils of expansive clay minerals which have been washed down from the adjacent basalt soils.

From Figure 1 it can be seen that Biu land system covers a wide area of Northern Nigeria. It can be assumed, therefore, that within the land system boundary, in response to high seasonal moisture contents, weak clay soils predominate with a corresponding lack of non-cohesive granular materials. Thus, with the information already at hand, a pattern of construction can be effectively applied throughout the extent of the land system. Soil subgrades are weak and, therefore, thick pavements would be required. At the same time, strong granular soils are lacking and there is little likelihood that such materials would be available for use as the base of the pavement. Therefore, in the event of further road building within the land system, survey effort could well be adapted to suit the nature of the terrain: centre-line sampling could be drastically reduced and the effort diverted in the direction where it would be most required, in this instance towards the location of supplies of sound rock for use in a crushed-stone base.

The granite soils, on the other hand, being stronger, are not only suitable for use as sub-base material, but from carefully selected sites would be capable of furnishing base material as well. Furthermore, the total thickness of pavement construction would be less in the granite area of Kwaya land system than that for the basalt of Biu land system.

In these examples the land systems are mainly determined by significant changes in the underlying parent rock. Elsewhere, topographic or climatic considerations, or even the extent of dissection, might outweigh the effects of parent geology and so determine the presence of a distinctive land system. In every case, however, the land system is determined by an assemblage of recurring land facets, whose nature and arrangement is responsible for the character of the land system as a whole.

Lugge land system is comprised of 6 land facets forming an inselberg landscape developed over Basement Complex granites and migmatites near Bauchi (Fig. 1). Analysis of a number of samples obtained within Lugge land system indicated that similar engineering materials were common to particular land facets and that different land facets and land elements within the land system have very different engineering characteristics.

In the first instance lateritic ironstone samples were obtained from two different sites within the upper pediment slope (land facet 3). Figure 3 shows a comparison of gradings and plasticity characteristics which were obtained from two sites – sites A and B. In Table 1 the values obtained for linear shrinkage, optimum moisture content, maximum dry density, and strengths are also shown. The values obtained are similar and for all practical purposes the materials are identical. The laterites provide a valuable source of road-building gravel and the location of these materials would play an important part in projected roadworks.

Figure 4A shows the gradings and plasticity characteristics obtained from a transported clay soil from land facet 5. Values of some other engineering

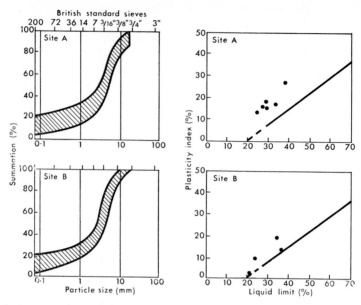

Fig. 3. A comparison of the gradings and plasticity characteristics of samples of lateritic ironstone gravel from two different sites within the same land facet (land facet 3 of Lugge land system).

TABLE 1

The engineering properties of samples of lateritic gravel obtained from two different sites within the same land facet (land facet 3 of Lugge land system).

Sample Number	Linear Shrinkage (%)	Max. Dry Density (lb/ft³)	Optimum Moisture Content (%)	Calif. Bearing Ratio (%)
SITE A				
14	4	135	8·2	78
22	7	134	10·9	96
25	10	138	7·9	80
26	Non plastic	134	10·2	82
27	6	135	8·8	94
29	8	137	8·5	94
30	8	133	9·4	116
SITE B				
110	4	137	10·5	63
102	2	140	8·4	88
101	8	132	9·8	82
1A	Non plastic	136	8·0	72
1B	6	132	10·5	94
2	Non plastic	133	9·7	96

properties are given in Table 2 (A). These values were found to be identical with those from other alluvial clays within the same land facet from many places in the land system.

Figure 4B shows the gradings and plasticity characteristics of a particular type of clay which sometimes occurs as an element of land facet 4 in Lugge land system. The high liquid limits, corresponding to CH soils in the Casa-grande classification, are typical of these soils which occur as dark grey expansive clays derived from small outcrops of ultra-basic gneisses within the Basement Complex. Table 2(B) shows the values of some other engineering properties of these soils.

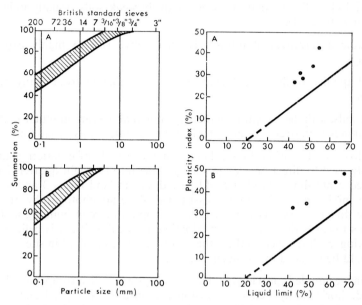

Fig. 4. The gradings and plasticity characteristics of alluvial clay (A) and of clays formed from ultra-basic gneiss (B) from Lugge land system (land facet 5).

TABLE 2

The engineering properties of alluvial clay (site A) and clay formed from ultra-basic gneisses (site B) in land facet 5 of Lugge land system

Sample Number	Linear Shrinkage (%)	Max. Dry Density (lb/ft³)	Optimum Moisture Content (%)	Calif. Bearing Ratio (%)
SITE A				
3	11	125	10·3	60
4	11	123	10·6	48
31	11	122	12·5	39
32	8	125	11·1	42
33	9	129	9·6	52
SITE B				
39	10	124	12·0	29
40	14	116	15·4	48
41	16	122	13·0	48
42	10	125	10·0	51

Because both kinds of clay are usually located in areas susceptible to a high water-table they create a special design problem within a land system which is otherwise characterized by comparatively strong, well-drained granular soils.

Within Lugge land system there are 5 major engineering considerations to be noted:

1. Lateritic ironstone provides a ready supply of good quality, relatively non-plastic gravel suitable for use as the base of the road pavement.

2. Alluvial clays form small areas of relatively weak soils, usually influenced by a high water-table.

3. Sporadic occurrences of ultra-basic gneiss give rise to highly expansive weak clays.

4. Good quality fresh unweathered stone is obtainable from many granite outcrops.

5. Most soils, with the exception of the clays noted above, are granular materials with relatively high strengths and offer little or no difficulty as a road foundation.

It follows that, within Lugge land system, stored information could be effectively used to direct pre-design survey effort into the right quarter. Rigidly controlled centre-line sampling could be reduced in land facets 3 and 4 to an absolute minimum, and with the assistance of aerial photography attention could be directed towards the location of supplies of road-building materials as well as towards those areas of predominantly weak soils. It is believed that by applying methods such as these the effort and time involved in site investigations could be reduced by as much as 70%.

The final example is provided by Doto land system, which comprises a heavily dissected, horizontally bedded sandstone, capped with a persistent lateritic ironstone. A description of Doto land system is shown in Table 3, while its location at two different sites in Northern Nigeria is shown in Figure 1. The engineering characteristics of the individual land facets are shown in some considerable detail in Tables 4, 5, and 6. These provide an example of the way in which relevant engineering intelligence can be stored in any system of land evaluation involving the identification of land systems and land facets.

TABLE 3

Doto land system

Climate—Semi-arid equatorial tropical (Sudan savanna zone): 3 humid months (July–September), 750–850 mm rainfall. Average daily maximum temperature above 33·5°C.

Rock—Medium- to coarse-grained sandstones of the Paleocene Kerri-Kerri Formation with subordinate conglomerates, clays, and siltstones; flat lying strata with an overall gentle dip to the north. Overlain by a thick, extensive lateritic ironstone which dips beneath Quaternary sediments of the Chad Formation.

Landscape—Extensive dissection has given rise to an intricate system of deep, steep-sided, flat-bottomed valleys, with tabular interfluves and residual mesas, frequently capped with lateritic ironstone. The form of the drainage pattern shows that the former stream courses were part of a system which flowed north-east to Lake Chad but has subsequently been captured by a tributary of the R. Gongola (R. Gaji) with a reversal of drainage. The accumulation of sediments on valley floors demonstrates that active down-cutting has now ceased. Five facets are identified in this land system.

Soils—Thin, stony soils on lateritic ironstone and sandstone. Sandy colluvium and alluvium of flat-floored valley bottoms.
Vegetation—Sudan savanna zone; with mixed *Detarium* woodland on stony upper slopes. Savanna 'parkland' on cultivated valley floors.
Altitude—500 m (approx.)
Relief—100 m.
Reference—Klinkenberg, K. *et al. Soil Survey Section Bull.* No. 21, 1963. Regional Research Station. Ministry of Agriculture, Samaru, N. Nigeria.

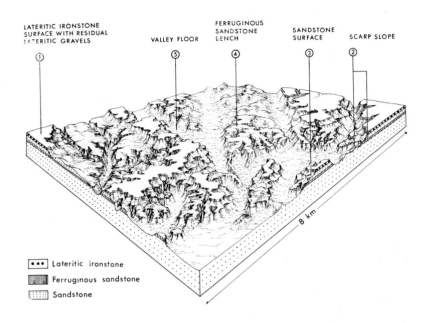

Land Facet	Form	Soils, Materials, and Hydrology	Land Cover
1	LATERITIC IRONSTONE SURFACE Flat to gently sloping surface at 600 m OD. Occurrences vary in size from 100m² to 2km². Occurs in flat interfluves and isolated mesa surfaces	Lateritic ironstone 8 cm thick occurs as surface capping to sandstone, the upper part of which is often heavily ferruginised. Surface materials comprise bare ironstone and thin stony soils. Where the laterite has been stripped away, stony soils overlie sandstone	Mixed *Detarium* woodland where sufficient soil occurs
2	SCARP SLOPE Uneven steep topography generally becoming steeper on upper part of slope below margin of land facet 1. Concave lower slopes with uneven bouldery microrelief. Steep rocky ribs and pinnacles and incised gullies are common	Lateritic ironstone and sandstone rock, talus and thin, stony soils subject to erosion by hill wash	*Detarium* woodland where sufficient soil occurs
3	SANDSTONE SURFACE Flat to moderately sloping ground corresponding to a structural bench formed by dissection of a flat-bedded sandstone	Rock and thin, stony soils	As above
4	FERRUGINOUS SANDSTONE BENCH As above, but more persistently developed and determined by the presence of a ferruginous sandstone horizon 0.5m thick, midway between land facets 1 and 5	Rock and thin stony soils. The indurated, ferruginous sandstone protects the underlying softer sandstone and forms a prominent bench, often bare rock, but sometimes overlain by rubbly soils	
5	VALLEY FLOOR Flat but steepening slightly at margin with land facet 2. Vary in width from 10m to 900m. Length may be as much as 13 m	Moderately deep, light grey to reddish brown sandy colluvial and alluvial soils. Permeable with no well-defined water courses. Active down-cutting of the gullies has now ceased	Savanna 'parkland' heavily cultivated

TABLE 4

Engineering characteristics of Doto land system — engineering properties of materials

Land Facet	Dominant Material	Depth	Drainage (Internal)	Symbol	Liquid Limit (%)	Plasticity Index (%)	Max. Dry Density (lb/ft³)	Opt. Moisture Content (%)	CBR at Equivalent BS Compaction (light) (%)	Gravel Coarse	Gravel Med.	Gravel Fine	Sand Coarse	Sand Med.	Sand Fine	Silt and Clay
1 LATERITIC IRONSTONE SURFACE WITH RESIDUAL LATERITIC GRAVELS	Ironstone rock, well graded gravel	Variable 5–15 ft	Generally well-drained. Short-lived local impedance due to lateritic caprock	GW	Non-plastic		138	10	36	5	2'	35	10	10	8	12
2 SCARP SLOPE	Wide range of engineering materials (sandstone rock, ill-sorted debris, etc.) Pockets of finer material		Well drained but subject to powerful erosion	GP	Sandstone rock Non-plastic					42	35	7	8	7	4	2
				GW	39	17				Nil	2	7	3	11	15	57
3 SANDSTONE SURFACE	Sand/silt, sandstone rock	Variable 6 in.–3 ft	Generally well drained, occasional perched water-tables form where clay-pans are present in the profile	SM	Non-plastic		124	9	36	Nil	Nil	2	11	12	17	58
4 FERRUGINOUS SANDSTONE BENCH	Indurated rock		Well drained	Rock	Rock											
5 VALLEY FLOOR	Silty sand and clayey sands with some sandstone fragments. Poorly graded		Well drained but considerable surface sheet wash in vicinity of scarp slopes	SM/SC	23–26	6–11				Nill	Nil	5	23	32	15	25
				SP	Non-plastic					Nil	Nil	Nil	15	45	32	8

TABLE 5

Engineering characteristics of Doto land system — engineering resources

Land Facet		Water Supply	Construction Materials				
No.	Name		Concrete Sand	Concrete Aggregate	Timber	Road Works	
						Sub-base	Base
1	LATERITIC IRONSTONE SURFACE WITH RESIDUAL LATERITIC GRAVELS	Very feeble supply from shallow wells in dry season contaminated by surface flow in wet season		Indurated surface rock after crushing and screening		Suitable but uneconomic Suitable, plentiful supply	Suitable, under caprock. Requires ripping and crushing Suitable but requires stabilization with lime or cement
2	SCARP SLOPE			Plentiful supply of medium-hard sandstone rock suitable for crushing		Gravels suitable but rock uneconomic	Rock suitable after crushing. Gravels suitable only when stabilized in cement lime
3	SANDSTONE SURFACE	Generally deep wells. Occasionally, perched water-tables supply shallow wells				Suitable	
4	FERRUGINOUS SANDSTONE BENCH			Indurated rock suitable for crushing			Suitable after crushing
5	VALLEY FLOOR	Perennial supply of potable water from deep wells. Liable to contamination by surface flow in wet season	Limited supply in local pockets deposited by sheet wash		Orchard bush. Suitable for kindling but not for construction	Suitable	

TABLE 6

Engineering characteristics of Doto land system — suitability for road location

Land Facet		Appraisal	Features
No,	Name		
1	LATERITIC IRONSTONE SURFACE WITH RESIDUAL LATERITIC GRAVELS	Unsuitable due to isolated facet situation. Where same facet is extensively developed in adjacent land system then suitable for road location	Flat to gently undulating topography. Abundant supplies of gravel. Generally well drained
2	SCARP SLOPE	Generally unsuitable because of steep slopes	Steep rock, with sliding and erosion
3	SANDSTONE SURFACE	Suitable when extensively developed	Soils are sandy and well drained with few well defined water courses
4	FERRUGINOUS SANDSTONE BENCH	Unsuitable because of isolated facet situation	Isolated situation and access is difficult. Dip of strata is favourable
5	VALLEY FLOOR	Suitable	Soils usually deep and well drained. There are no excessive slopes. Locally run-off from steep slopes of land facet 2 may create an erosion problem and intercepting ditches and culverts would be required

CONCLUSIONS

The following points have emerged as a result of the work that has been done in Northern Nigeria:

1. In addition to its agricultural uses, land classification provides a satisfactory basis for classifying and hence storing information about the engineering features of ground.

2. The extent and nature of road-making materials and of associated road-building problems can be displayed more effectively by using land classification methods than by employing geological and pedological mapping units.

3. At the level of the land system, broad but useful generalizations can be made about materials that are available, problems that exist, and construction methods that are applicable over quite large areas of ground. This information is particularly useful in the planning stages of regional road-building programmes.

4. At the level of the individual road project, engineers will be concerned with the engineering features of land facets and land elements. These can be used to retain and store design data which can subsequently be retrieved and used again in the design of new roads on similar ground.

5. As these are large areas in Northern Nigeria where in engineering terms the ground conditions are similar, the retrieval of data can effect substantial savings in the design effort required for new roads. It can also provide a means of alerting engineers to problems likely to be encountered in a particular terrain.

6. The frequency of soil sampling and testing in many site investigations is often disproportionate to that necessary for adequate design purposes. Land evaluation provides the means whereby an appropriate frequency of sampling can be decided. Studies made so far show that in a number of instances survey effort could have been reduced by as much as 70% if such information had been available.

In addition to the types of data referred to in the present study, land evaluation can be used to record other kinds of engineering information. An item that is considered particularly appropriate is some indication of the quantity of earthworks, associated with road building to different standards. Information on this could be obtained from completed road projects or could be estimated from photogrammetric traverses of land systems where suitable ground survey information was available. In either case, such information could provide a valuable indication in the planning stages of the eventual order of costs that are likely to be incurred.

Work is still needed before positive recommendations can be made about the way in which a system of stored data can be effectively applied. A land evaluation programme has been initiated in parts of Northern Nigeria by the Ministry of Agriculture. Before long it is hoped that a start will be made to extend this work to include information dealing with the engineering features of the ground. When this has been done, a means will have been found to provide simultaneously not only a sound and rational basis for agricultural land use planning but an equally effective foundation on which to make decisions about the planning and development of road communications.

This paper was contributed by permission of the Director of Road Research, United Kingdom. British Crown Copyright reproduced by permission of the Controller of H.M. Stationery Office.

REFERENCES

BAWDEN, M. G., and TULEY, P. (1966). *The land resources of Southern Sardauna and Southern Adamawa Provinces, Northern Nigeria.* Directorate of Overseas Survey.

BECKETT, P. H. T., and WEBSTER, R. (1965). *A classification system for terrain. Units and principles.* Military Engng Exp. Establ., Christchurch, England, Report 872.

BRINK, A. B., MABBUTT, J. A., WEBSTER, R., and BECKETT, P. H. T. (1966). *Report of the working group on land classification and data storage.* Military Engng Exp. Establ., Christchurch, England, Report 940.

CARTER, J. D., BARBER, W., and TAIT, E. A. (1963). The geology of parts of Adamawa, Bauchi, and Bornu Provinces in north-eastern Nigeria. *Bull. geol. Surv. Nigeria* **30.**

CLARE, K. E., and BEAVEN, P. J. (1965). Roadmaking materials in northern Borneo. DSIR, Road Research Laboratory. *Road Res. Tech. Pap.* No. 68.

CLAYTON, W. D. (1957). A preliminary survey of soil and vegetation in northern Nigeria Minist. Agric. Northern Nigeria (unpublished report).

DOWLING, J. W. F., and WILLIAMS, F. H. P. (1964). The use of aerial photographs in materials surveys and classification of land-forms. *Conference in Civil Engineering Problems Overseas.* London (Inst. Civil Engineers.)

KLINKENBERG, K., TOMLINSON, P. R., HIGGINS, G. M., and DE LEEUW, P. N. (1963). The soils of the Middle Gongola region. *Soil Survey Section Bull.* No. 21. Ministry of Agriculture, Regional Research Station, Samaru, Northern Nigeria.

MABBUTT, J. A. (1968). Review of concepts of land classification. In *Land Evaluation.* (Ed. G. A. Stewart.) (Macmillan: Melbourne.)

Terrain Analysis in Mobility Studies for Military Vehicles

J. T. Parry, J. A. Heginbottom and W. R. Cowan

*Department of Geography, McGill University,
Montreal, Canada*

*The terrain analysis system developed at McGill University has been applied in
the military training area of Camp Petawawa, Ontario. The study was undertaken
to determine the potential of large-scale air photographs (1 : 5000) in assessing
the specific environmental factors which affect the cross-country mobility of
military vehicles. Surface composition, macromorphology, micromorphology,
and surface cover were considered, and map overlays prepared for each factor.
Tests in the area indicated that vehicle performance was similar for areas with
similar arrays of terrain characteristics and on this basis successful predictions
of speed were made for cross-country test runs traversing a variety of terrain units.
Data storage and retrieval are very serious problems in any terrain classification
system. Two approaches to this general problem were investigated: the unit land
form approach and the computer map approach. In the former, the ground surface
is treated as a mosaic and small landscape units are outlined. Each of these is
uniform with respect to surface composition and macromorphology. The other
attributes of the unit are recorded by an array of symbols. The total composite
map of this type amounts to a data storage bank.
The second approach is a simple computer mapping programme in which the
lines and rows of the computer page are used as rectangular co-ordinates for the
area and the terrain data cards are keyed to this grid. The map output can show
single factors, associations of factors, or go–no go conditions for particular
vehicles.*

In 1967 the terrain analysis system developed at McGill University[1] was applied
in a small area of eastern Canada—the Canadian Forces Base at Petawawa,
which lies in the Ottawa valley about 80 miles north-west of Ottawa. The camp
is only 30 sq miles in area, but it includes quite varied conditions, and a small
area was mandatory because the study was designed to investigate three basic
problems:
1. Since air photo interpretation has been the main source of terrain information
for some time, and will probably remain so in the immediate future, a careful
evaluation of the quanta of terrain information which can be extracted from
large-scale air photos (1:5000) was attempted. It is seldom possible to obtain
vertical air photo coverage of any considerable area at scales larger than
1:5000, and so photos at this scale may be considered as the optimum information source for this type of remote sensing. In order to test the interpretation
procedures, the terrain analysis of the camp area was completed with a minimum
of on-site information.

[1]The research for this project was undertaken at the Department of Geography, McGill
University, for the Defence Research Board of Canada – Contract VC 69-500007
– Serial No. 2VC 5-1.

2. Data storage, retrieval, and display constitute a major problem area, and so some experimentation with suitable output forms was attempted.
3. In order to test the validity of the system as a whole it was decided that vehicle performance figures should be obtained for as many different terrain units as possible. Without this kind of test there is no way of knowing whether the terrain differences which appear at the interpretation stage are truly significant or not.

SIGNIFICANT TERRAIN FACTORS AND AIR PHOTO INTERPRETATION

The terrain at any locality is a complex of interacting factors. Not all factors affect ground mobility either directly or indirectly, and the first problem is to isolate those that are significant. Our work shows broad agreement with the studies undertaken at the Waterways Experiment Station (U.S.A.E.) in distinguishing the terrain factors significant in cross-country mobility. Four basic factors have been identified: surface composition, surface morphology including both macromorphology and micromorphology, surface cover including man-made features and vegetation, and surface climate. With the exception of the climatic factor, which demands an entirely different approach, it is possible to obtain a considerable amount of information about all the terrain factors by non-contact methods, such as air photo interpretation. For this reason, the climatic factor was not considered in the Petawawa study, although it is recognised that the local climate exercises an important control on the state of the ground, and thus on all types of surface movement. The other factors were assessed in turn and mapped at a scale of 1:25,000—each factor map being in the form of a coloured transparency, designed for use either singly, or in combination, as an overlay on a photo mosaic of the area.

   The production of the factor maps involved the adoption of suitable classification systems, which will be discussed in each of the following sections, and then the application of the system by air photo interpretation. The basic interpretation procedure is that of discrimination – areas or groups of objects which appear to have a separate individuality are recognised, and boundary lines drawn separating one from another. Some terrain factors are directly visible on the air photo, but others are not, and in these cases the classification of surface conditions within the delineated areas depends on the extent to which indirect evidence provides a convergence towards a particular identification.

Surface Composition

The surface composition is the most fundamental of the terrain factors because it determines the load which can be supported at a particular site, and the tractive forces which can be applied. Surface composition varies considerably: in mechanical terms the range is from a rigid elastic solid – consolidated rock – to a Newtonian fluid – water. Because of the tremendous variation in surface composition, even within a particular mechanical class, it is necessary to adopt specific classification systems for each surface type. The specific classification systems indicated in Table 1 were chosen from the existing systems because they are based on factors which have a direct bearing upon the trafficability of the material, and because they can be applied in both contact and non-contact situations.

   The photo interpretation of surface composition at Camp Petawawa proved to be fairly straightforward, since only a few composition types were involved and discrimination and identification were relatively easy. Some information on the surface composition was derived from published sources (Gillespie 1964; Gadd 1963); however, the plotting of the boundaries was based entirely on photo interpretation, and subsequent field checking showed that the accuracy was good. The major limiting factor was the obscuring effect of the vegetation, which resulted in the failure to identify several small rock outcrops and water bodies.

TABLE 1

Surface composition

Major Composition Type		Specific Classification System
Rigid elastic solids	Consolidated crystalline and sedimentary rocks	Miles system (Miles 1963)
Non-rigid solids in region of elastic behaviour	Unconsolidated rudaceous and arenaceous rocks	Miles system (Miles 1963)
	Frozen ground	*
Plastic and visco-plastic solids	Argillaceous rocks and mineral soils	Unified system (W.E.S. 1953)
	Organic soils	Radforth system (Radforth 1955, 1956)
Quasi-viscous solids	Snow	*
	Ice	*
Fluids	Water	—

*An appropriate classification has not yet been determined.

Surface Morphology: Macromorphology

Macromorphology is considered as the general surface configuration, including both the degree of slope and the slope form. In evaluating and mapping these elements the problems of scale and degree of generalisation are immediately introduced, and an arbitrary distinction has to be made between macromorphology and micromorphology. In the Petawawa study, the minimum slope segment which could be delimited at the mapping scale was 250 ft, and so larger slope segments were considered as macromorphology, whereas smaller features were treated as micromorphology.

The selection of class values for slope steepness and slope form (Table 2) was determined in part by the mapping requirements, and in part by vehicle performance—thus, 45° represents the maximum gradient for any current tracked vehicles, the shift from second to first gear takes place in wheeled vehicles around 26½°, and so on. Slope class values were determined from analysis of the air photos using a stereometer to measure the stereoscopic parallax, and the classification of slope form was based on careful stereoscopic examination of each slope segment. Even with the fairly wide range in the class interval, it was found necessary in the final mapping to make generalisations involving the combination of classes.

TABLE 2
Legend for terrain map (Fig. 1) and test courses (Fig. 3)

SURFACE COMPOSITION

☐ Consolidated rock — outcrops of granites and gneisses

⌇ Non-consolidated material

◉ Mineral soil — poorly graded sands and silty sands,
SP-SM Unified Soil Classification System

⊕ Organic soil — fine and coarse fibrous muskeg, types 9 and 12
Radforth Classification System

○ Water — water bodies more than three feet deep and one acre in area

SURFACE MORPHOLOGY : MACROMORPHOLOGY

Slope, steepness :			Slope form :	
△1	0 - 6°	0 - 10%	① Convex, smooth
△2	6 - 14°	10 - 25%	② Planar, smooth
△3	14 - 26½°	25 - 50%	③ Concave, smooth
△4	26½ - 45°	50 - 100%	④ Convex, rough
△5	Above 45°	Above 100%	⑤ Planar, rough
△6	Classes I and II		⑥ Concave, rough
△7	Classes II and III		⑦ Classes 1 and 3
△8	Classes III and IV		⑧ Classes 1,2,and 3
△9	Classes I, II, and III		⑨ Classes 4,5,and 6

SURFACE MORPHOLOGY : MICROMORPHOLOGY

⬛ Positive features of mineral soil in a random, linear pattern. Slopes △6 ⑦,
lengths 400 - 1800 ft, width-length ratio 1:4 - 1:20, amplitude 10 - 30 ft, spacing 10 per mile,
non - symmetric sigmoid in section. Aeolian — fixed sand dunes

▬ Positive features of mineral soil in a random, linear pattern. Slopes △6 ⑦,
lengths 50 - 400 ft, width-length ratio 1:2 - 1:8, amplitude less than 10 ft, spacing 18 per mile,
irregular sigmoid in section. Aeolian — sand sheets and ripples

⊖ * Negative features in mineral soil in a clustered, non-linear, overlapping pattern.
Slopes △7 ⑨, lengths 10 - 200 ft, width-length ratio 1:1 - 1:2, amplitude 10 -
50 ft, spacing 15 per mile, irregular cardioid in section. Glaciofluvial — kettle holes

❶ * Positive features of consolidated rock in a random, non-linear pattern. Slopes
△5 ⑤, lengths 20 - 100 ft, width-length ratio 1:1 - 1:2, amplitude 10 - 30 ft, spacing
calculation not possible, irregular rectilinear in section. Glacial — rock outcrops and erratics

* These symbols are not included in Fig.1

SURFACE COVER : VEGETATION STUCTURE

Height:	Stem type:	Form:
▲ More than 25ft	Woody	Trees
△ 5 - 25 ft	Woody	Young or dwarfed trees
▼ 2 - 5 ft	Woody	Tall shrubs or dwarfed trees
▼ Less than 2ft	Woody and non-woody	Low shrubs, grasses, sedges, and mosses

SURFACE COVER : VEGETATION SPACING (mean nearest neighbour distance)

⑨ 0 - 10 ft		④ 60 - 90 ft	
⑧ 10 - 15 ft		③ 90 - 140 ft	
⑦ 15 - 25 ft		② 140 - 220 ft	
⑥ 25 - 40 ft		① Greater than 220 ft	
⑤ 40 - 60 ft			

The field check revealed that almost all simple slopes without a tree cover had been correctly classified, but in the case of both simple and complex slopes under a tree cover, the steepness had been over-estimated in several cases and the slope form was frequently not identified.

Surface Morphology: Micromorphology

The detailed irregularities of the surface are probably of greater importance from the standpoint of ground mobility than the larger slope segments, because it is the micro features over which the vehicle actually travels. In the Petawawa study an attempt was made to identify all the small-scale surface features, and interpret some of the following characteristics: their composition, plan organisation, slope steepness and form, average length, width-length ratio, amplitude, cross section type, and genesis (Table 2). The scale factor prevented the mapping of such features individually, and so all that was attempted was the grouping of similar forms and the delimitation of the areas of occurrence of each type.

Micromorphology was found to be the most difficult of the factors to assess by air photo interpretation. This was in part a problem of detection: some features were too small to be resolved, while others gave such faint traces that they were very easily overlooked. There was also the problem of analysis: the image did not provide sufficient information to permit identification of its characteristics. No surface detail could be discerned at all beneath the forest and bush cover, and even in the open areas it was often impossible to determine such characteristics as steepness and form, amplitude and cross section type which could mean the difference between a successful mission and immobilisation.

Surface Cover: Man-made Features

Man-made features need no specific comment. They were differentiated from natural cover features, because of the fact that they often have special significance in military operations. The photo interpretation of man-made objects is usually easy, because the feature and its characteristics are directly visible. In the Petawawa study, all the man-made objects were identified, with the exception of some trenches and foxholes, and some building foundations.

Surface Cover: Vegetation

Vegetation is important from two points of view as far as military vehicles are concerned — concealment and penetration. Concealment is affected by three factors: vegetation height, canopy closure, and seasonal changes. The height classes adopted in the Petawawa study are given in Table 2, and the vegetation was stratified into the four cover types by stereoscopic examination of the photos. A more refined subdivision was attempted initially, but it was abandoned because of the difficulties of distinguishing and mapping small differences in height for the shorter vegetation types and the irrelevance of further subdivision once the understorey space permits the passage of vehicles.

Canopy closure can be readily determined by photo interpretation and standard scales are available. Phenological effects cannot be assessed from a single set of photos, and so no attempt was made to indicate the seasonal variation of cover.

Penetrability was found to be more difficult to assess than concealment. Two factors are involved — the stem diameter, which is important because it determines the facility with which the tree can be overridden, and the stem spacing, which provides a measure of the impedance, either in the sense of the number of stems which must be overridden per unit of path length, or in the sense of the manoeuvrability limits in situations where the vegetation cannot be overridden. No satisfactory method of measuring stem diameters from the air photos was devised; attempts to relate crown width and D.B.H. were unsuccessful, and direct measurement of D.B.H. on the photos was not possible.

In contrast, the assessment of stem spacing was found to be quite feasible. The spacing class values (Table 2) were selected with vehicle manoeuvrability in mind, and the values were determined by making individual stem counts within circular sampling areas carefully positioned on the air photos so that all discernible variations of the forest cover were sampled. Mean nearest neighbour distances were calculated according to the spacing formula of Mills (1964): $x = 0 \cdot 57 \sqrt{A/N}$, where x is the mean nearest neighbour distance, A is the ground area of the sampling plot, and N is the number of individual stems within the plot.

In concluding this section on the assessment of terrain factors from large-scale air photos, it should be noted that although a considerable amount of information about each terrain factor can be extracted from air photos at the 1 : 5000 scale there are definite limitations: firstly, the information derived from the photos does not provide any indication of seasonal changes, and yet in

Canada almost all attributes of a site vary with the season; secondly, at this scale it is difficult to retain an overall perspective, and to link up detail from one photo or flight line with another; thirdly, radical displacement can be a serious problem, especially when a short focal-length lens is used.

STORAGE AND PRESENTATION OF TERRAIN INFORMATION

The handling of any quantity of diverse information is always a difficult problem, especially when rapid retrieval is required. Two approaches, both with a mapping capability were investigated.

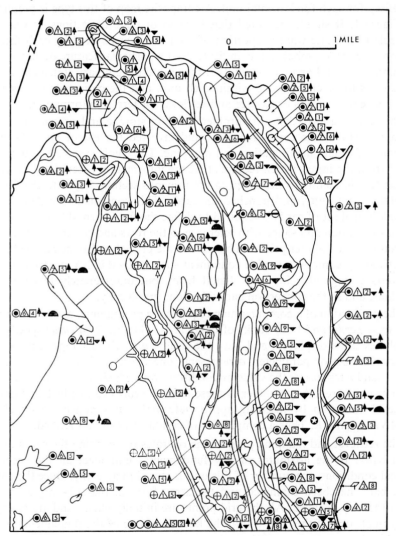

Fig. 1. Composite terrain map of part of Camp Petawawa, Ontario, Canada.

Both systems require the establishment of what may be termed fundamental terrain units. The surface in any area is an envelope, with a variety of inflections, and abrupt or gradual changes in composition. In nature the envelope is continuous, but it can be considered as a three-dimensional jigsaw puzzle, with the edges of the pieces determined by changes in either surface composition or macromorphology. Each piece is, therefore, homogeneous with respect to composition and morphology within the limits of the class values established for these two parameters. Such pieces constitute naturalistic subdivisions of the surface, and provide the fundamental terrain units required.

Theoretically, it is possible to take this subdivision of the surface envelope even farther by considering all the other terrain factors in turn, and producing units which are homogeneous with respect to every parameter considered. In practice, however, this is not possible, because of the scale problem in mapping, and so information relating to the other terrain factors can only be serialised for each fundamental unit. A composite map of this type is presented in Figure 1. It should be noted that because of scale limitations, it was not possible to indicate what proportion of each unit was covered by each factor; the presence of a symbol simply indicates that a particular feature occurs within the unit. The total array of symbols is thus a useful summary statement of the conditions to be encountered within each unit, and the composite map serves as a convenient means of storage and retrieval for terrain information.

The second approach to the problem of data storage and presentation was an outgrowth of the composite map, and involved the use of an IBM 7044 computer for data manipulation and mapping. The whole system is automatic, apart from the input, which requires that the information is serialised in terms of the terrain factors as described in the previous section, keyed to the fundamental terrain units, and punched on cards. This constitutes the data bank. An additional set of cards is required to define the fundamental terrain units in terms of location and shape with reference to the rows and columns of the page format of the computer printer. This part of the procedure can be handled most effectively by computer-graphic equipment such as D-Mac XY digitizer, which converts cartographic input to digital form, but unfortunately this was not available and so the conversion had to be done graphically.

The production of a computer map requires the programme, a set of *condition* and *logic cards*, and both banks of data cards. The *condition cards* specify the attributes to be displayed, and have the form $v/o/c$, where v represents a particular variable or parameter, o represents one operator from the set $=$, $\neq$, $>$, $<$, and c represents the value or condition, with which the specified variable is to be compared. Any number of these *condition cards* can be included in one retrieval operation by inserting appropriate *logic cards* punched with either an *AND* or an *OR*. Thus a complex set of conditions can be specified.

The retrieval and mapping programme operates by scanning the cards of the data bank. If the attributes of any fundamental unit meet all the specified logical conditions, the number of this unit is stored in an array. Once the entire data bank has been examined and the array formed, the sub-programme to print the map is called. All the grid points are initially blank, and are changed to symbols only if they fall within the bounds of one of the fundamental units listed in the array.

A sample computer map is shown in Figure 2. This is a simple *Go–No Go* map of part of Camp Petawawa for a hypothetical wheeled vehicle. The vehicle characteristics, which must be expressed in terms that can be directly related to the data bank, are listed below together with a verbal statement of the *condition* and *logic* sequence required for the programme.

Non amphibious	Surface composition $/=/$ water
	AND
Ground pressure requirements greater than those afforded by organic terrain	Surface composition $/=/$ organic terrain
	AND
Maximum climb 50% grade	Macromorphology $/>/$ 50% grade
	AND
Manoeuvrability requirements greater than 25 ft	Obstacle spacing $/</$ 25 ft

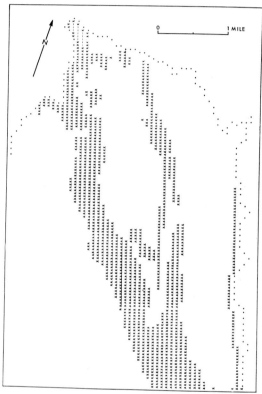

Fig. 2. Computer map of part of Camp Petawawa, Ontario, Canada.

It can be seen that the opposite of the required conditions was specified on each condition card. This was because the *No Go* areas were to be designated on the map. The programme involved the identification of all the fundamental terrain units which, for one reason or another, did not meet the vehicle requirements. Thus, the grid points within such units were printed with an *X*, while the areas where the vehicle could operate effectively remained blank.

There are certain problems inherent in the computer display of terrain data. With a computer of the type used in this project, output is via a line printer in the form of alphameric characters arranged in columns and rows. The page width is restricted to 13 in. (130 characters) and so for map output of large areas it is necessary to prepare the map in strips. There is no restriction in the other dimension since the paper is continuous.

Several quite serious problems arise out of the fixed dimension of the print characters ($\frac{1}{6}$ by $\frac{1}{10}$ in.). For example, in the study of Camp Petawawa where a mapping scale of 1:25,000 had been adopted for the terrain factors, each character of the line printer covered approximately 400 by 200 ft (nearly 2 acres). It followed that any feature smaller than these dimensions could not be included save at the expense of an adjacent feature. In addition, boundary lines could not be shown accurately since the character representing any segment of the line can only be printed at the centre of each row-column intersection. This means that at the 1:25,000 scale the boundary position may be incorrect by up to 200 ft along one axis and 100 ft on the other, and the error is proportionally greater at smaller scales. Boundaries which do not parallel the rows or columns have to be shown as a series of steps, which makes the mapping of irregular areas very difficult. This is a serious problem in dealing with terrain factors in cross-country mobility since many features of critical significance such as rivers, bluffs, etc. are narrow and irregular.

TERRAIN UNITS AND VEHICLE SPEED

An attempt was made to test the terrain analysis system at Camp Petawawa in July 1967, when three vehicles, a jeep (M38A1), a three-quarter ton truck (M37), and an armoured personnel carrier (M113) were made available for a two-week period. The effects of terrain conditions on vehicle performances are very complex, and include a whole range of factors, such as vehicle design, which are quite beyond the scope of a study of this sort, and so the only performance factor considered was that of vehicle speed. A relationship between average speed and surface conditions can be expected from a purely empiric point of view, thus a legitimate approach in validating a terrain analysis system is the demonstration that differences in average speed actually occur in different terrain units; the more severe the terrain conditions, the worse the vehicle performance.

A series of fundamental terrain units were selected, which provided a good sample of conditions at Camp Petawawa. The units were grouped, so that in any particular group several terrain factors remained constant, while for the other factors there were differences of the order of one or two class intervals. The tests consisted of cross-country passes between starting and finishing lines. The driver made the decision as to his actual path as he went along, the only stipulations being that he maintain as straight a path and as fast a speed as possible. Vehicles were at full combat load, and in the case of wheeled vehicles, tyres were at 25% deflection. Times were taken with a stop watch, and distances were measured with a range finder or a chain, thus permitting the calculation of speed-made-good[1] for each pass.

In some terrain units only a single pass was attempted, since the problem was simply that of establishing whether the vehicle could climb a particular slope or not, or whether it could complete the pass without becoming immobilised. In other terrain units, ten passes were planned in order to obtain average speed-made-good and standard deviations; however, in a few instances the vehicle sustained damage or became immobilised, while in other cases the speeds-made-good were so similar over five or six passes that the full set of ten was considered unnecessary.

Space does not permit a complete analysis of the results (Fig. 3), but a few comparisons can be made. Courses 8 to 14 involved the ascent of terrace edges

---

[1]Speed-made-good: The average speed between starting point and destination, with distance being measured as a straight line between these two points.

where the surface composition was either loose, bare sand or sandy soil. None of the vehicles surmounted the slopes greater than 45° (class 5), nor the slopes in class 4 ($26\frac{1}{2}°$–45°) where the surface material was bare sand. However, the

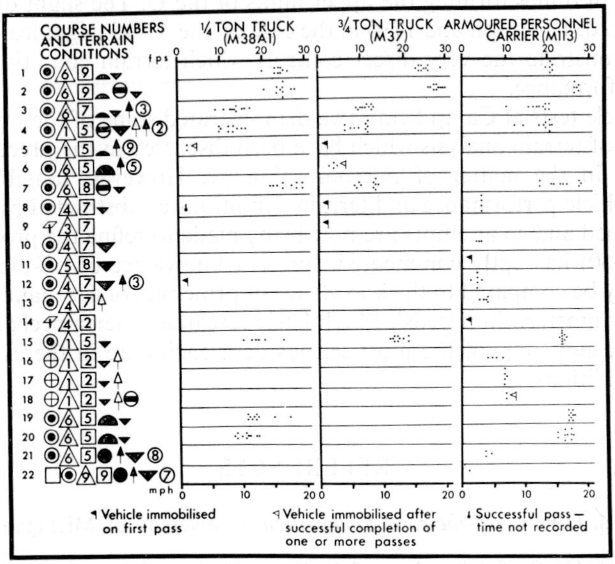

Fig. 3. Test courses and vehicle performance (legend for course descriptions is given in Table 2).

M38A1 was successful in course 8 (slope class 4 with a grass cover), where the maximum slope segment was 31°, and the M113 was successful on all the class 4 slopes even with a cover of bushes and trees (courses 10, 12, and 13): the range in average speed-made-good from 3·5 to 2·3 mph showing an inverse relation to the increase in steepness of the maximum slope segments from 28° to 35°.

Courses 17 and 18 were on enclosed muskeg, and were attempted only by the M113. The performance was very uniform, with average speeds-made-good of 6·9 and 7·1 mph. The immobilisation in course 18 resulted not from any undetected anomaly in the terrain, but from a man-made hazard in the form of a shell hole which had pierced the muskeg mat.

According to the terrain evaluation courses 1 and 2 were essentially similar; however, as can be seen in Figure 3, the vehicle performance figures were somewhat different (a t test showed that the differences were significant at the 1% level). This is an example of a situation where the occurrence of micro-morphological features not discernible on the air photos produced an appreciable effect, particularly on the performance of the M113.

The introduction of another variable, that of vegetation in course 3, produced a marked effect, as can be judged from the differences in mean average speed between courses 2 and 3: M38A1—16·9 mph and 11·6 mph; M37—19·1 mph and 7·6 mph; M113—18·7 mph and 12·4 mph.

The conditions on courses 4, 5, and 15 were similar apart from the density of vegetation. As can be seen from Figure 3 there was a direct relationship between the average speeds of all three vehicles and the differences in vegetation density for the three courses.

Courses 19 and 20 make an interesting comparison because the vehicles traversed the same terrain unit, but in different directions. The micromorphology consists of a series of fossil dunes (some of which are currently active), which form a broad U-shaped belt. In course 19 the vehicles made their way between the arms of the U and across the dunes at the point corresponding to the basal segment of the U, while in course 20 they were required to pass obliquely across both series of dunes forming the upper limbs of the U. The slight differences in average speed, 17·9 mph and 17·0 in the case of the M113 (significant at the 1% level), demonstrate the very direct controls which terrain conditions exert on vehicle performance.

The vehicle tests at Camp Petawawa demonstrated some of the weaknesses in the system of terrain analysis which have been discussed in the preceding pages, specifically in the matter of micromorphology. However, tangible relations between vehicle performance and terrain conditions as abstracted by the system were obtained and so attempts are now being made to refine the procedures. As Bekker (1960) has aptly commented, 'present knowledge of off-the-road loco-motion may be compared to the knowledge of principles of aeronautics available in the early nineteen hundreds'. Much basic research in terramechanics has yet to be done, and some of the most serious deficiencies are in the assessment of ground conditions.

REFERENCES

BEKKER, M. G. (1960). *Off-the-road Locomotion.* (University of Michigan Press: Ann Arbor.)

GADD, N. R. (1963). Surficial geology of the Chalk River area, Ontario-Quebec, Canada. *Geological Survey of Canada*, Map 1132 A.

GILLESPIE, J. E. (1964). Soil survey of Renfrew County, Ontario. *Ontario Soil Survey Report* No. 37.

MILES, R. D. (1963). A concept of landforms, parent materials and soils in air photo interpretation studies for engineering purposes. *Int. Arch. Photogramm.* **14**, 462–77.

MILLS, H. L. (1964). *The physiognomy of vegetation: a quantitative approach to vegetation geometry based upon the structural cell concept as the minimum sample size.* U.S. Army Engineer, Waterways Experiment Station, Corps of Engineers, Vicksburg, Mississippi. Contract DA 22-079-eng332-Marshall University, Huntington, West Virginia.

RADFORTH, N. W. (1955). *Organic terrain organization from the air.* Handbook No. 1. Report No. PR 95. Defence Research Board, Department of National Defence, Canada.

RADFORTH, N. W. (1958). *Organic terrain organization from the air.* Handbook No. 2. Report No. 124. Defence Research Board, Department of National Defence, Canada.

WATERWAYS EXPERIMENT STATION (1953). *The unified soil classification system.* U.S. Army Engineer Tech. Mem. No. 3-357. Waterways Experiment Station C.E. Vicksburg, Mississippi.

Land Assessment for Regional Planning: The Hunter Region of N.S.W. as a Case Study

C. C. Renwick

Director of Research, The Hunter Valley Research Foundation, Newcastle, Australia

This paper describes some uses of land evaluation techniques in regional planning in the Hunter region of New South Wales. The part played by the CSIRO's Division of Land Research in this work is set into the general framework of resources study pursued by the Hunter Valley Research Foundation, a regional research body concerned with guiding public and private investment in all forms of industry. The Foundation's basic research programme comprises depth studies of land and water resources together with economic structure and performance measurement by a physical and social sciences graduate team. Since the approach of the Foundation is not duplicated in any other Australian region the work is of interest in reviewing approaches to controlled growth in the fully employed economy and the place of land evaluation therein.

INTRODUCTION

The Hunter Valley Research Foundation was established in 1956 as a co-operative scientific venture to assess the investment structure and potential of the Hunter region of New South Wales. The graduates grouped for this task include economists, engineers, geographers, statisticians, mathematicians, agriculturalists, and geologists. The approach to the study of regional growth was determined on a tripartite basis under the heads of land studies, water studies, and economic structure and performance, the latter being a co-ordinating element.

In the past decade there has been no fundamental movement from this general approach although studies in depth have proceeded at different rates and to different stages. This paper gives principally an account of our land studies and relates these to the overall approach to the Foundation.

PRELIMINARIES ON ECONOMIC GROWTH

In the eighteenth and nineteenth centuries the accumulation of capital was a major private economic preoccupation. In the first half of the twentieth century the rising standard of living and the stabilisation of employment became targets of public policy. Now, in the second half of the twentieth century we are concerned with the setting of growth patterns and their stabilisation. This development represents the combination of a number of trends from the past and also represents a realisation by all groups within the affluent society that their affluence is interdependent.

Fundamental to the concept of growth is that of productivity. Productivity is the measured outcome of the combined efforts of capital, labour, technology, and research. When we look at growth and at productivity and indeed at the whole structure of resources both human and non-human on which these depend, the national patterns are fairly easily discerned. For example, in Australia, as the result of the work of the Committee of Economic Enquiry (Commonwealth of Australia 1966) it has now been established that a 5% growth rate in our gross national product is not only desirable but is a necessary target during the foreseeable future. Australians are now concerned about maintaining this growth rate over the years to come. But the establishment of a national growth rate, like the examination of a nation's balance of payments or its general fiscal situation, reveals only the end product of multiform activities. These occur within the nation itself and also are associated with the rest of the world through international transactions.

THE REGION'S GROWTH PATH

In order to interpret the growth path of a nation it is necessary to relate it to the growth paths of its several components and also to examine what is happening within the structure of the economy itself. It is at this point that the study of the region becomes of paramount importance. The region can be defined simply as a manageable area of study.

In looking at regions from the point of view of growth, certain factors are pre-eminent. First, a unity or environment of resources structure needs to be established. Second, clear lines of communication to other regions and to the rest of the world must be marked and flows along these lines recorded. Third, it must be possible to measure the major variables which affect performance within the area. These variables range over natural resources, human resources, industry, technology, investment, the outflow of commodities and services, and the inflow of capital. This is the range of variables to be examined within the region and it is in relation to these that the growth of the region will be established.

The region has an internal and external balance. From the internal point of view the development of its standards and the steady bringing into use of its resources is fundamental to its growth. Externally, the region provides a flow of goods and services to other regions and to the rest of the world, but it also requires from these sources savings which it cannot generate internally in order to provide more investment within the region.

Thus, a study of a nation on a regional basis can bring us clearly to understand what is required with regard to development within various areas of its resources and the extent to which interflows of capital will be necessary to maintain stability in overall growth. Unless the regional approach is taken, then a country such as Australia faces the prospect of continued affluence resulting largely from the development of a few metropolitan areas. In less developed countries, the prospect of unbalanced development is of even greater consequence.

THE RIVER BASIN AS A REGION

The river basin or watershed is a very convenient area on which to begin the delineation of a region. Excesses and deficiencies of water provoke crises of a kind that stimulate the communities of the river basin to various sorts of action. If the crises are sufficiently large and numerous and the river basin is sufficiently important in the national structure then these demands will become very strong at the political level. The decision-making processes with regard to meeting the demands for action will be increasingly difficult unless the whole watershed is taken into account. The region needs to be studied as a unit so that it can be adequately understood and valid comparisons can be made with other regions, and with the national growth picture.

To co-ordinate the multifarious range of resource studies which is possible, a simple approach, and as is proved by experience a most satisfactory one, is to group the study of resources under three broad heads, namely water resources, land resources, and economic structure (Hunter Valley Research Foundation 1962).

The grouping has the advantage of making it possible to integrate via the team approach scientists from a number of fields, both physical and social, and it leads also to the development of an overall point of view which tends to deepen the understanding of a particular scientist in exploring his speciality in the region.

The grouping of resources studies in depth under the three headings mentioned is co-ordinated by the concept of investment since it is on investment that the whole future planning of the river basin depends. This investment is both at the public and private level and is necessarily related to the profitability of such investment when considered in relation to alternatives available elsewhere.

REGIONAL LAND ASSESSMENT

Because of the integrated team approach of the Foundation, a comparable group was sought to undertake part of the land assessment. The total land assessment programme was first divided into rural and urban. Work was concentrated on rural studies to begin with, under the heads of land systems, land cover, and land utilisation. The land systems study was undertaken by the Division of Land Research and Regional Survey of the CSIRO and resulted in a set of studies being published (Story *et al.* 1963). Land cover and utilisation were studied by the Foundation team (Burley 1963).

Results of the land assessment have been set out in maps accompanied by reports, this having been determined as the best presentation for the purpose in view, viz., the guidance of investment policy, both public and private.

At a later stage urban land studies in terms of utilisation were undertaken and at this time a total land assessment is available for the region. A brief summary of findings in the rural land studies is pertinent at this point.

'It is probable that originally almost the entire Hunter Valley consisted of forestland, woodland or parkland, but today 48% of the region has a grassland or open parkland cover, and forestland occupies 46% of the land surface. However, only 10% of the grassland has benefited from pasture improvement and soil erosion is wide-spread in certain areas. Cropland and sown pasture are even more limited occupying only 4% of the region. Despite the efforts of interested organisations (particularly the Department of Agriculture and the Soil Conservation Service of New South Wales) and individuals, considerably more pasture improvement, sownland expansion and reafforestation are needed in the future. The present forested areas of the Valley should, in almost all cases remain in timber.

'Perhaps the most critical area with regard to land cover improvement is that of the flood plain. Almost the entire arable agricultural economy of the Valley is dependent upon the alluvial flats, but, even so, the potential of this section is far from being fully utilised. In some areas, conversion to sownland is almost complete, but there are many places where stretches of alluvium remain predominantly in grassland.

'The fertility of these areas is generally recognised but their utilisation is hampered by economic factors and problems created by periodic flooding.' (Renwick 1963).

USING LAND ASSESSMENT DATA

The CSIRO land systems team delineated 43 land systems within the Hunter River basin. These land systems were areas or groups of areas exhibiting characteristic combinations of geology, soils, vegetation, land form, and climate. The systems became meaningful for regional planning when taken in conjunction with other land studies (Atkinson 1966) and with the findings from water resources studies and economic evaluation of the region's industries.

The Foundation's Water Plan of 1965, recommending water resources development in the region for the next five years, settled, *inter alia*, for major conservation dams on two tributaries of the Hunter system. This recommendation for investment was based on integrated resources studies.

Basic data on the physical character and capabilities of the region were drawn from the land systems study and from research into land use by the Foundation. Water supply conditions were analysed, with particular attention to the extremes of flood and drought, their occurrence and magnitude and their economic and sociological, as well as ecological consequences. In all, 34 subcatchments were considered from an economic and hydrologic point of view. The accumulation of material concerning these various aspects of land, water, and economic development had been taking place since 1956. The Plan (Renwick *et al.* 1965) says:

'In the Paterson and Allyn River Valleys, [Fig. 1] there is a concentration of irrigators and large areas of potentially irrigable land. It is recommended that two major structures of a total capacity of 70,000 acre feet be constructed, one at Carrabolla on the Paterson River and the other at Eccleston on the Allyn River (compare Glenbawn; 185,000 acre feet for irrigation). The conservation of water by these structures, to provide two feet nett of irrigation water for at least 5000 acres and up to 12,000 acres at a reliability level of failure once in 50 years, would provide an excellent enlargement of the State's conservation programme. They are compact valleys, near to major markets and milk-processing plants, with excellent land potential. The efficient runoff characteristics of the Paterson and Allyn Rivers make them a logical choice in terms of the cost per unit of water yield for the siting of conservation dams in the Hunter Valley.'

These two river valleys were selected as the ones likely to yield the most profitable return on investment in irrigation. Such irrigation water would be used principally by dairymen who supply milk to the N.S.W. Milk Board and by vegetable growers whose production is geared to the expanding local market.

In mid 1967, at the request of the N.S.W. Government, the Research Foundation completed an economic feasibility study, incorporating a cost-benefit analysis, for a proposed conservation dam at Lostock on the Paterson River, Lostock having been considered a more suitable site than Carrabolla.

The State Government of New South Wales has now legislated for the dam on the Paterson River and preliminary work on the structure is underway. The Foundation's planning has been intensified in relation to this, considering the

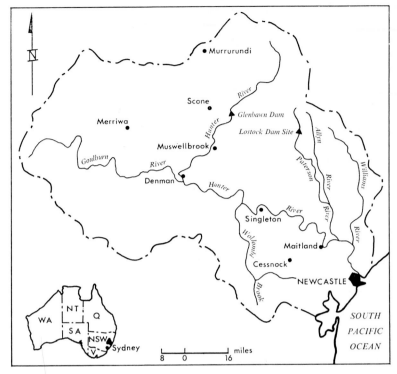

Fig. 1. The Hunter valley.

specific uses of the water to be made available. In this research, which is physical and economic, the land systems classification is being used.

PLANNING AGRICULTURAL DEVELOPMENT IN THE PATERSON SUBREGION

The Foundation is currently undertaking a major study in this subregion to determine the effect of the dam on land use, land tenure, and related socio-economic aspects. A major part of the study will be to determine the optimum allocation of agricultural resources.

The Paterson River watershed (and its tributary the Allyn River) has a total area of approximately 400 sq miles. Within this area there are 465 farm businesses ranging in size from a few acres to over 5000 acres. Classification of farms in a sufficiently detailed manner over such a large area is a complex task. Some form of classification is needed so that a stratified sample of the farms can be used to obtain the information required.

As time limits this study the more detailed land classifications such as a detailed soil map or a detailed land utilisation map cannot be used. The CSIRO's land systems report is being used as the basis for the classification of land in the valley. Within the subregion 10 land systems have been delineated.

Each farm within the Paterson subregion has been classified into the land system or land systems which cover the farm. Use of this approach has resulted in approximately 70 combinations of farm and land systems. Size of farms and their geographical location are also being considered. Thus the farm sample will be stratified in terms of land systems, farm size, and geographical location.

Data obtained from a survey of the sample farms will be used in a linear programming matrix. The linear programming matrix for each farm will be divided into a number of categories and each land system on each sample farm will be analysed separately. Also, each land system will be further broken down into its land units. This will allow a quite detailed analysis of each of the sample farms, based on the land systems approach.

From this analysis the optimum combinations of agricultural resources can be determined. This will indicate the extent of reallocation of agricultural resources required to optimise growth in the subregion and will enable the public and private sectors to see the size of the financial outlays involved in securing these changes in productivity.

STRENGTHS AND WEAKNESSES OF LAND SYSTEMS CLASSIFICATION: THE HUNTER EXPERIENCE

Most of the CSIRO's land systems work has been done in relatively under-developed regions and over large areas. In such cases little is usually known of land use, land potential, soil types, and the like and the land systems classification is the best available technique for a first study. In determining more of the potential of a region more detailed studies should follow.

Initially the CSIRO limited its analysis of land systems to such things as topography, soils, vegetation, and climate. Each land system was subdivided into land units which were similar in nature. Since the early 1960s however, there has been incorporated a land potential rating. Thus, each land unit now has a land use potential assigned to it and the estimated potential land use and the limitations of the land unit are taken into consideration. This inclusion of land potential in the classification is of great benefit. By a close study of a land systems classification it is possible to determine the likely topography, climate, soils, vegetation, and land potential of a particular area without the need for a detailed ground survey. The Hunter survey was the first to cover a highly settled region.

The Foundation in its work in the Paterson valley has encountered some problems in the formation of a sample. To make full use of the land systems classification each land unit should be analysed separately. However, with 70 possible farm-land system combinations and an average of three land units per land system the analysis becomes complicated.

A smaller number of land systems in a particular area would mean a smaller number of farm-land system combinations. This would make the analysis easier to handle while still providing a detailed analysis of each land unit. It would appear, then, that when the area and the number of land systems involved is large the land systems approach is not an ideal analytical tool for the purpose outlined above. However, with a different aim, or on smaller areas and with fewer land systems a classification based on these land systems would be of considerable use.

Although a land classification for the purpose outlined above is not ideal for a large number of land systems, this is not to say it is of no use. The Foundation has found that such a classification can be used when circumstances rule out alternatives such as a detailed soil analysis or a detailed land utilisation map.

The land systems classification in the Hunter valley did not include land potential classes. This has made the Foundation's task of application more difficult. However, as already stated, land potential classes are now being incorporated so that this problem should not arise in the future.

THE REGION'S ECONOMIC PERFORMANCE

Again referring to the case study of the Hunter region our calculations of gross regional product are significant. The region as a whole shows a steadily growing income level (see Table 1). The balance of primary, secondary, and tertiary activities parallels that of the nation as a whole with agriculture representing a comparatively small income component. As a result direct comparisons are valid and helpful in planning regional investment programmes (Renwick *et al.* in press). Agriculture exhibits the stresses of national agriculture as well as other trends, such as that to mechanisation and consequent improvements in productivity where the types and amounts of investment and scale of operation are satisfactory.

TABLE 1

Income generated in the Hunter region, 1947–1965
($'000)

	1947	1954	1955	1956	1957	1958
Primary industries						
Rural and fishing	8,372	23,690	21,336	20,556	22,656	21,140
Mining	13,286	45,386	44,410	42,248	41,156	39,052
Secondary industries	31,950	83,746	91,100	100,652	115,894	123,894
Tertiary industries	40,848	108,662	119,746	129,914	138,676	150,946
Total	94,456	221,484	276,592	293,370	318,382	335,032

	1959	1960	1961	1962	1963	1964	1965
Primary industries							
Rural and fishing	23,116	23,346	24,792	25,732	24,460	28,480	22,200
Mining	34,308	38,876	37,338	37,692	33,092	37,252	39,635
Secondary industries	125,042	137,652	149,988	152,200	154,540	167,072	185,104
Tertiary industries	158,790	174,492	198,000	214,000	232,000	250,000	269,000
Total	341,256	374,366	410,118	429,092	444,092	482,804	515,939

The price of land, both rural and urban, is a major element in location patterns and growth path determination. In the study of this market phenomenon land assessment of the kind discussed is significant. As a result of our regional experience more rational public and private investment decisions to assist in increasing productivity can be made, especially where matters such as irrigation are concerned.

CONCLUSIONS

The most important conclusions to be drawn here refer to rural land use and agricultural productivity. In reaching these conclusions land evaluation as described has played an important part. To look continuously with a favourable eye on the activities of agriculturalists who are prepared to make consumption outlays when they have finance but are not always prepared to make necessary capital investments, it is necessary to place squarely before the farmer as a businessman his requirement to make calculated business investments in land and water in order to help secure his own stability and to assist in achieving the required growth rate of the nation. If he fails in his task a wage gap will open inside our own economy, between rural industry on the one hand and secondary and tertiary on the other. Such a wage gap is currently a barrier to our entry into many foreign markets. To have it further develop within our own industrial structure will place unendurable burdens on the man on the land and could unsettle governments not prepared to approach national and regional resource development on a predominantly scientific basis (Renwick 1966).

REFERENCES

ATKINSON, W. (1966). *A review of the land systems of the Hunter valley, N.S.W.* Hunter Valley Research Foundation, Newcastle.
BURLEY, T. (1963). Agricultural land use in the Hunter valley: The present situation and future prospects. *Hunter Valley Research Foundation, Newcastle, Monograph No. 16.*
COMMONWEALTH OF AUSTRALIA (1966). *Report of the Committee of Economic Enquiry.* Vols. I and II (The Vernon Report) (Government Printer: Canberra.)
HUNTER VALLEY RESEARCH FOUNDATION (1962). *River basin research.* Hunter Valley Research Foundation, Newcastle.
RENWICK, C. (1963). Fundamental concepts of river basin planning. *The Living Earth* 8, 67–71.
RENWICK, C. (1966). A water plan for the Hunter valley. *Australian Quarterly* 38, 102–7.
RENWICK, C., PATTISON, A., MCMAHON, T., and MARSH, D. (1965). *A plan for water resource development in the Hunter valley.* Hunter Valley Research Foundation, Newcastle.
RENWICK, C. et al. (in press). *The Hunter Valley Region.* (A book reviewing the regional findings of the Foundation.)
STORY, R. et al. (1963). General report on the lands of the Hunter valley. *CSIRO Aust. Land Res. Ser. No. 8.*

Methods for Estimating the Suitability of Natural Conditions at Various Stages in the Drawing up of Architectural Plans

I. Bakhtina and E. Smirnova

Faculty of Geography, Moscow State University U.S.S.R.

The essential step for assessing land for architectural planning is to determine the specific possibilities available for exploiting a given region for every individual natural complex and to undertake a comparative economic assessment of these possibilities. Such assessment should be based on an objective synthetical study of landscapes and their morphological elements.

At subsequent stages of planning assessments will vary in accordance with given requirements. As far as recreation zones are concerned architectural-aesthetic assessments assume considerable importance.

At all stages of planning comparative assessments of natural territorial complexes, from the point of view of quality, are of prime importance.

INTRODUCTION

The problem of making the most expedient use of sites is considered by landscape architects who take their decisions after making a careful study of land. Plans are drawn up by various specialists whose number invariably includes landscape geographers.

Natural conditions and resources are always studied when such plans are drawn up. In this context geological, climatic, and soil data and a variety of maps are taken into account. However, these alone do not provide an idea of the correlations existing between the various components and possible changes involved in the natural conditions, which result from the interaction between the components. The application in practice of this complex approach to the study of natural conditions, which replaces the use of a series of different data, heralds in a new stage in the development of work in this field. The synthetic approach to the study of natural conditions facilitates the drawing up of plans in a number of ways. Since such an approach reveals the essential nature of the interaction between the different components, it facilitates the forecast of trends in their future development and forestalls the degradation of natural conditions through land use.

Synthetic landscape studies have been widely adopted in recent years and investigated: they have been used for a whole range of different economic purposes: for agricultural ends, for geochemical surveys in search of industrial minerals, for the definition of laws applying to medical geography and also for the production of landscape architectural plans. For several years now the landscape geographers at the Geographical Faculty of Moscow University have been participating in the drawing up of plans under the auspices of the Institute of the General Plan for Moscow, which is being supervised by architect V. Tobilevich, and also at other architectural centres. Recently similar work has been being conducted in the Baltic Republics, Siberia, Leningrad, Kiev, Chernovtsy, and many other major towns of the Soviet Union.

Practical experience has shown the essential importance of dividing territory up into different sections, which differ fairly widely one from another as far as their natural resources and general suitability are concerned. This in turn required a consolidation of the landscape approach to the study of natural conditions. However, as yet the term 'landscape' is not interpreted in the same way by geographers and landscape architects. It must be borne in mind that the way in which this term is interpreted determines the content and the methods adopted in the research to be carried out. In research in this field the meaning attributed to this term by N. Solntsev (1949) and the methods which he used are becoming more and more widely accepted. In the research into natural conditions designed to establish the feasibility of architectural projects landscape is interpreted as a regional unit, which exhibits uniformity as regards its lithological composition, relief, and climate–a unit which consists of a number of small natural-territorial complexes. Larger units (natural regions, provinces, etc.) represent genetically linked groups of landscapes which make up an integral complex. They all make up a regularly patterned system of coordinated units which form a network of physico-geographical divisons. The term landscape implies a regional (unique) category and its component parts, both those which are identical and those which display similarities as far as their natural features and the possibilities for practical exploitation are concerned.

The three stages involved in the drawing up of landscape architectural plans all involve special methods of research and assessment of landscape: regional planning, overall planning, and detailed planning.

REGIONAL PLANNING

The first stage in this work consists of the drawing up of the regional plan. In recent years drafts of regional plans have been widely used for a broad range of terrains and they now represent an essential stage in work concerned with the organization of productive forces and the rational exploitation of natural resources. A characteristic feature of regional planning is the particularly wide range of the questions under consideration–a simultaneous assessment of natural, economic, functional, and the architectural-aesthetic potential of a given territory is required.

The aim of regional planning is the plotting of functional zones; for agriculture, residential and industrial construction, and those for recreation. This initial stage involves the assessment of the area's functional potential, i.e. a comparative assessment of the suitability of the area for different types of exploitation. The rapid growth of towns, and their contiguous suburbs, the creation of large industrial complexes, and the working of new mineral deposits all demand that large tracts of land be prepared for the deployment of large sections of the population, the rational planning of new construction projects, and the logical development of cultural landscape. In this work comparative economical estimates are of supreme importance. In order to ensure that a regional plan is economically justified it is essential that the planned exploitation of a given territory should correspond as closely as possible to its given potential.

For the assessment of the potential advantages to be gained in the exploitation of a given territory it is essential to carry out landscape research and to this end to draw up an extensive medium-scale map of the landscape types of natural environment (1 : 50,000–1 : 300,000). It is also extremely important to evolve in advance, and select methods for, charting all the necessary indices on one map with a table of symbols that is as concise as possible. The work of the architects and the landscape geographers must on no account be undertaken at the same time. Geographical research must, as a matter of course, precede the eventual collaboration with architects on construction plans.

An extensive landscape map which provides a sufficient degree of precise and clear scientific information provides an adequate basis for the distribution of the various functional landscape zones, the necessary prelude to the drawing up of construction plans.

Work on the drawing up of an extensive landscape map and the distribution of the various functional landscape zones falls into three categories. The first stage, which determines the quantity and the nature of the subsequent work required, is the collection of existing literature and cartographical material relating to the given area and the drawing up of a provisional landscape map on the basis of this material. When a topographical map is already available and likewise a series of accompanying topical maps on the required scale (i.e. lithological and stratigraphical, geomorphological, hydrogeological, geobotanical, etc.) after carrying out an on-the-spot survey of the given territory geographers will be able to draw up an extensive landscape map comparatively quickly without having to carry out much field work. The second stage, a verification of the provisional landscape map drawn up in field studies, involves research to be carried out in sample areas and along specified routes in the given territory on the required scale needed to complement the hitherto insufficient amount of assembled data. The extensive landscape map, which can then be drawn up, reflects the nature of the territory in detail, taking into account all possible types of exploitation possible under contemporary conditions. The third and most responsible stage of this work is the assessment of the extent to which the territory can be exploited and the distribution of its functional zones. At this stage of the proceedings questions of future economic development of all kinds have to be considered in conjunction with one another, the rational distribution of different types of agricultural land, industrial enterprises, and settlements, is worked out, forecasts of possible population growth are drawn up and possible migration patterns plotted. These questions are worked on jointly by landscape geographers, economic geographers, and architects. They use as a basis in their work the landscape map, which is complemented by extensive prospect maps for various types of land use.

In order to distribute agricultural areas correctly a scientifically based appraisal is indispensable at the first stage of this planning work. The economic features must justify the use of the territory for agricultural purposes. If there is no completed cadastre of land types available when the draft for the district plan is being drawn up, an assessment of the area's natural potential can be used which, in its turn, is based on the correlation between the genetic features of the various soils, the contours of the relief, the subsoil and underlying rocks, which determine the moisture condition, intensity of erosion and plant growth conditions, the possibilities for employing agricultural machinery, and many other factors. The gradation of different qualities of agricultural soil can well be carried out on the basis of material gathered in the course of landscape research, but can, under no circumstances, replace cadastral estimates which take into account and systematise all information relating to the soil's productive capacity. However, this gradation provides initial material which can be elaborated through investigation of the economic aspects of sample areas, agricultural units, and systematisation of the correlations between the types of soil to be found in different landscapes. For example, among the agricultural areas of one landscape the dominating type could be gently undulating uplands and gentle slopes (up to 4°), easily drainable with a predominance of sod-podzolic soil on loess-type loam, on an underlying layer of sand at a depth of between one to three metres, suitable for various types of agriculture and fruit orchards. Another type of landscape could exhibit a predominance of flat uplands with average drainage, with small depressions and a catena of sod-podzolic and sod-podzolic gleish soils on a moraine base and peat-gleish soils on a basis of lake and swamp clays suitable for grain crops, flax, and low-quality fodder crops. The analysis of such types of agricultural soils can, in some cases, prove useful when decisions are being taken as to the allocation of poor land to construction sites, forest plantation, or recreation purposes.

Systematic methods for the drawing up of landscape maps for use in the planning of suburbs and complementary industrial complexes (for example in the development plans for the town of Chernovtsy) were evolved by Y. Dorf-man and V. Stanishevsky in 1966. Their work is of great interest both as regards their assessment of the suburb site from landscape and town planning aspects and their forecasts of population figures in the given landscape conditions. Their methods may well be applied in distributing residential and industrial zones in other areas with the appropriate modifications. The landscape map which they propose charts three types of conditions. The first group shows the existing 'soil-forming rock' base, complete with engineering and geological details. The second shows the existing 'landscape and architectural super-structure', with a clearly marked coincidence of the types of buildings adapted to the distinct types of terrains. The third charts the existing alternatives as regards possible landscape reconstruction. Large-scale work in the fields of geographical engineering and landscape research for district plans and town planning is being carried on at the present time by Professor T. Zvonkova at Moscow State University.

LAND PLANNING FOR RECREATION

In land immediately adjacent to large towns, and even that which is at a con-siderable distance from them, the selection of areas which are to be set aside for public recreation assumes tremendous importance. In keeping with the protection of people's health and the encouragement of outdoor activity, in the context of work devoted to the rational distribution of various economic zones at the present time, a great deal of attention is devoted to the organization of recreation facilities and the assessment of landscape units for this purpose. Experience gleaned in joint landscape research by teams from the geological faculty of Moscow University led by Zhukova in 1963, Golytsin in 1967, and architects from the Institute of the General Plan for Moscow (under the general supervision of Tobilevich in 1965) make it possible to draw up some general methodological principles for landscape research prior to the drawing up of plans for recreation zones at the three stages outlined above. In drawing up drafts for district plans for the selection of areas to be used for recreation purposes assessments of three basic types are required: assessments of the natural, functional, and aesthetic qualities of the given landscape. Each type of assessment should be made separately complete with its separate graduated scale for estimating with different numbers of points, the suitability of the particular territory for a recreation zone. Three diagrams should be drawn up to demonstrate the estimated quality of the natural, aesthetic, and functional aspects of the landscape units. Comparison of these diagrams makes it possible to work out the overall suitability of the given territory for a recreation zone, bearing in mind the interrelation of these various characteristics.

Natural qualities of a landscape are determined by the features of its morphological structure, the formation of its surface, the natural vegetation, the presence of reservoirs, and so on. The combination of these features in turn determines the particular character of the landscape and the various forms of its impact on man. The natural features determine first and foremost its potential as a recreation zone and are both of a direct and indirect health significance. This potential is determined by the surface contours (which in their turn determine the extent to which transport can be used), the properties of the surface rocks (which determine the degree of moisture and quality of the soil), the nature of the vegetation, and the size of the reservoirs (which bring to bear upon the micro-climate).

The assessment of aesthetic characteristics of landscape is bound up with the position of objects in relation to space and the picking out of the best spots for the appreciation of picturesque scenery. Aesthetic (spatial) aspects of a landscape depend on the various proportions of volumes to spaces between them, created by the combination of landscape contours, woodland, and buildings. The extent of open vistas determines the quality of broad-scale panoramas and should be assessed at various levels within the given area. At medium contour the 'view', the 'scenery', or the 'one-dimensional panorama' should be assessed from one or two small territorial units. From the highest vantage points multi-dimensional views and distant vistas of the landscape as a whole can be assessed.

The definition of a landscape's functional qualities for the organization of recreation facilities involves the assessment of the suitability of the given area for outdoor recreation on land and water (for walks and various types of sport, etc.), and for the construction of buildings providing recreation facilities. The best suited spots for zones of this sort are those where people can go in for the widest range of sports and types of recreation.

A general assessment of the possible recreation facilities which can be laid on in a particular zone is drawn up on the basis of a synthetical analysis of the qualities of the given territory and the definition of which parts of a given territory are the best suited in all respects. These then should be subdivided into those sections which are particularly valuable from an aesthetic or a scientific point of view which should then be preserved in their original state and organised as national parks. Such sections should be set apart from those which are deemed as suitable for recreation purposes since the presence of large numbers of people involves the risk of damage to unique natural treasures.

The above-mentioned methods applied by architect Bakhtina, using as a basis the landscape research carried out by geographers from Moscow State University, are of particularly positive significance since they are based on objective criteria. However, some of these methods are unnecessarily time consuming. Closer collaboration between geographers and architects would facilitate the elaboration of a unified scale of assessment criteria, the immediate determination of natural territorial complexes best suited for the organization of recreation zones both as far as natural conditions are concerned and bearing in mind aesthetic and functional factors.

At the second stage of planning, namely when plans are drawn up for areas which have already been singled out for some set purpose, a more detailed assessment is undertaken with regard to those qualities particularly important for a landscape of the given kind, complete with indices recording the individual characteristics of subsidiary landscape units on a scale between 1 : 10,000 and 1 : 25,000. At this stage, when the basic principles of the organization of architectural planning are being worked out, in addition to the assessment of the area's natural potential and the existing natural conditions, possibilities for necessary reorganization are also noted, such as the changes in relief contours in conjunction with the exploitation of local resources, reconstruction of vegetation distribution, the creation of new reservoirs. For this it is essential to carry out field research in sample areas and along specified routes for the drawing up, not only of landscape maps, but also for various topical maps and complementary diagrams. By this stage landscape maps are used not only for assessment but also for prognosis purposes. For example, the structure of a landscape predetermines, in the planning of recreation zones, both capacity and the extreme limits of the numbers for which the given zone can cater. When construction plans are drawn up a detailed study is made of the soil, where the foundations are to be laid, and also of the whole combination of natural conditions and the influence of all the various features of the landscape.

DETAILED PLANNING

At the detailed planning stage assessment and recommendations are elaborated for individual projects, for example, for individual sections of woodlands, depressions, stream valleys, slopes, etc., selective descriptions are made not only of small territorial units but also of their several subdivisions. A large-scale landscape map (1 : 2,000–1 : 10,000) is drawn up on the basis of an overall field landscape diagram. On the landscape map in addition to the natural complexes, details of processes which alter the face of the landscape are also marked in through signs and lines, such as the intensity of erosion, the development of landslides, karst phenomena, flooding, the abrasion of river banks, etc. At this stage it is particularly important to make use of a large range of additional complementary diagrams, for example diagrams of spatial structure which mark in open, half open, obstructed or partly obstructed areas, which are measured with the help of numerical indices and represent a decisive factor in the choice of construction sites.

At the third stage of planning recreation zones, the architectural–aesthetic qualities of a given region assume supreme importance, namely those features of a landscape which, as opposed to purely objective features of a landscape, are interpreted to a certain extent on a subjective basis. Architectural and aesthetic analyses of a given area are based on a whole series of observations, sketches and photographs taken at different times of the day and year. These analyses also depend on the place where the individual happens to be standing and his appreciation of the given landscape.

The first stage of architectural-aesthetic assessment consists in picking out the so-called 'architectural-landscape districts', that is, districts which produce different visual impacts. The basic feature or central focus of an architectural-landscape district may be a reservoir, flood-plains of big rivers, open spaces, stretches of woodland, etc. In districts where this central focus is a reservoir it will be noted that it is the reservoir which plays the decisive role in determining the overall impression produced by the given area. If, on the other hand, it is the banks or flood-plains of a river, the riverside vegetation, the relief and width of the flood-plains, the course of the river bed, and the nature of the terraces, will be the decisive features. All these features considered together create a complicated system of alternating spaces with varying local emphasis.

In landscapes where the central feature is an open space, the impression produced by the landscape as a whole will be determined by the relief of that open
space and other natural features. As far as woodland is concerned the decisive
features are the type of woodland, the type and age of the trees, and the correlation between the different clearings and the way they alternate with layers of
trees of varying thickness.

The second stage involves the picking out of the various elements that go
to make up the architectural-landscape zones and establishing how they will
appear to members of the public walking through these zones from all the
main angles. Distinctions are drawn between predominant, background, intermediate, and other elements. In connection with the aim of reaching synthetical
appreciation of the natural complex the above-mentioned elements can be
modified so that some stand out more while others are partly or completely
concealed from view.

The next stage involves the picking out of individual points and sites. The
most valuable are considered those which open on to multi-dimensional long-
distance panoramas: reservoirs, river valleys, groups of moraine hills, etc.,
river banks of varying steepness, groves, wood clearings framed with trees in
the distance which provide a backcloth for meandering rivers, the winding
beds of which are emphasised by the tops of willow trees. Distant ploughed
hills are divided up by patches of woodland. All these elements of landscape
are analysed and can be supplemented by groups of plantations and buildings.

The final stage consists in the working out of optimal routes for pedestrians,
cars, and water traffic. These routes are worked out by comparing a whole
range of routes that have been tried out at different times of the day and year.
The most interesting and those which provide the richest selection of visual
impressions are selected. The optimal routes, the best vantage points and sites
as far as views are concerned are marked out on diagrams used for architectural-
aesthetic analysis and the planned architectural-landscape districts. In this way
the most advantageous areas, from an aesthetic point of view, are picked out,
in which views of diverse natural scenery are provided on as wide a scale as
possible.

On the basis of such architectural-aesthetic analyses, carried out by architects,
decisions are then taken as to what features should be emphasised, changed, or
removed. How to achieve this is then decided by geographers on the basis of
objective landscape analysis of each natural complex.

CONCLUSION

In conclusion, it is important to note that in methods for estimating natural
conditions for drafting architectural plans, the essential step is to determine
the specific possibilities available for exploiting a given region for every individual
natural complex and to undertake a comparative economic assessment of these
possibilities. Such assessments should be based on an objective synthetical study
of landscapes and their morphological elements, which is of decisive importance
in the first stage of planning–regional planning and the rational distribution of
functional zones.

At subsequent stages of planning assessments will vary in accordance with
given requirements. As far as recreation zones are concerned, architectural-
aesthetic assessments assume considerable importance at this stage and with
regard to construction sites this is true of engineering geographical criteria.

At all stages of planning work where maximum use is made of quantitative methods in keeping with the enormous variety and quantity of factors to be taken into account, comparative assessments of natural territorial complexes, from the point of view of quality, are of prime importance; likewise, methods involving the simultaneous synthetical plotting of a variety of assessments on one and the same map which facilitates comparison of alternative draft plans.

The principles used in landscape research which are described in this paper are being adopted on an increasingly wide scale in the drawing up of large-scale architectural plans in the U.S.S.R.

REFERENCES

DORFMAN, Y. P., and STANISHEVSKY, V. A. (1966). An attempt to draw up landscape-town planning maps. *Second Scientific and Technical Cartographical Conference.* Lecture thesis. The Soviet Geographical Society Publishers: Leningrad.

GOLYTSIN, G. V., KAMYSHOVA, N. P., KUTEPOVA, L. T., and SMIRNOVA, E. D. (1967). *An attempt to draw up landscape maps to be used as a basis for the drawing up of architectural plans for the suburbs of large towns.* 'Nauka' Publishers: Leningrad.

ISACHENKO, A. G. (1966). Landscape science, architecture, and the organization of suburb sites. *Information VGO. (All Union Geographical Society)* vol. 98, 5th issue.

SOLNTSEV, N. A. (1949). On the morphology of natural geographical landscapes. *Questions of Geography* — Collection No. 16.

STOICHEV, L. I. (1963). *Some problems of district division and the classification of landscapes.* Moscow State University Publishers.

TOBILEVICH, B. P. (1963). *Physico-geographical district divisions in the Nechernozemny centre.* (Ed. N. A. Gvozdetsky and V. K. Zhuchkova.) Moscow University Publishers.

TOBILEVICH, B. P. (1965). The recreation zone at Klyazma reservoir. *The construction and architecture of Moscow.* No. 8.

ZHUKOVA, V. K. (1963). Landscapes in the wood and park belt of Moscow and the possibilities for using them in the organization of recreation facilities for the working people.

Automated Picture Interpretation

Azriel Rosenfeld

University of Maryland, College Park, Maryland, U.S.A.

This paper reviews some of the techniques which can be used to automatically classify and describe pictorial patterns. It outlines the general approach to pattern classification, and discusses representative 'preprocessing' and 'property measurement' methods, with emphasis on methods which may be useful in processing pictures of terrain. [The decision-making aspect of pattern recognition is not discussed.] Techniques for subdividing pictures into regions, and describing geometrical properties of such regions, are also considered. The paper is intended to serve as an introduction to the extensive literature in this field; it includes numerous references to this literature.

I. INTRODUCTION

The field of automatic pictorial pattern recognition is now nearly 15 years old. Workers in this field have dealt with a wide variety of classes of pictures, notably alphanumerical characters, biomedical photomicrographs, nuclear bubble chamber pictures, and aerial photographs. Regrettably, there is probably the least literature on this last class. [For a recent volume containing a number of papers in this area see *Pictorial Pattern Recognition* (Proceedings of the Symposium on Automatic Photointerpretation, Washington, D.C., 1967) Thompson, Washington, D.C., 1968.]

This paper reviews the pictorial pattern recognition field, with emphasis on techniques applicable to pictures of terrain. There is no 'standard' approach to automatic pattern recognition; each individual problem usually requires special methods of solution. This review therefore presents selected ideas, on a general level rather than from a problem-oriented standpoint, to give an indication of the tools available to workers in this field. Basic concepts are briefly described, in non-mathematical language where possible. References to the published literature are given; these should be consulted for further details.

2. PATTERN CLASSIFICATION

The general problem of automatic picture interpretation can be posed as follows: Given a picture, to generate a *description* of it, consisting of a set of statements about the picture in some appropriate language. Very little work has been done on this general level. The case normally treated is that in which one only needs to *classify* the picture into one of a set of prespecified categories. For example, in the case of an aerial photograph which shows only a single type of terrain the categories might be terrain types (or crop types, or tree cover types, etc.). Even if the photograph shows a diversity of regions, one might still only need to decide whether or not some particular phenomenon was present.

The process of automatic picture classification is usually carried out in several steps:

(a) Preprocessing. The given picture is transformed into one or more new pictures by performing various operations on it.

(b) Property measurement ('feature extraction'). A set of 'property functions' is applied, typically resulting in a set of real numbers $P_1, \ldots, P_m$ which can be regarded as properties of the original picture.

(c) Decision. The measured P's are compared with stored information about the classes. For example, if the classes $C_1, \ldots, C_n$ are represented by prototypes ('standard examples') for which the values of the properties are $P_{11}, \ldots, P_{m1}$; $P_{12}, \ldots, P_{m2}$; $P_{1n}, \ldots, P_{mn}$, then one might assign the picture having the measured property $P_1, \ldots, P_n$ to that class whose prototype has P_{ij}'s 'closest' to the P_i's.

In particular, if one knows the probability distribution of the values of the P_i's given that the picture is from the jth class, one can use Bayes' Theorem to determine the class to which a given set of P_i's most probably belongs.

There is an extensive literature on step (c), classification on the basis of a given set of properties. Since this is not a problem specific to *picture* classification, it will not be dealt with further here. [For a brief recent introduction to this area see C. A. Rosen, 'Pattern classification by adaptive machines', *Science, N. Y.* **156**, 1967, 38–44.] In the remaining sections of this paper we deal only with steps (a–b), preprocessing and property measurement. In what follows, we assume that a picture is a *function* f(x,y) defined on the plane; we usually assume that f(x,y) = 0 outside a finite region, often taken to be the unit square $0 \leqslant x \leqslant 1, 0 \leqslant y \leqslant 1$. The value of f at (x,y) should be thought of as measuring the 'gray level' (or 'density') of the picture at the point (x,y).

3. PREPROCESSING

(a) Uniform Operations on Pictures

Most of the operations which are performed on pictures for 'preprocessing' purposes are *uniform operations*—in other words, their effect does not depend on position within the picture.

More precisely, the operation F is uniform if it *commutes with the translations* —that is, if translating the picture by an arbitrary amount and then applying F produces the same result as applying F and then translating. (Another term for 'uniform' is 'space-invariant'.) An important type of uniform operation is a *local operation*, for which the value of the resulting picture at any point (x,y) depends only on the values of the original picture in a neighborhood of (x,y).

The operation F is called *linear* if

$$F(af+bg) = aF(f)+bF(g)$$

for all pictures f,g and all real numbers a,b. It can be shown that F is linear if and only if there exists a function g(x,y) such that

$$(F(f))(x,y) = \int_{-\infty}^{\infty} \int_{-\infty}^{\infty} g(x-u,y-v)\, f(u,v)\, dudv$$

In words: F(f) is the *convolution* of g with f. [From now on we shall abbreviate the convolution of g with f by $g*f$. In optics, g is called the *point spread function* of F; it is the two-dimensional analog of the *impulse response* in electrical engineering.]

The fact that any uniform linear operation is a convolution makes it possible to perform such operations in a particularly simple way using *Fourier transforms*. It can be shown that *the convolution of two functions is equal to the inverse Fourier transform of the product of their Fourier transforms*. It follows that one can convolve two functions by taking their Fourier transforms, multiplying them, and taking the inverse Fourier transform of the result. With the recent development of efficient algorithms for computing the Fourier transform, this procedure can actually be faster than convolving the functions directly.

Convolutions of pictures can be 'computed' optically in especially simple ways. On such implementations see D. McLachlan, Jr., 'The role of optics in applying correlation functions to pattern recognition', *J. opt. Soc. Am.* **52**, 1962, 454–59; J. K. Hawkins and C. J. Munsey, 'A natural image computer', *Optical Processing of Information*, Spartan 1963, 233–45; 'A parallel computer organization and mechanizations', *I.E.E.E. Trans.* *EC*-**12**, 1963, 251–62; 'Automatic photo reading', *Photogramm. Engng* **29**, 1963, 632–40; 'Eulogismographic nonlinear optical image processing for pattern recognition', *J. opt. Soc. Am.* **54**, 1964, 998–1003; 'Photographic techniques for extracting image shapes', *Photogr. Sci. Engng* **8**, 1964, 329–35; 'Image processing by optical techniques', *J. opt. Soc. Am.* **57**, 1967, 914–18; P. L. Jackson, 'Correlation function spatial filtering with incoherent light', *Appl. Opt.* **6**, 1967, 1272–3. Optical methods can even be used to convolve functions which are not necessarily nonnegative. For some interesting methods of doing this see D. H. Kelly, 'Image-processing experiments', *J. opt. Soc. Am.* **51**, 1961, 1095–101; A. B. Clarke, 'A photographic edge-isolation technique', *Photogramm. Engng* **28**, 1962, 393–9; E. A. Trabka and P. G. Roetling, 'Image transformations for pattern recognition using incoherent illumination and bipolar aperture masks', *J. opt. Soc. Am.* **54**, 1964, 1242–52.

Fourier transforms can also be 'computed' optically. See E. L. O'Neill, 'Spatial filtering in optics', *I.R.E. Trans.* *IT*-**2**, 1956, 56–65; G. F. Aroyan, 'The technique of spatial filtering', *Proc. I.R.E.* **47**, 1959, 1561–3; L. J. Cutrona *et al.*, 'Optical data processing and filtering systems', *I.R.E. Trans.* *IT*-**6**, 1960, 386–400; A. vander Lugt, 'Signal detection by complex spatial filtering', *I.E.E.E. Trans.* *IT*-**10**, 1964, 139–45; A. Kozma and D. L. Kelly, 'Spatial filtering for detection of signals submerged in noise', *Appl. Opt.* **4**, 1965, 387–92; B. R. Brown and A. W. Lohmann, 'Complex spatial filtering with binary masks', *Appl. Opt.* **5**, 1966, 967–9; T. M. Holladay and J. D. Gallatin, 'Phase control by polarization in coherent spatial filtering', *J. opt. Soc. Am.* **56**, 1966, 869–72; C. S. Weaver and J. W. Goodman, 'A technique for optically convolving two functions', *Appl. Opt.* **5**, 1966, 1248–9; J. E. Rau, 'Detection of differences in real distributions', *Appl. Opt.* **5**, 1966, 1490–4; as well as a number of papers in *Optical Processing of Information*, Spartan, Washington, D.C., 1963, and *Optical and Electro-Optical Information Processing*, M.I.T. Press, 1965.

Uniform operations can be performed on a picture very rapidly using a suitable special-purpose computer. On this approach see S. H. Unger, 'A computer oriented toward spatial problems', *Proc. I.R.E.* **46**, 1958, 1744–50; 'Pattern detection and recognition', *ibid.* **47**, 1959, 1737–52; L. A. Kamentsky, 'Pattern and character recognition systems—picture processing by nets of neuron-like elements', *Proc. Western Joint Comp. Conf.*, March 1959, 304–9; B. H. McCormick, 'The Illinois Pattern Recognition Computer—ILLIAC III', *I.E.E.E. Trans.* *EC*-**12**, 1963, 791–813; see also S. S. Yau and C. C. Yang, 'Pattern recognition using an associative memory', *I.E.E.E. Trans.* *EC*-**15**, 1966, 944–7. Special 'languages' designed to facilitate picture processing on conventional computers have also been developed. See R. Narasimhan, 'Labelling schemata and syntactic descriptions of pictures', *Inf. Control* **7**, 1964, 151–79, and 'Syntax-directed interpretation of classes of pictures', *Communs Ass. comput. Mach.* **9**, 1966, 166–73; and the papers by G. A. Moore and by J. L. Pfaltz *et al.* in *Pictorial Pattern Recognition*, Thompson, Washington, D.C., 1968.

(b) *Applications, 1: Matched filtering ('template matching')*

One often needs to determine how well two pictures 'match' each other, or to find a part of a picture which 'matches' a given picture. This problem can arise in pictorial pattern recognition situations where the 'patterns' are highly standardized (e.g., images of very specific objects). It also arises in such applications as automatic stereogrammetry, where the two images of the same point on a stereopair of pictures must be identified so that the parallax at that point can be measured.

For a brief historical review of the latter subject see G. L. Hobrough, 'Automation in photogrammetric instruments', *Photogramm. Engng* **31**, 1965, 595–603. One can also consider the converse question of detecting *differences* between two pictures, e.g., of the same scene taken at two different times. Even if the two pictures can be put into perfect registration, this problem of automatic 'change detection' can still be nontrivial if one wants to detect only *significant* changes, as opposed to 'changes' due to noise, differences in exposure, shadows, etc.

The most commonly used method of 'matching' two pictures f and g is based on the *Schwarz inequality*, which states that

$$\iint_R fg \leqslant \sqrt{\iint_R f^2 \iint_R g^2}$$

over any domain of integration R, with equality holding if and only if $g = cf$ for some nonnegative constant c. In particular, it follows that

$$\frac{\iint_R f(u,v)\, g(u+x, v+y)\, dudv}{\sqrt{\iint_R f^2(u,v)\, dudv}\, \sqrt{\iint_R g^2(u+x, v+y)\, dudv}} \leqslant 1 \qquad (*)$$

and $= 1$ if and only if $g(u,v) = cf(u-x, v-y)$ for some c—in other words, if and only if g exactly matches f over the region R, up to a multiplicative constant, after shifting by (x,y).

The numerator of (*) is called the *cross-correlation* of f and g; we shall denote it by $f \otimes g$. Let $\bar{g}$ be the function obtained from g by reflection in the origin, i.e., $\bar{g}(x,y) = g(-x,-y)$; then readily $f \otimes g = f * \bar{g}$, the convolution of f and $\bar{g}$. Note that the second integral in the denominator of (*) can be thought of as the cross-correlation of the 'characteristic function of R' (a function which has the value 1 in R, 0 outside R) with g; while the first integral in the denominator is a constant. Thus to 'find the pattern f in the picture g,' one can compute these cross-correlations and divide. [Under some circumstances one can regard the entire denominator as approximately constant, so that division is unnecessary.] It can be shown that even if the copy of f which is present in g is degraded by additive noise, f is still the best 'template' to cross-correlate with g in order to find the noisy f. These results are a two-dimensional analog of the theory of 'matched filters' in electrical engineering. For further discussion of two-dimensional matched filtering see W. D. Montgomery and P. W. Broome, 'Spatial filtering', *J. opt. Soc. Am.* **52**, 1962, 1259–75; J. L. Harris, 'Resolving power and decision theory', *J. opt. Soc. Am.* **54**, 1964, 606–11.

(c) *Applications, 2: Spatial frequency filtering*

As pointed out above, one can cross-correlate a template with a picture by multiplying their Fourier transforms and taking the inverse Fourier transform of the product. One of the chief advantages of this approach is that many useful preprocessing operations can be performed on a picture by performing very simple operations on its Fourier transform. This is because the values of the transform are the *spatial frequency* components of the original picture. Thus, for example, if one suppresses the part of the transform near the origin (i.e., multiplies the transform by a function which is 0 in a neighbourhood of the origin and 1 elsewhere), and then takes the inverse transform, the result tends to 'wash out' the 'smooth' regions on the picture while preserving the fine detail, since high spatial frequencies are preserved while low ones are deleted. Conversely, suppressing everything but a neighbourhood of the origin on the transform—in other words, preserving only the low spatial frequencies—has the effect of 'blurring' the picture, leaving smooth regions intact but degrading the detail. If the frequencies in an angular sector are suppressed, 'edges' on the picture in the direction perpendicular to the sector will be blurred, while edges parallel to that direction will be preserved. Periodic patterns superimposed on a picture (halftone dots, TV raster lines, etc.) can be largely suppressed by deleting selected spatial frequencies.

(d) Applications, 3: 'Smoothing' and 'sharpening'

One often wants to 'smooth' a picture in order to suppress noise which may be present in it, or to 'sharpen' it in order to reduce blur. As just pointed out, this can be done by 'low-pass' or 'high-pass' spatial frequency filtering; in the following paragraphs we briefly consider a number of other methods.

(1) Averaging—One can 'smooth' a picture by simply replacing its value at each point by the average—or more generally, by a weighted average—of its values over a neighborhood of the point. [This is a uniform linear operation; in fact, it is the convolution of the picture with a function representing the pattern of weights.] To prevent this operation from blurring 'edges', one can (e.g.) test for the presence of edges, and average only at points where edges are not present; this procedure is in general nonlinear. [On it, see R. E. Graham, 'Snow removal —a noise stripping process for picture signals', *I.E.E.E. Trans. IT*-**8**, 1962, 129–44.]

(2) 'Image restoration'—Suppose that a picture has been obtained via some imaging or transmission process which has degraded it. If the degradation process can be mathematically inverted, it is possible in principle to undo its effects and 'restore' the picture to an undegraded state. For example, suppose that the process is a uniform linear operation, so that the degraded picture is of the form f*g, where f is the undegraded picture. Then one can take the Fourier transform of f*g to obtain FG, the product of the Fourier transforms of f and g; divide by G; and take the inverse Fourier transform to obtain f. [Unfortunately, in practice the degradation is rarely given by a uniform linear operation, so that this procedure will not work perfectly.] For a good introduction to these concepts see J. L. Harris, 'Image evaluation and restoration', *J. opt. Soc. Am.* **56**, 1966, 569–74.

(3) The gradient and Laplacian—Since integration (=averaging) 'smooths' a picture, a natural approach to 'sharpening' is to perform some sort of *differentiation* operation. One such operation computes the directional derivative of the picture in the gradient direction at each point, i.e., the direction in which the gray level of the picture is changing fastest. Readily, the square of this derivative is given by

$$f_g^2 = f_x^2 + f_y^2$$

where f_x and f_y are the partial derivatives in the x and y directions. Another combination of derivatives which is of particular interest is the Laplacian

$$f_{xx} + f_{yy}$$

[On these operations and their applications see L. S. G. Kovasznay and H. M. Joseph, 'Image processing', *Proc. I.R.E.* **43**, 1955, 560–70; see also G. P. Dinneen, 'Programming pattern recognition', *Proc. Western Joint Comp. Conf.*, May 1955, 94–100, and J. D. Armitage *et al.*, 'Absolute contrast enhancement', *Appl. Opt.* **4**, 1965, 445–51.]

The Laplacian operation is essentially equivalent to a standard photographic technique known as 'unsharp masking'; in fact, it readily amounts to subtracting the picture f from a blurred copy f of itself. Neurons which perform Laplacian-like operations have been found in the visual systems of a number of animals. One can also use non-linear 'sharpening' methods involving the comparison of a blurred picture with the original. For example, let $\bar{\sigma}$ be the standard deviation of $\bar{f}$; then one could use $(\bar{f}-f)/\bar{\sigma}$ (rather than just $\bar{f}-f$) to 'sharpen' f. On operations of this type see W. S. Holmes *et al.*, 'Design of a photo interpretation automaton', *Proc. Eastern Joint Comp. Conf.*, December 1962, 27–35; 'Automatic photointerpretation and target location', *Proc. I.E.E.E.* **54**, 1966, 1679–86.

'Edges' in a particular direction can be emphasized by taking a derivative in the orthogonal direction—or, as a discrete approximation, taking the difference between the averages of f over two neighboring regions. [Neurons which perform such discrete operations have been found in the visual systems of certain mammals.] Alternatively, one can compare the frequency distributions (call them D_1 and D_2) of gray levels in the two regions, e.g., by computing $\int |D_1-D_2|$; see J. L. Muerle and D. C. Allen, 'Techniques for automatic segmentation of objects in a complex scene', *Pictorial Pattern Recognition*, Thompson, Washington, D.C., 1968.

4. PICTURE PROPERTIES

In discussing properties of pictures which can be used for automatic pattern recognition, it is convenient to distinguish between properties which can be defined directly for an arbitrary picture, and those which are meaningful only if a special subset of the picture (a 'figure') has been singled out. For example, one would not speak about the size or shape of a picture, since all pictures are defined on the unit square; one would only speak of the size and shape of a figure in the picture. Properties of figures will be discussed in Section 5; in this section we will be primarily concerned with picture properties which have natural definitions even if no figure is specified.

(a) Property Selection

Given a set of properties P_i, there are various ways of evaluating the contribution which each P_i makes to the classification decision. [See, e.g., P. M. Lewis, II, 'The characteristic selection problem in recognition systems', *I.R.E. Trans. IT*-**8**, 1962, 171–8; T. Marill and D. M. Green, 'On the effectiveness of receptors in recognition systems', *I.E.E.E. Trans. IT*-**9**, 1963, 11–17.] Many of the pattern recognition systems which 'learn' (that is, which can be 'trained' to make correct classifications) allow for modification of the properties which they use. However, there is no universal way of initially selecting properties appropriate to a given classification problem; this selection is up to the designer of the pattern recognition system.

In practice, properties are often selected on the basis of their mathematical simplicity or ease of implementation; sometimes they are chosen to simulate processes which are believed to occur in the visual systems of organisms. The soundest basis for property selection would be to formulate mathematical descriptions of the classes to which the patterns have to be assigned. For example, if all the patterns in a given class can be obtained by adding noise to an ideal ('prototype') pattern, the 'template match' with the prototype is in a sense an optimum property, as remarked in Section 3. [On the more general case in which each pattern is a union of given subpatterns see H. D. Block *et al.*, 'Determination and detection of features in patterns', *Computer and Information Sciences*, Spartan, Washington, D.C., 1964, 75–110.] Such complete class descriptions are rarely available, but partial descriptions can usually be formulated. For example, if a picture is known in advance to contain 'line-like' objects, certain types of properties (and preprocessing operations) are evidently more appropriate than others. Ideally, one might attempt to formulate descriptions of pattern classes using models for the classes of real objects which they represent; but such models are rarely detailed enough to provide adequate descriptions.

In many cases, two patterns always belong to the same class if they can be obtained from one another by a simple geometrical transformation (translation, rotation, scale change, etc.) or a simple transformation of the gray scale. Thus a partial description of the classes is provided by the fact that they are *invariant* under such transformations. In these situations it is evidently desirable to use properties which are also transformation-invariant. Such properties can be obtained in a number of ways:

1. For certain sets of transformations, invariants can be defined mathematically. [See, e.g., the references under (b) below on moment invariants; see also R. F. Meyer *et al.* 'Analytical approximation and translational invariance in character recognition', *Optical Character Recognition*, Spartan, Washington, D.C., 1962, 181–95.]

2. It is sometimes possible to define a procedure for 'normalizing' a pattern, such that patterns which differ only by a transformation in the given set will have identical 'normalized' forms. Examples:

(a) To normalize a pattern with respect to translation and rotation, the pattern can be translated so that its centroid is at the origin of the coordinate system, and rotated so that its principal axis of inertia lies along the x axis.

(b) The *autocorrelation* of a picture (i.e., its cross-correlation with itself) is easily shown to be the same for all pictures which differ only by translation. [See L. P. Horwitz and G. L. Shelton, Jr., 'Pattern recognition using autocorrelation', *Proc. I.R.E.* **49**, 1961, 175–85; R. Y. Kain, 'Autocorrelation pattern recognition', *ibid.*, 1085–6. See also M. B. Clowes, 'The use of multiple autocorrelation in character recognition', *Optical Character Recognition*, Spartan, Washington, D.C., 1962, 305–18, and D. N. Buell, 'Chrysler optical processing scanner', *Proc. Eastern Joint Comp. Conf.*, 1961, 352–70. There is evidence that certain insect eyes compute the autocorrelation of the visual field. On analogous methods of obtaining rotation or scale invariance see W. Doyle, 'Operations useful for similarity-invariant pattern recognition', *J. Ass. comput. Mach.* **9**, 1962, 259–67. One can similarly use the Fourier transform of the autocorrelation; see, e.g., J. D. Armitage and A. W. Lohmann, 'Character recognition by incoherent spatial filtering', *Appl. Opt.* **4**, 1965, 461–7.]

(c) If the transformations are linear and form a group, a pattern can be converted into an invariant form by (e.g.) applying all the transformations to it and taking the sum (or average) of the results. [See W. Pitts and W. S. McCullock,

'How we know universals—the perception of auditory and visual forms,' *Bull. math. Biophys.* **9**, 1947, 127–47.]

Evidently, if a pattern is normalized before its properties are measured, all patterns which differ only by one of the transformations will be classified in the same way, since they will have identical properties.

3. In some cases it is not impractical to apply 'all' of the transformations to any given pattern and to measure the properties for each of the transformed patterns. For example, when we cross-correlate a template with a picture (which is very easy to do optically) we are matching it with the picture in every possible position. One can then define 'invariant' properties by, e.g., taking the average (compare (2c) just above), the maximum, etc. of these measured values.

(b) Classes of Properties

Only a few of the many possible types of picture properties have been used for pattern recognition purposes. By a property of a picture we mean here a real number which is the result of some measurement made on the picture, or on some transformed picture which is the result of applying one or more 'pre-processing' operations to the original picture. [As already pointed out, pre-processing can be used to 'clean up' or simplify the original picture (smooth it, sharpen it, convert it from grayscale to binary form) or to normalize it. One can also use preprocessing to convert a picture into a form in which very easily computed properties yield useful information which would have been difficult to obtain directly. The Fourier transform has often been used for this purpose; see e.g., G. G. Lendaris and G. L. Stanley, 'An opticalogical self-organizing recognition system', *Optical and Electro-Optical Information Processing*, M.I.T. Press, 1965, 535–50; R. H. Brody and J. R. Ermlich, 'Fourier analysis of aerial photographs', *Proc. 4th Symp. on Remote Sensing of Environment*, April 1966, 375–92; R. H. Asendorf, 'The remote reconnaissance of extraterrestrial environments', *Pictorial Pattern Recognition*, Thompson, Washington, D.C., 1968.]

One can also consider 'properties' which are functions (of one parameter) rather than single numbers. For example, one can integrate the given picture over each of a one-parameter family of curves. In the case where the curves are all parallel lines, this is equivalent to 'collapsing' the picture onto a line perpendicular to the family of lines. [See, e.g., C. C. Heasly, Jr., 'Some communication aspects of character sensing systems', *Proc. Western Joint Comp. Conf.*, 1959, 176–80; W. E. Dickinson, 'A character-recognition study', *IBM Jl Res. Dev.* **4**, 1960, 335–48; W. T. Booth *et al.*, 'Design considerations for stylized-font character readers', *Optical Character Recognition*, Spartan, Washington, D.C., 1962, 115–28. A process of 'collapsing' onto the x and y axes is believed to play a major role in the discrimination of visual patterns by the octopus.] Similarly, one can use families of radial lines, concentric circles, and so on. [See, e.g., D. J. Innes, 'FILTER—a topological pattern separation computer program', *Proc. Eastern Joint Comp. Conf.*, December 1960, 25–37; M. R. Uffelman, 'Target recognition, prenormalization, and learning machines', *Pictorial Pattern Recognition*, Thompson, Washington, D.C., 1968.] One can compute such functions on a transformed picture rather than on the original picture; see, e.g., G. R. Tenery, 'Information flow in a Bionics image-recognition system', *Models for the Perception of Speech and Visual Form*, M.I.T. Press, 1967, 403–8.

(1) Local properties and 'textural properties'—The value of a property often does not depend on the entire picture, but only on a part of it. In particular, a property may be 'local' in the sense that the part is 'small'. A local property computed over a specific part of a picture is certainly not invariant under

translation, and so will usually be useful only in classifying that part. On the other hand, the *frequency distribution* of values of such a property is translation-invariant, and so are the statistics of this distribution. We shall call statistics of local properties 'textural properties'. Such properties have been used in a number of automatic terrain analysis studies; see, e.g., the papers by Gerdes and by Darling and Joseph in *Pictorial Pattern Recognition*, Thompson, Washington, D.C., 1968, as well as A. Rosenfeld, 'Automatic recognition of basic terrain types on aerial photographs', *Photogramm. Engng* **28**, 1962, 115–32, and A. Rosenfeld and A. Goldstein, 'Optical correlation for terrain type discrimination', *Photogramm. Engng* **30**, 1964, 639–46.

(*2*) *Linear properties*—Just as any uniform linear operation is a convolution, so it can be shown that any linear property is a 'template match'. In situations where the patterns to be classified are highly standardized (e.g., prototype plus noise) and can be normalized in position and orientation, it can be practical to use templates representing entire patterns as properties; more generally, one can use templates representing subpatterns. [To make template properties somewhat insensitive to position, one can 'blur' the picture before applying the template; see D. O. Clayden *et al.*, 'Letter recognition and the segmentation of running text', *Inf. Control* **9**, 1966, 246–64.] Another important class of linear properties are those in which the 'templates' are mathematically simple functions (e.g., polynomials, sinusoids, etc.). [For example, if the templates are the monomials $x^i y^j$, the properties are the *moments* of the picture. See (a) M. K. Hu, 'Pattern recognition by moment invariants', *Proc. I.R.E.* **49**, 1961, 1428; 'A mathematical model for visual perception', *Biological Prototypes and Synthetic Systems*, Plenum, 1962, 222–9; 'Visual pattern recognition by moment invariants', *I.R.E. Trans.* IT-**8**, 1962, 179–87. (b) V. E. Giuliano *et al.*, 'Automatic pattern recognition by a Gestalt method', *Inf. Control* **4**, 1961, 332–45; (c) F. L. Alt, 'Digital pattern recognition by moments', *Optical Character Recognition*, Spartan, Washington, D.C., 1962, 153–79; *J. Ass. comput. Mach.* **9**, 1962, 240–58. (d) S. Moskowitz, 'Terminal guidance by pattern recognition—a new approach', *I.E.E.E. Trans. ANE*-**11**, 1964, 254–65. Moments of the auto-correlation of a picture can also be used as properties; see Y. H. Katz, 'Pattern recognition of meteorological satellite cloud photography', *Proc. 3rd Symp. on Remote Sensing of Environment*, October 1964, 173–214.]

(*3*) *Random properties*—Many 'learning machine' pattern recognition systems employ properties which are defined randomly, e.g., by generating a random function and using it as a template. [In the 'simple Perceptron', each 'A-unit' computes a different property of this type. On Perceptrons see F. Rosenblatt *Principles of Neurodynamics*, Spartan, Washington, D.C., 1962.] One can also use properties which are not completely random, but which satisfy various constraints. One interesting example is that of properties which are generated 'without replacement', so that the subsets on which the random templates are defined are all disjoint. [See W. W. Bledsoe and I. Browning, 'Pattern recognition and reading by machine', *Proc. Eastern Joint Comp. Conf.*, December 1959, 225–32; G. P. Steck, 'Stochastic model for the Browning–Bledsoe pattern recognition scheme', *I.R.E. Trans. EC*-**11**, 1962, 274–82.]

5. FIGURE EXTRACTION AND FIGURE PROPERTIES

As pointed out at the beginning of Section 4, there exist 'properties' (size, shape, etc.) which are well defined only if some special subset of the picture—a 'figure'—

has been singled out. In this section we review methods of defining figures and also discuss properties of figures.

(a) *Figure Extraction from an Arbitrary Picture*

The commonest method of figure extraction is to simply 'threshold' the given picture f, or some picture F(f) obtained from it by a uniform operation; in other words, the figure is the set of points at which $F(f) \geqslant t$ (or $\leqslant t$), where t is a real number. Examples:
1. Thresholding f itself can yield meaningful figures in many cases (e.g., printed characters, clouds, etc.)
2. As described in Section 3, F can be chosen so that F(f) has high values only at 'edges', so that thresholding F(f) yields 'outline' figures (note, however, that there is no guarantee that these outlines will be closed curves).
3. If F is a matched filtering operation (Section 3), thresholding F(f) will select points at which a particular pattern is present in the picture.
[More refined figure extraction techniques can be devised using combinations of these methods. For a good example see R. Narasimhan and J. P. Fornango, 'Some further experiments in the parallel processing of pictures', *I.E.E.E. Trans. EC*-13, 1964, 748–50.] A key problem in this approach is that of selecting the threshold. In some cases this can be done once and for all in advance, while in other cases a threshold can be selected by examining the frequency distribution of gray levels in F(f).

An alternative approach to figure extraction is to determine the points of the figure *sequentially*, starting from some point of F(f) and searching for neighboring points which meet some acceptance criterion. 'Edge (or curve) following' and 'tracking' techniques fall under this heading. [See, e.g., W. Sprick and K. Ganzhorn, 'An analogous method for pattern recognition by following the boundary', *Proc. IFIP Cong.*, 1959, 238–44; E. C. Greanias *et al.*, 'The recognition of handwritten numerals by contour analysis', *IBM Jl Res. Dev.* 7, 1963, 14–21; R. S. Ledley *et al.*, 'BUGSYS: a programming system for picture processing—not for debugging', *Communs Ass. comp. Mach.* 9, 1966, 79–84.]

(b) *Figures Definable in Terms of a Given Figure*

Once a figure has been extracted from a picture, one can perform operations on the picture in which the points of the figure play special roles. Such operations can be used to derive new figures from the given one, e.g., by breaking it up into connected components or other types of 'pieces', by 'filling it in' (i.e., filling in a curve to obtain a solid figure), 'filling it out, (e.g., taking its convex hull, casting its 'shadow, [see H. A. Glucksman, 'A parapropagation pattern classifier', *I.E.E.E. Trans. EC*-14, 1965, 434–43]), and so on. If several figures are given, one can derive new figures from them by set theoretic operations (union, intersection, etc.).
(*1*) *Connected components*—There are a number of different methods of distinguishing, and in particular counting, the connected regions of which a figure is composed. See T. C. Nuttall, 'Apparatus for counting objects', U.S. Patent 2803406, August 20, 1957; R. A. Kirsch *et al.*, 'Experiments in processing pictorial information with a digital computer', *Proc. Eastern Joint Comp. Conf.*, December 1957, 221–9; H. von Foerster, 'Circuitry of clues to Platonic ideation', *Aspects of the Theory of Artificial Intelligence*, Plenum, New York, 1962, 43–81; P. Weston, 'Photocell field counts random objects', *Electronics* 34, 1961, 46–7; M. L. Babcock, 'Some physiology of automata', *Proc. Western Joint Comp.*

Conf., December 1961, 291–8; N. F. Izzo and W. Coles, 'Blood cell scanner identifies rare cells', *Electronics* **35**, 1962, 52–7; R. S. Ledley *et al.*, 'FIDAC: Film input to digital automatic computer and associated syntax-directed pattern-recognition programming system', *Optical and Electro-Optical Information Processing*, M.I.T. Press, 1965, 591–613.

(2) Isolated parts, clusters, elongated parts—It is relatively simple to compute the *distance* from every point of a picture to the nearest point of a given figure. In terms of this distance, one can set up criteria for defining isolated or elongated parts cf the figure, or 'clusters' of figure points. One can also define a sort of 'skeleton' of the figure which can be used to provide useful information about the shape of the figure. On these concepts see H. Blum, 'An associative method for dealing with the visual field and some of its biological implications', *Biological Prototypes and Synthetic Systems*, Plenum, New York, 1962, 244–60; 'A transformation for extracting new descriptors of shape', *Models for the Perception of Speech and Visual Form*, M.I.T. Press, 1967, 362–80; A. Rosenfeld and J. L. Pfaltz, 'Sequential operations in digital picture processing', *J. Ass. comput. Mach.* **13**, 1966, 471–94, and 'Distance functions on digital pictures', *Pat. Rec.* **1**, 1968. See also the papers by Rutovitz and by Philbrick in *Pictorial Pattern Recognition*, Thompson, Washington, D.C., 1968.

(3) Pieces of edges and curves; 'stream-following'—The edge of a figure can be broken up into pieces in various natural ways; some useful types of 'break points' are position extrema (locally highest, lowest, rightmost or leftmost points), points of inflection and curvature maxima. [On extrema see L. D. Harmon, 'A line-drawing pattern recognizer', *Proc. Western Joint Comp. Conf.*, May 1960, 351–64; 'Line-drawing pattern recognizer', *Electronics*, 1960, 39–43.] One can also look for pieces of edge which have given shapes, or shapes of a given type ('strokes', 'bays', 'notches', 'spurs', etc.). If the figure is line-like, these methods can be used to subdivide the figure itself; another possibility in this case is to use nodes (=line ends, and points where two or more lines meet), as break points [see H. Sherman, 'A quasi-topological method for the recognition of line patterns', *Proc. IFIP Cong.*, 1959, 232–7]. More generally, for any figure, one can 'track' its intersections with successive lines of a raster, and define beginnings and ends of pieces whenever intersections begin, end, change radically in size or position, merge, or split. [See R. L. Grimsdale *et al.*, 'A system for the automatic recognition of patterns', *Proc. I.E.E.* **106B**, 1959, 210–21; R. L. Grimsdale and J. M. Bullingham, 'Character recognition by digital computer using a special flying-spot scanner', *Comput. J.* **4**, 1961, 129–36; I. H. Sublette and J. Tults, 'Character recognition by digital feature detection', *RCA Rev.*, March 1962, 60–79; G. U. Uyehara, 'A stream-following technique for use in character recognition', *I.E.E.E. Int. Conv. Record*, March 1963.]

(c) Properties of Figures

Geometrical measurements made on figures can serve as useful properties for pattern classification, as well as being important in pattern description. The following are some important types of figure properties:

(1) Topological properties—Connectivity (=the number of connected components), order of connectivity (=the number of 'holes' in a connected component).

(2) Size properties—Area, height and width (measured along the coordinate axes—or more generally, 'extent' in any given direction), length and width (e.g., measured along and perpendicular to the principal axis of inertia, or given by the length and width of the circumscribed rectangle of smallest area), diameter (=greatest distance between points of the figure), perimeter. [On

these and other properties see H. Freeman, 'Techniques for the digital computer analysis of chain-encoded arbitrary plane curves', *Proc. Nat. Elect. Conf.*, October 1961, 421–32. On the use of the methods of integral geometry to measure figure properties, see A. B. J. Novikoff, 'Integral geometry as a tool in pattern perception', *Principles of Self-Organization*, Pergamon, New York, 1962, 347–68; H. L. Frisch and B. Julesz, 'Figure-ground perception and random geometry', *Percep. Psychophys.* **1**, 1966, 389–98.]

(*3*) *Shape properties*—Convexity, symmetry (about a point or line), straightness (e.g., arc length of curve/length of chord), total curvature (=total angle through which the tangent turns as the curve is traversed), complexity (e.g., perimeter^2/ area), randomness (of a point or line pattern). [On this last see M. F. Dacey and T. Tung, 'The identification of randomness in point patterns', *J. reg. Sci.* **4**, 1962, 83–96; M. F. Dacey, 'Description of line patterns', *Quantitative Geography*, Northwestern University, Evanston, Ill., 1967, 277–87.]

(*d*) *Functions of Figures*

Functions of one variable defined in terms of a figure can also be useful for pattern classification. Examples:

(*1*) *The intrinsic equation*—An arc is determined, independently of position and orientation, by specifying its curvature as a function of arc length (measured from some starting point). It is not difficult to modify this function so that it is also independent of starting point and of scale.

(*2*) *Functions of distance*—The area of the region within distance r of a figure (or the arc length of the locus of points at distance exactly r from the figure), as a function of r, provides useful information about the shape of the figure.

(*3*) *Intercepts with families of curves*—The manner in which each of a family of curves C_λ intersects the figure (for example, the total length of intersection, the number of intersections, etc.), as a function of λ, can be used to describe the figure. Alternatively, given a collection C_μ of such families of curves (e.g., the families of parallel lines at all orientations), one can compute statistics of the intersections of the curves in each family with the figure, and take any such statistics as a function of μ. [See, e.g., E. C. Greanias *et al.*, 'Design of logic for recognition of printed characters by simulation', *IBM Jl Res. Dev.* **1**, 1957, 9–18; W. Doyle, 'Recognition of sloppy hand-printed characters', *Proc. Western Joint Comp. Conf.*, May 1960, 133–42; M. E. Stevens, 'Abstract shape recognition by machine', *Proc. Eastern Joint Comp. Conf.*, December 1961, 332–51.]

(*4*) *Statistical distributions*—The frequency distribution of the values of any local figure property can be used as a figure function. A useful example is the *directionality spectrum*, i.e., the distribution of slopes around the boundary of the figure. [See H. Freeman, 'On the digital computer classification of geometric line patterns', *Proc. Nat. Elect. Conf.*, October 1962, 312–24.]

6. PROSPECTS

There has been significant progress in automatic pictorial pattern recognition over the past 15 years. Equipment for reading printed characters is coming into widespread use, and there has also been considerable success in reading hand printing. A number of systems for automatically scanning and analyzing nuclear bubble and spark chamber pictures are now operational. Work on more complex pictures, such as biomedical photomicrographs and aerial photographs, is still largely experimental, but many specific tasks are well within the range of current capability. It should be entirely possible to develop solutions to a variety of problems in the automatic photointerpretation of terrain. Such solutions are particularly desirable in cases involving very large numbers of photographs, or where computer processing of the pictures is already being performed for other reasons.

There are many tasks at which machines are better than humans—notably, tasks involving quantitative measurement. Man-machine collaboration in the analysis of aerial photographs could be very advantageous. If a picture is scanned and input to a computer, at the same time that it is viewed by an interpreter, the interpreter can point out objects or outline regions (using a light pen, Rand tablet, or the like) for analysis by the computer. As a capability for automatic interpretation is developed, the computer can be programmed to make tentative analyses and display them for confirmation or correction by the interpreter. In this way, the testing and application of new techniques can keep pace with their development, and rapid progress can be made toward the goal of fully automated picture interpretation.

A Geographic Information System for Regional Planning

R. F. Tomlinson

Department of Forestry and Rural Development,
Government of Canada

As a tool in its program of rural development, Canada is developing a computer-based information system for the storage and manipulation of map-based land data. The system and its capabilities are described.

Canada, like many countries, faces an immense problem in both understanding and guiding the development of its land, water, and human resources. One of the major agencies created specifically to implement policy to attack this problem is the Rural Development Branch of the Department of Forestry and Rural Development. A primary task facing this agency is to assemble social (demographic), economic, and land data for an integrated analysis to enable problems of rural development to be specified, development programs to be implemented, and their effectiveness evaluated.

Parallel with the gathering of data has been the development, by the Regional Planning Information Systems Division of the Branch, of interrelated computer-based information systems to handle and analyse the data. The Geographic Information System, for the storage and manipulation of land data is the most developed of these systems. Its design and development started in 1963, implementation began in 1965, and is now in its final stages; routine use is scheduled for September 1968. It is perhaps worthwhile to recount our progress with this system at this time.

Early in the life of the Branch (1962) a start was made with the gathering of some kinds of land data by the Canada Land Inventory. The data they collect is restricted to five types: the present use of the land, the capability of the land for agriculture, the capability of the land for forestry, the capability for recreation, and the capability for supporting wildlife. These data alone, if gathered in sufficient quantities for the summaries to be directly applicable to provincial and federal resource policy and regional planning, will generate an estimated 30,000 map sheets, at various scales. The Inventory has currently produced 7000 map sheets, of which 3000 have been prepared for computer input. The maps contain an average of 800 distinct areas on each sheet, and have been found to contain as many as 4000. Additionally, other types of maps covering watersheds, climate, geology, administrative boundaries, and land titles are generated by other agencies.

The need for a computer-based system, whereby map and related data can be stored in a form suitable for rapid measurement and comparison, is apparent as soon as the magnitude of the problem of handling large numbers of maps is appreciated. Lack of trained personnel makes it impossible to examine such large amounts of data manually in any sensible time, much less to provide a meaningful analysis of the content. A situation can be reached where the amount of data precludes its use. The end product of countless hours of survey can remain unused, with the result that administrators do not receive information necessary for a sound basis to decision making.

From the first, it was the intention to produce the maps generated for the Canada Land Inventory in such a way that their data could be related on a nation-wide basis by the geographic information system. This made it necessary to establish a common basis of data description. Classification systems were evolved for each type of data by discussions with the federal and provincial agencies concerned in the original survey, under the guidance of a federal co-ordinator. In each case, the classification systems were subject to trial in pilot areas in various regions of the country. Regional variations are incorporated into the classification system by development of ratings which recognize equivalent values. The classification systems vary from a relatively simple, one-letter code for present land use to a complex, multi-level description used for forestry.

The maps, essentially interpretations of existing data in terms of the classification system, are usually produced by the federal and provincial agencies most closely related to the collection of the original data (over 100 agencies are involved). The manuscript maps are sent to Ottawa to be edited and prepared for computer input.

The basic capability of the geographic information system is that it accepts and stores all types of location-specific information, that is, any information which can be related to an area, line, or point on a map. Information relating to land resources is most frequently location-specific in character. For example, census data (perhaps not usually thought of as location-specific) are collected from specific areas of land called enumeration areas, which are recorded on maps; a highway is a location-specific line; a campsite can be thought of as a location-specific point on a map.

The system can best be described as comprising two parts: the data bank and the set of procedures and methods for moving data into the bank, and for carrying out the manipulations, measurements, and comparisons of the data, once there. These two parts will be referred to as the 'data bank' and the 'information system', respectively. It is quite possible to have the entire geographic information system with full operating capability and have no data in the data bank. The amount of data which can be put into the data bank is infinite, as any number of magnetic tapes can be generated and stored. Additional data related to any area can be inserted at any time.

The system has the following capabilities:

It will accept maps containing data represented as areas or lines or points. The maps can be of any scale and on any map projection, and they can contain linear distortions. All of these characteristics will be adjusted to a standard format (normalized) when they are put in. Data relating to points only can be put in independently of maps. They are simply related to their latitude and longitude points.

The system compacts and stores information. The compaction is most efficient. For maps at a scale of 1 : 50,000 with an average density of information it is expected that a complete coverage of the farmed area of Canada (approximately 600 map sheets) can be recorded on two reels of magnetic tape.

The system can measure any data in the data bank. If the data have been inserted in the form of areas, then each area can be measured. For example, a soil map might be represented by different areas of different soils. The area of each patch of soil or the total area of any one type of soil can be calculated.

Similarly, the lengths of lines can be measured and the occurrences of points counted.

The region from which area, line, or point measurements are required can be limited in a variety of ways. Data can be retrieved within any boundary already described to the system. If, for example, a map of administrative region boundaries has been put into the data bank, measurements can be carried out within a specific administrative region. If a desired boundary has not already been described to the system it can, of course, be drawn on a clean sheet and inserted in the normal way, or if it is simple enough in shape to be described by a straight line joining points, then it is only necessary to put in the co-ordinate values of the points.

It will also be possible to limit retrieval by reference to any line or point already described to this system. The system can be asked, for example, to measure the area of patches of land crossed by the line of a highway or within a band of specified width along the highway, or to determine the areas suitable for sub-divisions within 20 miles of the center of a city.

A major system capability is comparison of two types of mapped data relating to the same area. Just as two maps can be manually overlaid to allow the relationships between the data to be examined, the system can overlay any two or more types of data to measure the exact amounts of each type of land in juxtaposition to the map or maps below.

This can be applied as a search capability, whereby a comparison of various types of information is made to find out where a selected set of characteristics occur together. For example, a request to find suitable landing sites for a helicopter would require an examination of the vegetation map to determine treeless areas, the topographic map to make sure that the area was flat, and the present land use map to make sure that the area was not populated. These three coverages would be compared to identify and describe all points having the desired characteristics.

A further extension of the search capability could result in a 'search in context'. A potential helicopter landing-site, for example, would be of limited value if, while being perfectly treeless, flat, and uninhabited, it occurred as an island in the middle of a swamp. The search routine can be instructed to ignore otherwise desirable sites if they do not occur in a desirable context.

Another search capability that can be implemented is referred to as the 'nearest neighbour search'. This would be employed when the limit of the search is not definite enough to be specified. The search command would simply request the nearest examples of the desired character to be located. A composite example of some of these capabilities might be an instruction to locate the nearest potash mine which is served by a main highway, north and south railroad connections, and is surrounded by a minimum of 10,000 sq miles of good farmland.

The system can produce information in two different forms. The commonest form is perhaps the normal printed alphabetical and numerical data produced on the regular computer printer. In addition to the printer will be a graphic plotter which, under the control of the system, produces a map showing the location of the desired areas, lines, or points which satisfy the request.

An inherent danger of information systems is that the data entered into the system may vary widely in reliability, but may be assumed to be equally reliable in subsequent multifactor assessments. The system can accept a reliability identifier with any type of information and can keep track of reliability tags so that degrees of reliability are printed out beside the answer to a request.

The advantages of information which is kept up to date, compared with data which have to accumulate for several years before it is economically desirable to reprint a map, are well known to users of map information. Data can easily be added to the system without waiting for large amounts of new data to accrue. Old coverage can be erased and replaced on the magnetic tapes or, if desired, both the old and the new coverage can be retained. New survey data at a more detailed scale can be incorporated with previous data at smaller scales, provided, of course, that the classification systems are compatible.

For many of the day-to-day information needs of administrators of land resource policy, simple forms exist to allow the administrator to initiate the request without the assistance of a computer programmer. Although more detailed assessments requiring the full flexibility and capability of the system would best be handled by someone acquainted with the data formats, a considerable amount of programming effort has been eliminated even at this level by use of programs already written and incorporated into the system. It is estimated that, with no previous computer knowledge, an administrator could be taught to complete normal form-originated requests in one week. Three weeks training and practice thereafter are expected to be necessary for the same administrator to handle more detailed requests. The unusual or very complex requests will need a programmer working in conjunction with the system librarian.

In many ways the system is self-monitoring. On accepting a request for information, the first response of the librarian will be to use the system's KWIC[1] index to check whether that particular request has been made before and, if so, to indicate where the answer is stored in the filing cabinet. If the request has already been partially answered, this also is determined. If the request requires new manipulation of data, the system indicates which tapes have the requisite data stored on them.

The tapes then are selected from the library, put on to the computer and the assessment is executed. An extension of this capability is to provide a cost estimate of the work, prior to processing, based on a preliminary analysis of the amount of data on the requested tapes. Such estimates will be necessary in more complex applications.

The system is independent of peripheral devices such as input scanners or output plotters. While the IBM cartographic scanner is now in use, in conjunction with a D-Mac X-Y digitizer, to convert graphic data to digital form, instrumentation is likely to be developed in the next two or three years to combine these functions.

The normalization step, which converts digitized graphic information to the format required by the data bank, is independent of the main system functions and can be changed accordingly.

The system is designed for use on the IBM System 360 Model 50, with 512 thousand bytes[2] of storage, 6 magnetic tape drives, and 3 magnetic disc drives under the control of the standard operating system. Greater operating efficiency is achieved if the System 360 Model 65 is used. The practical application of the data bank concept and the entire system capability is available by use of this general-purpose computer.

SYSTEM DESCRIPTION

Boundary data to be put into the data bank are traced (scribed) on to a clean

---

[1] KWIC — Key Word In Context document indexing and cross-referencing system based on computer sorting of key words in the title. Ref. IBM Publ. E20-8091.
[2] Byte — a unit of computer storage space made up of eight digits, or bits, in the binary system (using only 0 or 1). Each byte is capable of storing one letter, two decimal digits, or a binary value.

sheet from the source map (Fig. 1). The unique areas or 'map elements' are numbered on a transparent overlay and the corresponding classification is transcribed to a data sheet for punching into cards to be read by the computer.

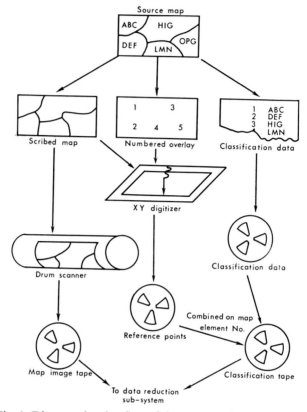

Fig. 1. Diagram showing flow of data preparation procedures.

The traced boundary sheet is placed on the drum scanner, and the scanning operation produces a digitized map of the boundaries on magnetic tape. The drum scanner was developed to meet Rural Development Branch requirements by the International Business Machines Company. The possible use of the drum scanning approach was first considered in 1963. The preliminary design criteria were established by the Rural Development Branch in 1964 and development work was contracted to the International Business Machines Company in 1965. The scanner consists of a cylindrical drum on which a map or chart can be mounted, and a movable carriage which slowly moves the scanning head across the front of the revolving drum. The scanning system consists of the scanning head proper, its associated electronics, and controls leading to a standard IBM magnetic tape drive.

The technique employed is to detect the changes in intensity of light reflected from black or white areas on the map or chart surface and to record this information as a series of binary bits written on magnetic tape. The scan head is a device utilizing fibre optics and is capable of scanning eight scan lines simultaneously. The drum scanner can accept a map up to 48 in. × 48 in. in size. A full-size map takes approximately 15 minutes to scan, including the time for mounting and dismounting it. Smaller sheets take a correspondingly shorter time.

It is not within the scope of this paper to give a detailed description of the drum scanner, though it is hoped that the engineering aspects will be covered in detail in a future paper. The format of the map-image data on tape is, however, pertinent to the discussion. One map-image record is produced for each 0·032 in. along the X-axis of a map sheet, and the height of each record area is 0·004 in. along the Y-axis. The 0·032 in. record, comprising one byte of computer storage, is divided into eight bits. Each bit thus represents an area or spot 0·004 in. wide. Lines drawn on the map are usually 0·008 in. wide. If the scan heads on the scanner identify 50% or more of a spot as part of a line, then a '1' bit is generated; otherwise a '0' bit is generated. A line in this manner is represented as a collection of bits which are usually either one, two, or three spots in width.

The traced boundary sheet with the transparent numbered overlay is placed on a D-Mac cartographic X-Y digitizer where the four reference corner points and the co-ordinates of one reference point per 'map face' are coded in digits. A map face is any one of the distinct areas that together make up the surface of the map. As noted before, information related to a face is considered to be homogeneously distributed within that face. The output from the X-Y digitizer is produced on magnetic tape by means of an NCR encoder; this will revert to punched cards if it is found that the error-edit capability of cards is needed. The classification data sheet is now also directly transcribed on to magnetic tape, though this may be taken back to punched card output. Classification data and the digitized reference points are combined on the basis of map face number to result in a classification tape.

Entering Data into the System

The basic approach to feeding map data into the system is to reconstruct a line segment, or the part of a line that lies between adjacent vertices, from the point comprising the scanned map image. These segments are then combined with the classification information to produce map faces which are a basic unit of storage.

The following are some of the steps in this input procedure. As a preliminary, the identification of the scanner and classification tapes, coverage and map identification, and similar data are put into the procedure which controls the flow in the subsequent update[1] operation. The classification tape is edited for data consistency and is changed into system format during this stage (Fig. 2).

The map-image tape then enters the main map-data reduction procedure. Since a 30-in. by 30-in. map generates over 56 million bits, occupying over 7 million bytes of computer storage on an IBM System 360, the data reduction of the map image is performed sequentially on smaller units known as 'sections'. The use of a square (or nearly square) section results in considerably longer lines being available from the map for processing at one time than would be the case if a long, thin rectangle were used. A computer with 512 thousand bytes of core storage can handle a section in the order of $1\frac{1}{2}$ in. $\times 2\frac{1}{4}$ in.

Each spot in the cloud of spots which make up the lines is assigned a 'V' value. This is a measure of the number of information-carrying spots surrounding it.

[1] Update — A computer procedure to combine new data being entered into the system with data already existing in the system. This may take the form of correcting, replacing, or deleting existing data, or inserting or adding new data.

This minimizes the effect of irrelevant bits and tends to pick out the center points along the line. The search follows the highest V values; it eliminates the redundant spots in the cloud.

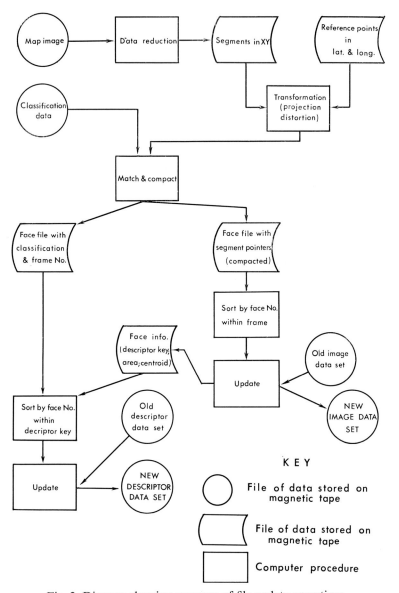

Fig. 2. Diagram showing sequence of file update operations.

The center points are coded to identify line intersections (or vertices) and the sense of direction of the line. Having thus located the points which comprise boundary lines, it is a simple task to record the X and Y co-ordinates of each point along a segment.

The system requires descriptive information to be related to map elements. One method of accomplishing this is to apply an identifying tag to both sides of the line. This tag also indicates in which direction the line was first followed, this being necessary if the sides of the line are to have a constant meaning.

The identifying tags are called 'system colors'. They are analogous to the colors in a political map. A sort-and-search of these colors enables the segments to be connected with each other, and hence faces to be assembled.

Using the reference points in latitude and longitude taken from the four corner points of the map, a transformation is carried out which locates the X-Y digitizer map-element reference points within the scanner. Map projections, which can vary from one map to another, are normalized. Calculations are made to correct for linear distortion and skewed orientation of the map on the scanner or digitizer. The transformed 'map-image data set' and the classification (or 'descriptor-data set') then are matched and compacted. During this match-and-compact operation, the map-image co-ordinates are recorded in terms of a standardized geodetic co-ordinate system. This allows a uniform base for storage and the subsequent measurement and overlay procedures.

The choice of a standard co-ordinate system was a major consideration. The eventual measurement needs (i.e. area, length, and centroid) required the chosen system to be locally cartesian. However, a co-ordinate system based on a projection can result in a system of regions, each with its own co-ordinate system. This problem is particularly pertinent when one considers an area as extensive as Canada.

Careful investigation indicated that a system comprised of the geodetic latitude and longitude had many advantages. The smallest division in the geodetic co-ordinate system used in the data bank is called a unit grid. It represents an angular displacement of $1/2^{24}$ degrees. This was derived quite empirically. Using a 4-byte unit, 1 byte allows a span of 128 degrees which is sufficient to encompass Canada. The remaining 3 bytes represent the possible subdivision of any one degree.

The theoretical resolution of the system is determined by the actual distance on the ground covered by this unit grid, which at 45 degrees latitude is just over 1/4 in. in the latitudinal (or X) direction. This is considered adequate for the data being put into the system.

Scale within the system is in terms of the unit grid distance. Factors from 2^0 to 2^{31} have been devised to provide coarser resolution.

To handle map information within the system, it is convenient to subdivide the co-ordinate system into regions called 'frames'. A frame has an equal angular displacement in the X and Y directions, hence is a square in the geodetic co-ordinate system.

A relatively simple calculation reveals that a map of average density (30 in. by 30 in., with 800 in. of boundary lines), will occupy 200,000 bytes of storage if no scale change or transformation is performed. With up to 30,000 maps envisaged as the primary content of the data bank, a compact notation for storage of co-ordinates was essential.

With a code based on direction change between co-ordinates and distance between co-ordinates, a sequence of simple codes can be used to describe co-ordinates. A sample line, requiring 864 bits for normal X-Y recording, occupies 76 bits in compact notation. If required, lines with regular patterns can be further compacted by storing the pattern with an indication of how many times the pattern is repeated.

In the match-and-compact phase, routines are carried out to calculate the area of each face, the centroid of face elements, and the length of line elements. In the same phase, an extensive error analysis is performed to ensure that the map is topologically correct. Errors found at this stage are documented by a series of error messages on the computer printer.

The match-and-compact operation produces two index files. The first of these is a face file with classification and frame number which, when sorted, is used in updating the descriptor-data set. The second is a face file with segment identifiers which is used to update the image-data set. Incorporated in the second file is the basic compact notation of co-ordinate data by frame number. The routine for updating the image data set provides the geodetic properties (area, centroid, and length) as required to update the descriptor-data set. Both of these update routines can produce error listings as new data are matched with data already in the data bank. Again, error correcting is carried out as an update to the primary map-data reduction phase.

The best approach to take with regard to error correction will only be found by trial with a working system. Given a high percentage of errors requiring reference back to source documents or even to field survey, the relatively expensive method using cathode-ray tube displays would add little, if anything, to the efficiency of the error-correction procedure. On the other hand, given a high percentage of errors of a strictly cartographic nature and not requiring reference to source documents, the cathode-ray tube approach, by which images displayed on the tube can be corrected by 'drawing' on it with a beam of light, would have considerable merit. Both approaches will be investigated during the system trials.

Data Bank Organization

The data bank is divided into classification data contained within the descriptor-data set and boundary data contained within the image-data set. Three levels of file organization are envisaged. These are: (1) consecutive, (2) regional, and (3) indexed. These file organizations, together with an unstructured or structured version of the classification data within the descriptor-data set, have been combined into six levels. Five of these will be possible within the present scope of the data bank.

Using the descriptor-data set as an example, the relationship between the various levels can be thought of as follows: Level 1 represents the basic descriptor-data set arranged by consecutive face number; Level 2 represents a sorted Level 1, grouped according to some selected characteristic or set of characteristics; Level 3 is the equivalent to Level 1 for a specific region or group of regions; Level 4 can be thought of as a Level 3 which has been structured by grouping the faces relating to a certain characteristic or set of characteristics; Level 6 is a Level 2 or 4 which is not only structured but has an index of its contents available to facilitate further search. Level 5 is not implemented as an indexed consecutive file is not an advantage.

In the descriptor-data set for each map element, there is a list of pointers to the frames containing relevant parts of the boundary information for that map element. The format of this key varies with the level of file organization, but in all cases, it serves to relate the image-data set to the descriptor-data set. The record formats of the various levels of descriptor-data set are illustrated below.

Level 1, 3

Record Type	Cover-age Number	Map Element	Geodetic Data	Factor Data	Frame List	Level 3 Region List

Level 2, 4, 6

Record Type	DDS Key Classification Data	Geodetic Data	Non-Key Factor Data	Frame List	Region No. List

Data Retrieval

As the boundary information is kept separate from the description information it is only necessary to use the boundary information if actual boundaries have to be compared or output. Otherwise, all retrieval can be done from the description information files. This leads to extremely efficient use of the data bank, as most requests will not require use of the boundaries.

A computer needs a detailed description of the location and organization of data within itself before it can bring it out or manipulate it. These detailed descriptions are themselves kept in computer storage and are indexed by key words. These key words have been made to be the normal words that would ordinarily describe the maps such as PRESENT LAND USE or AGRICULTURAL CAPABILITY. The use of such key words automatically generates computer programs that both describe the data and actually bring it out of the computer.

In the same way key words are used to describe the types of manipulation that can be carried out by the system. When data is to be retrieved the request is written by combining the key names of the data and the key words of the desired analysis. This results in a very powerful set of instructions being available that are also very flexible. This flexibility in data specification statements is made possible by use of the PL/1 language. Uncomplicated requests will be extremely simple to address to the computer. The more complex requests will necessitate a small program being written, but even this will be facilitated by the use of these key words which represent already written small programs.

Overlay Procedure

The overlay procedure of the system is the well-known function of putting one map over another and examining the resulting data relationships.

Firstly, the two maps in the data bank are brought to the same scale. Then a section of one map of a size that can be handled by the computer is brought into core and the corresponding section of the map being overlaid is similarly brought into core and superimposed on the first. This, in effect, creates a new map with new faces. The new faces are 're-colored' and identified as new homogeneous areas. The first description data set is then brought in and the proper description is applied to each of the new faces. The description data set from the overlay map is similarly brought in and applied to the new map faces. Each of the new faces has now got a double name, one from each of the original two maps. The process is thus one of creating one 'new' map from the two original maps being overlaid. The new map can then have its areas measured and summarized in the same way as any other map in the system. It is stored and kept in the system as if it were an original map coverage. Up to eight maps can be overlaid in the same operation but obviously this is not a limitation, as the results of two overlays can subsequently be themselves overlaid.

Data Control

Data control within the system is achieved by the system monitor. The system monitor accepts pertinent data on the history of map-data manipulation within the system at all times. Many of the responsibilities for system control in such an open-ended system must rest with the system librarian.

The librarian's responsibilities include deciding whether coverages are permanent or temporary, selecting the resolution at which boundary lines for various coverages need to be stored, and deciding the way in which the descriptor-data sets are filed for ease of retrieval and comparison. He is also responsible for providing the procedures which edit the classification data in the preliminary phase of the map-data reduction sub-system. He must tailor the key words that describe the different types of map and different types of manipulation to efficient, specifically applicable retrieval requirements. He is in control of the flow of individual maps within the system and, similarly he must evaluate the practicability of assessment requests, including the avoidance of duplicate assessments.

CONCLUSION

The Geographic Information System of the Rural Development Branch is still in an early stage of its development. Not all the procedures described have yet been fully implemented and at present rates of progress it will be several years before the data bank contains maps for any one type of information that cover the whole of the settled portion of Canada. The effectiveness of the system will of course depend as much on the quality of the data entered into the bank as on the capabilities for handling data. Nevertheless, the system is further advanced than any other major land data bank and contains several new concepts and techniques, especially those relating to the compact storage of boundary data and the rapid comparison of one map with another. Such a system is essential to effective rural planning in any country and offers for the first time the possibility of rapid and efficient geographical analysis which has application in any nation where the developing economy is concerned with the natural resources.

The author gratefully acknowledges the support and encouragement given this work by ARDA, particularly from A. T. Davidson, L. E. Pratt, and W. A. Benson, Chief, Canada Land Inventory, and from the International Business Machines Company of the IBM/Ottawa staff associated with the programming and computer applications of the project; specifically: Guy Morton, Frank Jankulak, Don Lever, Art Benjamin, Robert Kemeny, Peter Kingston, and Bruce Ferier.

An Integrated System for Exploiting Quantitative Terrain Data for Engineering Purposes

Warren E. Grabau

U.S. Army Engineer Waterways Experiment Station, Vicksburg, Miss., U.S.A.

Modern planning and operational activities require quantitative evaluations of the relations among the environments and the activities being planned or conducted. With mathematical models of these relations, an integrated and largely automated system for performing a terrain evaluation can be designed. The system involves the development of mathematical performance prediction models, the acquisition of terrain data on the basis of model requirements, information processing to convert it into useful form, and the automatic construction of performance prediction maps on tabulations. Major modules of the system are in existence, but the components have not yet been assembled into an integrated procedure.

There is a widely held opinion that any description or classification of terrain constitutes a terrain evaluation or terrain analysis. This is true in only the most limited sense, even when the terms of description or classification are obviously chosen with reference to engineering activities or operations. A statement that a specific region is 'characterized by rolling hills, sparse vegetation, and firm soils, making it easy to construct roads', is of course an evaluation of that region. However, such a qualitative generalization is scarcely of use to a modern engineer who must obtain the maximum practical efficiency from the deployment of his available men and machines. It is scarcely more useful to the planner, who must allocate meagre resources in the most productive way possible.

There appear to be two general levels of generalization involved in terrain evaluation, and there is normally a good deal of confusion as to which level is being addressed at any given time. At the first level, for example, the road construction engineer is interested in a precise estimate of cost and time, based on a specific centre line alignment of a stretch of road. Obtaining such an estimate requires very great detail on all elements of the engineering problem. In general, terrain evaluation for this type of problem can only be accomplished by using photogrammetry on large-scale air photos, and by meticulous ground sampling. These procedures are all well understood and widely employed.

At the second general level, however, the user is what might be called a 'development engineer'. His interest is in obtaining approximate solutions for general problems. He needs to know approximately how many kilometres of road he will need to serve a newly developing area, and what he can expect in time and cost as an approximation of sufficient precision to tell·him the general magnitude of the task. He will not, by and large, be interested in exact road alignments. The terrain evaluation processes for this type of analysis are somewhat different and require much less detail than the first. The air photos are, by and large, subjected to interpretation as opposed to photogrammetry.

Ideally, a terrain evaluation system should incorporate the potential capability for both levels, as well as any intermediate ones, even though the system cannot be supplied with information for both for all geographic areas in the immediate future. The integrated terrain evaluation system hypothesized here is potentially capable of both, although at this time it is specifically addressed to the second, more generalized level.

Study of the nature of the terrain evaluation problem has revealed that more is at issue than simple description or classification. Instead, truly useful terrain analysis for engineering purposes has proven to consist of a number of inter-dependent problems, all of which must be solved in concert before a true terrain evaluation can be usefully achieved. Terrain evaluation is thus revealed as a relatively complex system for providing specific kinds of information to the engineer user.

The function of terrain analysis for engineer purposes is to provide the planner or field engineer with such precise information about the terrain in the operational area that he can calculate the effects of the terrain on the work forces and machines with reasonable reliability. With such calculations, the engineer can lay out his plans with confidence that the terrain itself will not confront him with a devastating surprise.

Since the objective is to make it possible to calculate the effects of the terrain on the various activities comprising a construction operation (or alternatively, on the operation as a whole), it follows that a prerequisite of the terrain evalua-tion system is a set of analytical models relating terrain to the activity in such a way that the performance of any given activity can be predicted in any given terrain context. Such performance prediction models must be entirely objective, and therefore quantitative, if the predictions are to be of more than marginal utility. Thus, a manager of earth-moving equipment must be able to predict with relatively high reliability the average speed of his vehicles along a specified route (e.g., from borrow pit to fill) if he is to maintain a realistic schedule; this presupposes a quite sophisticated cross-country locomotion model. The canal builder must be able to predict how long it will take to cut a given ditch; those concerned with logistics must be able to select areas for base development with great speed and reliability; and so on. Finally, the economists who planned the construction effort must have taken the effects of the terrain on all of the related activities into account in order to develop a realistic operational plan. These prerequisites of the terrain evaluation process are indicated in column 1 of Figure 1.

The research, on which the terrain evaluation scheme proposed herein is based, has been focused entirely on military problems; Figure 1 is therefore a diagram of a system intended for use by the military. However, since many military activities, especially those involved in civil engineering effects, differ only (or at least largely) in degree from civilian projects, it is probably safe to assume that a nearly identical scheme would also be suitable for civilian purposes.

The development of usefully reliable analytical performance prediction models has proven to be both difficult and time-consuming. Perhaps this is understandable in view of the fact that the development of analytical models was not even considered to be a requirement of terrain evaluation until very recently. At the present time, a relatively sophisticated mathematical model for predicting the cross-country locomotion of vehicles of standard configuration is available (WES 1965). It must be emphasized that no attempt has yet been made to adapt the model to earthmoving equipment or any other specialized kind of engineering vehicle. It seems unlikely that such an adaptation would prove particularly difficult. Relatively crude but nonetheless useful analytical models for predicting the effort required to construct roads and airfields are also in being.

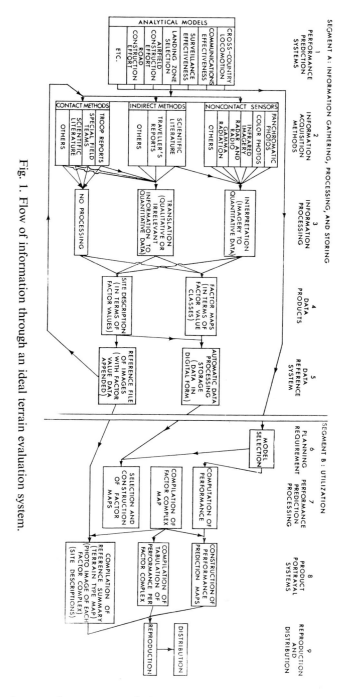

Fig. 1. Flow of information through an ideal terrain evaluation system.

The various performance prediction models provide not only the capability for estimating performance; the task of developing them also results in the isolation of the terrain factors that affect each activity. Because each model interrelates terrain and activity, the models require measurable attributes of the terrain (i.e., terrain factors) as input values. For example, the airfield construction effort model (which is very crude and highly generalized) requires values for five highly specialized factors:

1. Characteristic slope, which is the most common topographic slope occurring in the area selected for construction; it affects the ease of providing drainage, the movement of construction equipment, and the volume of grading.

2. Soil grain-size distribution, which is related to the relative ease with which the soils are handled with normal construction equipment and to the difficulty of providing drainage.

3. Soil moisture content which affects the workability of soils.

4. Depth of rock (the vertical distance from the surface of the ground to bedrock) which is related to the volume of grading and proportion of soil to rock.

5. Mean basal area of plants per unit area, which is a measure of the difficulty of cutting and removing the vegetation on the construction site.

With the significant terrain factors isolated, the terrain analyst is then faced with the problem of acquiring data on those factors. It must be emphasized that the choice of factors is not open to preference; the analytical models require certain factors measured in specific ways, and no others. Given those factors, the terrain analyst must acquire that specific information whether he likes it or not. Thus, information acquisition methods (column 2, Fig. 1) are a matter of legitimate interest to terrain analysts since these methods must ultimately yield the quantitative data required as input by the analytical models. The most highly sophisticated information acquisition system in the world is useless unless it provides data which can be used. Unfortunately, most information acquisition systems used up to the present time have furnished only (or at least largely) qualitative information, whereas the mathematical performance prediction models require quantitative data. The terrain analysts are therefore faced with the necessity of developing both information acquisition systems and procedures for either interpreting or translating (column 3, Fig. 1) the output of the data acquisition systems into the quantitative formats required by the models.

There are three general classes of information acquisition systems, each with its specific sphere of utility.

1. The non-contact sensor systems are devices or techniques which yield either an image of the terrain or a machine-recorded value of some property of, or reflectance or emission from, the terrain. Examples include panchromatic photography, infrared imagery, gamma radiation level, magnetic field strength and direction, radio and radar frequency images, and so on. The major difficulty with these sensor systems, at least from the point of view of the engineer analyst, is that the systems rarely if ever directly yield factor value information as required by the analytical models. A stereopair of panchromatic air photos may contain all of the information required to provide data on topographic slope, but the data are not directly obtainable; an interpretation process is required to extract them from the imagery. Gamma radiation levels may contain information relevant to soil properties (such as shear strength), but the sensor output must be interpreted in suitable terms before the inherent information is available for use in a mathematical model. Thus, the terrain analyst is faced with the staggering task of learning how to interpret non-contact sensor outputs in terms of the factors required by the performance prediction models. Unfortunately, nearly all previous work on sensor interpretation, including standard photo interpretation, has been geared to the qualitative information requirements of other scientists (geologists, pedologists, botanists, agronomists, etc.), and the products of their research on inter-

pretation are not directly relevant to the needs of the engineer analyst. For example, only one major effort has been made to date to obtain quantitative factor value data for cross-country mobility analysis by air photo interpretation (Shamburger and Grabau 1968).

2. Information and data can also be gained by contact methods. For example, specially trained field teams can visit sites of interest and obtain direct measurements of the significant properties. To provide data for the airfield construction effort model, for example, they could directly measure the topographic slope, thickness of soil, and so on. Some scientific literature contains terrain data for geographic locations in forms directly usable as model input, and therefore qualifies as a 'contact' method. Construction reports could also presumably be used, especially if the personnel were trained to obtain the specific data required. For the most part data obtained by contact methods can be used directly (as indicated by the flow diagram, Fig. 1) without significant processing, since they will have been acquired in the format required by the models. However, it must be emphasized that not all information or data acquired by contact means are usable in the form in which they are collected. For example, a team of agronomists collecting data on soils in the field will normally collect data relevant to their scientific discipline and, while these data often contain information of interest to the construction engineer, the data must normally be translated (column 3, Fig. 1) from an agronomy-oriented format to an engineer terrain evaluation format. As a case in point, data on soil texture and moisture content, of direct interest to the agronomist, can to some extent be correlated with shear strength, which is a factor of interest to the construction engineer.

3. Finally, indirect methods of acquiring terrain data can be employed, although ordinarily this method is used only in the absence of either contact or non-contact data. Since nature is ordered, it follows that two areas characterized by the same geological history, climate, and cultural exploitation will strongly resemble each other. Thus, if the history, climate, and cultural exploitation of an unknown area can be determined, either directly or by inference, the general terrain characteristics of the area can be predicted within certain limits by comparing it to some known area with similar background. The prediction will be statistical at best, rather than specific; that is, the terrain description will normally be in terms of estimates of percentage of coverage by specific factor value classes or factor value class sets, rather than in terms of the planimetric distributions of those classes or sets. However, if even relatively reliable maps are available, quite detailed and surprisingly accurate factor value class maps can sometimes be generated (van Lopik and Kolb 1959).

Of the three information acquisition methods, by far the most reliable from the standpoint of engineering evaluation is the contact method, chiefly because it yields direct, and directly usable, quantitative measures of significant factors. The major disadvantage is that it provides only site descriptions; mapping any large area by this method is prohibitively costly and time-consuming, at least at the present time. The interpretation of non-contact sensor outputs is significantly less reliable, even in areas where adequate ground control (i.e., measurement of factor values in selected sites by contact methods) is available. Reliability decays rapidly as ground control points become more sparse. The most impressive advantage of non-contact methods is the speed and ease by which large areas can be studied and mapped, assuming of course that suitable imagery is available. By far the least reliable of the three data acquisition methods is the indirect procedure; at its worst, it yields information which is hardly more than an educated guess. At best, when supported by adequate topographic maps and literature sources, it may provide a data store only somewhat less reliable than photo interpretation. Obviously, all three methods can play a useful role, depending upon the situation.

The function of the various information acquisition methods, along with the parallel translation and interpretation processes, is to provide specific data on areas of interest in a form that can be used as input for the several performance prediction models. The most convenient method thus far developed for recording the planimetric distribution of factor value data appears to be the factor map (column 4, Fig. 1). In this mapping procedure, the total range of variation of value of each factor in the area of interest is established. These ranges are then subdivided into convenient classes, with the class ranges selected in such a way that the errors introduced by using the class ranges as input into the relevant mathematical models are small enough to be acceptable. For example, in the factor maps designed for use with the present airfield construction effort model, the characteristic slope factor is subdivided into four classes: 0 to 2, 2 to 10, 10 to 30, and more than 30%. These classes were chosen largely because the error introduced by using the midpoint of the class ranges as entry values in the mathematical model gave predictions which were acceptable approximations of the values which would be obtained by the 'class envelope'. As an illustration, the variation introduced by using 0° as opposed to 2° as input values in the airfield construction effort model would, all other things being equal, result in a change of estimated construction time for a light lift airfield of less than one day. Since the model is assumed to be reliable to only the nearest day, this class of slope values is entirely acceptable.

The various factors are mapped independently, if possible by different analysts, to ensure that the maps are as objective as possible. The actual mapping is done on the basis of all of the information available; such information is usually a combination of the products of two or more of the information acquisition systems described above. Factor maps of this form have been produced and used in practical exercises (Shamburger and Grabau 1968). An example of a slope factor map, intended for use as input to a cross-country locomotion model, is given in Figure 2.

Simple line maps, such as the factor maps, are relatively easy to convert to digital form for storage in computer memory (Spartan 1962). While this seems at first glance like a difficult way to file a map (why not put the map sheet in a library?), there are in fact some very significant advantages to computer storage. For example, the map can be recovered from storage, using an automatic incremental plotter to actually draw the map at any desired scale or on any desired projection so that a transparent overlay can be made to fit any convenient map series without further processing. Another not quite so obvious advantage is retrieval. The terrain evaluation system being hypothesized will eventually include factor maps covering a large proportion of the earth's surface. Further, since there must be as many factor maps for each area as there are significant factors, the number of maps for each area will be large. The number of maps which must be stored soon becomes almost astronomical. It is obvious that a mechanical method of extracting the pertinent maps from the file will be a necessity, and this logic inevitably leads to the storage of both object and its retrieval data in the same form in the same place. The most space–and time–conserving method is to use digits on a few feet of magnetic tape. There is also a fringe benefit: the data could be sent to any point on earth by radio or telephone within minutes of demand.

An ideal terrain evaluation system should also incorporate a device whereby the rationale for making the various interpretations and translations would be preserved for future reference. Two steps are involved: the recording of measure-

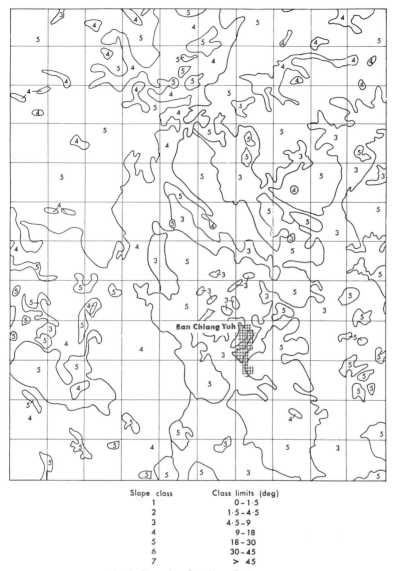

Slope class	Class limits (deg)
1	0 – 1·5
2	1·5 – 4·5
3	4·5 – 9
4	9 – 18
5	18 – 30
6	30 – 45
7	> 45

Fig. 2. Sample of a slope factor map.

ment and sampling procedures to ensure uniformity of measurement among all data collectors, and the recording of interpretation rationale for acquiring data from sensor imagery.

The most sophisticated system for recording measurement procedures at the present time is a partially developed one involving the recording of all significant factor values on a standard format, which in turn is designed to be readily transcribable into automatic data processing (ADP) formats (WES 1968). For those sites visited by field teams, this process is simple and direct, consisting only of making prescribed measurements, filling out the data forms, and transcribing the data to ADP storage (columns 4 and 5, Fig. 1).

The United Kingdom has developed a workable system for recording interpretation rationales (Leibowitz 1966). Basically, the U.K. system envisions a store of both qualitative and quantitative site data, supplemented by appropriate noncontact imagery which is annotated in such a way that future interpreters will find it easy to follow the logic used in interpretation. The system assumes the availability of imagery. Where no ground control is available, the best that can be done is to isolate a sample of the imagery (if imagery is available) relevant to each factor value class, and annotate the imagery with all real or interpreted information derived for that area. A carefully designed system for accomplishing this task has been developed by the U.K. (MEXE 1962). These records, of whatever type, should be stored in some ready-access library, with appropriate subject and location references so that they could be easily removed. This problem has not yet been systematically investigated.

The file of factor maps, on which is recorded the planimetric distributions of the significant value classes of all relevant terrain factors, constitutes the basic store for the terrain evaluation system; but the actual process of evaluation of terrain for engineer purposes has not yet been accomplished. The evaluation process is indicated schematically in segment B of Figure 1.

As an example of the operation of the evaluation process, let it be assumed that a planner is concerned with an operation involving the construction of airfields in some specified geographic region. The first step is to identify the pertinent performance prediction model (column 6, Fig. 1); in this case, the airfield construction effort model is used. The input requirements of the model specify that data on four factors are required: characteristic slope, soil workability, soil depth, and mean basal area of vegetation. Assuming that machine storage systems are successfully developed, the maps displaying these factors could then be withdrawn from machine storage and constructed with an automatic plotter at some convenient scale (column 7, Fig. 1).

The assembled factor maps contain all of the terrain data required to calculate the construction effort required to build an airfield of specified type at any point in the area of interest, but these data are not assembled into the most convenient form. Ideally, the data should be presented in such a way that only the minimum of calculations need be made. For example, let it be assumed that the area of interest is covered by a single 1 : 50,000 quadrangle, and that the user is concerned with locating the site in that area at which construction time for a light lift airfield will be least. The obvious thing to do would be to calculate the construction effort for every point in an arbitrary grid of, say, 1 km. This would mean that the factor value classes for more than 600 points would have to be extracted from the five-factor maps, and the set for each point run through the mathematical model. That point with the minimum predicted value would be the sought-for location. This procedure is obviously time-consuming and laborious. A potentially faster and far more flexible method is to first compile all of the pertinent factor maps into a 'factor complex' map, by sequentially overlaying all of the factor maps (column 7, Fig. 1). Such a map delineates all areas exhibiting the same arrays of factor value classes. In any one quadrangle, there are rarely more than 30 or 40 different arrays; thus, the process of recording all possible array combinations for any one small area is enormously simplified.

There are, quite naturally, some disadvantages. Since the factors were mapped independently and the factors are independent attributes of nature, the map unit boundaries on successive factor maps coincide only in part; as a result, the factor complex maps are usually relatively complex. Several hundred or even several thousand different aggregations of factor value classes may occur in any large geographic area. It must be emphasized that a factor complex is *not* a land form (except by coincidence). For example, a land form such as a cuesta may be subdivided into a number of factor complexes on the basis of slope variations, vegetation differences, soil depth variations, and so on. The large number of factor complexes is, of course, a significant data storage and retrieval problem when dealing with large and complex areas.

At the present time, factor complex maps have only been compiled by hand (Shamburger and Grabau 1968). This is at best an inordinately tedious and costly process. However, a computer program for accomplishing this process has been written and is reported as nearly ready for utilization (Spartan 1962).

Since each factor complex is characterized by a discrete combination of factor value classes, it follows that each factor complex will be characterized by a single construction effort value. The products of the evaluation computations (column 7, Fig. 1) can be placed on the map in the appropriate map units (i.e., in the chosen example, a construction effort number is substituted for the equivalent terrain type number). The user can now read the average number of days required to build an airfield of the specified type at all points in the area of interest directly from a performance prediction map (column 8, Fig. 1), which in this case would be a map delineating areas requiring the same number of days to build the specified airfield. Such maps have been produced manually, and an example is given in Figure 3, but no procedure has yet been devised for producing them with automatic data processing machines. However, since the process from factor complex map to performance prediction map is entirely mechanical, there appears to be no reason why the process cannot be automated.

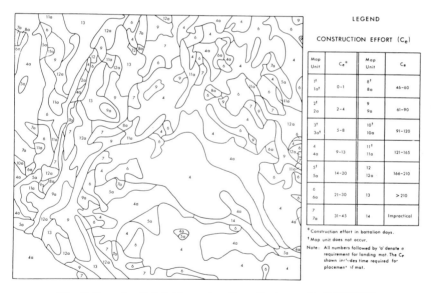

Fig. 3. Sample of airfield construction effort map (1 : 2,500,000).

It would also be convenient for the user if a tabulation were available showing the total range of construction times that could be expected in the geographic area of interest, as well as the proportoin of total areas exhibiting various levels of required construction effort, and so on. Since each construction effort level (or value) is delineated as a map unit on the final map, the areas of each can be readily measured or calculated and the results tabulated with great ease (column 8, Fig. 1).

Even this may not be enough. The basic performance prediction model in the example chosen is based on the assumption that the work force is a standard

Engineer construction battalion. It is quite possible to imagine a situation in which the time required for such a standard battalion to construct the needed airfields would be tactically unacceptable, but in which a specially constituted force of equivalent size might accomplish the task. For example, in heavily forested flat terrain, the work force might be modified by increasing the tree-felling and disposal capability at the expense of grading capability. However, before a decision to change the composition of the work force can logically be made, the user must know in some detail the nature of the terrain environment. Accordingly, in at least some situations it would be useful to provide the user with not only the basic factor complex map (column 7, Fig. 1) but also perhaps a compilation of site descriptions and air photo images relevant to the area of interest. Since these will presumably be stored in a readily accessible file (column 5, Fig. 1), of the general form developed by the United Kingdom (Leibowitz 1966), compilation of these into a reference summary (column 8, Fig. 1) would be simple and direct. Since the factor complex maps contain all of the relevant terrain data, the analyst could (at least theoretically) determine which factors were responsible for the greatest amount of construction effort. Thus, in the example cited above, the terms of the construction effort model devoted to grading and vegetation clearing would be examined independently, and an optimum balance between the work forces devoted to each could be calculated. By obvious extension, this also implies that the size and composition of the work force required to do a particular job in a previously specified length of time could be calculated. It must however be emphasized that the existing models have not yet been used in this way.

Compilation of all pertinent information into a prototype presentation is still not quite enough to meet the practical needs of the development engineer; the information must be reproduced in sufficient quantities to be available to all potential users, and it must be distributed to such users in time to be of benefit (column 9, Fig. 1). The U.S. Army Engineer Topographic Laboratories are continuing the development of integrated reproduction and distribution techniques and machines to deal with the problems raised by these requirements.

Thus, a completely integrated and largely mechanized terrain evaluation system for use by engineer and land development agencies can be visualized. Further, major modules of the integrated system are in being, albeit still in experimental form, so that the successful operation of the entire system can be confidently anticipated.

REFERENCES

LEIBOWITZ, T. H. (1966). *Techniques Required to Build Up a Library of Annotated Aerial Photographs*. (Soil Science Laboratory, University of Oxford: Oxford, England.)

MILITARY ENGINEERING EXPERIMENTAL ESTABLISHMENT (1962). *A data storage system for desert terrain*. Military Engng Exp. Establ. Christchurch, England.

SHAMBURGER, J. H., and GRABAU, W. E. (1968). *Mobility environmental research study. A quantitative method for describing terrain for ground mobility*. U.S. Army Engineer Waterways Experiment Station, CE. Vicksburg, Miss.

SPARTAN AIR SERVICES LIMITED (1962). *Evaluation of land use techniques for processing military geographic intelligence*. Contract report prepared for U.S. Army Engineer Geodesy, Intelligence and Mapping Research and Development Agency: Ft. Belvoir, Va.

U.S. ARMY ENGINEER WATERWAYS EXPERIMENT STATION (1968). *Environmental Data Collection Methods*. Vol. 4, Vegetation.

VAN LOPIK, J., and KOLB, C. R. (1959). *A Technique for preparing desert terrain analogs*. U.S. Army Engineer Waterways Experiment Station, CE. Vicksburg, Miss.

Aspects of a Computer-Based Land Evaluation System

T. Pearcey and T. G. Chapman

Respectively Division of Computing Research and Division of Land Research, CSIRO, Canberra, Australia

The current major obstacles to more comprehensive use of computers in land evaluation are technological rather than conceptual. An outline of the data-handling requirements for an Australian land evaluation system shows that they will be within the capacity of computer technology in the next decade. The most important advances in this field will be the development of very large rapid access stores and sophisticated data-input devices.

Data representations appropriate to such a system will probably consist of hierarchies of linked lists. The final form of a computer-based land evaluation system could be a public utility, which might be developed from, or in connection with, data banks created for other purposes.

INTRODUCTION

The science of land evaluation requires the co-ordinated study of a wide variety of subject matter, ranging from the sciences associated broadly with geophysics and biology to economic and social aspects of rural and urban culture. While the use of computers is increasing rapidly in individual disciplines and in broad treatments of interdisciplinary problems, comprehensive and detailed land evaluation is not yet feasible. The three main limitations are the lack of data in computer-compatible form, the lack of capacity of existing computers to handle the large volumes of data requiring analysis, and the lack of conceptual models of the processes and interrelationships involved. The last limitation is usually the result of the first or second (Chapman 1968; Nix 1968), and we must therefore look to improvements in technology as a means of achieving substantial progress in quantitative land evaluation.

It is the object of this paper to outline the probable effects on land evaluation studies of currently foreseeable advances in computer technology, over a time span of the next 10–20 years. These advances will be characterized by a great increase in the availability of computing services, in the data handling and data manipulation powers of computing systems, and corresponding reductions in the actual cost per operation of these systems. This increase in power and availability will be realized by the use of new techniques in computer design and construction. These techniques include the use of production-line batch fabrication methods now becoming established, and the development and provision of large-scale rapid access stores.

DATA TYPES

Data relevant to land evaluation include both the natural characteristics of land areas and the effects of human activity on land. The data therefore cover such parameters as topography, geology, climate and hydrology, soils, vegetative cover, geophysical parameters such as gravitational and geomagnetic fields, agriculture, plant and animal ecology, population and production statistics, and transport systems.

In general, land data can be classified as alphanumeric or graphic. Alphanumeric data describe or define land parameters (or variables which are relevant to land processes) at a point or within an area. Thus, rain gauge and soil auger data relate essentially to a point, while examples of area data would be a scientist's 'site' description, or crop yield from a particular plot under specified conditions. Much of this data is dependent on time or other variables (such as the various treatments in an agronomic experiment), and requires expression in arrays or arrayed lists, of two or more dimensions. In particular, descriptive data will naturally be held as linear arrays of characters.

Graphic data describe or define representations of one or more variables in two dimensions, and thus constitute maps of these variables. The examples in Figure 1, of the commonly occurring types of graphic, show that the structure may define areas of given attributes, as in the area-attribute (slope class, land

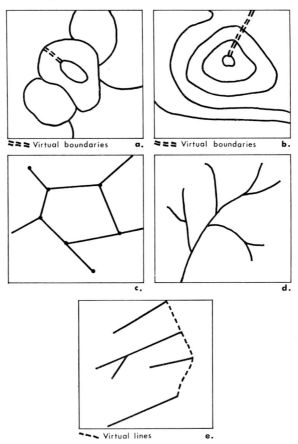

Fig. 1. Categories of land data maps: (a), area-attribute maps; (b), topographic and geographical contour maps; (c), communication and route maps; (d), drainage nets; (e) fault line maps.

system, etc.) and the topographical contour map, or lines with given attributes, as in the communication map and the drainage net. Another type of map is seen in the geological fault line map which usually consists of isolated lines or groups of lines (Fig. 1). In either case, the graphic is associated with alphanumeric data corresponding to the attributes of particular areas or lines.

Pictorial data, such as aerial photographs, are also used in land evaluation, and are interpreted in terms of associations of tone (or colour) and texture, usually as seen on a stereo model. Whether the interpretation is subjective or a programmed result of a high-speed scanning process. it will be expressed in the form of a graphic, i.e., a line diagram. We may therefore retain pictorial data in their original form outside the system (for possible re-interpretation), and make the abstracted graphics available to the system.

Both alphanumeric and graphic data may be objective or subjective, but the proportion of subjective data is higher in graphics, owing to general lack of information on spatial variations of land parameters. Objective graphics include statistical and legal maps, topographical contour maps, communication route maps, and drainage nets. Examples of subjective graphics are land system and soils maps and isohyetal maps.

DATA VOLUME

Alphanumeric Data

The following estimates are based on raw data, which should be available to the system at some level, though not necessarily in the immediate access stores.

We can obtain a first estimate of the requirements for an Australia-wide system by considering some specific examples:

1. *Hydroclimatic data* (climate, stream flow, groundwater levels) are numeric and time-variable. The current collection rate is 10^7 items per year and the total current storage is about 15×10^7 items (Chapman 1967). Taking each item as requiring 20 characters, the storage requirement in 10 years would be 5×10^9 characters. The immediate access data might be averages or totals for daily or longer periods.

2. *Agronomic data* are alphanumeric and mainly time-invariant (e.g., the crop yield at a stated location under specified conditions). The current collection rate could be 10^7 to 10^8 items per year (M. J. T. Norman, private communication), and the present storage probably represents 10 years at the current collection rate. Taking each item as requiring 10 characters, the storage requirement in 10 years would be 2×10^9 to 2×10^{10} characters. The immediate access material might be data summaries in correlational form.

3. *Geological data* are alphanumeric and time-invariant. The data content of point observations on a 1:250,000 map (in terms of position, geological observations of rock type and structural attitude, and the results of chemical analyses on samples) is about 4×10^6 characters (T. Quinlan, unpublished data). The storage requirement in 10 years would be about 2×10^9 characters.

Taking into consideration the other types of alphanumeric data under collection, we can estimate a total storage requirement rising to 10^{12} characters in the next 10–20 years.

Graphic Data

The actual storage requirements of graphics are currently very difficult to assess even when they are constrained to the minimum for machine storage. A rough estimate for the contents of a normal 1:50,000 topographic map gives a set of about 10^6 items each of about 12 characters. A typical set of such maps (not all at 1:50,000 scale) for Australia might then require about 10^{12} characters. If we then allow for the range of objective and subjective maps of relevance to land evaluation, the total storage volume would be of the order of 10^{14} to 10^{15} characters.

It may not be necessary to hold graphic data in digital form, as an essentially fixed picture representation of a map could be read optically and converted into a digital form immediately before use. We would, however, still require all the alphanumeric data in digital form, and the requirement for 10^{12} characters of digital storage therefore remains, although the volume needed for immediate access would be at least one order lower.

COMPUTER CAPABILITIES

It is clear that we are still only on the fringe of the use of computers for land evaluation. The greatest restriction to full development of computer use is due to the difficulty of cross-referencing data of different categories, frequently held on different storage media or storage areas, which the complexity of full appreciation of land data requires. For computer design the difficulty is therefore primarily one of obtaining adequate ready access storage space which will allow cross referencing of data at high speed. Aspects of computing capability and speed constitute only a secondary difficulty.

The data processing computer, and the computer technology and industry, have developed almost entirely in the past 20 years, and there has been a series of revolutionary advances in the technology from the old vacuum tube to the present micro-integrated circuitry. Micro-integrated technology will result in much greater reliability and reduced size with correspondingly reduced power loads. It will also provide additional speed at very much lower cost for the same computing capability (Fig. 2) (Pearcey 1966).

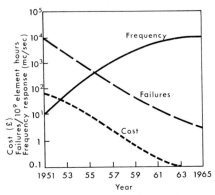

Fig. 2. Transistor performance and cost.

The use of micro-integrated techniques is just one aspect of a much wider change taking place in computer technology, the use of batch fabrication methods. These methods tend to make the computer a product of mass production technology, using highly automated continuous production line methods. The components, being mass fabricated in large batches, become correspondingly cheaper. Batch fabrication techniques do not stop at the production of electronic logic circuitry but are applied to interwiring, storage media, peripheral devices, and so on.

With the reduction in the cost of units and corresponding increases in reliability it will be possible to provide greater data processing and storage capability to larger and larger units or groups of units. This will particularly apply to the design of cheap and simple communication and input and output terminals. It will therefore be possible to hold data in considerably greater volume than we do at present and to provide information contained within the system to a wider variety of users. With the foreseeable techniques we can expect storage capacity of high speed access, e.g., a few microseconds, to rise to the neighbourhood of from 10^7 to 10^8 characters, backed with larger stores, with longer access times as illustrated by Table 1.

TABLE 1

The hierarchy of storage media

Storage Type	Logic Type*	Order of Maximum Capacity (Characters)	Access Times (Microseconds)
Internal processing	Electronic transistor	$10^4 - 10^5$	$0 \cdot 1 - 1 \cdot 0$
Immediate access	Magnetic film or core	$10^7 - 10^8$	$1-5$
Medium access	Magnetic drum and disc	$10^8 - 10^{11}$	$10^4 - 10^5$
Large-scale backing	Cryogenic	$10^8 - 10^{11}$	$5-20$
Main data banks	Magnetic and optical cards	$10^{14} - 10^{15}$	$5 \times 10^5 - 2 \times 10^6$

* For comparison one magnetic tape stores about 15×10^6 characters but may have an access time from a few seconds to some minutes.

From this table it will be seen that the size of the immediate access storage will be able to handle the digital representation of at least one map and its associated alphanumeric data amounting to about 10^8 characters.

Increases in speed of data manipulation to operation rates of about 5×10^7/second are foreseeable, although there is a physical upper limit to the rates attainable with a single processor, and with multiprocessor complexes the actual operation rates of 10^8 to 10^9 operations per second may become available. Figure 2 shows how recent technologies have increased the speeds of electronic operation, have improved reliability, and decreased the cost of computing equipment other than peripheral units in which progress is somewhat slower.

INPUT, OUTPUT, AND MEDIA

Within the next few years, we may envisage an improvement in the types of, and particularly the ease of use and suitability of, input and output devices and media. At present, current media, e.g., punched cards, paper tape, and printed output, are not suitable to the data handled. It is clear that a considerable proportion of data to be handled by a land evaluation computer system will be textual and the use of character readers for direct input of textual data from documents will become common practice. In addition, we must envisage a large class of input via picture scanners which will accept monotone photographs and represent them by a digitization of the varying level of greyness of the photograph produced, possibly by subjecting it to a linear scan.

Although the aerial or other type of photograph is usually very complex, so that interpretation will inevitably be complex and require abstraction of the data contained within it, many pictures will be of the line drawing or graphic type in which no data will be lost in transfer to internal representation.

We may anticipate a considerable increase in the speed of printing of textual output but we will also have available visual facilities through the use of display consoles on which pictures or diagrams will be output for visual inspection (with textual annotations). Systems will also be provided for input via keyboards and by facilities for indicating positions within a displayed area, in an on-line fashion, so that the user may guide the progress of an investigation as it proceeds. In association with this display facility there will naturally be a photographic or other facility for recording diagrams required for study at leisure. One can also envisage a need, at the level of a public information retrieval utility, of both input and output via a telephone only.

An important medium which is capable of very high density is the optical film store. This can provide storage densities considerably higher than are available on magnetic media which are limited by the physical size of the magnetic reading and writing gap. We may expect, for instance, that much of the essentially static data needed for land evaluation may be transferred to optical film frames, each being selected and scanned under program control. In particular, we can envisage a system, as yet not developed, which would combine the advantages of both the optical and magnetic type stores by using selectable card decks, each of which contains two areas, an area containing mainly diagrammatical map data (giving a higher density of information from which a digital picture may be reconstructed) and a magnetic film area on to which textual data may be encoded. This latter will be data containing keys to the associated diagram, and the relevant textual information concerning the areas or entities in the picture, and any descriptive data relating to points within the areas represented by the diagrams. With such a combination of media it would be possible to update the textual data until it becomes necessary to reconstruct the picture component, and thereafter the textual data would be transferred to a new card and a new picture exposed on its photographic area through a suitable output device.

DATA REPRESENTATION

We have indicated that the main sets of the alphanumeric and pictorial data may be held on an optical-magnetic type of storage medium and that the medium would contain the detail of the main data bank. The ready access store would contain program sequences transferable from drums and discs or large-scale immediate access stores, together with suitable directories leading to items of data in the main bank and any other additional data which may be required sufficiently frequently to justify very rapid access.

So far as internal representation of data is concerned it will be necessary to hold picture data and some selected and associated textual data for manipulation and assessment and we have seen that the ready access store would probably hold such a set of associated data together with one digitized picture at any one time.

When required to handle a picture and related textual data (a picture on an optical-magnetic card would consist mainly of a line drawing and related text would be entirely on the magnetic textual area), the picture could be scanned linearly and the line structure of the picture could be reconstructed in the internal store. One method of representation would, for instance, allow the data to be held as a set of data arrays representing the vector elements of curves or straight lines constituting the picture. Thus, a closed loop of lines would constitute a ring of elementary vector arrays, each array defining the start and end points of a line and its path between them. The ring would be formed in store by linking the sequence of arrays together in a form of a circularly linked list. Thus, a ring of such arrays, each array of which represents the path from one node to the next, would define an enclosed region of the picture, and a set

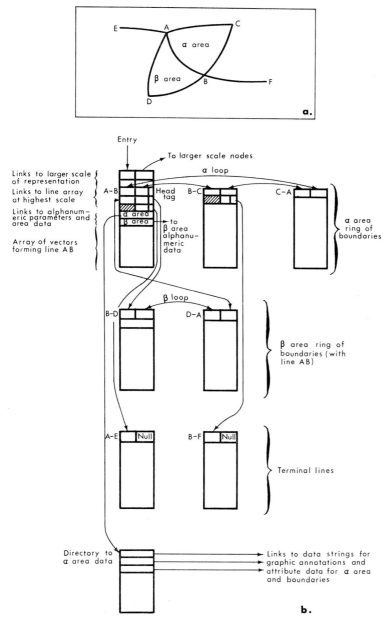

Fig. 3. A possible form of internal data structure for handling line maps and related alphanumeric data: (a), the line map; (b) the data structure.

of regions would be represented by linked rings connecting at the appropriate nodes. Common lines separating regions would be common to neighbouring rings.

Thus for instance, land form maps which usually consist of groups of adjacent areas would be well represented by rings of line segment arrays. However, in the case of contour maps and land form maps which contain multiply-connected areas, it would be possible to define arbitrary starting points to denote the ring origin as would be done with normally adjacent areas, and to define a pair of virtually coincident boundaries (Cook 1967) so as to reduce the original complex of areas effectively to a set of simply connected areas, so that a continuous trace of all area boundaries would be internally represented by connected array rings (see Fig. 1). A typical possible internal structure is illustrated in Figure 3 for areas ABC and ABD.

In this representation of a picture which contains virtual boundaries the program utilizing the array ring structure may trace from an initially defined starting point in the structure to any point in the boundary net. With this facility, it would be possible to carry out computations on a picture, such as finding areas marked by boundaries.

Somewhat different map forms are those like drainage nets, in which the lines on the map form a type of tree structure instead of a ring structure. In such cases the internal representation of the picture would have the form of a tree structure of arrays, each array representing the sequence of elementary vectors of the stream paths between nodes, or from a node to a source, or from an initial main node to the main boundary of the figure.

Terminal arrays would thus not point to any next array and the link would be left null (see Fig. 3, lines BE and BF). However, at all nodes, the links to neighbouring arrays would point both forward and backward so that searching within an array net may be made easy.

It may be noted that a communication net is of an intermediate type between a contour or land form map and a drainage net, in that it contains both ring type loops and terminal routes connected only at one end, and may contain more than one system of communication.

Descriptive or other specific data, related to a line, line ring, or enclosed area will be pointed to by inclusion in the appropriate array of line vectors and list, of links to other lines and a further link to a directory leading to the appropriate alphanumeric data array for the associated vector and/or area. Thus the data at the head of the first array of a ring or list would contain reference data related to the ring, line, or area enclosed and would also lead to data relating to points with defined co-ordinates within the areas represented by the associated array ring (see Fig. 3; data referred to at head of AB array). Data relating to more than one area would be linked to the same node and array. The relevant area represented by the data pointed to may be determined from the order of the linkage and the order of the angles at the node in a particular chosen direction of rotation.

Alphanumeric data will contain parameter data related to area or line segments including annotations, which would be placed on the picture if displayed on an output display, and data related to neighbouring points within the area concerned. It is evident that a hierarchy of forms of significant items in a data set will exist and that data may become more detailed as one passes down the hierarchy of a data structure. These levels of structure would be analogous to representation of the data at different scales of mapping. Thus at one higher level a number of areas, probably adjacent, would be considered as a single area. In such a case a record must be kept of the structure of the data forms at higher levels. It is suggested that the individual basic area or line elements, e.g., as in land form and communication maps respectively, be further associated with a group of links between nodes and that each such group should represent a network of nodes at a high level of abstraction. These would be initially determined by the originator of the map or by use of a suitable automatic selection system determined by prescribed characteristics, and would be held with alphanumeric data related to the first property array formed on entering the data structure of a picture (see Fig. 3). The form of the level structure reconstructs the complete picture at any chosen level with annotations to the user, via a suitable output display system.

By associating a group of different but related pictures and their associated alphanumeric data, new maps of association of areas etc. would be constructed and textual data created for them. These would form part of an extending field of data within the system.

It will be necessary at times to recover alphanumeric data independently of the associated map figures so that an additional directory to the full list of alphanumeric data must also be provided. This is not indicated in Figure 3.

SYSTEM CAPABILITIES AND THE LAND EVALUATION UTILITY

The system must first have the ability to grow from any input of alphanumeric or pictorial data. As stated above, the complexity of pictorial material will be reduced to graphics for system storage. Development of automated techniques to achieve abstractions of pictorial material, for particular purposes, will probably be the most difficult part of the whole task of system design and implementation (Rosenfeld 1968).

The system must next provide facilities to the user to access array elements of data in the hierarchical structure from the highest to the lowest level, the lowest scale corresponding to the individual map or graphic and its associated alphanumeric parameters and point-descriptive data. The higher levels of data and those which may be most frequently accessed will naturally be held on a more rapidly accessible storage, but the bulk of the data will be held on a special medium such as the magnetic or optical-magnetic storage bank. Provided the data access facility is available, the system becomes essentially an information retrieval system for land data (such as Tomlinson 1968), probably operated in an on-line manner. This will require output media such as teletype, visual displays, and telephonic output.

While the development of a computer-based system could probably be justified solely on the benefits from its use as an information retrieval tool, the facility to access data, and to cross refer between files related to the same geographical areas in different contexts, would provide the research worker with the tools to develop land evaluation as a science. The system would enable the testing of hypotheses and models at any level of sophistication. The resulting increased understanding of processes and inter-relationships would lead to more definitive and accurate predictions at the local, regional, and national level.

As part of the research facility it will be possible to create new associations of data from new and existing data, through control of the system by the user. In this way the stock of information which will be directly available will be continually improved, as new data associations are created and placed permanently in the internal storage.

The system must also be capable not only of creating related data by derivation from data already provided, but must also be able to modify, update, and extend existing files.

In order to provide the user with requested abstractions from both alpha-numeric and graphic data, the system must be capable of forming, at any chosen level of detail, suitable data structures for output as an annotated graphic.

To perform these functions, an appropriate control language must be defined and implemented for input/output and internal data manipulation. The input and output features of such a system have been described in a previous section. Such a language must allow for interaction, e.g., by request and response, between system and user, so that the user may guide the system through a desired course of operation. This is particularly important for the land assess-ment research worker.

The foregoing discussion has assumed that the land evaluation system will be complete in itself and hold all data relevant to its purposes. It would be more realistic to suppose that it will obtain some of its data (particularly at levels of considerable detail) through links with other data banks, such as those for meteorology and census and statistics. We can therefore envisage a number of related data banks (with fixed or translatable formats for common usage) as together providing a computer-based land evaluation public utility.

Such a system would be used by government, other public utilities, private industry, and individual citizens, and its effectiveness would be continually increased by the access of new data and the development of more powerful analytical procedures by research workers.

CONCLUSION

It will become feasible for an efficient and useful technique of land evaluation to be created on a computer-based system. Such a system would comprise a continuous hierarchy of storage systems of various levels of accessibility, and would contain a large volume of data relevant to a wide range of forms of land assessment and prediction. The data required would cover a very wide context, and would preferably be derived from a combination of the mass of data now available to unconnected and widely different organizations.

The formation of a comprehensive computer-based land evaluation system could be the basis of a public information and land development utility. It would be useful to a wide range of organizations and professions, and would constitute an important facility for the economic development of Australia.

REFERENCES

CHAPMAN, T. G. (1967). Measurements for water resource assessment. In *The Collection and Processing of Field Data*. pp. 131–48. (Wiley: New York.)

CHAPMAN, T. G. (1968). Catchment parameters for a deterministic rainfall-runoff model. In *Land Evaluation*. (Ed. G. A. Stewart) (Macmillan: Melbourne.)

COOK, B. G. (1967). A computer representation of plane region boundaries. *Aust. Comput. J.* 1, 44.

NIX, H. A. (1968). The assessment of biological productivity. In *Land Evaluation*. (Ed. G. A. Stewart) (Macmillan: Melbourne.)

PEARCEY, T. (1966). The new technologies and their effects on computers and computing. *Comput. Bull.* 10, 43.

ROSENFELD, A. (1968). Automated picture interpretation. In *Land Evaluation*. (Ed. G. A. Stewart) (Macmillan: Melbourne.)

TOMLINSON, R. F. (1968). A geographic information system for regional planning. In *Land Evaluation* (Ed. G. A. Stewart) (Macmillan: Melbourne.)

The Role of Humans in Land Evaluation

Frank R. Gibbons, J. N. Rowan, and R. G. Downes

Soil Conservation Authority of Victoria, Australia

There are three basic stages in land evaluation – receiving stimuli, recognizing whatever gave rise to them, and interpreting, or assessing the significance of, that information.

People can detect many of the features of the land, and may be more efficient than instruments in doing so, but their important role lies particularly in their ability to interpret intuitively and also to develop a purpose and to make decisions quickly in the process of achieving it.

These capabilities are based upon the reception and storage of abundant and varied impressions continuously over long periods of time.

The role of people in the intrinsic or general-purpose approach to land evaluation lies in their ability to recognize areas with high covariance of the various land features and so to provide the essential initial hypothesis for investigation by other means. Similarly, in the extrinsic, specific-purpose approach, they can direct attention to those relationships between the land features and the proposed use which it is most useful to investigate further by other means. The ability of people to do those things depends mainly on their having had suitable experience and training.

Humans are likely to keep the directive role in land evaluation, and leave the routine operations increasingly to instruments.

THE IMPORTANCE OF INTERPRETATION

Evaluation is assessing the value, or usefulness, of an object for some purpose of the user.

There are three basic stages in evaluation. The first is the receiving of stimuli. This is the physical reaction of a body to external conditions; for example, a tree may cause chemical changes, corresponding to its image, on the retina of an eye.

The second stage is elucidating the received stimuli—assigning meaning to them, or recognizing whatever caused them. This is the referring, to previous reactions, of that reaction to the received stimuli. The recognition may be at different levels, because it answers the question 'what is the nature of the phenomenon which has given rise to the stimuli?', and there may be various aspects of that nature. One aspect is 'what are the attributes of the phenomenon?', and another is 'what is the phenomenon and how is it related to other phenomena?'. For example, elucidating the chemical changes may provide the information that there are brown, rough surfaces progressively divided and then ending in shiny green surfaces. Everyone can recognize the phenomenon as a tree, but only people familiar with trees can recognize it as a brown stringybark.

The third stage is interpreting the phenomenon which has given rise to the stimuli, relative to some purpose of the interpreter. This is the referring, to previous recognitions, of the information obtained about the phenomenon. It answers the question 'what is the significance of the phenomenon to the interpreter?'. For example, in land evaluation, it is not enough that the tree should be recognized as a brown stringybark; it should also allow the observer to assess its significance, such as that the site on which it grows is freely drained but chemically infertile.

As a result of interpreting the phenomena, the interpreter may acquire some further purpose, for example, to gather more information of a particular kind. This is distinct from the prior purpose involved in the interpretive stage and is in response to the interpretation; it may be followed by a decision as to the means of achieving the newly acquired purpose.

Therefore, assessing the significance of the information received previously and continuing that assessment until a satisfactory conclusion is reached depend mainly on the interpretive stage.

THE BASIC CAPABILITIES OF HUMANS IN LAND EVALUATION

The receptive stage by humans in land evaluation is mainly in sight and touch, the senses of taste, smell, and hearing not often being used. The limitations, as compared with instruments, are in the inability to receive any stimuli other than a particular range of wave-length, in those limitations associated with remoteness, such as not seeing distant objects clearly, oblique vision for land-scape, and finally in the inability to touch beyond arms' length. An advantage is the greater facility, in practice, although not in principle, for the continuous use of various faculties together, for example, continuous, stereoscopic, colour vision while moving, thus allowing an appreciation of a wide variety of shapes, sizes, colour, and perspective.

The stages of recognition and interpretation by humans have as their basis the abundance of the information being received continuously over long periods of time, the storage of some of it, and the close linkage of the interpretive and receptive organs. For these two stages, people as compared with instruments such as digital recorders and computers, have two chief limitations. The first is that they cannot treat the data quantitatively—that is, as measurable and therefore transferable, comparable, capable of being correlated, and amenable to testing. The second limitation is the incomplete and transient storage, result-ing in distorted records. A photograph stays the same, but the ability of humans to recall a memory is notoriously unreliable.

Humans, however, do have advantages for these stages. One is the greater storage effected. This is partly because of the relatively large storage capacity and partly because of the abundance of data received. As Williams (1963) pointed out, the human brain is incomparably more efficient than any com-puter; consider also the variety and scope of impressions received during just one minute when observantly walking through the bush – what, then, of the experience of years? This advantage allows humans to relate readily the data stored at different times, thus resulting in the capacity for intuition, which is the immediate comprehension, or unconscious assessing, of the significance of information. Another advantage is the relatively closer linkage, in practice, if not in principle, between the receptive, interpretive, and motor-organs, which allows the deliberate and informed seeking of further information as the immediate result of interpreting information previously received. These faculties for almost immediate interpretation and for continuous planned, purposive action are human characteristics, and, at a different level, that of the desire which activates the purpose, form one of the essential differences between humans and computers (Williams 1963).

Humans and instruments, then, have relative advantages and disadvantages in both the receptive stage and the stages of recognition and interpretation. Consequently, in land evaluation, people and instruments can be used together, each to varying extents. For example, although some soil features such as surface temperature can be determined by remote instrumental sensing, it is impracticable to detect other features such as the structure of the soil-profile without direct human examination. Similarly, it is possible to determine the various topographic features – aspect, slope, and elevation – by remote sensing alone, but it may be easier to determine these more directly if people happen to be at a particular site in order to examine the soil.

For a better understanding of the human role in land evaluation, it is useful to list the reasons for using instruments. These are:

1. To detect stimuli which humans cannot receive;
2. To obtain data more easily than people can get it, or from places inaccessible to them;
3. To obtain the data objectively or consistently;
4. To obtain measurable data;
5. To obtain correlations and elucidate interrelationships (including constructing systems of classification and evaluation);
6. To test the reliability of conclusions.

The first four of these reasons are involved in the receiving stage, and the last two are involved in the stage of recognition. It is not possible, however, to use instruments alone in the interpretive stage, which involves the essentially human faculty of purpose.

THE TWO BASIC APPROACHES TO LAND EVALUATION AND THEIR REQUIREMENTS FOR USEFULNESS

Land evaluation is assessing the value or usefulness of land for one or more uses of it. If the land assessed has a range of value for the proposed use, land evaluation includes classification of the land, which is the grouping of different kinds of land according to their value for one or more uses. Consequently, the concepts of classification may be applied to evaluation.

The usefulness of a system of classification depends on its predictive ability for the value of an attribute, the reliability of the estimate, and the relevance of the predicted information to the proposed use (Goodall 1966; Gibbons 1968). Because of interaction between the attributes or between them and other environmental features, the relationships between the attributes and a measure of the proposed use may alter, and thus the relevance may be diminished or destroyed. For example, if soil texture be a relevant feature for plant growth, because of its effect on the wetness of the site, then a difference in climate is likely to alter that relevance of soil texture for plant growth, because climate, also, will affect the wetness of the site.

So also with land evaluation – its usefulness depends on its predictive ability for the characteristics of an area of land, the reliability of the prediction, and the relevance of the predicted information to the proposed use. The relevance, and therefore the usefulness of the evaluation, may be diminished by interaction between the various features of the land.

The requirements for high predictive ability, reliability and relevance in land evaluation depend on the approach adopted, which is determined by the purpose of the evaluation.

There are two main approaches. The first is where there may be any use – proposed uses or uses not yet known – for the land being evaluated; here, the proposed use is regarded as infinite and the evaluation is termed intrinsic. Examples of intrinsic systems of land evaluation are those devised for the land surveys of the CSIRO Division of Land Research, Soil Conservation Authority of Victoria, and Canadian Department of Forestry. The requirements for high utility in an intrinsic system of evaluation are, for high relevance, a large number of different attributes so that the relevant attributes are likely to be included, and, for high predictive ability, a high degree of covariance between them. This latter is essential for the effectiveness of an intrinsic system.

The second approach is where there is a limited number of proposed uses for the land; here the evaluation is termed extrinsic. An example is surveys to determine the suitability of land for citrus crops in irrigation areas. There are three requirements for high relevance in an extrinsic system. The first is a knowledge of the relationships between the various attributes of the land and some measure of the proposed use, so that the appropriate ones can be chosen as the basis for the system of evaluation, and their significance for the proposed use be known. For example, if the drainage-status of the soil is important in the growing of oranges, then the fact must be known so that that feature can be included in the basis of the system; furthermore, it will be necessary to know the effect of the various degrees of drainage on the yield of oranges if predictions are to be made. Secondly, a knowledge is required of the inter-actions so that the conditions may be known under which particular features are relevant, or the relevant features be known for a particular set of conditions. For example, both soil texture and soil structure may affect the drainage status, so that, for texture to be the relevant feature, a particular soil structure is required; conversely, if the soil be of a particular texture, it will be known that structure is the relevant feature. Thirdly, a knowledge is required of the conditions under which there will be no interaction. High predictive ability will follow if the chosen feature be one of known relationship with the proposed use.

THE ROLE OF HUMANS IN THE INTRINSIC APPROACH TO LAND EVALUATION

For intrinsic systems of land evaluation to be effective, high covariance between a large number of environmental features is required. In the intrinsic approach, therefore, the main functions are:

1. To recognize areas with such high covariance because it is only within them that a particular intrinsic system can be expected to be useful.
2. To determine the features and their values for the area so recognized, in order to construct the system.

Over large areas, there is often but little overall correlation between the various environmental features. This happens where two or more of the relatively independent variables of the environment do in fact vary independently – for example, an area across which the climate shows gradual change and in which there is a range of topographic positions or a number of rock types. There, because there is no covariance of the chief factors, because there may be inter-action between those factors, and because similar end products among the dependent variables may be produced by different combinations of the in-dependent factors, there is no general high covariance amongst those dependent features.

However, locally within that area, even at all places within that area, correla-tions between the features of the environment may be high. This happens in those smaller areas where only one independent factor varies, for example, topography in a restricted part wherein the climatic differences are slight and with the same rock type. There, the variations in each of the dependent features will reflect only the variations in that independent factor and consequently will covary with each other; as a result, each such smaller area is one in which a particular intrinsic system may be effective.

These areas with relatively high covariance can be recognized by people, often without the need for instruments to calculate the correlations, although greatly helped by the use of instruments to detect the various features. This human recognition of areas is based upon a realization that, as described above, a high covariance is more likely where fewer of the independent factors vary. It is facilitated first by assessing the degree of relative dependence and independence of the various features in the area, then by determining the circumstances under which fewest of those relatively independent factors vary, and finally by selecting some diagnostic features on the bases of which to recognize the area.

The first of these operations (assessing the degree of dependence) requires an understanding of the principles, although not the detail, of the causative relationships between the various features of the land. The second of the operations may be simple if there be sharp discontinuities in an independent factor – for example, where there are sudden changes in rock type or topography. In areas with gradual change in the independent factors, however, it may be necessary to investigate the relationships between them, and with the dependent features, over an area, in order to determine the rationale of their variation. Once an area has been recognized as likely to show high covariance, the nature of the various features can be determined most efficiently by examining them along the line of variation of the most variable and independent factor, for example, from ridges to valleys. As a result of the more detailed relationships then revealed, the entire hypothesis that the area is one which shows the highest local covariance may be reviewed and, if necessary, modified or discarded. Diagnostic combinations of features on the basis of which to recognize the extent of the area may then be selected – the third operation – and further information sought from any source, including the use of instruments for detection or for recording, to locate the various areas. In short, people can recognize areas with high covariance of features because, with training, they can know how to go about determining what it is most efficient to look for, can decide how and where it is most efficient to look, and in the process can call upon a large amount of data stored in their minds.

This human role is possible in localities unfamiliar to the investigators, but it is likely to be done better when they are in a district which they know. This is not only because of a knowledge of the various visible features of the land, but also because of a familiarity with the relationships between them. Where this familiarity has been deepened by observations and reasoning to that degree of understanding which will allow intuitive assessment, is there any reason to use instruments instead of people to recognize areas in which the intrinsic approach may be used?

To answer this, consider again the reasons for using instruments in land evaluation, as listed previously.

The first four reasons apply to the detection of stimuli, and only the other two reasons are considered at this point.

Thus, the use of instruments to obtain correlations and elucidate inter-relationships is of great assistance, however complex the situation (Webb *et al.* 1967). But the results do not indicate the areas in which there is high covariance – they can only indicate the degree of covariance in the selected area. Therefore, for the essential step in the intrinsic approach (that is, the recognition of areas with high covariance) the quantitative estimate of covariance is useful not as a means of arriving at the conclusion that particular areas are those with high covariance, but as a test of such a conclusion reached intuitively by humans – or else to resolve doubtful situations.

Indeed, it may be claimed that the use of instruments to obtain the correlations is unnecessary in the intrinsic approach because, if there be sufficient doubt about the closeness of the correlation to warrant a quantitative estimate, it is unlikely that the correlations would be high enough for the intuitive approach to be effective. In such an attitude, however, there is the assumption that the human diagnosis is likely to be correct – an assumption which is not justified until there have been studies of the reliability of human intuitive assessment. Such studies are needed now, because, if this particular human role is reliable, then an effective intrinsic approach to land evaluation is feasible, but if not, then, however valid the intrinsic approach may be in an area, it is not practicable at this stage without the reliable preliminary guide by humans as to the areas involved.

There is a subjective element in the human recognition of areas within which an intrinsic approach may be adopted, as shown by the variety of solutions proposed. In the CSIRO Division of Land Research, for example, only one scale of pattern has been used until recently, while in the Soil Conservation Authority of Victoria, three different scales of pattern are adopted, distinguished fundamentally by the number of independent factors (or subgroups of factors) which vary, and hence in the degree of covariance to be expected amongst the features of the land.

In testing the reliability of these various solutions, however, one must distinguish the three basic stages of evaluation. For example, in an area for which an intrinsic system has been proposed because there is a high correlation between visible features, for the approach to succeed, the invisible features (such as the analytical properties of the soil) must also be correlated; if they are not, the approach will fail, but human sensing alone cannot predict the failure. The approach is expected to succeed, but does not. The fault here lies not in the interpretive stage, the unreliability of human intuition, but in the inadequacy of detection, because the situation will occur when a further, hidden factor, such as the content of some chemical in the rock, varies independently of the observed and varying independent factor. This is one of the big drawbacks of the intrinsic 'integrated land survey' and a cause of its harshest criticism – that unreliable predictions have been made. That, however, is a criticism of the fact that neither humans nor instruments can detect the nature of the land adequately and that some people have not realised and kept within such a limitation, but it is not a criticism of the basic role of the human interpretive faculty.

THE ROLE OF HUMANS IN THE EXTRINSIC APPROACH TO LAND EVALUATION

For extrinsic systems of land evaluation to be useful, a number of requirements must be met, as detailed previously.

In the extrinsic approach, to meet these requirements, there are five main functions and, for each of these, the place of human interpretation or purpose may be discussed briefly.

The first is to decide what is the proposed use of the land. This may appear redundant for an extrinsic system, but it is surprising how widely used are some systems of evaluating the land, or particular features of it – for example the Seventh Approximation (U.S. Soil Conservation Service 1960) – in which an extrinsic approach is used, but a general purpose is claimed. The decision is a necessary one in the extrinsic approach and a human one.

The second function is to find out the relationships between the various features of the land and some measure of the proposed use so as to know which features are the most relevant (and thus most suitable to choose as a basis for constructing the system), and also to know their significance for the proposed use (thus allowing predictions to be made). Because this may involve detailed analyses of experimental work (Butler 1964), with the construction of a system of evaluation by the monothetic methods of numerical taxonomy and calculating the predictions for the various classes of the system, all of which can be done by calculators, the human role here is restricted to the programming of computers.

The third function is to analyse the interactions of the environmental features so as to know the conditions under which particular features are relevant, or the relevant features for a particular set of conditions. This requires observations of the relationships between each of the relevant features and some measure of the proposed use, under various combinations of those features. Again, computers can analyse these relationships and so determine the conditions under which particular features will be relevant and determine the relevance of the various features in a particular set of conditions. With this information, it is possible to construct systems of evaluation of known usefulness for particular sets of conditions, and also to know the set of conditions in which a particular system can be applied usefully. However, because these relationships are immersed in the welter of numerous natural situations, as distinct from the carefully planned treatments of experimental work, the computations can be more complex than for the function described just previously. Furthermore, it is in just such natural situations that rough, qualitative assessments of relationships can be made as a result of observation, familiarity, informed thinking, and intuitive interpretation by experienced ecologists. Therefore, it is not a question of whether to use human interpretation or to use instruments, or even that the matter is one of deciding when it is most efficient – or feasible, or cheaper – to use the one or the other. Rather, it is a matter of determining how to use both human and instrumental facilities so that they are complementary. Just as in the intrinsic approach, human interpretation can assist in recognizing areas of high covariance by providing the initial hypothesis which can be tested instrumentally, *so in the extrinsic approach the human assessment of interactions can direct attention to those relationships which are most profitable to be investigated further* – either by people or with instruments. This is an invaluable contribution, and may not necessarily diminish in importance as the use of instruments becomes more efficient – or feasible, or cheaper.

The fourth function is to recognize the areas within which there will be no interaction, so as to know where the relevance is, or is not, altered – that is, where predictions can be made about land use as well as about the features of the land. Interference of this kind as a result of interaction will be less likely where the features covary (Gibbons 1968); consequently, this function is the same as the main function in the intrinsic approach. To recognize areas with high covariance of the various features is the *sine qua non* of the intrinsic approach, but it is not widely realized that it is also indispensable in the extrinsic approach. As pointed out before, people can greatly assist in this function because they can provide the initial hypothesis most efficiently.

The final function is to observe the values of the particular land features chosen as the basis of the system and so to construct the system. This is similar to the second function in the intrinsic approach and the same human techniques as described previously can be applied.

THE FUTURE ROLE OF HUMANS IN LAND EVALUATION

Future developments in land evaluation may be difficult to predict. Consequently, the continuing role of people in land evaluation may depend on their capability to perceive and interpret the unexpected.

The computer can provide unexpected information. Williams' (1963) computer, for example, indicated a correlation between plant communities and parish boundaries which was the result of historical events quite unknown to the investigators at the time of collecting the data. This ability, however, is restricted to revealing unexpected relationships and does not include observing and interpreting unexpected phenomena. This latter, which is serendipity, is a human faculty, based upon the storage of abundant and varied impressions continuously over long periods. Its basis is similar to that of the intuitive interpretation of the land features which provides the hypotheses necessary for the different approaches to land evaluation. Like such intuition, this faculty of apprehending, by apparently happy accident, the significance of events, relies largely on the people involved having suitable experience, familiarity with their subject, and training. How many people, for example, could have emulated Fleming in his discovery of penicillin?

Will the importance of the intuitive interpretation, which provides the hypotheses, diminish with greater power and sophistication of instruments? The answer depends on the nature of the work to be tackled; if that work be the amassing and correlation of data, then the intuitive role will gradually diminish as the accumulation of data provides the basis for the hypotheses. If, however, that work be the solution of fresh problems, then the importance of the intuitive role will remain and will increase with the importance of the problem. Because people have the capacity and purpose to seek fresh problems to solve, the answer lies in their own hands.

In our view, therefore humans are likely to keep the directive role and leave the routine operations more and more to instruments.

It is a pleasure to acknowledge the helpful discussions with Patricia Gibbons and with the Reverend J. D. Martin of Geelong College, together with their generous assistance.

REFERENCES

BUTLER, B. E. (1964). Assessing the soil factor in agricultural production. *J. Aust. Inst. agric. Sci.* **30**, 232–40.

GIBBONS, F. R. (1968). Limitations to the usefulness of soil classification. *Proc. 9th Int. Soil Science Congress* (in press).

GOODALL, D. W. (1966). Classification, probability and utility. *Nature, Lond.* **211**, 53–4.

UNITED STATES SOIL CONSERVATION SERVICE (1960). *Soil Classification: A Comprehensive System. 7th Approximation.* (U.S. Govt. Printer: Washington.)

WILLIAMS, W. T. (1963). The computer botanist. *Observer*, London, December issue.

WEBB, L. J., TRACEY, J. G., WILLIAMS, W. T., and LANCE, G. N. (1967). Studies in the numerical analysis of complex rainforest communities. I. *J. Ecol.* **55**, 171–92.

Parametric Description of Land Form

J. G. Speight

Division of Land Research, CSIRO, Canberra, Australia

The concepts of land element, being a simple component of landscape, and land system, a landscape pattern formed by the arrangement of such components, are used as a basis for setting up a parametric model of land form applicable to erosional situations. Parameters used for land-form elements are slope, rate-of-change of slope, contour curvature, and unit catchment area; those for land system are ridginess, ridge reticulation and ridge vector magnitude and orientation. For a test area of 3·7 sq km, values of land-form element parameters are obtained from maps with a scale of 1 : 2400 and contour interval of 1.52 m. Parametric definitions of crests, hill slopes, foot slopes, swales, plains, and water courses are formulated, and a map of these elements constructed. The size and distribution of the elements differs systematically between land systems as previously mapped. Combinations of ridge crest parameters, evaluated for sample areas 2000 ft square are used to define synthetic land systems which prove similar in distribution to those previously mapped, suggesting that land system mapping by the use of these parameters alone may be feasible. The advent of automatic photogrammetric machines with digital output is expected to reduce the labour involved to a level that is practical for resources surveys.

LAND ELEMENTS AND LAND SYSTEMS

The complexity of form of the surface of the earth has discouraged attempts at rigorous description. It is difficult to conceive of a sufficiently realistic model of land form that is at the same time mathematically simple enough for general use. The land system and land element concepts, by separating forms into two orders of complexity, appear to offer the prospect of a solution.

The concept of a *land element*, defined by Brink *et al.* (1966) as 'the simplest part of the landscape, for practical purposes uniform in lithology, form, soil, and vegetation' (cf. *site* of Christian and Stewart 1968) is descended from the *site* of Bourne (1931) – 'an area which appears, for all practical purposes, to provide throughout its extent similar local conditions as to climate, physiography, geology, soil, and edaphic factors in general' and, on the land form side, from the *facet* concept of Wooldridge (1932), facets being either *flats* or *slopes* that are not susceptible to subdivision on the basis of form (Linton 1951). Linton's comment that *slopes* 'may be gentle or steep, concave or convex, smooth or rugged' and that *flats* may 'differ in respect of absolute altitude, extent, and relation to the water table' points to the simplicity of the concept: an element may be characterized morphologically by a very small number of parameters specifying the general shape of its surface, its extent, its roughness, and some aspects of its external relationships.

From the conceptual point of view, the *land unit* of the Australian Land Research approach (Christian 1952; Christian and Stewart 1968) and the *land facet* of the Oxford working group on land classification (Brink *et al.* 1966) are transitional categories. They are defined purely on the basis of descriptive convenience, and range in practice from *land elements* to complete landscapes.

Unfortunately, the *land systems* considered below have been defined as assemblages of *land units* or *land facets* rather than of *land elements* or *sites*. However, since both the Land Research and the Oxford working group definitions state that *land units* (or *land facets*) are groups (or associations) of *sites* (*land elements*) it is completely justifiable, and conceptually desirable to discuss *land systems* as assemblages of *land elements* rather than of *land units*.

A *land system* was defined in the following terms. 'We have defined this unit, which is a composite of related units, as an area, or groups of areas, throughout which there is a recurring pattern of topography, soils, and vegetation. A change in this pattern determines the boundary of a land system.' (Christian and Stewart 1953.) The concept of pattern – in the sense of an arrangement of components – is fundamental here; it is noteworthy that pattern plays no part in the definition of *land element*. Conversely, if the component elements have been comprehensively described in terms such as Linton suggested for the morphology of slopes and flats (plus others for vegetation and soils), the land system description need specify only the *patterns* that characterize the landscape as a whole, patterns that result from the extent, shape, and areal relationships of land elements. The relation between land element and land system may then be considered analogous to that between word and sentence. The syntax that relates the two would repay detailed study, but for the present purpose it is sufficient to point out that (1) the two are susceptible to description in fundamentally different terms, (2) there need be no redundancy, in the form of assigning the same parameter to both land system and land element, and (3) there is a need to consider land element relationships in two ways: looking outward from the land element and looking inward from the land system.

Thus far, the units discussed have embraced all aspects of the physical landscape, but the argument applies with equal force to land form alone. The remainder of the paper is restricted to the consideration of land systems and land elements defined (as they sometimes are) solely on land-form characteristics. The term land-form element has been used here for land elements so defined.

LAND-FORM ELEMENTS

Parameters for Land-Form Element Description

Savigear (1956) has evolved a technique of morphological mapping which depends on the recognition of *facets* of constant slope and *elements* of smoothly curved profile, delimited by boundaries observed in the field. This clearly involves only two parameters: slope, and rate-of-change of slope. A third parameter, contour curvature, is incorporated in a scheme proposed by Troeh (1965). This scheme approximates local land form to a paraboloid of revolution expressed in cylindrical co-ordinates as:

$$Z = P + SR + LR^2$$

were Z is in the vertical direction. This model matches only those land-form elements that have (i) contours that are arcs of concentric circles and (ii) profiles whose slope (as a tangent) varies at a constant rate. In fact, however, this situation is common enough to make the model widely applicable. There are five unknowns involved: P, S, L, and two others specifying the position of the axis of rotation. As the necessary five points of known co-ordinates, Troeh (1964) used the centre and corners of sample squares of side 80 ft. He obtained good correlation of soil type with values of the parameters G, L, R, where

$$G = dZ/dR = S + 2LR$$

is the slope at the centre of the figure;

$$L = \tfrac{1}{2}(d^2Z/dR^2)$$

is half the rate-of-change of slope (a constant); and R is the radius of curvature of the contour at the centre of the figure. The present paper adapts these three parameters for use in mapping. Another useful parameter, slope orientation, has not been investigated in this study.

Parameters defining land-form geometry at a point should be supplemented by others that take account of the relationships between neighbouring land forms that may be inter-dependent with that at the point. The area of particular interest is that which is upslope from the point, and the only relational parameter developed in the present study is a measure of the size of this area, that is, the unit catchment area.

Materials

The area selected for testing the feasibility of parametric land-form mapping was the catchment of a small tributary of Woolshed Creek, above Gladefield Homestead in the Australian Capital Territory. The area included was 3·7 sq km (1·3 sq miles), a stream catchment being specified to minimize edge effects that might arise from the use of arbitrary boundaries such as map sheet edges. The area was covered by highly detailed contour maps (Fig. 1a) with a scale of 1 : 2400 and a contour interval of 1·52 m (5 ft), produced by the Survey Branch, Department of the Interior, from 1 : 12,000 scale air photos and ground control precise to ±8 cm (3 in.) horizontally and ±15 cm (6 in.) vertically. The density of ground control points is of the order of 40 per sq km (100 per sq mile). Altitudes shown as contours on the map are precise to ±45 cm (18 in.) and the position of detail is precise to about 2 m (6 ft). The precision of contour line position is inversely proportional to the slope; at 100% slope the precision is of the same order as the thickness of the contour line, but at 1% slope the precision is only ±45 m (150 ft), which is 19 mm ($\frac{3}{4}$ in.) on the face of the map.

The work described below is based exclusively on analysis of these maps. It is considered that detail that is not presented on them is largely irrelevant to the land-form elements to be mapped, and that no amount of field work would improve on the data they contain for land-form element mapping, except at a few points where specific plotting errors appear to have occurred.

The contours do not adequately depict slopes of less than 1%, but this is an aspect of the general problem of plain-land morphometry. At characteristic plain-land slopes in the neighbourhood of 0·1%, even 10 cm (4 in.) contours are barely adequate for land-form element definition.

Measurement of Parameter Values

Slope—The test area was mapped into slope categories bounded by equal increments of the logarithm of the tangent of the slope angle. This scheme divides low angle slopes such as alluvial fans and plains into several slope categories without excessively subdividing hill slopes, and it has the property that a land surface with a constant rate-of-change of slope appears as a succession of bands of slope categories of equal width on the map. The usefulness of the scheme depends on the categories being (a) fine enough to provide an adequate slope description and (b) coarse enough to be reliably mapped. The common ratio between categories was 1·8:1, which is as fine a subdivision as is justified on any map whose contour spacing (and therefore slope information) is subject

Fig. 1. Detail maps to demonstrate the method of mapping of land-form elements. a, contour map, contour interval 1·52m (5 ft); b, slope categories, log-tangent scale; c, slope gradient (rate-of-change of slope); d, contour curvature, concave and convex; e, down-slope flow lines; f, line printer map of land-form elements.

to an error of up to ± 30%, which is usually the case.

The categories mapped were as follows:

1	56%–100%	
2	32%– 56%	
3	18%– 32%	

4   10%– 18%
5   5·6% – 10%
6   3·2% –5·6%
7   1·8% –3·2%
8   1·0% –1·8%
9   0·56%–1·0%

The method of mapping required a set of gauges representing a contour spacing appropriate to the slope category limits. These gauges were moved around the contours with the marks on the gauge always parallel to the contour lines, and marks were made wherever the contour spacing was the same as the spacing of the marks on the gauge. In this way, areas of given slope categories were delineated (Fig. 1b).

Slope Gradient (Rate-of-change of Slope)—Slope gradient was derived from the slope category map and the original contour map in combination. Several categories of concavity and of convexity were envisaged, but a total of four proved to be the practical limit. Notably concave or convex areas could be identified by a transition completely through one slope category in some arbitrarily short distance along a line normal to the contours. After consideration of the nature of the land forms and the precision of the map, the critical distance was fixed at 25 m, or 0·40 in. at map scale. This corresponds to a change of slope by a factor of 1·8 in 25 metres (81·9 ft) or, in Troeh's terminology, $L = \pm 0·036 \ m^{-1} (\pm 0·011 \ ft^{-1})$. In the terminology of Savigear (1956) and Young (1964) notably concave or convex zones would mainly be slope elements rather than slope segments, though Young measures rate of change in *degrees* per hundred metres, so the two concepts are not congruent.

It was also possible to judge with some confidence the position of a line separating areas within which slopes were *not* concave from those within which slopes were not convex, though straight slopes might appear in either. The four categories of slope gradient mapped as in Figure 1c, were thus:
1 Notably concave; $L \geqslant 0·036 \ m^{-1}$
2 Slightly concave to straight; $0 \leqslant L < 0·036 \ m^{-1}$
3 Straight to slightly convex; $0 \geqslant L > (-0·036) \ m^{-1}$
4 Notably convex; $L \leqslant (-0·036) \ m^{-1}$

Contour Curvature—Contour curvature was assessed in terms of radius of curvature of the equivalent circular arc. Again the critical values had to be assessed on both an estimation of the range of curvatures of significance to the mapping of land-form elements in the area, and an appreciation of the limits of accuracy of the mapped contours. Very small radii of contour curvature are significant only for the investigation of microrelief rather than relief, and they may arise on the map from error in photogrammetry or draughting; very large radii of curvature are similarly irrelevant and are difficult to assess on the map because they are masked by irregularities in the contour trace. The only radii which may be mapped unambiguously on the available maps are in the range from 10 m to 100 m. One has a further problem in deciding the smallest length of curved contour to consider as significant to land element definition. Finally one critical radius of curvature and one minimum length of contour segment were made to serve both the convex and concave cases. The radius chosen was 48·3 m (158·5 ft), required to persist for a chord-distance of at least 25 m along the contour, corresponding to a change in slope facing of exactly 30° in that distance. As in the case of slope gradient it was possible to separate non-convex and non-concave areas of gentle curvature, leading to a map such as Figure 1d, with a fourfold classification of contour curvature:

1 Notably concave; R $\geqslant$ 48·3 m
2 Slightly concave to straight; 0 $\leqslant$ R $<$ 48·3 m
3 Straight to slightly convex; 0 $\geqslant$ R $>$ ($-$48·3) m
4 Notably convex; R $\leqslant$ ($-$48·3) m

Unit Catchment Area—In determining values for this parameter, a square grid of points 100 ft apart was laid over the map, and from every point a line was traced downslope so that it was normal to every contour that it crossed. This resulted in a dendritic pattern of flow lines, down which water and materials would move over the surface of the ground under the action of gravity (Fig. 1e). Next, a line with a scaled length of 100 ft was laid with its mid-point on each grid point in turn, and parallel to the adjacent contour. The number of flow lines crossing this line, including the flow line beginning at that grid point, was counted: the total represents the catchment area above the 100 ft sampling line in units of 10^4 sq ft. This is not quite true in detail; for example, where the flow lines diverge from a hill crest, an over-estimation results, but it is not significant to the overall pattern. Values of unit catchment area vary from 1 up to the total number of grid points in a given stream basin, which may be measured in thousands, but in an erosional landscape only a small proportion of the values exceed 9 and such values are usually, but not always, found to fall within recognizable water courses[1].

Water courses were arbitrarily defined by consideration of the unit catchment area values and the flow-line map. Points with catchment area values greater than 99 were designated water courses without qualification; points with catchment area values less than 100 were designated water courses if the grid point fell beneath a single line representing 5 or more convergent flow lines, or beneath a narrow zone of flow concentration with equivalent unit catchment area of 10^4 sq ft per *ft* of contour. When the zone width attained 100 ft this criterion became the same as the first mentioned.

Collation of Data

The grid system employed for generating unit catchment areas was overlaid on maps of slope, slope gradient, and contour curvature, and values of all four parameters were read off against their grid co-ordinates and punched on computer cards.

Land-form Element Mapping

From the four land-form parameters a very large number of land-form elements, each different from all others in at least one respect, might be set up. The present investigation was confined to the mapping of formalized versions of a few commonly accepted types of land-form element that are distinguishable on the basis of form alone, in such a way that no point either failed to be assigned to an element or was assigned to more than one, and that a reasonably comprehensive and consistent description of the total landscape was achieved.

The elements chosen for mapping, listed with their mapping symbols, were:

Crests	C
Hill slopes	H
Concave foot slopes	T

---

[1]The lack of provision for over-bank flooding from stream channels is a fundamental limitation of the method described in this paper.

Convex foot slopes   F
Swales   S
Plains   A
Water courses   W

Definitions of the typical characteristics of these were as follows:

Crests were areas notably convex in either slope gradient or contour curvature. They could occur at any values of slope, but at lower angle slopes they could not have high unit catchment areas.

Hill slopes had slopes in excess of 5·6% and any values of slope gradient or contour curvature except notably convex, but high unit catchment areas were permitted only at steeper slope angles.

Foot slopes had slopes between 3·2% and 18%, but the steeper angles occurred only at high values of unit catchment area. A dichotomy was made between foot slopes that were convex in contour curvature and those that were concave. The convex type (F) embraced the form assumed by a small undissected alluvial or colluvial fan.

Swales were areas notably concave in either slope gradient or contour curvature and notably convex in neither. They had slopes less than 10% and high values of unit catchment area.

Plains were areas of slope less than 3·2%.

Water courses have been defined in a previous section.

These conceptual definitions permit considerable ambiguity and the possibility of areas remaining undefined. This may be avoided only by the construction of an exhaustive table of combinations, which was done as shown in Figure 2. It will be seen that many categories of unit catchment area and some categories of slope are not held to have decisive value in this particular table of purely empirical definitions.

Fig. 2. Diagram showing the definition of land-form elements in parametric terms.

The diagram plots **Contour convexity** (columns 1–4) against **Profile convexity** (rows 1–4) for each combination of **Slope category** (≤3, 4, 5, 6, ≥7) and **Unit catchment area** (≤5, 6–9, ≥10).

Unit catchment area ≤5

Slope ≤3	1	2	3	4
1	H	H	H	C
2	H	H	H	C
3	H	H	H	C
4	C	C	C	C

Slope 4	1	2	3	4
1	H	H	H	C
2	H	H	H	C
3	H	H	H	C
4	C	C	C	C

Slope 5	1	2	3	4
1	T	T	F	C
2	T	H	H	C
3	T	H	H	C
4	C	C	C	C

Slope 6	1	2	3	4
1	T	T	F	C
2	T	T	F	C
3	T	T	F	C
4	C	C	C	C

Slope ≥7	1	2	3	4
1	A	A	A	C
2	A	A	A	C
3	A	A	A	C
4	C	C	C	C

Unit catchment area 6–9

Slope ≤3	1	2	3	4
1	H	H	H	C
2	H	H	H	C
3	H	H	H	C
4	C	C	C	C

Slope 4	1	2	3	4
1	H	H	H	C
2	H	H	H	C
3	H	H	H	C
4	C	C	C	C

Slope 5	1	2	3	4
1	T	T	F	F
2	T	T	F	F
3	T	T	F	F
4	T	T	F	F

Slope 6	1	2	3	4
1	S	S	S	F
2	S	T	F	F
3	S	T	F	F
4	T	T	F	F

Slope ≥7	1	2	3	4
1	S	S	S	A
2	S	A	A	A
3	S	A	A	A
4	A	A	A	A

Unit catchment area ≥10

Slope ≤3	1	2	3	4
1	H	H	H	C
2	H	H	H	C
3	H	H	H	C
4	C	C	C	C

Slope 4	1	2	3	4
1	T	T	F	F
2	T	T	F	F
3	T	T	F	F
4	T	T	F	F

Slope 5	1	2	3	4
1	S	S	S	F
2	S	T	F	F
3	S	T	F	F
4	T	T	F	F

Slope 6	1	2	3	4
1	S	S	S	F
2	S	T	F	F
3	S	T	F	F
4	T	T	F	F

Slope ≥7	1	2	3	4
1	S	S	S	A
2	S	A	A	A
3	S	A	A	A
4	A	A	A	A

Assignment of each mapped point to one land-form element or another was accomplished by a series of logical 'IF' statements in a computer program which listed the points, parameters, and land-form elements, totalled the areas falling into each element, and printed out a slightly distorted map made up of land-form element symbols on a line-printer (Fig. 1f). The visual interpretation of this map was found to be rather difficult without some further hand-work, involving the marking in of the water courses and of smooth boundaries between blocks of the same land-form element. Indeterminacy arose when identical symbols were diagonally adjacent as, for example, in the configuration $^{FS.}_{SF}$. This was solved by assigning a priority in linking such points, depending on the likelihood of the land-form element being reticulated. Swales were given the highest priority, followed by crests, plains, hill slopes, convex and concave foot slopes, in that order. Finally the map was hand coloured, in a presentation similar to that shown in Figure 3.

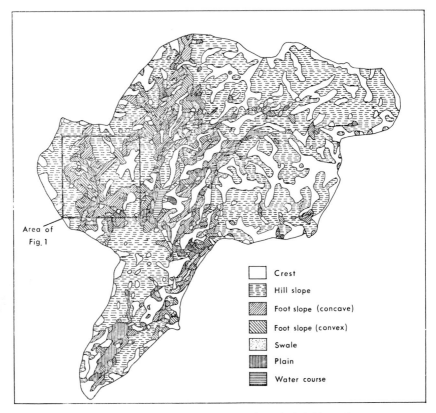

Fig. 3. Land-form element map for the Gladefield catchment.

The Gladefield Catchment Land-form Element Map

The test area comprised two hilly areas of contrasting appearance, separated by an area of undulating country with some alluvial flats. The land-form element map (Fig. 3) showed the eastern hilly area to consist mainly of crests and hill slopes, the crests having a pronounced continuity and reticulation. The western hills, on the other hand, had small and discontinuous areas of crest, and the hill slopes commonly graded down into foot slopes. The undulating area consisted of a fine-textured mosaic of all the elements. These three areas had independently been mapped into separate land systems by a land resources survey team (Gunn *et al.*, in preparation), who were working at a very much smaller mapping scale, and Mr R. H. Gunn kindly mapped the land system boundaries precisely where they traversed the Gladefield catchment, as shown in Figure 4a. The western hills fell within Gibraltar land system described as rocky hills on granite or volcanics, the eastern hills within Woolcara land system described as hills on Palaeozoic sediments, and the undulating area within Gundaroo land system described as undulating lowlands on Palaeozoic sediments. Thus, both relief categories and lithologic categories were correlated with distribution of land-form elements as here defined.

Where land system boundaries have been independently recognized, one can be specific about land element distribution, though one cannot be sure that the included sample is representative without sampling other occurrences of the same land systems elsewhere. Table 1 shows the striking quantitative differences that were derived from Figure 3.

TABLE 1

Land element distribution and mean size within land systems

	Land Element						
	C	H	T	F	S	A	W
Gibraltar land system							
Area (%)	21	51	12	8	2	3	3
Mean size (ha)	0·32	2·66	0·35	0·26	0·14	0·44	—
Gundaroo land system							
Area (%)	28	16	18	15	8	5	10
Mean size (ha)	0·40	0·26	0·22	0·20	0·20	0·18	—
Woolcara land system							
Area (Œ)	35	55	3	1	1	0	6
Mean size (ha)	1·15	1·90	0·11	0·10	0·12	—	—

LAND SYSTEMS

Parameters of Pattern

The land-form patterns that render land systems indentifiable may be divided into two kinds, linear patterns and areal patterns. Investigation of the geomorphic aspects of either kind is facilitated by the construction of a map of rigorously defined land-form elements such as the one described above. As to the areal patterns shown by the distribution of land-form elements, though a relationship to independently mapped land systems has been demonstrated, it was not feasible to map land system boundaries by comparing the land-form element composition in sample areas distributed over the catchment. Quite large areas of the western hills that happened to include no foot slopes would have been indistinguishable on this basis from areas in the eastern hills. On the other hand, consideration of sample areas sufficiently large to include the typical proportion of foot slopes when sampling the western hills would have resulted in the sample areas that were centred on the undulating country also taking in considerable parts of the hilly areas on either side. This problem of obtaining an adequate sample to assess a characteristic without overflowing the physical boundaries of apparent land systems applies also to such parameters as relief and grain (Wood and Snell 1960), and to many others summarized by Carr and van Lopik (1962).

Linear patterns appear to occur at a finer scale in the landscape than areal patterns, and therefore offer more chance of discrimination between land systems. Parameters were selected for their analysis as follows:

Ridginess: the total length of crest per unit area (analogous to drainage density).

Reticulation: the total length of the largest connected network of crests that projected into a sample area.

Orientation: the directional properties of crests within a sample area, expressed as a vector magnitude[1] and direction (Curray 1956).

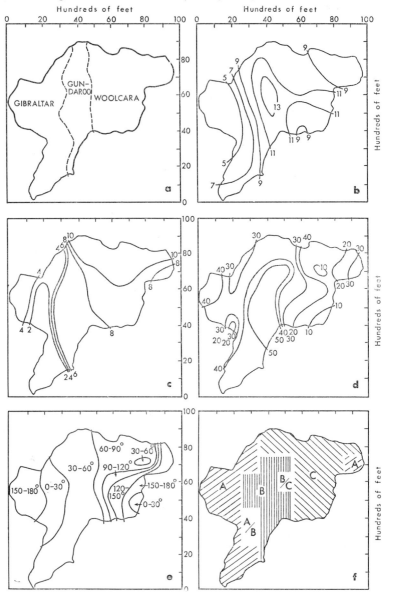

Fig. 4. Land systems and ridge pattern parameters in the Gladefield catchment. a, land systems after R. H. Gunn; b, ridginess (in thousands of feet per 2000 foot square); c, reticulation (length in thousands of feet of longest network entering each 2000 foot square); d, vector magnitude (%, by 10° classes); e, vector orientation (degrees E of N); f, land systems synthesized from ridge pattern parameters.

[1]Vectors were computed in 10° categories from 1° to 180°. A vector magnitude of 0% signifies a uniform distribution, 100% signifies that all data fall in one 10° category.

Crests, if consistently defined, are more informative than drainage lines in their pattern characteristics because of (a) the strong tendency to complete reticulation in a drainage system which prevents the use of reticulation as a parameter, and (b) the oscillatory (meandering) behaviour of running water, which adds a great deal of 'noise' to the orientation distribution.

Synthetic Land System Mapping

Ridge pattern parameters were assessed in sample areas of optimum size and spacing (determined by trial and error as squares 4×10^6 sq ft area, on centres 1000 ft apart) and maps were prepared to display the resulting patterns of areal variation (Figs. 4b, 4c, 4d, 4e).

As an assessment of the usefulness of these parameters for land system mapping, the value of each parameter that appeared to be typical was assessed for each land system in turn, and a 'likelihood' rating of 3 was applied to these values. Ratings of 2 were applied to adjacent values, and of 1 to those next adjacent. (In the case of vector orientation, which was not very significant, the highest rating applied was 2). For each sample square the most likely land system was assessed by adding the ratings for the four parameters, with the results shown on the map (Fig. 4f). The clear division of the map into three large areas, rather than a chaos of fragments, indicated that the desired geomorphic regionalization was being achieved. The land systems have been labelled with letter symbols only, as it is not necessarily true that the parametric definitions developed from this small area are adequate or accurate in the context of the survey area as a whole, but this could be verified by analysis of a number of other areas of 1 or 2 sq miles.

DISCUSSION

This study has demonstrated that, at least in this erosional situation, the classification of land systems and land units (land elements) on the basis of land form can be put on an entirely numerical footing, so that the element of subjectivity does not extend beyond the initial definitions. On a given set of definitions, mapping may proceed in a self-consistent way that allows of no ambiguity and permits the quantitative comparison of landscapes from place to place. A method of work that suggests itself is analysis of selected stereo-pairs of air photos to replace the present technique of field examination of selected sites. The laborious handwork involved in mapping slope and other parameters is unlikely to remain an obstacle with the advent of automatic photogrammatic machines capable of recording X, Y, Z co-ordinates of the land surface on magnetic tape for computer analysis.

In this connection Greysukh (1966) has described a computer-oriented technique for identifying 6 classes of land form by the distribution of slope vectors around a point. From each point of known X, Y, Z co-ordinates, lines are drawn connecting it to a ring of adjacent points forming a 'concentric figure'. The pattern assumed by a diagram of slope versus azimuth is then taken as diagnostic. For instance, if all slopes are negative, this indicates a hill (more precisely, a peak); one positive maximum and two negative maxima indicates a cape (spur); one positive and one negative maximum indicates a regular slope; similarly a ravine (swale), depression, and saddle may be identified. The suggested mapping method consists of first constructing quite large concentric figures, which in general will be distorted by being transitional between the classes of land form. Such distortion is identified by progressively reducing the size of the figure—an 'ideal' figure should retain the same characteristics, while those of a distorted figure should change. If the figure is distorted, it is possible to find the direction in which the figure should be displaced to reduce the distortion. The figure is then appropriately shifted, and reduced again to test for distortion. By this process, the location of the axes of linear features may be found, then, by expansion of the figures, the extent of each land-form element may be delineated. The paper does not cite experimental results, and it seems clear that precisely the same problems of scale would arise as in the present study. For instance, in the definition of a cape (spur), which is analogous to the definition of a crest in this paper, the degree of contour curvature necessary to distinguish a cape from a regular slope is implicit in the spacing of the points in Greysukh's concentric figure. Greysukh's method may well prove a starting point, however, for the investigation of the fundamental problem of scale in land form. Its simplicity in comparison with that of Troeh is a great advantage where large numbers of data points are to be computed.

REFERENCES

BOURNE, R. (1931). Regional survey and its relation to stocktaking of the agricultural and forest resources of the British Empire. *Ox. For. Mem.* **13.**

BRINK, A. B., MABBUTT, J. A., WEBSTER, R., and BECKETT, P. H. T. (1966). *Report of the working group on land classification and data storage.* Military Engng Exp. Establ., Christchurch, England. Report 940.

CARR, D. D., and VAN LOPIK, J. R. (1962). *Terrain quantification, Phase I: Surface geometry measurements.* U.S. Air Force Cambridge Research Laboratories, Bedford, Massachusetts. Report AFCRL 63–208.

CHRISTIAN, C. S. (1952). Regional land surveys. *J. Aust. Inst. agric. Sci.* **18**, 140–6.

CHRISTIAN, C. S., and STEWART, G. A. (1953). General report on survey of Katherine–Darwin region, 1946. *CSIRO Aust. Land Res. Ser.* No. 1.

CHRISTIAN, C. S., and STEWART, G. A. (1968). Methodology of integrated surveys. In *Aerial Surveys and Integrated Studies.* Proc. Toulouse Conf. 1964, UNESCO. pp. 233–80.

CURRAY, J. R. (1956). The analysis of two-dimensional orientation data. *J. Geol.* **64**, 117–31.

GREYSUKH, V. L. (1966). The possibility of studying landforms by means of digital computers. Translated in *Soviet Geography* **8**, 137–49 (1967).

LINTON, D. L. (1951). The delimitation of morphological regions. Ch. 11 In *London Essays in Geography.* (Longmans Green: London.)

SAVIGEAR, R. A. G. (1956). Technique and terminology in the investigation of slope forms. *Premier Rapport de la Commission pour l'etude des Versants.* Union Geographique Internationale, Amsterdam, 66–75.

TROEH, F. R. (1964). Landform parameters correlated to soil drainage. *Proc. Soil Sci. Soc. Am.* **28**, 808–12.

TROEH, F. R. (1965). Landform equations fitted to contour maps. *Am. J. Sci.* **263**, 616–27.

WOOD, W. F., and SNELL, J. B. (1960). *A quantitative system for classifying landforms.* Quartermaster Research and Engineering Command, U.S. Army, Tech. Report EP-124.

WOOLDRIDGE, S. W. (1932). The cycle of erosion and the representation of relief. *Scott. geogr. Mag.* **48**, 30–36.

YOUNG, A. (1964). Slope profile analysis. *Z. Geomorph. Suppl.* **5**, 17–27.

Quantification of Vegetation Structure on Vertical Aerial Photographs

P. C. Heyligers

Division of Land Research, CSIRO, Canberra, Australia

Specific properties of photo images are used to classify vegetation on air photographs. The scale of the photography determines whether these are structural characteristics or tones and textures caused by the unresolved features of the vegetation. As an example the vegetation typing for the Aitape–Ambunti survey area in New Guinea is outlined.

The use of photo keys, especially of stereograms, is recommended as a means of standardization as the feasibility and accuracy of measuring photo image properties has still to be evaluated.

INTRODUCTION

Every plant has its specific requirements of, and tolerances to, the whole gamut of environmental conditions. A community reflects the requirements which its plants have in common. Hence vegetation can be used as an indicator of environmental conditions. This is one of the reasons for studying vegetation in land evaluation surveys.

An adequate description of vegetation is necessary as a basis for deductions about the environment. There are two aspects of description; one relates to floristic composition, which is expressed by the range of species and their quantities; the other to structure, which is determined by the various forms of plants in their spatial relationships. A variety of techniques is available for describing vegetation in the field. However, complete reliance on field descriptions for land evaluation surveys is both slow and costly. Vertical aerial photographs provide a record of a number of properties of vegetation and are widely used in vegetation studies. The techniques used for field description can seldom be applied, because the features to be identified or measured are usually too small or are not visible. The photo image, however, provides new clues which compensate partly for these restrictions.

In this paper the practicability of quantifying various aspects of vegetation structure from air-photo imagery will be examined. The purpose of quantification is to reduce the subjectivity that is involved in photo interpretation. Moreover, quantification will be necessary if machinery is to play a role in the interpretation procedure.

INFLUENCE OF STRUCTURE

Scale is the most important factor influencing the portrayal of structure, assuming that the pictures have been taken and processed as well as possible. It must be realized, however, that even on large-scale vertical photographs only part of the vegetation can be seen.

Each structural element has a critical photo scale, which is the smallest scale at which this element can be identified. The relationship between critical photo scale and actual photo scale determines whether or not the structural characteristics of the components will play a major role during interpretation. If not, then pattern, which pertains to the distribution of tones and textures of a photographic image, becomes an important element. Therefore, for a photo of any scale, different description techniques may have to be used because of differences in critical scales of the vegetation types.

AN EXAMPLE OF QUANTIFICATION

An outline of the vegetation classification used for the natural resources reconnaissance survey of the Aitape-Ambunti area is given below as an example of quantification, or at least as an approach towards quantification.

The Aitape-Ambunti area lies in the north-west of the Territory of New Guinea. It comprises about 11,500 sq km (4500 sq miles) of country stretching from the coast over hilly tracts and ranges up to 1700 m (5500 ft) to the swamps and flood-plains of the Sepik River. Black and white photography at a scale of 1 : 50,000 taken with a 153 mm (6 in.) lens was used.

The first step in the preliminary mapping was to separate native gardens, plantations, and regrowth vegetation from natural vegetation. Natural vegetation was then split up into major vegetation types: forest (F), woodland (W), savannah (V), palm vegetations (M, N), scrub (S), grassland (G), and mixed herbaceous vegetation (H).

Distinguishing between scrub, grassland, and mixed herbaceous vegetation is difficult because of the increasing discrepancy between their critical scales and the photo scale. The major types were further divided into more homogeneous units, called air-photo vegetation types,[1] which were coded by capital letters (as mentioned above) followed by other letters expressing distinctive properties.

During July, August, and September 1966, 360 observations were made in the field to check the preliminary mapping and to gather information about aspects not visible on the air photos. The ecologists in the New Guinea section of the Division of Land Research employ forms for these observations, one of which is used in forest and scrub (Fig. 1a), a second in other vegetation types (Fig. 1b). The forms (devised by K. Paijmans) have been in use since 1963, but those illustrated were prepared in a revised form in 1967. The more important structural characteristics are noted in a systematic semi-quantitative way. Most of the abbreviations will be self-evident: e.g., c.p.r. means common, present, rare. The blank spaces are filled in with actual values or, in the case of frequency, with a category of a five-step scale as given after 'climbers'. Of the other items the appropriate category will be ticked off or underlined. The forms are printed on 20·5 cm × 13 cm sorter cards with punched-hole margins. The time available to make an observation is usually 20 or 30 minutes.

The mapping was also checked and amended from the air during transport by helicopter from and to base camp and between query sites. Examples of the air-photo typing will be given below in conjunction with what the observations brought out.

Identification of Regrowth

As long as traces of abandoned gardens can be seen, separation of regrowth

---

[1] Howard (1967) coined the phrase 'aerial photographic community' from which 'air photo vegetation type' is adapted.

Final classification

		Query no.
FOREST, SCRUB: mangrove, beach, swamp, riparian; lowl., hill, submont.,		Date
mont., subalp., alp.; adv.second., semi-decid., decid.		Airph.
Emergents: height ; scatt., very scatt.; reg., irreg., groups		Mapp.type
Canopy: height ; cover %; de., mod.de., open; even, uneven		Photogr.
Lower tree strata: cover %; de., mod.de., open; layering dist./indist.		Herbar.
Stem form: straight c.p.r., branchy c.p.r., crooked c.p.r., leaning		Woodsa.
c.p.r., bent at base c.p.r.		Landf.
Buttresses: low c.p.r., medium: narr.c.p.r.,wide c.p.r.; high:		Alt.
narr.c.p.r.,wide c.p.r. Girths: sm.c.p.r.,mod.c.p.r.,large c.p.r.		Soil
Species: Leaves: sm.c.p.r.,mod.c.p.r.,large c.p.r.		W.table
	L.S.

Shrub layer: cov.   %; de., mod.de., open; reg., irreg., patchy; type: spreading, slender
Herb layer: cov.   %; reg., irreg., patchy; type: herbs,grasses,ferns,seedlings, mosses, ...
Visibility: good, mod., poor, very poor
Climbers: abu., very co.,co.,pres.,rare;
type: thick woody, thin woody, fleshy, ferns, bamboo, rattan, ...
Epiphytes: freq. in crown layer   , midway   , lower down
type: woody, ferns, mosses, lichens, aroids, orchids, ...
Palms: freq. in can.   lo.tr.str.   shrubl.   herbl.   ; type: Strangling figs: c.p.r.
Bamboo: freq. in can.   lo.tr.str.   shrubl.   herbl.   ; type:
Pandanus: freq. in can.   lo.tr.str.   shrubl.   herbl.   ; type:
Tree ferns: freq.   lo.tr.str.   shrubl.   herbl.   ; type:
Zingib./Marant.: freq.in shrubl.   herbl.   ; type:
Freq.of: pneumatophores , stiltroots , aerial roots ; cauliflory ; (semi-)decid.trees
Leaf litter/humus layer: thin, thick, springy; cont., discont.
NOTES: seral stage, dominance, habitat indicators, phenology, human interference, animals,
boundaries with adjacent veg.types, flooding, comparison photo aspect - field obs.

Fig. 1a. Form used to record forest and scrub vegetation in reconnaissance
surveys in New Guinea.

	Query no.
	Date
	Airph.
	Mapp.type
	Photogr.
	Herbar.
	Woodsa.
	Landf.
	Alt.
	Soil
	W:table
	L.S.

Final classification

NATIVE GARDEN, PLANTATION. crop   health
GARDEN REGROWTH. age   height   density/cover
  spec.:

WOODLAND/SAVANNAH: dry, wet; tree, shrub. PALM and/or PANDAN VEG.
GRASSLAND: dry, wet; alpine; tall, mid-h., low.
HERBAC. VEG.: dry, wet; floating, submersed; type: sedges, ferns,
  gingers, Hanguana, ...
Trees: height: max.   average
─density: mod.de., scatt., very scatt., odd ind.; distr.: reg.,irreg.,groups
  girths: sm.c.p.r.,mod.c.p.r.,large c.p.r.; leaves: sm.c.p.r.,mod.c.p.r.,large c.p.r.;
  freq.of (semi-)decid.trees   epiphytes   climbers
  spec.:

Shrubs: height   Visibility: good, mod., poor, very poor.
  density: mod.de., scatt., very scatt., odd ind.; distr.: reg.,irreg.,groups
  spec.:

Ground layer: height   cover   %; distr.: reg., patchy, tussocks
Grasses: abu., co., mod.co., sc., odd ind.; spec.:
Sedges: abu., co., mod.co., sc., odd ind.; spec.:
Ferns: abu., co., mod.co., sc., odd ind.; spec.:
Climbers: abu., co., mod.co., sc., odd ind.; spec.:
Other herbs: abu., co., mod.co.; sc.; odd ind.; spec.:

NOTES: recently burnt, young/mature regrowth, charred trees, other traces of burning;
  seral stage, dominance, habitat indicators, phenology, human interference, animals,
  boundaries with adjacent veg.types, flooding, comparison photo aspect – field obs.

Fig. 1b. Form used to record other vegetation in reconnaissance surveys in New Guinea.

from natural vegetation is straightforward. Difficulties arise mainly with older regrowth forest; irregularities in canopy together with juxtaposition to other regrowth types then provide the criteria. Of the 13 cases in which the preliminary mapping was wrong 10 were misinterpretations of forest, the others of sago palm vegetation.

Grassland

In grasslands a distinction based on experience in previous surveys was made between mid-height grassland (G, about 0·5 to 2 m (2–6 ft) tall) and tall grassland (Gt, more than 2 m (6 ft) tall). At the photo scale used it is only possible to judge the height in very favourable conditions. Therefore texture and tone formed the main criteria: G, medium light tones, smooth texture; Gr, medium light tones, rather rough texture; Gt, medium dark tones, rough texture. The type Gr was in six of the eight observations a vegetation dominated by ferns and sedges; thus, in fact, a type of mixed herbaceous vegetation which should have been mapped as Hr. Forty-three observations were made in G. According to the dominance of certain species a number of communities could be distinguished. These communities, however, could not be correlated consistently with tonal variations within the G type as they could not be distinguished from old burn patterns.

A pattern very similar to Gt but somewhat darker and slightly more irregular in texture was mapped as scrub (S). Aerial observations showed this distinction to be correct; this scrub was an almost pure stand of a low, much-branched *Pandanus* species.

Palm Vegetation

The types of palm vegetation, namely *Nypa* (N) and sago (*Metroxylon*) (M), are usually distinguishable on their textural and tonal qualities: N, a very fine-speckled pattern of even tones; M, a coarser-speckled pattern of less even tones.

One case was encountered where these differences failed to show, and even after aerial checking it was impossible to establish the boundary on the photographs. Probably because of marginal conditions the palms were smaller than usual and their characteristics did not show at the photo scale used.

Forest

Since the critical scale for forest was smaller than the photo scale used, structural criteria such as height, crown spacing and size, and lower storey features, could be employed. Heights were estimated using the three classes established in previous surveys: low (l), mid-height (m), and tall (no symbol[1]), with boundaries at 15 m (50 ft) and 30 m (100 ft).

The canopy was classified as open or rather open (o) when the crowns were more or less clearly separated from each other; as irregular (i) when showing considerable variations in crown height and spacing; and as closed or rather closed (no symbol) when spacing was narrow and crowns often touched. The symbol s was used to indicate predominance of small crowns.

---

[1] In theory every class should have its symbol to avoid misunderstanding, but practical considerations, such as space available on a map, demand that symbols be kept as short as possible.

The lower storey, even if the canopy is open, can add little to the distinction of types unless it is really dense. The presence of sago palms (M) in the under storey is an example. They could be seen in mid-height forest with an open canopy (FmoM), but in the case of tall forest with an open canopy (FoM) reliance was placed on inference, supported by evidence from larger-scale photography. In mid-height forest with a small-crowned, irregular canopy (Fmsi) the presence of sago was only discovered by field work.

Tone and texture were also used; the symbol d indicated the presence of light-toned crowns, the tone probably being caused by a flush of leaves or flowers; w was used for woolly textured crowns, and v for a very evenly textured canopy.

Although a total of 40 preliminary natural forest types were delineated (excluding mangrove and *Casuarina* forests), only 25 types were used in the final mapping. Some preliminary types occupied areas too small to be mapped and were combined with adjacent types, and some similar types were grouped according to their affinities to facilitate mapping. The diagnostic descriptions for the more common types are:

Fo: Tall forest with a rather open canopy; the photo image is a rather evenly textured pattern of crowns with mid-grey tones and an occasional lighter-toned one. Height variations in the canopy tend to be regular. Crowns are relatively widely and evenly spaced and of a large range in size.

Fi: Tall forest with an irregular canopy; the photo image is of a rather rough texture owing to irregular height and crown spacing variations. Crown sizes tend to be rather uniform, at least large crowns are very rare. Tones fall in the medium and lighter greys, but very light-toned crowns are rare.

Fid: Tall forest with an irregular canopy with light-toned crowns; the photo image is similar to that of tall forest with an irregular canopy (Fi), except for very light-toned crowns which are prominent.

Fmi: Mid-height forest with an irregular canopy; the photo image is of a fine but rather rough texture composed of small and very small crowns in various tones of grey to very light grey which are irregularly spaced horizontally as well as vertically.

Fms: Mid-height forest with a small-crowned canopy; in comparison with mid-height forest with an irregular canopy (Fmi) the photo image of this type is of a less rough texture, owing to a more even spacing of crowns which tend to be less variable in size as well, and a lesser height of emerging trees.

Diagnostic descriptions of the regrowth forests are:

FRy: Young regrowth forest, up to 20 m tall; the tone in the photo images is uneven and varies between light and medium grey and small crowns are distinguishable in the rather rough-textured canopy.

FRm: Medium-aged regrowth forest, 20–30 m tall; the photo image shows a canopy of rather small crowns, rather dark toned, often with a lighter tone at the illuminated side. Crowns tend to be detached and of irregular height.

FR: Old regrowth forest, 30 m or more tall; the photo image is rather similar to that of medium-aged regrowth forest (FRm), but crowns are larger. Scattered lighter-toned crowns occur. The image resembles that of tall forest with an irregular canopy (Fi, Fid).

In Table 1 an evaluation is made of the criteria used in the mapping of forest types in terms of the number of times the preliminary typing had to be adjusted for the final mapping. The table shows that canopy characteristics could be interpreted more reliably than height. This is to be expected, because canopy features can be seen and height can only be estimated.

TABLE 1

Evaluation of characteristics used in the stratification of forest

Structural Characteristic	Designation during Preliminary Air-photo Interpretation	Number of Field Checks	Number of Checks showing the Interpretation to be Wrong	Corrected Designations for the Wrong Interpretation
Height	Tall	92	26 (30%)	Mid-height
	Mid-height	58	16 (26%)	Tall
	Low	7	4 (56%)	Mid-height
	Total	157	46 (29%)	
Crown spacing and size (Fe types excluded)	Open	47	4 (9%)	Irregular (3x), closed (1x)
	Irregular	87	16 (18%)	Open (5x), closed (11x)
	Closed	24	5 (21%)	Open (4x), irregular (1x)
	Small	33	7 (21%)	—
	Total	191	27 (14%)	

As an exercise in possibilities of classification and correlation, a classification was developed with more or less the same criteria as used for air-photo typing but based entirely on the ground observations. An outline of this classification is presented in Table 2, together with the correlation to the air photo forest types. Discrepancies in height around the 30 m boundary are mainly due to a different emphasis on the position of the 30 m height group. In the air-photo types this group is included in tall forest, but in the other classification it is split up according to presence or absence of emerging trees, and combined with the type with a larger average canopy height and the type with lower average canopy height respectively. As the distinction of two height classes above 20 m on air photos can often not reliably be made, it is not feasible to differentiate height further during photo typing notwithstanding the fact that it can easily be done by ground observations. Canopy cover expresses as a percentage the proportion of sky obscured by foliage. The cover classes show only some correlation with the canopy types as distinguished on the air photos: 46%, 26%, and 5% of the observations in the 15–30%, 40–50%, and 60–80% cover classes, respectively, were made in forest types with an open canopy, the complementary percentage in forest types with an irregular or a closed canopy. These differences are caused by the fact that the air-photo canopy criteria are a mixture of crown closure and height variations, factors difficult to assess from the ground. The forest form of Figure 1 was revised after the survey to take better account of canopy features.

Undoubtedly it will be possible to develop more extensive classifications from the ground observations, taking into account other structural features and also life forms, but unless a classification can be related to the air-photo typing or to land form features which can be assessed from the air photos, it is not of any help in air-photo interpretation. The question can be reversed, namely to what extent do features not visible on the air photos correlate with the photo forest types? Table 3 and Figure 2 are extracted from the observations

TABLE 2

Comparison of a classification based on ground observations with the air-photo forest types

Classification on Ground Observations			Air-photo Forest Types																									No. of Obs.
Distinctive Features	Canopy Height (m)	Canopy Cover (%)	Fm	Fmo	Fmi	Fmio	Fms	Fmsv	F	Fo	Foi	Fos	Fod	FodM	Fi	Fid	Fmop	Fmop	FmoW	FmoCW	FmW	FmCW	FmRW	FoW	FRm	FR	
	20–25	15–30		2	2	1	1	1		1						2		1									9
		40–50		1	3	1	2	1		1																	6
		60–80			3		3	3																			9
	26–29; or 30 without E*	15–30	3	1	7	1	3									1											18
		40–50	1		2		3						1			2											9
		60–80					2	3								1											5
	30 with E; or 31–35 without E	15–30	1						1	7	3	1	1	2	6	7											29
		40–50							1	3	1	2	1		2	3						1					11
		60–80								1					1	1								1			3
	31–35 with E; or ≥36	15–30							2	2	1		4		3	1											21
		40–50							3	2	1			1		3											9
		60–80								1																	1
Pandanus common in canopy	22–30	15–40													1		4	1									6
Sago palms common in undergrowth	23–28; or 30 without E	10–40																	5	1	2	2	1	2			13
	30 with E; or ≥31	50–60																						2			2
Regrowth forest	20–29; or 30 without E	15–30																							15	7	22
		40–70																							7		7
	30 with E; or ≥31	15–30																								4	4
		40–70																								4	4
Number of observations			5	4	17	3	14	8	7	18	6	3	7	3	13	21	4	2	5	1	2	3	1	5	22	15	188

* E means emerging trees.

TABLE 3

Height and cover of selected air-photo forest types

		Air-photo Forest Types							
		Fo	Fi	Fid	FR	Fmi	Fms	FRm	FRy
Height (m)									
Tallest trees	Median	40	40	36	35	32	33	32	20
	Range	35–45	37–45	30–45	33–42	27–40	28–35	28–35	15–22
Canopy	Median	33	34	30	30	27	27	25	13
	Range	30–36	30–35	25–35	28–35	20–30	20–30	20–28	8–20
Cover (%)									
Canopy	Median	25	25	30	25	30	30	23	20
	Range	15–50	20–40	20–50	15–50	15–60	20–40	15–60	15–25
Subcanopy	Median	50	40	50	35	40	40	28	40
	Range	30–60	30–60	30–60	20–60	30–60	30–50	10–60	20–60
Canopy (if sub-canopy indisitnct)	Median					55	68		40
	Range					40–70	50–70		15–80
Shrub layer	Median	15	10	10	10	5	15	5	10
	Range	5–30	5–30	5–25	5–30	5–30	5–30	3–40	5–30
Herb layer	Median	1	3	3	10	4	1	10	30
	Range	1–5	1–20	1–10	2–50	1–40	1–3	3–80	3–95
Number of observations		18	13	23*	17*	17	15*	22	20
Number of observations with sub-canopy indistinct						2	6		16

* These figures are higher than those in Table 2 because some observations were incomplete and could not be used for Table 2.

for forest types, including regrowth forest, for which 13 or more observations
were available.

Table 3 summarizes values for height and cover in terms of the median and
the penultimate values of the series of observations. The height is given only
for the canopy and the tallest trees that emerge from the canopy. As layering
in tropical forest is often indistinct, height estimates of lower layers are omitted.
As to be expected, the average height values follow faithfully the classification.
The range of the heights of tallest trees for Fid and Fmi is larger than for Fo
and Fms: this is consistent with the photo typing. Fi, however, does not fit in.
The cover is estimated in steps of 5% up to 40% and in steps of 10% for higher
values. The subcanopy is formed by those trees that remain below the trees in
the canopy and are sheltered against the full impact of the macroclimate.
Table 3 shows again that this cover estimate does not correlate with the spacing
characteristics as determined from the air photos. The subcanopy tends to have
slightly lower cover values in mid-height forests than in tall forests, but not so
low as in medium-aged and old regrowth forest. The shrub layer is equally
variable throughout. The herb layer is densest in regrowth forest, and the
density decreases with aging of the forest.

Figure 2 summarizes observations on the occurrence of some life forms.
Epiphytes are uncommon in the mid-height forests, but are common in the
tall forests. In the regrowth forests their frequency reflects the enrichment with
epiphytes in course of time. Mid-height forest with an irregular canopy (Fmi)
is conspicuously poorer in palms than the other natural forest types and old
regrowth forest (FR). Mature rattan is usually common and never absent in
tall forest with a rather open canopy (Fo). Rattan is rare in young regrowth
forest but gains importance when the forest ages. Tree ferns are usually absent
in natural forest except in mid-height forest with an irregular canopy (Fmi).
Selaginella, a ferny herb, is usually common in regrowth forest and uncommon
or absent in natural forest. The conclusion from Figure 2 must be that trends
are recognizable, but that correlations are hardly ever absolute.

FEASIBILITY OF QUANTIFICATION

From the previous section it may be concluded that terms like rough texture,
light tone, or rather open canopy are still qualitative rather than quantitative.
On the other hand, FmoM, meaning 'mid-height forest with an open canopy
and with sago palms in the under-storey', reveals more about the structure of
this forest than 'sago forest' or 'swamp forest'. Quantification could be carried
further by measuring parameters such as crown size, crown spacing, number
of crowns per unit area, and variation in canopy height, or – at larger scales –
tussock size, ground cover, etc. The measurements, however, are time consuming
and the results may not be very accurate. Application of an overall measuring
procedure for reconnaissance surveys does not seem feasible, but a forthcoming
research programme will evaluate the influence of scale on the portrayal of
structural characteristics and on the accuracy of measurements. This programme will also try to bridge the gap between the results of air-photo typing
and field observation classifications. It is envisaged that the results will lead to
an improved interpretation of small-scale photographs.

Meanwhile, a certain degree of standardization could be reached by a more
frequent use of photo keys. Stereograms (photographs correctly mounted for
stereoscopic viewing) of vegetation types analyzed on the air photos and in the
field are especially useful, because these form a reference collection, can be

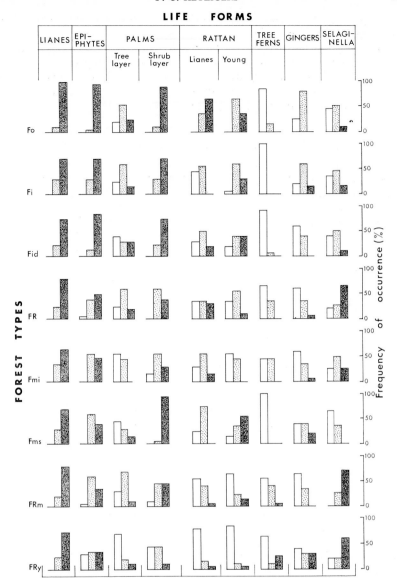

Fig. 2. Frequency of occurrence of certain life forms in selected forest types. Blank histograms denote absent, light stippling denotes uncommon, heavy stippling denotes common or very common.

used for instruction purposes, and illustrate vegetation classifications based on structure, for instance the system to be used in the survey of the vegetation types of Australia as part of the International Biological Programme. As it will be applied by various workers a key of stereograms will ensure consistency.

CONCLUSION

The possibilities of quantification of vegetation characteristics on air photos depend on the nature of the vegetation and the photo scale. There is little doubt that structural characteristics as long as they are discernible will be of great value in classification of vegetation. It is desirable to express these characteristics at least in a semi-quantitative way if accurate measurements cannot be obtained. When structure is unrecognizable the interpreter can use only tone and texture. If the relationships between these and structural properties are better understood interpretation could become more reliable.

It is unlikely that the subjective element in interpretation will be completely eliminated by measurements. Therefore, photo keys and stereograms should be used to minimize the influence of subjectivity.

REFERENCE

HOWARD, J. A. C. (1967). Ecological analysis in photo-interpretation. *Revue Photo-interprétation* **6**, 31.

A Computer-Compatible System for Quantitatively Describing the Physiognomy of Vegetation Assemblages

Warren E. Grabau and William N. Rushing

*U.S. Army Engineer Waterways Experiment Station,
Vicksburg, Miss., U.S.A.*

A rigorous procedure for obtaining and recording physiognomic data describing vegetation assemblages has been developed. The sample size is based on an extension of the minimal area concept; the basic sample area is called the 'structural cell'.

Most of the description consists of direct measurements of various physical properties, such as factors relating to stem sizes, shapes, and distributions; branch sizes and attitudes; crown shapes, etc. All data are recorded on forms adapted to computer input requirements. With a site description stored in computer memory, a very large number of analyses can be performed. Several examples are given.

RATIONALE

Vegetation imposes significant effects on many engineering and land exploitation activities. With but few exceptions, these effects are produced by the gross physical attributes of the vegetation as a whole rather than by its taxonomic or genetic characteristics. A bulldozer 'senses' only the particular size, shape, and strength of a plant; it does not sense the distinction between a maple tree and an oak. Thus, for most engineering purposes, the description of vegetation need incorporate only those physical attributes of plants and plant assemblages which can be demonstrated to produce an effect on an engineer machine or activity. For the purposes of this discussion such attributes will hereafter be called *factors*.

The practical exploitation of this simple notion, however, presumes the prior identification of the significant factors to be included in the description. Further, since a description of vegetation must be based upon some sort of areal sample, practical utilization also presumes the prior development of a rational procedure for determining an adequate sample size.

The identification of factors is complicated by the fact that vegetation affects a large number of different engineering activities, no two of which respond in exactly the same way, or to precisely the same combination of factors. For example, cross-country locomotion is known to be affected by stem sizes, stem spacing, stem base spread, branching height, branching angle, branch diameter, and in some instances crown diameter. On the other hand, road construction is affected chiefly by stem diameter, stem spacing, stem base spread, and perhaps some attributes of the root system. While both activities appear to have some factors in common, they are actually affected by somewhat different ranges of values within these factors. Thus, even an apparent overlap of factors is often misleading. From this it is clear, first, that any multiple-purpose description must include data on a large number of factors and, second, that those factors must be measured over their total ranges of variation in order to be sure that all significant factor values have been recorded.

A truly general description system (e.g., one that would contain the factor data required for *any* purpose) is probably impractical at the present time. This is because the factors cannot properly be selected until a useful performance prediction model is available – and such models are presently available for only a few machines and activities. The obvious course is to design a basic structure which can be indefinitely expanded to include new factors as they are identified but which will accommodate such additions without affecting the fundamental organization. Such a system can also be abstracted; that is, data can be collected for a single purpose, and the factor values recorded according to system procedure, even though many other factors, not needed for the purpose at hand, are omitted.

This very useful capability is, however, logically concomitant with a rigid restriction: every factor must be completely independent. There should be no redundancy, and there *must* be no derived factors, such as ratios.

The development of a rational sample-size selection procedure is even more troublesome than factor identification. The solution which was eventually found derives basically from the minimal area concept (cf. Greig-Smith 1964), but the idea has been significantly modified. The basis of the present sampling system is the 'structural cell'. Briefly stated, the theory holds that in any essentially homogeneous structure there exists a minimal area, the structural cell, which will incorporate a specified proportion of the variations of spatial positions exhibited by *any* selected structural characteristic of the components comprising a plant assemblage. The development of the theory (Mills and Clagg 1964) is discussed in detail in a paper by Addor and Fife (unpublished 1967).

In practice, the theory indicates that the spatial distribution of any population which is approximately uniformly distributed can be adequately described by a circular area which encloses 20 members. One implication is that the sampling areas are completely relativistic; the size (i.e., the diameter of the structural cell) is dependent upon the structure of the vegetation itself. Thus, the size of the structural cell is as fundamental a characteristic of the structure as is the size, shape or for that matter, the taxonomy of the component plants.

The data recording procedure should be such that it can be done by relatively non-technical people. Also it should be designed to minimize 'interface errors'; that is, the errors which occur when data are transferred from one format or medium to another. Since it is assumed that the extraction of significant data from the general description will eventually be accomplished by automatic data processing (ADP), it follows that the data should be recorded in the field on a form adapted to making the transfer to ADP storage as simple and direct as possible. The usual process of going from field notebooks to data summaries to ADP data forms to keypunch cards (or magnetic tape) should be avoided at all costs, because errors will occur at every interface. A form which minimizes such errors is illustrated in Figure 1. Data are recorded in the field on this form, which is then given directly to the keypunch operator. The numbers at the heads of the columns on the form are the column numbers on the standard ADP card.

DESCRIPTION SYSTEM

The vegetation structure description system is presented, in somewhat abbreviated form, in Appendix 1. The numbered paragraphs in the appendix

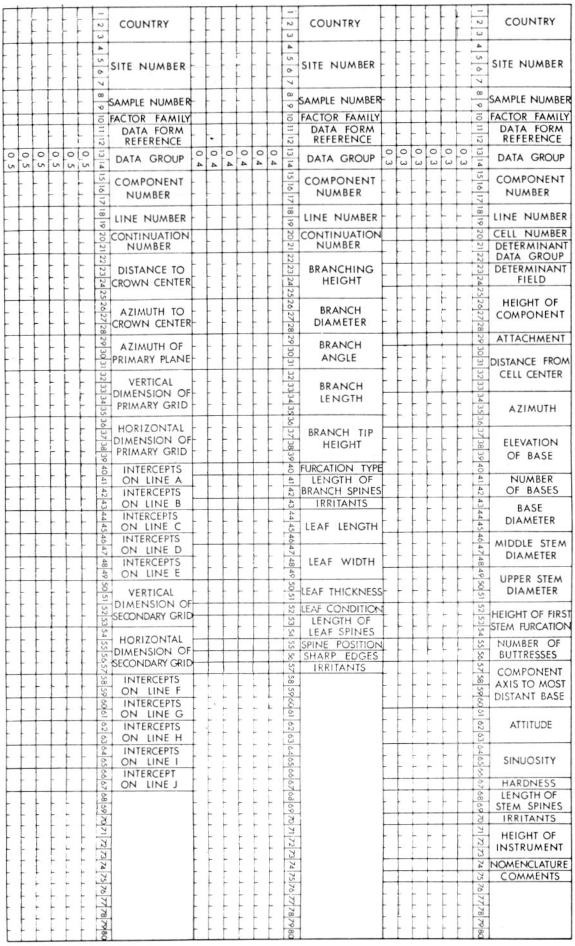

Fig. 1. Vegetation structure data form.

Form — Column 1: COUNTRY · SITE NUMBER · SAMPLE NUMBER · FACTOR FAMILY · DATA FORM REFERENCE · DATA GROUP · COMPONENT NUMBER · LINE NUMBER · CONTINUATION NUMBER · DISTANCE TO CROWN CENTER · AZIMUTH TO CROWN CENTER · AZIMUTH OF PRIMARY PLANE · VERTICAL DIMENSION OF PRIMARY GRID · HORIZONTAL DIMENSION OF PRIMARY GRID · INTERCEPTS ON LINE A · INTERCEPTS ON LINE B · INTERCEPTS ON LINE C · INTERCEPTS ON LINE D · INTERCEPTS ON LINE E · VERTICAL DIMENSION OF SECONDARY GRID · HORIZONTAL DIMENSION OF SECONDARY GRID · INTERCEPTS ON LINE F · INTERCEPTS ON LINE G · INTERCEPTS ON LINE H · INTERCEPTS ON LINE I · INTERCEPT ON LINE J

Form — Column 2: COUNTRY · SITE NUMBER · SAMPLE NUMBER · FACTOR FAMILY · DATA FORM REFERENCE · DATA GROUP · COMPONENT NUMBER · LINE NUMBER · CONTINUATION NUMBER · BRANCHING HEIGHT · BRANCH DIAMETER · BRANCH ANGLE · BRANCH LENGTH · BRANCH TIP HEIGHT · FURCATION TYPE · LENGTH OF BRANCH SPINES IRRITANTS · LEAF LENGTH · LEAF WIDTH · LEAF THICKNESS · LEAF CONDITION · LENGTH OF LEAF SPINES · SPINE POSITION SHARP EDGES IRRITANTS

Form — Column 3: COUNTRY · SITE NUMBER · SAMPLE NUMBER · FACTOR FAMILY · DATA FORM REFERENCE · DATA GROUP · COMPONENT NUMBER · LINE NUMBER · CELL NUMBER · DETERMINANT DATA GROUP · DETERMINANT FIELD · HEIGHT OF COMPONENT · ATTACHMENT · DISTANCE FROM CELL CENTER · AZIMUTH · ELEVATION OF BASE · NUMBER OF BASES · BASE DIAMETER · MIDDLE STEM DIAMETER · UPPER STEM DIAMETER · HEIGHT OF FIRST STEM FURCATION · NUMBER OF BUTTRESSES · COMPONENT AXIS TO MOST DISTANT BASE · ATTITUDE · SINUOSITY · HARDNESS · LENGTH OF STEM SPINES IRRITANTS · HEIGHT OF INSTRUMENT · NOMENCLATURE COMMENTS

are referred to as 'items' in the text. The appendix contains only those statements which are directly relevant to the vegetation description itself; filing data, such as country, site number, sample number, etc., have been omitted from discussion. In the numbered items in the appendix, the first word (or words) is a heading on the field data form (Fig. 1). The initial words are followed by a number (or numbers) in parentheses, which indicate the column numbers on the data form. Following the parentheses, there is in many instances a bracket; the word in the bracket indicates the unit of measure prescribed for that factor (the word 'code' in the brackets implies that a numerical code is used for a more or less subjective classification of that factor, and 'count' indicates the total number in a group of things). Definitions, comments, and data collection instructions follow the parentheses or brackets. The definitions are illustrated, as appropriate, in Figures 2–5.

However, prior to beginning the process of filling out the data form, it is necessary to establish the area which is to be described. If possible, this area should be the structural cell of the assemblage. Since the cell is a sample to define spatial distributions, the thing whose distribution is to be described must be selected. The 'thing' is some factor value of the vegetation structure;

it may be selected for any purpose, but it must be isolated before the structural cell can be identified, and it must be emphasized that the resulting cell is an attribute of the distribution of that factor value, and *only* that factor value. The factor value chosen to determine the cell size is called the determinant; the factor containing the *determinant* is the *determinant factor*.

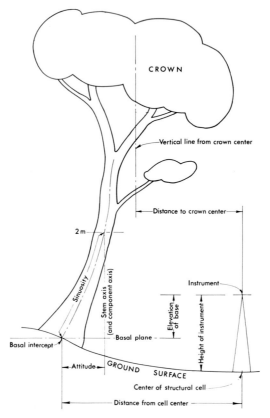

Fig. 2. Basic definitions.

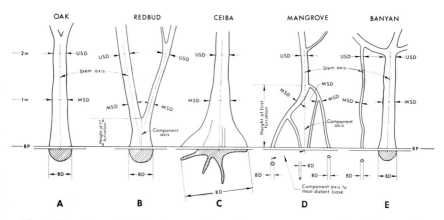

Fig. 3. Stem characteristics. Assumption: all components more than 500 cm tall. USD = upper stem diameter, MSD = middle stem diameter, BD = base diameter, BP = basal plane.

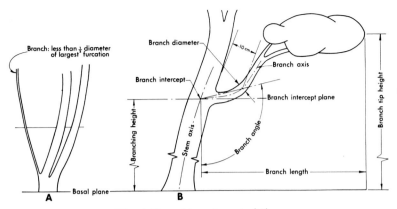

Fig. 4. Branching characteristics.

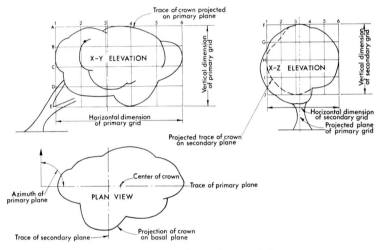

Fig. 5. Crown shape characteristics.

It should be noted that the structural cell theory holds that *any* attribute can be used as the determinant. Thus, it may be a single factor value (such as specific stem diameter), or it may be two or more factor values *in combination*.

If for any purpose it is desired to establish the spatial distributions of two or more *separate* determinants in the same assemblage, it is appropriate to establish concentric structural cells for each. In most cases, the two cells will be of different sizes, since it is unlikely that two different determinants will have identical spatial distributions. When cells of two or more sizes are recorded, the *largest* cell at any given sample point is called the *primary cell*. Successively smaller cells (and there may be many, depending upon the purposes for making the description) are called secondary, tertiary, etc.

It should be noted that the description of components, and of geometric associations of one component with another, can be accomplished without recourse to the structural cell. If for any reason a description of a small area or of a highly non-uniform area in which a valid structural cell cannot be established is desired, the circular area designated for the description is called a *sample area*. This fact *must* be noted in the record. Figure 6 shows the planimetric distribution for a sample area.

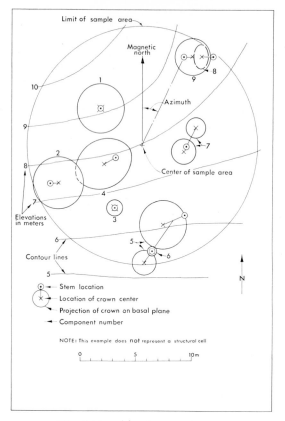

Fig. 6. Example of a sample area.

TIME REQUIREMENTS

The data recording process described above seems to be extraordinarily complex and unnecessarily elaborate, but that impression is largely illusionary. After a day or two of experience, a previously unskilled field team can completely describe a normal temperate-zone forest sample in a few hours. Even the complex second-growth rain forests of Panama or South-east Asia take only one day in most cases. This is largely because the process is almost entirely routine; once the team members have become accustomed to taking the measurements, and have memorized the sequence in which they should be taken, the data can be accumulated more rapidly than the recorder can write the numbers in the data form.

UTILIZATION OF DATA

It must be emphasized that the description scheme was designed primarily to fill the needs of military performance prediction models. It is obvious that the input for the models must be extractable from the recorded data, or the whole effort will have been in vain.

The U.S. Army has a quite sophisticated mathematical model for predicting the speeds of military vehicles going across-country. The model requires vegetation information in terms of the spacings of stems as a function of successive stem diameters. The card deck, which has been obtained by direct transcription from the data forms, is used as program input; the machine reads the 'distance from cell centre' field (item 9), the 'middle stem diameter' field (item 14), and the 'height of component' field (item 7). From these values, the program calculates the number of stems (in diameter increments of 1 cm) for seven arbitrarily defined height classes of components in an arbitrarily assigned area (called an 'expanded cell', which need not be directly related to the size of the structural cell). The program also calculates accumulations of numbers of stem sizes, and spacing as a function of accumulated numbers of stem sizes. These are the values specifically required as input to the cross-country speed prediction model.

If a graphic visualization of these data is required, that too can be provided. Figure 7 is an example of graphs produced by an on-line incremental plotter, illustrating the same data as in Appendix 1.

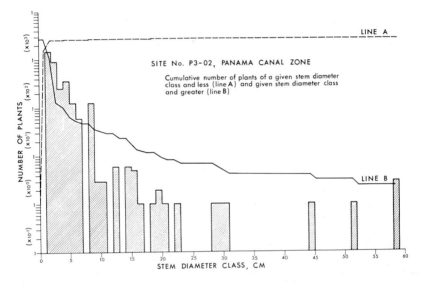

Fig. 7. Histogram and graph; stem diameter class versus number of plants.

It is quite possible that a forester or ecologist might want to study the precise locational geometry of plant assemblages. For example, it might be necessary to establish the degree of association of two species, or the forester might want information on the way in which stem diameter classes are organized in space. An easy way to convey such information is to construct an annotated map of the sample areas. Again the card deck is used as direct input. The computer reads the 'component number' field (item 2), the 'distance from cell centre' field (item 9), the 'azimuth' field (item 10), and the 'middle stem diameter' field (item 14), and with an on-line plotter, constructs a map such as that illustrated by Figure 8. The numbers beside the crosses are item numbers, placed there by the machine so that we mere humans can refer to cards in data group 06 and identify the species. The sizes of the crosses are coded according to arbitrarily designated stem diameter classes.

It is apparent that many other combinations of data can be extracted from the descriptions; the potentialities seem almost limitless. The only requirement is a computer and a competent programmer.

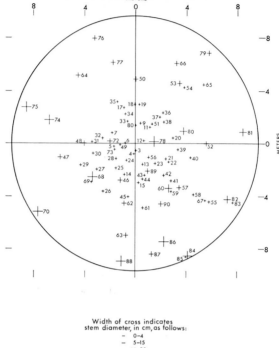

Fig. 8. Automatic plotter map of stem distributions. Note: numbers adjacent to
each cross correspond to item numbers in columns 11–13 on data form
and printout.

The description system which has been developed meets all of the criteria
and considerations previously described. It is both open-ended and abstractable,
and modification to suit civilian requirements would be simple and
straightforward.

REFERENCES

GREIG-SMITH, P. (1964). *Quantitative Plant Ecology*. 2nd Ed. (Butterworth: Washington.)
MILLS, H. L., and CLAGG, SAM E. (1964). *The Physiognomy of Vegetation: A Quantitative
Approach to Vegetation Geometry Based Upon the Structural Cell Concept as the
Minimum Sample Size. Concepts and Analytical Methods.* (U.S.A.E. Waterways
Experimental Station: Vicksburg, Miss.)

Appendix 1

INSTRUCTIONS FOR FILLING OUT VEGETATION DESCRIPTION DATA FORMS

Stem Characteristics (Data Group 03; see Fig. 1)

1. Data group (13–14). This is a file number to identify specific kinds of
information in the card deck.

2. Component number (15–17). A component is any numbered individual plant, or any aggregation of plants so closely associated that they cannot logically be separated (e.g., a clump of bunch grass, or bamboo).

3. Line number (18–19). Enter the number of lines on the data sheet necessary to describe the component. The numbering sequence is continuous through data groups 04 and 05 (Fig. 1).

4. Cell number (20) [count]. The order number of the structural cell of which the component is a part. All components exhibiting the determinant which was chosen as the basis for a structural cell are identified by the same number in this field. The cells are numbered sequentially, with '1' being assigned to the primary cell.

5. Determinant data group (21–22) [code]. The data group (columns 13–14, Fig. 1) in which the determinant factor is recorded according to the following:

Code No.	Data Group
03	Stem characteristics
04	Branch and foliage characteristics
05	Crown characteristics

6. Determinant field (23–24) [code]. The column number in Figure 1 of the first column in the field of the determinant factor.

7. Height of components (25–28) [cm]. The vertical distance from the basal plane (a horizontal plane passed through the intercept of the stem axis and the ground surface; see Fig. 2) to the highest point of the component.

8. Attachment (29) [code]. If the base of the plant can be identified, place a '1' in this column; if not, place a '2' therein.

9. Distance from cell centre (30–33) [cm]. The horizontal distance from the cell centre to the basal intercept (the intercept of the component axis and the basal plane, Fig. 2).

10. Azimuth (34–36) [degrees]. The horizontal angle clockwise from magnetic north to the basal intercept (component 9, Fig. 6).

11. Elevation of base (37–40) [cm]. The relative elevation of the basal plane with respect to the instrument height. If the stem base is above the instrument level, place a '+' in column 37; if below, a '−'.

12. Number of bases (41–42) [count]. The number of individual stems entering the ground (example D, Fig. 3).

13. Base diameter (43–45) [cm]. The diameter of each stem(s) at ground level (Fig. 3).

14. Middle stem diameter (46–48) [cm]. The diameter of the stem(s) at a point above the basal intercept in accordance with the following (and see Fig. 3):

Height of Component (cm)	Height of Diameter Measurements (cm)	
	Middle	Upper
< 30	1	2
30–100	10	20
100–200	30	60
200–500	60	120
> 500	100	200

15. Upper stem diameter (49–51) [cm]. The diameter of the stem(s) at a point as specified in the table in item 14 (and see Fig. 3).

16. Height of first stem furcation (52–54) [cm]. The vertical distance from the basal plane to the first stem furcation.

17. Number of buttresses (55–56) [count]. The number of buttress terminations, if the component has a 'star-shaped' cross-section at or slightly above the basal plane (example C, Fig. 3).

18. Component axis to most distant base (57–60) [cm]. The horizontal distance from the component axis to the most distant secondary stem (or stilt root; example D, Fig. 3).

19. Attitude (61–63) [cm]. The horizontal distance from the basal intercept to the intercept in the basal plane of a vertical line dropped from the component axis at a point 200 cm above the basal plane (Fig. 2), or from the highest point of the crown if the component is less than 200 cm high.

20. Sinuosity (64–66) [cm]. The length of the stem axis, from the basal intercept to a point 200 cm above the basal plane, or to the highest point of the crown if the component is less than 200 cm high.

21. Hardness (67) [code]. The depth to which a standard wooden pencil (approximate diameter 7 mm, sharpened to a conical point about 25 mm long) can be driven by hand into the component stem after removal of the bark.

Code Number	Depth (mm)
1	< 7
2	7–25
3	> 25

22. Length of stem spines (68–69) [mm]. The approximate average length of any hard, sharp protrusion capable of inflicting a wound on unprotected human flesh. If there are none, record '00.'

23. Irritants (70) [code]. If there are irritating hairs or any other type of irritant on the stem, place a '1' in this field; if none, record '0.'

24. Height of instrument (71–73) [cm]. The vertical distance between the optical axis of the instrument at the centre of the structural cell and the ground surface at that point (Fig. 2).

25. Nomenclature (74) [code]. If taxonomic or other data relating to plant identification are obtained for this component, place a '1' indicating the existence of a 'vegetation nomenclature' card (data group 06), in this field; if none a '0.'

26. Comments (75) [code]. If any additional descriptive material is desirable for complete description of a component, place a '1' in this column, indicating the existence of a 'comment' card (data group 07) on which additional information is recorded. If none, place a '0.'

Branch and Foliage Characteristics (Data Group 04; see Fig. 1)

The branching description, as given in the following items, defines selected factors of individual branches. It is possible to describe those factors for every branch in a component, and for certain purposes this procedure is justifiable. For many other purposes, it is normally adequate to describe only those branches which: (a) form the bottom of the crown; or (b) determine the geometry of the structure which ultimately forms the crown; or (c) protrude significantly into the space around the stem, thus effectively increasing the space occupied by the component in the zone in which most human activities take place. Columns 1–19 in this form are reserved for filing and retrieval information.

27. Continuation number (20–21). This number identifies the line in data group 03 of which this line is a continuation.

28. Branching height (22–25) [cm]. The vertical distance from the branch intercept plane (a horizontal plane passed through the intercept of the stem axis and the branch axis) to the basal plane (Fig. 4). If the branching height is less than 200 cm, the branch must be *less than* one-half the diameter of the largest stem (see items 14 and 15); larger structures are defined as stems.

29. Branch diameter (26–28) [cm]. The diameter of the branch at a point 10 cm from the *surface* of the stem to which it is attached (Fig. 4).

30. Branch angle (29–31) [degrees]. The vertical angle between a vertical line dropped from the branch intercept and a straight line projected from the branch intercept through the axis of the branch at the point at which its diameter (item 29) was measured (Fig. 4).

31. Branch length (32–35) [cm]. The horizontal straight-line distance from the branch intercept to the farthest extension of the branch, including its twigs and leaves, if any (Fig. 4).

32. Branch tip height (36–39) [cm]. The vertical distance from the basal plane to the point at the branch tip selected in item 31 (Fig. 4).

33. Furcation type (40) [code]. The basic branching organization. There appear to be six fundamental categories.

Code No.	Definition
1	Continuous central axis; stem goes vertically through the entire crown.
2	Partial central axis; stem goes part way through crown, then furcates into two or more large branches.
3	No central axis; stem furcates into two or more large branches at or near base of crown.
4	Stem furcation; stem divides into two or more large branches well below leaf and twig mass.
5	Radial; branches radiate from common or nearly common point; very few or no branches below point of major furcation.
6	Entangled; branches emerge at odd angles and places, and tangle amongst themselves and other plants.

34. Length of branch spines (41–42) [mm]. The approximate average length of any spines on the branches.

35. Irritants (43) [code]. Place a '1' in this field if there are irritants of any kind on the branches; if none, a '0.'

36. Leaf length (44–46) [mm]. The approximate average longest dimension of any leaflike organ. A 'leaf' includes any leaflike organ, such as fern fronds. Each leaflet in a compound leaf is treated as an individual leaf as are also the segments of leaves which are dissected to the midrib, as in many palms. If the leaf is of the typically spatulate form the term applies only to the blade, and not the petiole.

37. Leaf width (47–49) [mm]. The greatest distance across the leaf at right angles to the line along which length was measured.

38. Leaf thickness (50–51) [mm]. The thickness of the leaf blade, *not* the large veins. For tapered or fleshy leaves, measure the maximum thickness of a cross section at the midpoint between the point of attachment and the blade tip.

39. Leaf condition (52) [code]. The presence or conditions of the leaves.

Code No.	Condition
0	No leaves present.
1	Present and living.
2	Dead, but still clinging to component.

40. Length of leaf spines (53–54) [mm]. The average length of any spines on the leaf.
41. Spine position (55) [code]. The position of the armature on the leaf.

Code No.	Location of Armature
0	Spines absent.
1	On leaf margin only.
2	On leaf tip only.
3	On both leaf margin and leaf tip.
4	On entire surface.

42. Sharp edges (56) [code]. A sharp or cutting edge which is capable of inflicting an abrasion or wound on unprotected human flesh. If present, place a '1' in this field; if none, a '0.'
43. Irritants (57) [code]. Place a '1' in this field if there are irritants of any type on or in the leaves; if there are none, record '0.'

Crown Shape Characteristics (Data Group 05; see Fig. 1)

This data group records information relevant to the size and shape of the crown of the component, and the location of the crown with respect to the centre of the structural cell.
44. Distance to crown centre (22–25) [cm]. The horizontal distance from the centre of the structural cell to the geometric centre of the figure which would result from projecting the crown of the component vertically to the basal plane (Fig. 2).
45. Azimuth to crown centre (26–28) [degrees]. The horizontal angle between magnetic north and the crown centre, measured clockwise.
46. Azimuth of primary plane (29–31) [degrees]. The azimuth of a vertical plane passed through the crown centre (item 45) in that direction which will result in the largest projected crown area if the surface of the crown were projected to the plane along lines normal to it (Fig. 5).
47. Vertical dimension of primary grid (32–35) [cm]. The primary grid is formed by placing a rectangle on the primary plane in such a way that top and bottom of the rectangle just touch the tip of the crown and the lowest part of the crown, respectively, *of that part of the crown intercepted by the primary plane,* and with the vertical sides of the rectangle just touching the widest projections of the portion of the crown intercepted by the same plane (Fig. 5). Some judgment is required, especially with respect to identification of the lowest portion of the crown. As a general rule, the crown is the envelope enclosing the leaf and twig mass. The vertical dimension of the primary grid is the vertical dimension of the rectangle described above.
48. Horizontal dimension of primary grid (36–39) [cm]. The horizontal dimension of the grid described in item 47 (Fig. 5).
49. Intercepts on line A (40–41) [code]. Divide the grid into vertical and horizontal zones. Number and letter the zones as shown in Figure 5. Construct the intercept of the crown margin on the grid. The grid intercepts on line A are the numbers of the vertical lines closest to the points at which the crown trace crosses line A. If the trace touches only one point on line A (as is often the case), record only the code for the single nearest vertical line, and place it in column 40 of the data form; place a '0' in column 41. If there is no crown, place '0' in both columns.

50. Intercepts on lines B through E (42–43, 44–45, 46–47, 48–49) [code]. Same procedure as for item 47.
51. Vertical dimension of the secondary grid (50–53) [code]. Construct a second grid passing through the crown centre in the same fashion as for the primary grid, but at right angles to it. The vertical dimension of the secondary grid (Fig. 5) is measured in the same way as that of the primary grid (item 45).
52. Horizontal dimension of the secondary grid (54–57) [cm]. Measured in the same way as for the primary grid (item 46; and see Fig. 5).
53. Intercepts on lines F through J (58–59, 60–61, 62–63, 64–65, 66–67) [code]. Record in the same fashion as on the primary grid (item 47).

Vegetation Nomenclature Data (Data Group 06; Not Illustrated)

If it appears desirable to record nomenclatural information about a component, it is recorded on a separate form. The first 12 columns are devoted to filing and retrieval information, as in the other data groups. Columns 13–14 record the data group number; columns 15–16 record the component number; and the remainder of the card can be utilized for other information. A suggested specified order is: common name, botanical name, the name of the person making the identification, and the name of the reference used to assist in the identification (if any).

Comments (Data Group 07; Not Illustrated)

Any individual information about either individual components, or about the assemblage as a whole, which the field team considers to be worthy of recording is referenced in the same manner as specified for data group 06, and then written out. As many lines as are needed are used, with the lines numbered sequentially for sorting.

Soil Water and its Effect on Soil Engineering Parameters

B. G. Richards

Division of Soil Mechanics, CSIRO, Syndal, Victoria, Australia

The design of foundations for highways and house dwellings is based on engineering parameters which are strongly dependent on the soil water potential. It is shown that the controlling soil water potential is governed entirely by the potential gradient below the depth of seasonal moisture variation. The engineering performance of these structures can therefore only be determined from land evaluation procedures which delineate on the earth's surface areas of significantly different soil type, and subsurface moisture conditions.

INTRODUCTION

In most fields of engineering and materials science, use is made of materials whose properties can be assumed to be reasonably constant and independent of environment. Soil engineering, on the other hand, is concerned with materials whose properties not only vary with time, but also are strongly dependent upon both natural and man-made environment. Perhaps the most important environmentally-controlled factor in determining engineering soil properties is soil water.

Until recently, adequate techniques for the quantitative expression of soil water variables were not readily available. This resulted in soil engineers being limited to determining the relevant soil engineering parameters in simulated environments, particularly the stress system, density, and soil water conditions. In general, it was only possible to simulate those conditions that existed at the time of the investigation and not those that might be expected to occur in the future. However, recent advances in techniques for the measurement and prediction of soil water variables have now reached a stage where the empirical and simulated procedures can in many cases be improved or replaced by a more rational approach through a more basic and fundamental understanding of the problems. While it is not true to say at this time that environmental or soil water variables can always be confidently included in engineering design techniques, it is now possible to predict how they could be in the future. This paper therefore attempts to review simply and briefly the present state of utilizing soil water variables in engineering practice.

QUANTITATIVE EXPRESSION OF THE SOIL WATER VARIABLE

Moisture Content

In the past, soil water has mainly been expressed in engineering practice in terms of the gravimetric water content as a percentage of the dry weight of the soil which can be measured in the laboratory relatively easily. However, because of the extreme variations in moisture content with practically every soil variable, e.g., soil type, clay content, porosity or density, structure, externally applied stress, etc., no meaningful expression of moisture content *in situ* can readily be found (Aitchison and Richards 1965). Even if an effective moisture content can be obtained using statistical methods, it can only be used in empirical approaches.

Pore Pressure or Soil Water Potential

Terzaghi (1925) made one of the most important advances in soil mechanics when he formulated his effective stress law for saturated soils, viz. in its most familiar form:

$$\sigma' = \sigma - u \qquad (1)$$

where σ' = total normal stress, u = pore water pressure, σ = the effective stress.

In most cases, the term effective stress can only be satisfactorily defined as that stress which is instrumental in controlling soil behaviour (Donald 1964). Numerous workers have tried to attribute physical significance to effective stress, but none has been successful for all real soils.

The simple definition of effective stress as given by equation (1) has been well tested over the past few decades for describing shear strength and volume change phenomena in saturated soils, i.e. soils which are pore space saturated (Skempton 1960; Bishop 1959). However, when the soil voids contain both air and water, the pore pressure u does not act uniformly over all the soil particles and equation (1) becomes unsatisfactory. Theoretical treatments using statistical considerations gave rise to a number of modified effective stress equations (Aitchison 1957; Jennings 1960; Croney, Coleman, and Black 1958), but the present common form (Aitchison and Bishop 1960) is:

$$\sigma' = \sigma - u_a + \chi(u_a - u_w) \qquad (2)$$

where u_a = pore air pressure, u_w = pore water pressure, $u_a - u_w$ = pore water suction, χ = an empirical parameter depending mainly on the degree of saturation.

This equation has not yet been tested rigorously, mainly because of lack of adequate measurement techniques, but it has been used successfully to explain the shear strength behaviour of a number of unsaturated cohesionless and clay soils (Bishop *et al.* 1960; Donald 1964; Blight 1965b, 1966). There is also very limited evidence that equation (2) is also applicable to volume change in soils (Blight 1965a, 1966).

Several attempts have been made to attribute physical significance to χ, but as with effective stress, it must be considered at this time as an empirical factor dependent upon a number of variables. In most cases, however, equations (1) and (2) have been found to be quite satisfactory at an engineering level, providing certain limitations due to a lack of understanding of effective stress are observed.

Total Potential or Thermodynamic Variable

Perhaps the most readily measurable soil water variable is the total potential (Marshall 1959). The Kelvin equation, viz., in its simplest form:

$$h = RT \log_e \frac{p}{p_0} \qquad (3)$$

where h = total potential, R = gas constant, T = absolute temperature, $\frac{p}{p_0} = \frac{H}{100}$ = relative vapour pressure or humidity, describes the relationship between total potential and vapour pressure. The psychrometric technique

(Spanner 1951; Richards 1965, and unpublished data), has now been developed to a stage where it is a very satisfactory engineering technique for measuring soil water potentials in partially saturated soils. Peck and Rabbidge (1966) have developed an osmotic technique for the measurement of total potential, which shows promise for the future.

The solute suction or osmotic potential, which is the difference between the total suction and matrix suction or potential is related to the electrolyte concentration of the soil water and has generally been ignored by engineers in the past. However, measurements of solute suctions in a range of Australian soils (Aitchison and Richards 1965) have shown that solute suctions can be very high indeed, particularly in arid areas, where values in excess of -2000 lb/in.^{2} have been measured.

Bolt (1955), Waidelich (1958), Lambe (1960), and Quirk (1963) among others have clearly demonstrated the importance of the pore fluid and therefore solute suction on engineering soil properties, particularly volume change. Not only has its presence obviously resulted in substantial errors in conventional pore pressure measurements, but it must also be included in any effective stress relation. Experience so far has suggested that over the whole range of values found in soils, the relative effects of matrix and solute suctions are not necessarily the same. Thus it appears that measurement of both components rather than the total suction itself is necessary and the relative effect of each accounted for by two empirical χ factors (Richards 1967).

Considering the present state of knowledge and experience it is now clear that the only satisfactory expression of the soil water variable is by the total suction or potential and its two components, viz., matrix and solute components. Further weight is added to this argument by the fact that predictions of soil water variations beneath engineering structures can only be made in terms of these same variables, as will be discussed later.

ENGINEERING SOIL PARAMETERS

The main problem confronted by soil engineers in practice can generally be analysed in terms of the shear strength and deformation parameters of the soil. If a true effective stress could be found, then the deformation of soil could be related entirely to effective stress. Because of limitations in the effective stress concept, it is preferable at the present time to consider deformation problems in two categories, viz., deformation where applied stress is the main factor, e.g., pavement deflections, and secondly, deformation where moisture changes are the main factor, e.g., settlement and heave. Furthermore, when using effective stress concepts with any engineering soil parameter, care must be exercised in extrapolating measured parameters to field conditions. Some of the difficulties in doing this are created by the stress and moisture history of the soil (e.g., over-consolidation effects on soil parameters); time effects (e.g., creep and secondary compression); soil structure alterations due both to chemical and physical effects (e.g., collapse of soils when suddenly wetted).

Shear Strength

The general expression used in soil engineering for the shear strength of a soil mass is:

$$S = C' + \sigma' \tan \varphi' \tag{4}$$

where S = shear strength of the soil mass and C′ and φ′ are purely empirical parameters for shear strength defined as: C′ = apparent cohesion with respect to effective stresses, φ′ = angle of shearing resistance with respect to effective stresses.

The angle φ is relatively constant, varying only slightly with soil structure. However, C′ varies significantly with both the soil water variable and soil structure. Various attempts have been made to interpret both C′ and φ′ as more fundamental parameters, e.g., Hvorslev (1937), Parry (1960), Trollope (1964). While certainly aiding the understanding of the shear strength of soils, they only have limited application to engineering practice.

Equation (4) is the best expression available at the present time for both saturated and partially saturated soils, providing its limitations are taken into consideration.

Stress Controlled Deformation

While soil deforms under changed stress conditions in most engineering applications, it is probably in the field of pavement performance that these deformations are most important. In all approaches used to the present time, the soil is assumed to be a 'pseudo-elastic' material, enabling the theories of elasticity to be used (Whiffin and Lister 1962). Although soil is in reality a non-linear material, properly determined effective elastic moduli enable the simpler linear theories to be used. As modern high-speed computers become more accessible, non-linear theories could be applied to practical applications. However, the problem of describing the non-linear properties of soils simply and quickly may not warrant this increased sophistication in most practical cases.

Hveem (1955) first introduced the term 'resilient' deformation for those recoverable deformations, which, depending on the magnitude and repetition of load, lead to fatigue failure. The term 'resilient' was used as the deformations

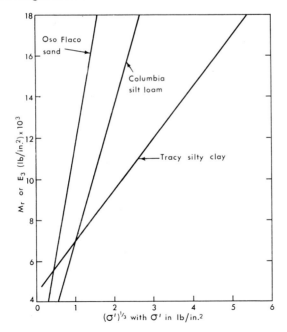

Fig. 1. Relationship between subgrade moduli and effective stress for three soils.

are not truly elastic. Seed *et al.* (1965) have investigated extensively resilient strains and deformations in a wide range of materials and have shown conclusively that the only satisfactory modulus of the pavement layers is the effective elastic modulus, which they defined as the 'resilient' modulus M_r.

Although the effect of soil water variable is not well known, the theoretical model of Brutsaert (1964) and experimental results of a number of workers (Hardin and Richart 1963; Seed *et al.* 1965; Brutsaert and Luthin 1964; Monismith and Richards unpublished data) have shown that the resilient modulus of soil could be related to the nth power of effective stress, where n varies from $0 \cdot 2$ to $0 \cdot 6$, but is generally approximately $0 \cdot 3$.

Figure 1 shows trends of M_r against the third power of effective stress for three soils (Brutsaert and Luthin 1964; Monismith and Richards unpublished data) which are adequate for engineering purposes over a limited range of effective stress, based on pore pressures or matrix suctions. The effects of solute suctions are unknown at this time.

Moisture-controlled Deformation

The most important deformation of this type is the volume change that takes place in the soil under engineering structures resulting in heave or settlement. These volume changes are due to moisture changes which may be the result of changes in applied stress, e.g., consolidation, or environmental changes, e.g., shrinkage settlement. In both saturated soils and soils with negative pore pressure, and 100% pore space saturation, volume change can be predicted quite accurately using the effective stress law, providing care is taken to avoid the limitations of over-consolidation and stress and moisture history.

Experimental proof of the equivalence between negative pore pressures or matrix suctions and applied stresses for producing volume changes in soils has been given by Croney, Lewis, and Coleman (1950); Aitchison and Donald (1956), and others over part of the range of engineering interest. However, when shrinkage cracks appear, the equivalence between suction and applied stress fails due to the different nature of the stresses within the soil mass. Apart from this limitation, the effective stress concept is useful to explain volume changes in saturated soils in practical applications.

Volume changes in partially saturated soils are not sufficiently understood and are consequently difficult to predict. An effective stress law similar to equation (3) has been used to describe the behaviour of partially saturated soils with some success (Blight 1965a, 1965b, 1966), but the parameter χ is probably different from the χ relevant to shear behaviour (Aitchison 1957). The effects of solute suction are again not properly understood and are generally neglected in practice.

Soil Engineering Parameters in General

As the above discussion has shown, soil engineering parameters depend on the nature and arrangement of the soil itself and the soil water. For a given soil type, the soil can, at the practical level, be defined quantitatively by the density or void ratio with a qualitative understanding of its structure, which is generally assumed to remain unchanged. The density or void ratio can in many instances be controlled by proper design and construction procedures, so that it remains constant or varies only as a function of the soil water potential. This is particularly true in pavement design where experience has shown that pavement materials placed at a higher density than a certain percentage of standard density, e.g., a percentage of modified AASHO density, which is related to the traffic conditions, will undergo no further change in density and therefore deformation.

Soil water variables on the other hand, are environmentally controlled and cannot be generally controlled. Consequently, soil water potential and how it changes with time are important factors in determining the relevant soil engineering parameters.

PREDICTION OF SOIL WATER POTENTIAL

The prediction of soil water potential (expressed as pore pressure or suction) has been adequately described elsewhere (Aitchison and Richards 1965; Richards 1967). Consequently, only a brief summary need be given here.

On a very broad basis, it has been found that the total suction (and therefore matrix suction to a lower degree) beneath covered areas tends to be related to climate as expressed quantitatively by some factor such as Thornthwaite's moisture index, I, as shown in Figure 2 (Russam and Coleman 1962; Aitchison and Richards 1965; Scala unpublished data). The relation in Figure 2 has been established empirically from a large number of observations throughout the world. While quite large departures do occur from this relationship due to local environmental factors, it is quite useful in preliminary or broad-scale planning.

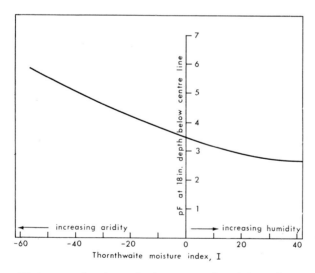

Fig. 2. Equilibrium suction beneath the centre of sealed road pavements as a function of Thornthwaite's moisture index, I.

At the local level, the ultimate equilibrium suction (generally matrix suction) can be more accurately predicted from the subsurface suction profile using the equation:

$$h_z = h_{z_0} + \rho(z_0 - z) \qquad (5)$$

where h_z = equilibrium suction beneath covered area at depth z, h_{z_0} = suction at a depth z_0, which is below the depth of seasonal moisture variation, and ρ = density of water.

Equation (5) is based on several approximate assumptions which have been verified both theoretically and experimentally at a practical level (Richards

1967, in press). It has physical significance in that it defines the suction profile with no upward flux of water through the soil profile (i.e. $q = 0$ in Fig. 3). This approach is summarised graphically in Figure 3. The solid lines show typical seasonal ranges of suction profiles, and the dashed line the predicted equilibrium profiles using equation (5).

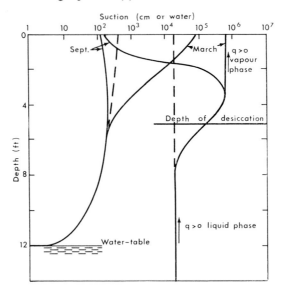

Fig. 3. Typical suction profiles away from engineering structures and the graphical constructions to obtain the equilibrium profiles. Equilibrium profile extrapolated as if $q = 0$ (i.e. equation 5).

In general this approach tends to be conservative, but much more accurate than empirical procedures now in use. With shallow water-tables, the procedure has been shown to be very accurate (Croney 1952), but in other cases, it must only be considered to be a good approximation. As an engineer can measure the soil water potential prior to construction, and estimate the ultimate value at all depths, he is therefore in possession of both the likely change and the critical values of soil water potential relevant to his design. A word of caution should be added, however, in using equation (5) as a lack of understanding and experience of soil water behaviour could lead to erroneous conclusions.

DESIGN PROCEDURES

In many soil engineering problems, the soil parameters discussed above must be considered in detail at the local level, necessitating considerable soil testing. These problems are not relevant to this Symposium and need no further discussion. A large number of problems, on the other hand, due to both economic as well as technical reasons, are best handled regionally either as units of length or of area. Perhaps the two main areas of interest are highways and house dwellings, the performance of which will be discussed briefly.

Design of Road and Aerodrome Pavements

Soil volume changes, i.e., heave or settlement due to moisture variations beneath the pavements are often important (Williams 1965). The resulting deformation can cause severe cracking, reducing the life and increasing the maintenance of the pavement as well as affecting the trafficability. This problem of volume change will be discussed later under design of buildings.

The major problem in the design of pavements is the determination of the most critical strength or resistance to deformation of the subgrade. In Australia, as in many other places, the determination of the California bearing ratio (CBR) of the soil in the soaked condition is still the basis for designing pavement thicknesses, although some road authorities do allow reduced pavement thicknesses or the use of poorer grade materials in drier areas.

The CBR method of design is at best a very empirical method, that allows little scope for possible future development. A new and rational method that has recently been proposed (Dorman and Metcalf 1965; Klomp and Dorman 1964), but not developed as a practical method to date, does show exciting promise. One of its main advantages is that it takes a number of important factors into account, viz., wheel loading, traffic intensity, and fatigue criteria of the pavement materials. The basic principle in this method is the prevention of excessive stress or strain in the pavement or in the underlying soil or subgrade. This is accomplished by investigating the strain conditions at certain critical locations in the pavement and then designing to maintain these strains within safe limits. Dorman and Metcalf (1965), using data from the AASHO road test, produced design curves for the conditions at the test road. Figure 4 shows typical curves for 10^6 equivalent 9000 lb wheel loads while other curves can be prepared for other load repetitions.

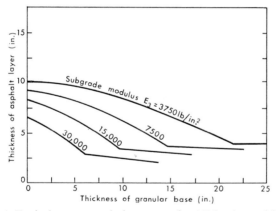

Fig. 4. Typical pavement design curves for 10^6 load repetitions.

While no attempt has been made to extrapolate these curves to other road sites, the method does suggest that the curves are independent of the base materials, providing adequate material specifications and placement densities are achieved. However, they will be dependent on the fatigue properties of the asphalt surface layer and particularly on the temperature in that layer.

The curves in Figure 4 give the thickness of granular base for any thickness of asphalt layer or *vice versa*. It is clearly evident that the modulus of the subgrade has a very large influence on pavement thicknesses and therefore on performance. The effect of environment and particularly the soil moisture variable can now be included in this design method (Richards in press) by incorporating the relation between resilient modulus of the subgrade and effective stress (Fig. 1) into the design curve in Figure 4. For say a 4 in. thick asphalt layer, this gives the design curves in Figure 5 relating base thickness directly to the soil water potential or suction as the overburden stresses can be ignored in this case. These curves clearly show the significant savings in pavement thicknesses which can be achieved when soil water is taken into account.

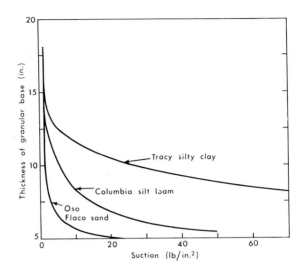

Fig. 5. Design curves for three soils (based on data in Fig. 1) showing the effect of the soil water variable, suction. Asphalt layer 4 in. thick, 10^6 repetitions of 18,000 lb axle loads.

Design of House Dwellings

In contrast to pavements, the strength of the soil is rarely of importance for house dwellings on clays, which are our main concern in this discussion. Consolidation type settlement under structural load is generally insignificant. However, it must be realized that consolidation is only a particular case of the more general problem of water movement and should not be considered separately in any complete analysis.

The most common problem met in the performance of buildings is the heave or settlement of the soil due to the climatic and drainage environment and changes in this environment brought about by the erection of the building. Some of the most common causes of failure based on experience in a number of countries are seasonal soil moisture variations under the extremities of the structure, long-term wetting or drying under the structure as a result of the new soil environment caused by the structure, hydrological changes over the general area (Willoughby 1965), and localized man-made effects, e.g., broken water pipes, etc.

The environmental factors which cause damage, can now more or less be predicted, but the man-made factors will always remain an uncertainty, although with reasonable care, they can be minimized.

The moisture changes that will occur under the centre of the structure relative to the seasonal changes occurring at the edges can now be predicted. Using volume change-effective stress relationships for various depths in the soil profile and integrating over a sufficient depth of the profile the total surface movement can be estimated.

CONCLUSIONS

The general discussion above clearly indicates that there are very large gaps in our knowledge of soil engineering parameters and particularly the effect of water on them. However, it is equally clear that the techniques used in design procedures, some of which are extremely empirical, have worked successfully in the past and will continue to do so in the future. Furthermore, new measurement techniques and more rational and fundamental design techniques are becoming available, which it is hoped will lead to more efficient and economic designs.

One point that does stand out in this discussion, which must be of importance to this Symposium, is that for both types of structures discussed, the performance of the structure at the broad practical level depends on a single parameter of the soil *in situ* which is a function of the soil type and the soil water potential. In the case of highway pavements, the parameter is the dynamic stress-controlled deformation characteristic as a function of the soil water potential, whereas for house dwellings it is generally the deformation characteristic under constant static stress, also as a function of the soil water potential.

It is further shown that the controlling soil water potential is governed entirely by the soil water potential profile below the depth of seasonal moisture variation for a properly designed structure. This therefore leads to the conclusion that the engineering performance of the structures mentioned can be determined from any land evaluation procedure which delineates on the earth's surface areas of significantly different soil type and subsurface moisture conditions.

REFERENCES

AITCHISON, G. D. (1957). The strength of quasi-saturated and unsaturated soils in relation to the pressure deficiency in the pore water. *Proc. 4th Int. Conf. Soil Mech. Fdn Engng* **1**, 135–9.

AITCHISON, G. D., and DONALD, I. B. (1956). Effective stresses in unsaturated soils. *Proc. 2nd Aust.–N.Z. Conf. Soil Mech. Fdn Engng* 192–9.

AITCHISON, G. D., and BISHOP, A. W. (1960). Discussion in *Pore Pressure and Suction in Soils*. (Butterworths: London.) 63–69.

AITCHISON, G. D., and RICHARDS, B. G. (1965). A broad-scale study of moisture conditions in pavement subgrade throughout Australia. In *Moisture Equilibria and Moisture Changes in Soils Beneath Covered Areas*. (Butterworths: Sydney.) 184–232.

AITCHISON, G. D., RUSSAM, K., and RICHARDS, B. G. (1965). Engineering concepts of moisture equilibria and moisture changes in soils. In *Moisture Equilibria and Moisture Changes in Soils Beneath Covered Areas*. (Butterworths: Sydney.) 7–21.

BISHOP, A. W. (1959). *The Principle of Effective Stress*. (Teknisk: Ukeblad.)

BISHOP, A. W., ALPAN, I., BLIGHT, G. E., and DONALD, I. B. (1960). Factors controlling the strength of the partly saturated cohesive soils. *Proc. Conf. Shear Strength of Cohesive Soils*, Am. Soc. Civ. Engrs, Colorado, 503–32 and 1027–42.

BLIGHT, G. E. (1965a). A study of effective stresses for volume change. In *Moisture Equilibria and Moisture Changes in Soils Beneath Covered Areas*. (Butterworths: Sydney.) 259–69.

BLIGHT, G. E. (1965b). Shear strength pore pressure in triaxial testing. *J. Soil Mech. Fdns Div. Am. Soc. civ. Engrs, Proc.* **91** (SM6), 25–39.

BLIGHT, G. E. (1966). Strength characteristics of desiccated clays. *J. Soil Mech. Fdns Div. Am. Soc. civ. Engrs, Proc.* **92** (SM6), 19–37.

BOLT, G. H. (1955). Physico-chemical analysis of the compressibility of pure clays. *Géotechnique* **6**, 86–93.

BRUTSAERT, W. (1964). The propagation of elastic waves in unconsolidated unsaturated granular mediums. *J. geophys. Res.* **69**, 243–58.

BRUTSAERT, W., and LUTHIN, J. N. (1964). The velocity of sound in soils near the surface as a function of the moisture content. *J. geophys. Res.* **69**, 643–52.

CRONEY, D., LEWIS, W. A., and COLEMAN, J. D. (1950). Calculation of the moisture distribution beneath structures. *Civ. Engng publ. Wks Rev.* 45.

CRONEY, D. (1952). The movement and distribution of water in soils. *Géotechnique* 3, 1–16.

CRONEY, D., COLEMAN, J. D., and BLACK, W. P. M. (1958). The movement and distribution of water in soil in relation to highway design and performance. *Highw. Res. Bd Spec. Report* No. 40.

DONALD, I. B. (1964). The influence of water on the engineering properties of soils. In *Mechanisms of Soil Stabilization*. (CSIRO: Melbourne.) D5-7-D5-16.

DORMAN, G. M., and METCALF, C. T. (1965). Design curves for flexible pavements based on layered systems theory. *Highw. Res. Record* No. 71, 69–84.

HARDIN, B. O., and RICHART, F. E. Jnr, (1963). *J. Soil Mech. Fdns Div. Am. Soc. civ. Engrs* (SM1), 33–65.

HVEEM, F. N. (1955). Pavement deflections and fatigue failures, design and testing of flexible pavements. *Bull. Highw. Res. Bd* No. 114, 43–87.

HVORSLEV, M. J. (1937). Uber die Festigkeitseigenschaften gestorten bindiger Boden. *Ingenieridenskabelige Skrifter*, A No. 45, Copenhagen.

JENNINGS, J. E. (1960). A revised effective stress law for use in the prediction of the behaviour of unsaturated soils. In *Pore Pressure and Suction in Soils*. (Butterworths: London.) 26–30.

KLOMP, A. G. J., and DORMAN, G. M. (1964). Stress distribution and dynamic testing in relation to road design. *Proc. 2nd Bienn. Conf. Aust. Rd Res. Bd*, 2, Pt 2, 701–28.

LAMBE, T. W. (1960). A mechanistic picture of shear strength in clay. *Proc. Res. Conf. Shear Strength Cohesive Soils*, Am. Soc. civ. Engrs. Colorado, 555–80.

MARSHALL, T. J. (1959). Relations between water and soil. *Tech. Commun. Commonw. Bur. Soils* No. 50.

PARRY, R. H. G. (1960). The role of latent interparticle forces in the behaviour of clay. *Proc. Symposium on Interparticle Forces in Clay–Water–Electrolyte Systems*, CSIRO, Melbourne.

PECK, A. J., and RABBIDGE, R. M. (1966). Soil water potential: direct measurement by a new technique. *Science, N.Y.* 151, 1385–6.

QUIRK, J. P. (1963). The role of surface forces in determining the physical behaviour of soils and clays. *Proc. 4th Aust.–N.Z. Conf. Soil Mech. Fdn Engng*, 205.

RICHARDS, B. G. (1965). Measurements of the free energy of soil moisture by the psychrometric technique using thermistors. In *Moisture Equilibria and Moisture Changes in Soils Beneath Covered Areas*. (Butterworths: Sydney.) 39–46.

RICHARDS, B. G. (1967). Moisture flow and equilibria in unsaturated soils for shallow foundations. In *Permeability and Capillarity of Soils*. Am. Soc. civ. Engrs, STP417, 4–34.

RICHARDS, B. G. (in press). Role of environment in flexible pavement design. *Civ. Engng Trans. Instn Engrs Aust.*

RUSSAM, K., and COLEMAN, J. D. (1962). The effect of climatic factors on subgrade conditions. *Géotechnique* 11, 22–28.

SEED, H. B., MITRY, F. G., MONISMITH, C. L., and CHAN, C. K. (1965). *Predictions of pavement deflections from laboratory repeated load tests*. I.T.T.E. Report No. TE-65-6, University of California, Berkeley.

SKEMPTON, A. W. (1960). Contribution to *From Theory to Practice in Soil Mechanics*. (Wiley: N.Y.)

SPANNER, D. C. (1951). The Peltier effect and its use in the measurement of suction pressure. *J. exp. Bot.* 2, 145–68.

TERZAGHI, K. (1925). Principles of soil mechanics I — Phenomena of cohesion in clay. *Engng News Rec.* 95, 19.

TROLLOPE, D. H. (1964). On the shear strength of soils. In *Mechanisms of Soil Stabilization*. (CSIRO: Melbourne.) D4-5-D4-13.

WAIDELICH, W. C. (1958). Influence of liquid and clay mineral type on consolidation of clay — liquid systems. *Highw. Res. Bd Spec. Report* No. 40.

WILLIAMS, A. A. B. (1965). The deformation of roads resulting from moisture changes in expansive soils in South Africa. In *Moisture Equilibria and Moisture Changes in Soils Beneath Covered Areas*. (Butterworths: Sydney.) 143–55.

WILLOUGHBY, D. R. (1955). Ground water movement observed during the initial period of urban development at Elizabeth, South Australia. In *Engineering Effects of Moisture Changes in Soils*. (Texas A. & M. Press.) 31–44.

WHIFFIN, A. C., and LISTER, N. W. (1962). *Proc. Int. Conf. on the Structural Design of Asphalt Pavements*, 499.

Reconnaissance Estimation of Stream Discharge—Frequency Relationships

K. D. Woodyer and P. M. Fleming

Division of Land Research,
CSIRO, Canberra, Australia

Constant bankfull frequency appears to be the most promising index for the estimation of discharge-frequency relationships based on reconnaissance observations. Bankfull level has been identified for streams in New South Wales on the basis of channel morphology and vegetation. Two methods of extrapolating from this base flood frequency are considered. A fixed frequency technique appears best suited to the inaccuracies associated with determination of bankfull levels in catchments smaller than 100 sq miles. Moreover, this method does not require daily rainfall observations. The strength of the bankfull frequency approach is that it represents an integration of all catchment characteristics.

INTRODUCTION

This paper examines the feasibility of assessing stream flow on the basis of a reconnaissance survey. Attention is focused here on flow from small catchments rather than from large catchments, where, if a major engineering work is envisaged, the delay and expense involved in the collection of stream flow data is justified. It is not generally realised that large sums of money are expended on the numerous minor works situated on small catchments. It is estimated by Langbein and Hoyt (1959, p. 139) that one-quarter of the capital expenditure on roads in the United States of America is used for the construction of bridges, culverts, and other drainage works. It is likely that a similar proportion applies to Australia where the average annual expenditure on roads for 1961–66 was $367 million (Commonwealth of Australia 1966, p. 15) – almost double the expenditure during that period on water supply, irrigation, and sewerage works. On this basis Australian expenditure on minor works situated on small catchments must be considerable. Figure 1 shows that over much of Australia there is a dearth of gauging data for small catchments necessary for the design of minor works. The concentration of these gauging stations in south-eastern Australia is apparent. Since it will never be feasible to gauge other than a minor proportion of small catchments it is important to investigate methods of estimating discharge.

Geomorphic characteristics of catchments have been related to peak discharge by many workers (see Gray 1965). These characteristics include area, size, and shape of catchments; density and distribution of water courses; overland slope or general land slope; size, length, slope, and condition of stream channels; depression storage and channel pondage. However, these relationships have to be calibrated in terms of local runoff and in the reconnaissance context the only hydrological data we can assume is a sparse network of daily read rain gauges. Moreover, these methods do not supply the design information essential for engineering works, namely stage-discharge-frequency relationships.

The problem can be resolved into three aspects:

1. Estimation of the stage (river height)-discharge relationship.
2. Association of a mean recurrence interval with a particular discharge or stage.
3. Extrapolation from this base discharge-frequency relationship to a general discharge-frequency relationship.

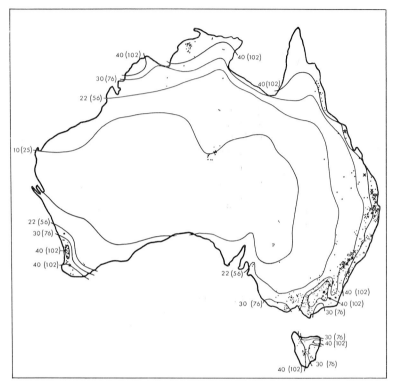

Fig. 1. Gauged catchments less than 100 sq miles (259 sq km) in area shown by dots, and isohyets (median annual precipitation) in inches with millimetres in parentheses. Location of catchments referred to in Tables 1 and 2 shown by crosses.

ESTIMATION OF THE STAGE-DISCHARGE RELATIONSHIP

Use of Uniform Flow Formulas

The estimation of stage-discharge relationships for natural streams presents difficulties. Uniform flow, where the gradient of the water surface is parallel with the bed, seldom occurs because of the occurrence of irregular bed profiles and mobile bed forms. Steady varied flow, where the water depth remains constant with time at any section, but varies along the stream, is a more common situation. The theory of channel hydraulics for uniform flow can be adapted to steady varied flow by use of the energy gradient in place of the water surface gradient in the appropriate formula. The most widely used of all uniform flow formulas is the Manning formula (see Chow 1959) which is expressed as:

$$V = (1/n) R^{\frac{2}{3}} S^{\frac{1}{2}} \tag{1}$$

where V is the mean velocity in metres per second, R is the hydraulic radius in metres i.e. (wetted cross sectional area) ÷ (wetted perimeter), S is the water surface gradient, and n is a coefficient of channel roughness known as Manning's n.

Slope Area Methods

The direct use of a uniform flow formula such as equation (1) for the determination of discharge for a particular stage is known as the slope-area method. In the absence of direct observations of the water surface gradient, it is customary to use high-water marks left by floods and to derive the energy gradient by successive approximation (see Chow 1959, p. 146–8; Dalrymple 1956). In the case of bankfull flow, which is used as a base index for a discharge-frequency relationship in this paper, it seems logical to use the gradient along the banks as the water surface gradient.

In the slope-area method, a comparatively regular channel reach free from bends is selected, and the cross sectional area of the channel is surveyed so that the hydraulic radius R in equation (1) can be determined for any particular stage. The estimation of the stage-discharge relationship is complicated by the fact that the roughness coefficient and the energy gradient vary with stage. Cowan (1956) developed a procedure for estimating Manning's n. However, the estimation of n is largely a subjective procedure based on experience. On the other hand, the water surface gradient (for estimation of the energy gradient) can be approximated at several stages. Two bench levels have been observed along streams in New South Wales (Woodyer 1968; and below), and the gradient along these benches can be assumed to approximate the water surface gradient. In addition debris marks, if available, provide the water level gradient for one or more flood discharges. An observation of discharge, during the course of the reconnaissance survey, may provide another useful water surface gradient measurement. At the same time, such an observation would provide a check on the estimated values of n and the calculation of the energy gradient. In this way it may be possible to estimate several points on the stage-discharge relationship.

The main weakness of uniform flow formulas is that they do not allow for the mobility of the channel boundary and the effect of changing bed forms on the stage-discharge relationship. This problem has not been adequately solved to date, as indicated by Garde and Ranga Raju (1966), and the subsequent discussion of their paper.

In spite of this weakness and the subjectivity involved in estimating the value of n, the accuracy claimed for the slope-area method is surprisingly good. Dalrymple (1956), in the United States of America, reports a maximum error of $9 \cdot 7\%$ and an average error of $4 \cdot 3\%$ in cases where it was possible to check discharge estimates accurately. In other cases, 75% of estimates had an indicated error of less than 15%. These estimated accuracies suggest that the majority of discharge estimates were made in reaches not seriously affected by mobility of the channel boundary.

THE RECURRENCE INTERVAL OF A PARTICULAR DISCHARGE OR STAGE

A number of methods of linking discharges with frequencies have been suggested. Some of these are considered below in the context of a reconnaissance survey.

TABLE 1

Queensland catchments

Station Index Number	Gauging Site — Stream and Location	Catchment Data Area (sq miles)	Area (sq km)	M_{10}	P_{10}^{48} (mm)	Frequency Parameters* a_p	a_q	Error of q_{10} (%)
125001	Pioneer River at Pleystowe	530	1350	9·4	481	1·4	2·4	−1
130306	Don River at Rannes	2650	6800	1·8	193	1·3	N.L.	+50
136201	Barkers Creek at Holbrook	590	1540	0·3	124	1·05	N.L.	+220
136202	Barambah Creek at Moffatdale	250	650	1·3	124	1·05	N.L.	−25
138001	Mary River at Miva	1865	4830	3·6	266	1·1	1·9	+26
138002	Wide Bay Creek at Brooyar	263	680	3·2	204	1·2	1·35	−7
138004	Munna Creek at Marodian	465	1200	5·0	241	1·3	2·0	−22
138105	Yabba Creek at Imbil	230	600	4·9	290	1·0	N.L.	+5
142101	North Pine River at Youngs Crossing	138	360	5·1	213	0·95	1·75	−37
143103	Reynolds Creek at Mogerah	74	200	3·7	234	1·7	N.L.	0
143203	Lockyer Creek at Helidon	137	350	1·2	165	0·8	N.L.	+67
145001	Logan River at Beaudesert	570	1480	2·1	197	0·95	1·40	+30
145101	Albert River at Lumeah	67	170	2·9	222	1·15	N.L.	+18
145102	Albert River at Bromfleet	210	540	6·0	272	1·20	N.L.	−22
146004	Little Nerang at Neranwood	16	40	7·5	388	1·25	1·10	+1
422310	Condamine River at Warwick	530	1370	1·0	139	1·10	N.L.	+28

* Frequency parameters a_p and a_q are coefficients used in equation (6). N.L. = non-linear.

TABLE 2

New South Wales catchments

Station Index Number	Gauging Site		Catchment Data				Frequency Parameters*		Error of q_{10} (%)
	Stream and Location	Area (sq miles)	Area (sq km)	M_{10}	P_{10}^{48} (mm)		a_p	a_q	
210017	Moonan Brook at Moonan Brook	38	98	1·30	122		0·90	2·41	−23
210019	Omadale Creek at Roma	40	104	0·99	122		0·90	1·67	−17
210042	Bowmans Creek at Ravensworth	79	204	0·71	136		1·10	N.L.	+54
210045	Saltwater Creek at Plashetts	16	41	1·71	126		1·08	1·46	0
212008	Coxs River at Bathurst Road	77	199	1·28	142		1·00	2·87	−28
410009	Jounama Creek at Talbingo	52	134	1·18	125		0·75	1·56	+33
421003	Bindo Creek below Gum Valley Creek	13	34	1·13	142		1·00	2·00	−73

* Frequency parameters a_p and a_q are coefficients used in equation (6). N.L. = non-linear.

Frequency of Responsible Storms

Nash (1956) calculates the frequency of particular discharge, given the unit hydrograph and rainfall frequency data, by adding the frequencies of all storms which produce this discharge. This method assumes that the percentage of rainfall which appears as channel flow is known, and that catchment characteristics have been correlated with the instantaneous unit hydrograph. In the absence of a network of gauging stations to define these relationships, this method is impracticable.

Modified Myers' Formula

Table 1 presents the results of an analysis by Ward (1967) of data from 16 streams in north-eastern Australia (mostly in south-east Queensland) using a modified Myers' formula. These streams are all associated with the eastern escarpment but cover a fair range of land types and land uses. The dominant land use is rangeland for cattle. The original Myers' formula was a function of the square root of the catchment area (Jarvis 1942, p. 535) but has now been generalized to relate discharge to a power of catchment area

$$Q = MA^f \tag{2}$$

where Q is flood peak discharge in cubic metres per second; A is catchment area in kilometres; M is called Myers' coefficient, and f is a constant, originally with value $0 \cdot 5$. Ward showed that, in common with experience in France and the U.S.A., his Australian data indicated f should have the value $0 \cdot 8$ and then examined a special case of equation (2),

$$Q_{10} = M_{10}A^{0 \cdot 8} \tag{3}$$

where Q_{10} is the peak discharge, in cubic metres per second, with a mean recurrence interval of 10 years in the annual maximum series (see below), and A is the area of the catchment in square kilometres. Ward gave data which have been shown to give a highly significant correlation ($r = 0 \cdot 975$) between the Myers' coefficient (M_{10}) defined by equation (3) and the 48-hour duration rainfall (P_{10}^{48}) having a mean recurrence interval of 10 years (annual maximum series). The parameter, (P_{10}^{48}) was derived from daily read rain gauge data at selected sites on or near each catchment for which M_{10} was calculated.

To avoid any bias from the selection methods used by Ward, (P_{10}^{48}) values for all available rainfall stations on each of Ward's catchments were averaged to provide new values of (P_{10}^{48}) and an equation of best fit determined for the data. Errors of ± 20 mm in rainfall and $\pm 0 \cdot 3$ for M_{10} were allowed for in the equation (see Morgan 1960). The data are plotted in Figure 2 and the correlation coefficient was $0 \cdot 745$ (significant at the $0 \cdot 1\%$ level).

$$M_{10} = 0 \cdot 025 \, (P_{10}^{48}) - 2 \cdot 13 \tag{4}$$

where (P_{10}^{48}) is in millimetres.
When the likely error in (P_{48}^{10}), indicated above, is considered, it is apparent that the relative accuracy of equation (4) is low for values of (P_{10}^{48}) below about 150 mm.

The N.S.W. catchments in Table 2 were also investigated and the values of M_{10} plotted in Figure 2. The values of P_{10} range from 122 to 142 mm and, while the absolute differences in M_{10} are less than $\pm 0 \cdot 5$, the relative errors in M_{10} and so Q_{10} are as high as 70%. The N.S.W. catchments were all less than 100 sq miles (259 sq km) in area and also covered a considerable range of land types and land use.

Only three of Ward's 16 catchments were less than 100 sq miles (259 sq km) in area, while six were greater than 500 sq miles (1300 sq km). However, the smaller catchments fitted the relationships expressed in equation (4) very well, so that there is no reason to doubt the applicability of the equation to small catchments, although further data from small catchments is desirable.

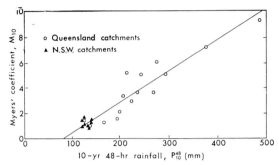

Fig. 2. Correlation of Meyers' coefficient with rainfall. Queensland data after Ward (1967), N.S.W. data after French (unpublished).

Bankfull Frequency

There are strong indications that bankfull flow may be associated with a constant frequency. If this is so, it would provide a link between channel morphology and flood frequency which might be used to extrapolate to floods of other frequencies. Therefore, the evidence for a constant bankfull frequency is considered briefly.

Wolman and Leopold (1957), Dury (1961), and Leopold, Wolman, and Miller (1964) found that there is a remarkable similarity in bankfull frequency for a variety of rivers in areas of diverse physiography and climate. Bankfull level has been defined in these investigations as the general flood-plain level. Dury, Hails, and Robbie (1963) claimed that there is widespread evidence that many streams have incised their former flood-plains in very recent times, which they suggest is probably due to a slight shift in climate. Certainly some apparent flood-plains are only covered by major floods. In an investigation of bankfull frequency in New South Wales, Woodyer (1968) assumed that due to recent incision, the present active flood-plain may be represented at some sites by a relatively inconspicuous, narrow depositional bench occurring below the apparent flood-plain. Therefore, all benches occurring within the channel cross section were considered. As many as three benches were observed, the 'low', 'middle', and 'high' benches. The high bench appears to represent the present flood-plain level, where streams are incised, and was grouped with the apparent flood-plain (where not incised) in considering bankfull frequencies. It was found, by appropriate statistical tests (McGilchrist and Woodyer 1968) that the bankfull frequencies associated with the present flood-plain level (i.e. the grouped high bench and apparent flood-plain levels) and the middle bench could each be regarded as being 'constant'. Constant in the sense that the bankful frequencies associated with each level could be regarded as samples drawn from a single population of bankfull frequencies characteristic of that level. The mean bankfull recurrence interval for the present flood-plain level, weighted for lengths of record, was 369 days. Thus bankfull discharge for the present flood-plain level closely approximates the 1 year flood in the annual exceedance series, which is defined below.

These benches were identified initially in terms of their relative elevation above the bed of the stream at a particular site. Subsequently, it was possible to identify them *per se* mainly on the basis of their vegetative cover. Bench expression in small rocky upland catchments was often confused, when compared with larger catchments of up to 50,000 sq miles (129,000 sq km) in area. In the present context, however, interest centres on catchments less than 100 sq miles (259 sq km) in area, so that some inaccuracy in defining bankfull level is to be expected.

THE EXTRAPOLATION OF THE BASE DISCHARGE–FREQUENCY RELATIONSHIP

Annual Maximum and Exceedance Series

In hydrological studies, it is normal to distinguish between two types of data, annual maximum values and exceedance values. The annual maximum is the largest of all observations taken in a year. There are thus n values in n years and these constitute the annual maximum series. If all the observations taken in the n years are ranked in descending order then the top n values constitute the annual exceedance series (which is a partial duration series). Chow (1953) has shown that if the annual maximum series follows the extreme value distribution then the associated annual exceedance series follows an exponential law. Alexander (1954) shows that this also applies to annual maximum series which satisfy a log-normal distribution, for a limited range of standard deviations. Both types of series have already been referred to in this paper and are virtually identical for mean recurrence intervals greater than 10 years.

Frequency Functions

Events of different recurrence interval may be related by means of a frequency function F_y which may be defined in general form

$$X_y = F_y \cdot X_1 \qquad (5)$$

where X_1 = variable with a chance of being equalled or exceeded on the average once in one year and X_y = value with the chance of being equalled or exceeded on the average once in y years. Equation (5) defines an annual exceedance series and since the annual maximum series of flood and rainfall events commonly fit extreme value or log-normal frequency distributions (McGuinness and Brakensiek 1964), the form of F_y often satisfies an exponential law:

$$F_y = 1 + a \log y, \qquad (6)$$

where a is a constant for any single set of observations. The symbols F_{qy} and F_{py} will represent frequency functions for runoff and rainfall respectively and a_q and a_p the appropriate values of a. Gerny (1958) has shown that a modified form of equation (6) fits rainfall and runoff data in South Australia:

$$F_y = 1 + b \log \frac{1+y}{2} \qquad (7)$$

where b is a constant for any single set of observations.

Daily rainfall data of reasonable length of record (40 years or greater) are commonly available. Therefore, it is logical to try to relate rainfall events and flood events of the same recurrence interval and also to establish relationships between frequency functions for rainfall and runoff. Three sets of Australian data will be examined for such relationships and the possible conditions of applications of derived relationships will be suggested.

Relationships Between Frequency Functions for Rainfall and Runoff

French of the University of New South Wales (in preparation) interpreted the rational method[1] formula as a statistical model linking rainfall and runoff events of the same recurrence interval y

$$q_y = C_y p_y^t \qquad (8)$$

Here C_y links the stochastic variables q_y (peak discharge) in inches per hour and p_y^t (the mean rainfall intensity for time of concentration t) in inches per hour.

French examined data from 67 catchments in eastern New South Wales less than 100 sq miles (259 sq km) in area and concluded that C_y could be considered independent of recurrence interval and catchment area but varied with location and could be interpolated by isopleths on a map. The independence of recurrence interval means that F_{py} equals F_{qy} for small catchments in N.S.W. French found, that if the rainfall for 1 hour duration p_y^1 was substituted for p_y^t, C_y remained relatively independent of recurrence interval. In this case F_{py} satisfies equation (6) with a value of a_p of $1 \cdot 0$.

Gerny (1958) demonstrated that, for associated frequency distributions of rainfall and runoff, b_q in equation (7) should always be greater than b_p. By analogy a_q should always be greater than a_p in equation (6). This trend is evident in all except one of the catchments in Tables 1 and 2 for which simultaneous values of a_p and a_q are available. In all the non-linear cases, i.e. where the frequency function is not of the logarithmic form of equation (6) this trend was evident and increased with recurrence interval. On the average, in Table 2, a_q is approximately twice a_p, and in Table 1, a_q is $1 \cdot 5$ a_p, which could be used as a guide in the estimation of the frequency function for runoff from rainfall data.

Extrapolation of Bankfull Frequency to Other Recurrence Intervals

Seven of the catchments studied by French had also been examined by Woodyer (1968) in respect of bench levels and the data from these catchments (see Table 2) were analysed to see if floods could be estimated from the following assumptions:

1. Bankfull flow has a mean recurrence interval of one year.
2. The frequency distribution follows equation (6) with $a_q = 1 \cdot 0$.

Figure 3 shows the data in a non-dimensional form, normalized with respect to bankfull flow. They indicate that the data fit the assumptions in a fairly

---

[1] This well known formula (Jens and McPherson 1964; Ogrosky and Mockus 1964) is usually written

$$Q = CIA \quad \text{or} \quad q = CI$$

where Q is peak discharge rate in cubic feet per second accurate to about 1 %, q is peak discharge rate in inches per hour, C is a runoff coefficient, I is rainfall intensity for time of concentration in inches per hour, and A is catchment area in acres.

satisfactory manner, with the exception of Bindo Creek. In this analysis all available catchments less than 100 sq miles (259 sq km) were included. In the case of Bindo Creek with a catchment area of only 13 sq miles (33·7 sq km), the catchment is very rocky, the benches are poorly formed, and the presence of a weir may interfere with bench expression, so that this discrepancy is not surprising.

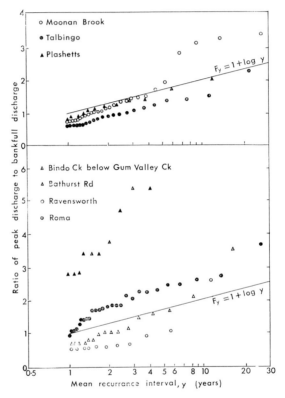

Fig. 3. Extrapolation of bankfull discharge for N.S.W. catchments shown in Table 2, compared with actual data.

The significance of this result must be appreciated in the context of available methods of estimating design discharges for small catchments. In the estimation of runoff by the 'rational method' the combination of errors in runoff coefficient, time of concentration, and rainfall intensity can give large errors in discharge. French, in his investigation of 67 catchments by a number of different methods of computation of components of the 'rational method' formula, found an almost uniform distribution of errors between -50% and $+200\%$ with much larger errors not uncommon. Examination of errors in q_{10} in Tables 1 and 2 indicates that the methods proposed in this paper may result in smaller errors. However, a much larger sample is desirable, particularly in the case of Table 2.

In situations where benches are clearly expressed and confidence can be placed in the estimate of bankfull flow the frequency function could be derived, as indicated above, from rainfall data.

CONCLUSIONS

The two sets of stream flow data examined (Tables 1 and 2) come from regions of different rainfall intensity and the way they group on Figure 2 suggests that different approaches are appropriate in each area.

In areas with high rainfall it is to be expected that runoff should be fairly simply related to the readily available parameters of area and 48-hour rainfall. It has been demonstrated by Ward (1967) that the modified Myers' method can be applied in wetter parts of northern and eastern Australia and the Myers' coefficient for the 10-year peak discharge deduced from 48-hour 10-year rainfall.

In areas where the 48-hour 10-year rainfall is less than about 150 mm other catchment parameters more strongly influence the peak discharge and account must be taken of them. Constant bankfull frequency offers a method of effectively integrating all the catchment parameters involved. Woodyer has demonstrated that bankfull flow has a mean recurrence interval of one year if account is taken of the possibility of recent incision. Peak discharges at other recurrence intervals can be estimated from bankfull flow by use of a simple constant frequency function, or where sufficient data is available, by estimation of a local frequency function.

In the reconnaissance context, where local knowledge of rainfall and runoff relationships will be minimal, the constant bankfull frequency technique offers the greatest promise for the reduction in gross errors in estimated discharge. Moreover, the use of the constant frequency function in association with bankfull frequency enables the method to be used in areas where daily rainfall data are not available, as in remote areas and in high-altitude catchments.

We are indebted to Mr R. French of the School of Civil Engineering, University of New South Wales and Mr J. S. Ward of the Irrigation and Water Supply Commission, Queensland for providing access to unpublished data.

REFERENCES

ALEXANDER, G. (1954). Discussion of rainfall intensity-frequency data for N.S.W. stations. *J. Instn Engrs Aust.* **26**, 119–21.

CHOW, V. T. (1953). Frequency analysis of hydrologic data with special application to rainfall intensities. *Univ. Illinois, Engineering Exp. Sta. Bull. Ser.* No. 414.

CHOW, V. T. (1954). The log-probability law and the engineering applications. *Proc. Am. Soc. civ. Engrs* **80**, No. 536.

CHOW, V. T. (1959). *Open-Channel Hydraulics.* (McGraw-Hill: New York.)

COMMONWEALTH OF AUSTRALIA (1966). *National income and expenditure 1965–66.* Parliamentary Paper No. 305.

COWAN, W. L. (1956). Estimating hydraulic roughness coefficients. *Agric. Engng, St Joseph, Mich.* **37**, 473–5.

DALRYMPLE, T. (1956). Measuring floods. *Int. Ass. scient. Hydrol.*, Publ. No. 42, 380–404.

DURY, G. H. (1961). Bankfull discharge — an example of its statistical relationships. *Int. Ass. scient. Hydrol. VIᵉ Annee*, No. 3, 48–55.

DURY, G. H., HAILS, J. R., and ROBBIE, M. B. (1963). Bankfull discharge and the magnitude frequency series. *Aust. J. Sci.* **26**, 123–4.

GARDE, R. J., and RANGA RAJU, K. G. (1966). Resistance relationships for alluvial channel flow. *Proc. Am. Soc. civ. Engrs* **92**, HY4, 77–100.

GERNY, J. S. (1958). Rainstorms and flood run-off in South Australia. *J. Instn Engrs Aust.* **30**, 221–30.

GRAY, D. M. (1965). Physiographic characteristics and the runoff pattern. *Proc. Hydrology Symposium No. 4*, p. 321, National Research Council of Canada.

INSTITUTION OF ENGINEERS, AUSTRALIA (1958). *Australian rainfall and run-off.* First Report of Stormwater Standards Committee.

JARVIS, C. S. (1942). Floods. In *Hydrology*. (Ed. O. E. Meinzer). (McGraw-Hill: New York.)

JENS, S. W., and MCPHERSON, M. B. (1964). Hydrology of urban areas. In *Handbook of Applied Hydrology*. (Ed. V. T. Chow). (McGraw-Hill: New York.)

LANGBEIN, W. B., and HOYT, W. G. (1959). *Water Facts for the Nations Future*. (Ronald Press Co.: New York.)

LEOPOLD, L. B., WOLMAN, M. G., and MILLER, J. P. (1964). *Fluvial Processes in Geomorphology*. (Freeman: San Francisco.)

MCGILCHRIST, C. A., and WOODYER, K. D. (1968). Statistical tests for common bankfull frequency in rivers. *Wat. Resour. Res.* **4**, (2), (in press).

MCGUINNESS, J. L., and BRAKENSIEK, D. L. (1964). Simplified techniques for fitting frequency distributions to hydrologic data. *U.S.D.A. agric. Handb.* No. 259.

MORGAN, W. A. (1960). Determination of the straight line of best fit to observational data of two related variates when both sets of values are subject to error. *Q. Jl R. met. Soc.* **86**, 107–13.

NASH, J. E. (1956). Frequency of discharges from ungauged catchments. *Trans. Am. geophys. Un.* **37**, 719–25.

OGROSKY, H. O., and MOCKUS, V. (1964). Hydrology of agricultural lands. In *Handbook of Applied Hydrology*. (Ed. V. T. Chow) (McGraw-Hill: New York.)

WARD, J. S. (1967). Frequency analysis of floods and droughts. Paper presented at Institution of Engineers, Australia, Hydrology Symposium, Brisbane, November 27–28, 1967.

WOODYER, K. D. (1968). Bankfull frequency in rivers. *J. Hydrol.* **6**, (in press).

WOLMAN, M. G., and LEOPOLD, L. B. (1957). River flood-plains: some observations on their formation. *Prof. Pap. U.S. geol. Surv.* No. 282-C.

Estimation of Evaporation Using Meteorological Data

I. R. Cowan

Division of Land Research CSIRO
Canberra, Australia

Methods of estimating evaporation from land surfaces by use of meterological measurements are reviewed. The combination approach, which uses the principle of energy conservation together with equations for the turbulent transfer of heat and vapour, is considered in detail and sources of error are examined. The complications which arise in estimating evaporation, due to spatial variations of the characteristics of the ground cover, are outlined. Attention is given to the problems of predicting, as opposed to measuring, the evaporation from a finite area of land, and the concept of 'potential' evaporation is discussed.

INTRODUCTION

Meteorological methods for the estimation of evaporation from natural surfaces depend, wholly or in part, on equating the evaporation from the ground cover to the vertical flux of vapour in the atmosphere where measurements are made. They can only be applied with precision where there is an extensive area of homogeneous ground cover—because of the difficulties of obtaining a representative average of the flux in the atmosphere with a variable surface condition and of defining the surface area from which the vapour originated. With some methods, estimates of the vapour flux cannot be made at all unless certain conditions of uniformity are satisfied. Thus the meteorological approach has usually been developed for and tested in conditions where the height of the boundary layer—the layer of air adjacent to the earth's surface in which the vertical fluxes of heat, vapour, and momentum are substantially constant with height—is greater than the greatest height at which measurements are made. The depth of the boundary layer increases with distance downwind from the nearest discontinuity in the characteristics of the surface. The rate at which the depth increases with this distance—or 'fetch'—depends on aerodynamic factors; and the depth itself, being based on an arbitrary condition of uniformity, depends on the nature of the discontinuity. As a rough indication however, Table 1 shows estimates by Dyer (1963) of the boundary layer height above

TABLE 1

Estimates of height of boundary layer for different values of the fetch by Dyer (1963)

Height (m)	0.5	1	2	5	10	20	50
Fetch (m)	70	170	420	1350	3300	8100	26,500

grass (based on a 10% variation of vapour flux) for different fetches, the discontinuity being a change in the wetness of the surface.

Three methods of estimating evaporation will be examined in this paper under the heading 'precise methods' and one 'imprecise' method will be discussed at length under the heading 'combination method'. The term 'precise' is relative; the combination method involves some assumptions about the surface properties of vegetation and soil while the others do not. Finally, problems will be discussed which occur in the real world due to spatial variation of surface conditions. Such problems involve advection—that is the horizontal transport of vapour, heat, and momentum—and thus are essentially concerned with the theory of boundary layer development. The subject of 'potential' evaporation is introduced as an incidental aspect of this kind of problem.

In this treatment of the meteorological approach to the study of evaporation, attention will be given to the principles rather than the details of measurements; for the latter, one may refer to Slatyer and McIlroy (1961) and Tanner (1963). This writer has also found particularly helpful the accounts by Priestley (1959) and Webb (1965) of many relevant aspects of micrometeorological theory.

PRECISE METHODS OF ESTIMATING EVAPORATION

The Energy Partition Method

The net energy, Φ, received by vegetation and soil due to exchanges of solar and longwave radiation is dissipated primarily as latent heat of vaporization of water, λE, sensible heat conducted into the atmosphere, H, and sensible heat conducted into the ground, G; the amounts of energy involved in changes of heat content of plants are relatively small. Thus the net radiation received per unit area of land in unit time may be written

$$\Phi = \lambda E + H + G \tag{1}$$

Φ can be measured with a net radiometer. G can be measured with a soil heat flux plate or estimated from changes of soil temperature and knowledge of the thermal capacity of the soil; a precise method is often unnecessary since G tends to be small compared with other terms in equation (1), particularly if the cover of vegetation is complete. The terms E and H remain. If they can be identified with the upward fluxes of vapour and heat in the atmosphere each may be expressed as the product of an eddy diffusion coefficient, K, and an appropriate concentration gradient, i.e.,

$$E = -K\rho\frac{\partial q}{\partial z} \tag{2a}$$

$$H = -Kc_p\rho\frac{\partial T}{\partial z} \tag{2b}$$

where ρ, c_p, q, and T are respectively the density, specific heat, specific humidity, and temperature of the atmosphere and z is height. It is assumed that the K's for water vapour and heat are identical, both being determined by the turbulent mixing of the atmosphere. The flux equations may also be written in integral form as

$$E = \rho\frac{q_1 - q_2}{R_{12}} \tag{3a}$$

$$H = c_p\rho\frac{T_1 - T_2}{R_{12}} \tag{3b}$$

where the subscripts 1 and 2 distinguish quantities measured at heights z_1, and z_2 respectively and

$$R_{12} = \int_{z_1}^{z_2} \frac{dz}{K} \tag{4}$$

From equations (3a) and (3b) the Bowen ratio is evaluated as

$$\beta = \frac{H}{\lambda E} = \frac{c_p}{\lambda} \cdot \frac{T_1 - T_2}{q_1 - q_2} \tag{5}$$

Using equation (1) it is found that

$$E = \frac{(\Phi - G)/\lambda}{1 + \beta} \tag{6}$$

Thus the problem of estimating evaporation devolves on the measurement of the energy terms Φ and G and the differences of humidity and temperature between two heights. The differences are usually measured using wet- and dry-bulb psychrometry. Slatyer and McIlroy (1961) approximate the humidity difference by differences in wet- and dry-bulb temperatures and obtain the particularly convenient expression

$$E = \frac{\Phi - G}{\lambda} \left[1 - \frac{1}{1 + \varepsilon} \cdot \frac{T_1 - T_2}{T_{w1} - T_{w2}} \right] \tag{7}$$

where T_w is wet-bulb temperature and

$$\varepsilon = \frac{\lambda}{c_p} \frac{dq'}{dT} \tag{8}$$

in which q' is the specific humidity of air saturated at temperature T. The dimensionless quantity ε is the rate of increase of the latent heat constant of saturated air with increase of sensible heat content. It has a temperature coefficient of about $0 \cdot 06°C^{-1}$ but has been taken as constant; the error is negligible if ε is evaluated using the mean wet-bulb temperature.

This method of estimating evaporation is extremely powerful. The only contentious assumption is that of equating the eddy diffusion coefficients for water vapour and heat, and this assumption has received valuable experimental support recently (Swinbank and Dyer 1967; Dyer 1967). The instrumentation required is sufficiently simple for the method to be used on a routine basis. Frequent automatic recording of the variables is required, however, and a considerable degree of technical resource is necessary. Since the turbulent transport process has been described as a diffusion, smoothed values of temperature and humidity are used. Slow response sensors may be employed and data should be averaged over periods of at least 10 minutes. However, the period of averaging should not be sufficiently long for marked systematic changes of microclimate to occur or the estimate of evaporation will be in error due to correlations between the variables used—$\frac{1}{2}$ hour is probably a good compromise.

Aerodynamic Methods

The most direct means of estimating the upward flux of water vapour in the atmosphere is as the product of the specific humidity and the upward flux of air mass measured at the same point. The mean value of the latter flux over a horizontal surface tends to zero if averaged over a sufficient period of time. Therefore, vapour flux averaged over a period of time which includes a representative sample of the turbulent fluctuations in the atmosphere depends primarily on the correlation between the deviations of humidity from the mean value and the corresponding air flux. Hence techniques of measuring vapour flux which employ this principle are termed 'eddy correlation'. The principle may equally well be used to determine the flux of heat in the atmosphere and, because of the complementary nature of sensible and latent heat (see equation

(1)), such a measurement is almost as useful as a direct measurement of the flux of vapour. The approach was first outlined by Swinbank (1951) who also made estimates of the heat flux using continuous records of temperature and the vertical component of windspeed. Later developments have resulted in instruments (Dyer 1961; Dyer and Maher 1965) in which the correlation is performed automatically. Because of the necessity of closely following the rapid fluctuations of atmospheric variables, sensors with short time constants are used ($\sim 0 \cdot 2$ sec) and tend to be rather delicate. As a result of this, these instruments, while they have already proved to be most valuable research tools, are probably not at present sufficiently robust for use in routine measurements of evaporation.

Another method which may be termed aerodynamic adopts a diffusion approach to the estimate of vapour flux and therefore, in common with the energy partition approach, employs smoothed values of atmospheric variables. It depends on the estimation of the aerodynamic resistance R_{12} in equation (3a) from an examination of the profile of windspeed within the boundary layer. The starting point is the expression for the downward flux of the horizontal momentum of the atmosphere (equivalent to the shearing stress), as a turbulent diffusion process,

$$\tau = K\rho \frac{\partial u}{\partial z} \tag{9}$$

where u is the mean horizontal windspeed. Assuming that the diffusion is due to forced convection in which neither viscosity or buoyancy play an important role, a dimensional approach to the dependence of K on other variables yields

$$K = ku^* z \tag{10}$$

where k is an empirical constant (von Karman's constant) and $u^* \equiv (\tau/\rho)^{\frac{1}{2}}$ is known as the shearing or friction velocity. Experiment yields $k \approx 0 \cdot 4$. Using equation (10) in equation (9) the well-known logarithmic profile of windspeed emerges

$$u_2 - u_1 = \frac{u^*}{k} \ln \frac{z_2}{z_1} \tag{11}$$

and, from equation (4), the resistance is

$$R_{12} = \frac{1}{ku^*} \ln \frac{z_2}{z_1} \tag{12}$$

Thus the resistance may in principle be determined from measurements of windspeed at two known heights. Corresponding measurements of humidity and the use of equation (3a) yield the vapour flux. This method is due to Thornthwaite and Holzman (1942). Within the layer of air occupied by vegetation or very close to the surface of a bare soil, it is known that the logarithmic profile does not hold. One may define a height z_0, the roughness length, at which the windspeed extrapolated from the logarithmic profile in the turbulent boundary layer is zero and equation (11) is then rewritten as

$$u = \frac{u^*}{k} \ln \frac{z}{z_0} \tag{13}$$

With bare soil surfaces or short vegetation, z_0 (which is of the order $0 \cdot 1$ of the roughness elements—soil aggregates or plants) is invariant with windspeed. Thus a determination of z_0 may be subsequently used in conjunction with measured windspeed at one height only to provide an estimate of R_{12}. With tall vegetation z_0 depends on windspeed (Inoue 1963); moreover the height z must be measured from a hypothetical plane within the vegetation whose displacement from the ground surface d (also dependent on windspeed) must emerge from an examination of the wind profile using measurements made at a minimum of three heights. Essentially, d is found as the value which will preserve the logarithmic form of the wind profile.

All that has been written on the estimation of the aerodynamic resistance so far depends on the assumption that bouyancy effects on turbulence are small; more generally atmospheric phenomena are modified due to the air density gradients associated with temperature gradients and sensible heat flux in the atmosphere. As results of this modification the logarithmic wind profile does not hold in all conditions and the eddy diffusivity for momentum is not identical with that for heat. Deacon and Swinbank (1958) describe a means of surmounting the first difficulty but the method does not help with the second. A more general approach to the problems, stemming from the work of Monin and Obhukov (1954), Swinbank (1964), Swinbank and Dyer (1967), and Dyer (1967)—see also Priestley (1959)—is required. We distinguish between the eddy diffusivity for momentum by the subscript M and that for heat and vapour by the subscript F, and write, as modified versions of equation (10),

$$K_M = \frac{k\,u^*z}{\varphi_M(z/L)} \tag{14a}$$

$$K_F = \frac{k\,u^*z}{\varphi_F(z/L)} \tag{14b}$$

where the φ's are functions of z/L, L being the Monin–Obhukov length defined as

$$L = -\frac{c_p\rho Tu^{*3}}{kgH} \tag{15}$$

with H, as before, the upward flux of heat in the atmosphere. The length L is negative for lapse and positive for inversion conditions; z/L is the ratio of the rate of work of buoyancy forces to the rate of work of shearing forces in conditions in which the effects of the former on turbulent structure are negligible. Swinbank (1964) and Dyer (1967) provide what are probably the best available expressions for the φ functions:

$$\varphi_M = \frac{z}{L}\left[1 - \exp\,(\,-\,z/L)\right]^{-1} \tag{16a}$$

$$\varphi_F = (1 - 15z/L)^{-0.55} \tag{16b}$$

the second expression being developed empirically for unstable conditions only. The first expression leads, using equations (9) and (14a), to Swinbank's 'exponential wind-profile', i.e.,

$$u_2 - u_1 = \frac{u^*}{k}\int_{z_1}^{z_2}\frac{\varphi_M}{z}\,dz = \frac{u^*}{k}\ln\left[\exp\,(z/L)-1\right]\Bigg|_{z_1}^{z_2} \tag{17}$$

For normal values of L in the lowest 10 m of the atmosphere little change is engendered by replacing the power -0.55 in equation (16b) by -0.5 and, using equation (14), one finds

$$R_{12} = \frac{1}{ku^*}\int_{z_1}^{z_2}\frac{\varphi_M}{z}\,dz = \frac{1}{ku^*}\ln\left[\frac{(1-15\,z/L)^{\frac12}-1}{(1+15\,z/L)^{\frac12}+1}\right]\Bigg|_{z_1}^{z_2} \tag{18}$$

These equations are the counterparts of equations (11) and (12); some simplification is obviously possible if z/L is small. The evaluation of R_{12} now requires an estimation of L and thus the heat flux H. If measurements of dry bulb temperature are available at heights z_1 and z_2 this does not present a major problem since R_{12} applies to both the sensible and latent heat fluxes (see equations (3a) and (3b)). However the general approach cannot be recommended as a routine method of estimating evaporation. It places a heavy burden on the accuracy of the estimate of R_{12} and does not appear to have any advantages over the energy partition method. The method has been treated at length primarily because the discussion is relevant to an understanding of the method next to be examined.

THE COMBINATION METHOD OF ESTIMATING EVAPORATION

General Theory

The term 'combination' describes those equations, the best known of which is due to Penman (1948, 1953) that combine considerations of the supply of radiant energy to the evaporating surfaces and the capacity of the atmosphere to act as a sink for water vapour. The method is the least demanding, in terms of the instrumentation required, of those that use meteorological measurements to estimate evaporation. At the same time it involves adventurous assumptions about the conditions which obtain at plant surfaces and about heat and water vapour transport in the atmosphere.

Rewriting equation (3b) in terms of q' by use of equation (8) and combining the result with equation (2a) it is easily shown that

$$F = K_F \rho \frac{\partial \delta}{\partial z} \qquad (19)$$

where F represents $E - \varepsilon H/\lambda$ and $\delta = q' - q$ is humidity deficit in the atmosphere. K has been explicitly replaced by K_F in view of the discussion in the previous section. Clearly if F can be determined E is easily found from the energy balance in equation (1) as

$$E = \frac{\varepsilon(\Phi - G)/\lambda + F}{\varepsilon + 1} \qquad (20)$$

Consider, now, the distribution of humidity deficit not only within the atmosphere above the vegetation but also within the layer of air occupied by the plants. Within this lower layer, the detailed distribution will be very complex indeed. However, it is possible to show that throughout the atmosphere the spatial variation of the deficit conforms closely to a second-order linear and homogeneous differential equation in which the coefficients depend only on the pattern of flow and the statistical properties of the turbulent air stream. Let us assume that the plant and soil surfaces are wet, i.e., that the humidity deficit there is zero. From the properties of linear equations it follows that the pattern of the distribution of humidity within the atmosphere will be quite independent of the absolute magnitude of the humidity deficit at any fixed reference position. Thus equation (19) may be rewritten as

$$F = \frac{\rho \delta}{R} \qquad (21)$$

where R depends on the reference height chosen and the characteristics of air flow over and amongst the vegetation. Hence the problem of estimating E has been reduced to one of measuring net radiation and soil heat flux (as in the energy partition method), humidity deficit at one height, and–most difficult–of determining R.

The Aerodynamic Resistance

Often, when mean daily values of the relevant variables are used to estimate evaporation, R is expressed as an empirical function of the windspeed at a fixed height (Penman 1948). The use of a single such function neglects the differing aerodynamic characteristics of differing plant communities. Businger (1956) suggested what is, at any rate superficially, a more fundamental approach which has been used by Tanner and Pelton (1960), Monteith (1963), and van Bavel (1966). The resistance R is assumed to be identical with the analogous resistance to momentum transport, R* say. We leave aside, for the present, problems associated with effects of stability on the evaluation of the resistance by this means to consider another difficulty.

The identity of R and R* demands not only that the coefficients for vertical transport of the fluxes F and τ are identical at all heights, but that the attenuations of these fluxes within the air layer occupied by plants are identical also. This cannot be so because the analogy between mass and heat transfer on the one hand and momentum transfer on the other breaks down entirely in the vicinity of the leaves. The point may be quantified by comparing the resistance to heat and vapour transfer between a single leaf and the ambient air, with the resistance to dissipation of momentum due to the same leaf. On the basis of such a comparison and a number of assumptions Cowan (1968) has suggested that

$$\frac{R_i}{R_i^*} \approx 0\cdot 56 \, (c^2 r_1^2 \, u_h)^{\frac{1}{3}} \tag{22}$$

where R_i and R_i^* are the parts of R and R* associated with transfer processes within the layer of air occupied by plants, c is the mean coefficient of drag per unit area of leaf, r_1 a quantity related to the boundary layer resistance of the leaves to vapour and heat transfer (and which increases with leaf size) and u_h is the windspeed at the top of the vegetation where $z = h$. The derivation depends on the assumptions that the profiles of windspeed and eddy diffusivity within the air layer are similar, and that c, r_1 and the concentration of leaves is constant with height. Therefore, equation (22) provides rough estimates only. Setting $c = 0\cdot 25$, $r_1 = 3$ (for a leaf of width 5 cm) we find $R_i/R_i^* \approx 0\cdot 5 \, u_h^{\frac{1}{3}}$. Windspeeds in excess of 3m sec^{-1} at $z = h$ are unlikely and thus the value of R_i/R_i^* is unlikely to exceed 3. For smaller leaves and windspeeds it will be less.

Estimates of R_i/R_i^* should be considered in relation to values of R_i^*/R^*. The greater the reference height at which measurement of δ is made, the smaller is the relative importance of an error in the estimate of R_i. From the logarithmic wind profile,

$$\frac{R_i^*}{R^*} = \frac{\ln (h/z_0)}{\ln (z/z_0)} \tag{23}$$

Numerical examination of equation (23) indicates that, as a rough guide, it is necessary that z should be at least 5 times the height of the vegetation to ensure that errors in 1/R are less than 30%; in some cases the requirement could be more exacting.

If measurements are made at a height of several meters it will often become necessary to take account of the effects on R of atmospheric density gradients. In unstable conditions R is then to be estimated from equations (17) and (18) taking $u_1 = 0$ at $z_1 = z_0$. The use of these equations involves no extra instrumentation but entails a considerable complication in data processing.

The Effect of Leaf Resistance to Vapour Loss

The assumption that the humidity deficit is zero at the plant and soil surfaces strictly is valid only if the surfaces are wet due to precipitation or condensation. It may nearly be valid with plants well supplied with water and having small stomatal resistances; it certainly is not true of plants with limited water supply. Slatyer and McIlroy (1961) modify the combination equation by writing

$$E = \frac{\varepsilon(\Phi - G)/\lambda + \rho(\delta - \delta_0)/R}{\varepsilon + 1} \tag{24}$$

and define δ_0 as the humidity deficit at the leaf surfaces. Clearly, if R is taken as R^*, δ_0 is the value found by extrapolating the δ profile to the level $z = z_0$. Penman (1953) and Monteith (1963) introduce a stomatal or group resistance, R_c say, by setting $\delta_0 = ER_c$ and equation (24) becomes

$$E = \frac{\varepsilon(\Phi - G)/\lambda + \rho\delta/R}{\varepsilon + 1 + R_c/R} \tag{25}$$

Neither of these developments takes account of the architecture of vegetation and the pattern of energy exchange within the air layer occupied by the vegetation. The form of equation (25) is not substantiated by detailed analysis (Cowan 1968)—in the sense that R_c is a function not only of the internal resistance of leaves to loss of vapour and other properties of the vegetation, but of climatic parameters also. The computation of the role of leaf resistance in reducing transpiration is complex and, in view of this and the difficulty of obtaining data on leaf resistance in the field, it seems unlikely that such computations could be incorporated in a routine method of estimating evaporation. In any event, such computations are peripheral to the central problem because they do not include the reaction of the stomata to soil and plant factors. Van Bavel (1967) found with alfalfa from which irrigation water was withheld that the course of transpiration during the day suggested 'a proportional control system that, by first closing, and later opening, the stomata, appears to maintain an (approximately constant) evaporation rate in spite of a highly variable demand'. A plant-soil model based on proportional control of the type suggested by van Bavel has been developed by Cowan (1965). It is assumed that evaporation from a crop takes place at one of two rates. The first is the potential rate of transpiration, E_t, which depends primarily on climatic environment and represents the rate of transpiration from a crop when the leaves are turgid. The other, termed the supply function, E_w, depends on the water content of the soil together with the hydraulic characteristics of soil and plants and is a measure of the ability of the soil-crop system to supply liquid water to the sites of vaporization in the leaves. The actual rate of transpiration at any time is equal to either E_t or E_w, which ever is least. Cowan (1965) has given estimates of E_w as a function of soil water content for a crop of assumed characteristics. These include the rather restrictive assumption that the concentration of absorbing roots within the rooting zone in the soil is uniform with depth. More sophisticated treatments of soil: root interactions (Gardner 1964) will facilitate better estimates of E_w. However, empirical information for particular types of vegetation and particular soils of the type collected by van Bavel (1967) will be essential in making practical use of the supply concept.

PROBLEMS ASSOCIATED WITH VARIATION OF SURFACE COVER

Heterogeneity

The problem of estimating evaporation in a large part of the real world is complicated by variations in the properties of the surface cover. The variability of the earth's surface takes on different aspects according to the distance from which it is viewed. Even within an area of uniform vegetation micro-variations occur; vegetation itself is discontinuous, leaves of plants and plants themselves have their own boundary regions in which the microclimatic influences of their individual geometric and other properties are marked. Provided instruments are not placed too close to the surface, the meteorological approach tends, with advantage, to smooth out the effects of small random or repetitive variations in the surface cover. The greater the characteristic linear dimension of the variations the greater will the height of the instruments need to be, and it may be advantageous in some circumstances to develop methods of estimating vapour flux at considerable heights using instruments which are air-borne. Unfortunately, the frequency spectrum of the characteristic lengths of natural variations in surface cover (including, for example, variations in composition of the plant community due to the multiplicity of factors which affect the competition between species, variations of surface relief due to geomorphological factors, etc.) tends to be continuous and it will rarely be possible to site instruments in positions free from the influence of the unwanted effects of local variations in cover and yet firmly entrenched within the boundary layers due to all variations of larger characteristic length. An alternative approach is to attempt the demanding exercise of obtaining measurements of the upward flux of vapour close to the surface and at a sufficient number of sites to give a mean value representative of the evaporation from a given area of land. Both the energy partition and the eddy correlation methods would in principle be suitable; the aerodynamic method would not. It is doubtful whether this kind of operation could be carried out using estimates at fixed sites; a more practicable approach might be developed using instruments mounted on vehicles. With vegetation well supplied with water a modification of the energy partition approach appears to be feasible, for use with low-flying air craft (Costin and Rose, private communication). Measurements of the net vertical flux of radiation and of the upward flux of terrestrial radiation would be required, together with measurements of atmospheric humidity, q, and temperature, T. Using the measurement of terrestrial radiation to obtain an estimate of the temperature of the ground cover, T_0, (see Rose and Thomas 1968) the Bowen ratio could be computed as

$$\beta = \frac{c_p}{\lambda} \frac{[T_0 - T]}{[q'(T_0) - q]} \tag{26}$$

and used as in equation (6) to obtain the evaporation. G would be either neglected (with dense covers of vegetation) or estimated from the diurnal variation of T_0 and approximate values of soil thermal properties (with bare soil). Problems which might arise due to possible differences in the transport coefficients for heat and vapour in the atmosphere, and due also to the variability of the fluxes of heat and vapour with height, would require careful examination.

Finally, mention of the application of the combination method is relevant. In principle, the combination equation can be applied also to a limited area of heterogeneous vegetation provided leaves and soil act effectively as wet surfaces. Some reframing of definitions is required however Φ and G are average values over the area considered, δ is the humidity deficit at a fixed reference point and R, the aerodynamic resistance, will depend not only on the aerodynamics of flow over the vegetation but on the reference position chosen. It will clearly be impossible to estimate R on the basis of theoretical considerations. Its value will need to be determined empirically by adjustment to give satisfactory agreement between the combination equation and evaporation estimated by other means, such as catchment water balance studies (Chapman 1968) or using lysimeters (McIlroy and Angus 1964; Pruitt and Lourence 1966). At first approximation level, it may be assumed that R is inversely proportional to the windspeed. Two considerations enter into the fixing of a reference position at which to determine δ and u. First, it should be removed from the influence of random local variations of the vegetative cover. Second, standardization is desirable. Both conditions are met by adoption of standard recommendations for the siting of meteorological instruments.

The 'Oasis' Problem

A somewhat more tractable problem, from a theoretical point of view, concerns evaporation from an irrigated area in a dry surround. Here man creates a surface of considerable uniformity—at least in terms of its humidity—and in doing so creates a sharp discontinuity in energy relationships at the boundary. The question to be discussed is not the one of how to estimate evaporation from the irrigated surface (wherever the boundary layer development is adequate, this can be done using one of the methods described earlier) but of how one may predict what the evaporation will be from a knowledge of the properties of the air masses which encroach on to the irrigated area from the dry land surround, and the radiant energy input. It will be recognized that this is a quite different problem from the others that have been discussed, because one attempts to use variables which are independent of the behaviour of the evaporating surface. Thus, the irrigated area need not actually exist; its existence can be projected and, in fact, the usefulness of the answer to the problem which is posed lies in the help it can give to the planning of irrigated systems. The subject is one of considerable difficulty, however, and the theory of it is not well advanced. For detailed information, we may refer to Priestley (1959), de Vries (1959), Philip (1957), Rider, Philip, and Bradley (1963), Dyer (1963), and Dyer and Crawford (1965).

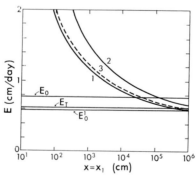

Fig. 1. Potential evaporation rates for the Nanneella irrigation district (redrawn from de Vries 1959). Curve 1—'local potential evaporation rate' in relation to distance downwind, x; curve 2—'average potential evaporation rate' for an area of width x_1 in the wind direction in relation to x_1; curve 3 —'lower potential evaporation rate' (i.e. constant evaporation rate at which water becomes non-limiting at a fixed distance downwind, x_1) in relation to x_1. E_0—Penman's value (calculated from dryland data) for a water surface; $E_T = 0.8\ E_0$—Penman's value for a transpiring crop; E_0—value for a hypothetical water surface with reflectivity 0.23. †

† It was noted, during reading of proofs, that Curves 1 and 3 have been interchanged in this reproduction of de Vries' figure. The 'error' has been allowed to stand, for it seems evident that the lower potential rate of evaporation must of necessity be somewhat greater than the local potential rate.

De Vries (1959) applied physical principles to the computation of the effects of advection during a particular period of 14 days in the Nanneella irrigation district in the Riverina plain of Australia. Assuming that the rate of evaporation was determined by the sum of the amounts of irrigation and rain received (this sum not being sufficient to maintain transpiration at the potential rate, E_t), he was able to compute the expected changes of temperature and humidity down-wind over the irrigated area. A reasonable agreement was obtained with measurements taken in four standard meteorological stations. Further calculations gave estimates (shown in Fig. 1) of the potential rate of evaporation as a function of distance downwind in the irrigated area. The sense in which the term 'potential' is used here requires amplification.

The adjective 'potential' has often been used to describe evaporation calculated using a formula of the Penman, or combination, type. Its use in this context is confusing because such a formula, while it provides a means of estimating actual rate of evaporation from wet soil and turgid vegetation, cannot be used to *predict* what the evaporation from a surface of limited humidity would be if the supply of water to the surface were increased. The formula cannot be used to predict in this way because the variables it employs—in particular atmospheric humidity and temperature—are measured within the boundary layer of the surface and themselves depend on the humidity and rate of evaporation at the surface. This is not to say that 'potential' evaporation cannot be invested with a valid physical meaning. It may properly be defined as the rate of evaporation which would be sustained by a given surface in a given macroenvironment if the surface were plentifully supplied with liquid water. This is the sense in which de Vries uses the term 'potential' to describe curves 1 and 2 in Figure 1. De Vries uses the term in a more subtle way in defining the 'lower potential evaporation rate' of evaporation. It is recognized that vegetation close to the leading edge of an irrigated area may not be capable of maintaining turgidity in the face of the high local potential rate of evaporation which obtains there. Hence, there may be a region adjacent to the leading edge in which the rate of evaporation is approximately constant despite the variation in microclimate in the downwind direction. This rate is determined by the hydraulic characteristics of soil and plants as they affect stomatal aperture and is in essence, the supply function E_w introduced in earlier discussion. With increasing distance, downwind stomatal aperture increases as the vapour deficit in the atmosphere decreases due to the accumulated transfer of water vapour to the air stream. Beyond a certain distance, x_1, which depends on the value of E_w, the vegetation is fully turgid and the rate of evaporation declines with further increase of distance. The relation between E_w—or the lower potential rate of evaporation—and x_1 estimated by de Vries for the Naneela irrigation district is shown in Figure 1 (curve 3).

In order to make computations of the type illustrated in Figure 1 it is necessary to specify the temperature, humidity, and windspeed profiles in the air encroaching on to the irrigated area, that is to say over the upwind dry land where the properties of the atmosphere are very little, if at all, affected by the proximity of the irrigated area. De Vries' data included measurements of solar radiation and the reflection coefficient of the surface; cloudiness; precipitation; temperature, humidity, and windspeed at a fixed height; and soil temperature. It required ingenuity and empiricism to reconstruct the energy balance of the dry land surface, to obtain an estimate of eddy diffusivity, and thus to be able to compute profiles. Information on the roughness coefficient of the surface, the upward and downward components of terrestrial (long-wave) radiation, and of evaporation would have been desirable. In the absence of sophisticated micrometeorological instrument little improvement could be made on de Vries' assumption that the evaporation from the dry land equalled the precipitation during the same period. The problem which has been outlined is one of a wider class of problems which are central to the application of micrometeorology in land evaluation studies. These concern the effects of change in land use on the energy balance and climate of a given land area. At the present time theory is not adequate to give quantitative answers in most instances.

CONCLUSION

It is impossible to summarize in a short space the many points that have been raised in this discussion of the meteorological approach to estimating evaporation. One broad conclusion emerges, however. Micrometeorology is a quite difficult subject; in common with other earth sciences, the fundamental physical knowledge is well established but the boundary conditions imposed by the real world are complex and variable. Because of this, general procedures cannot be recommended and techniques must be suited to the particular circumstances of the problem in hand. This need for matching techniques to circumstances points to the necessity of employing micrometeorologists in land evaluation studies if micrometeorological theory is to be exploited.

REFERENCES

BUSINGER, J. A. (1956). Some remarks on Penman's equation for the evapotranspiration. *Neth. J. agric. Sci.* **4**, 77.

CHAPMAN, T. G. (1968). Catchment parameters for a deterministic rainfall-runoff model. In *Land Evaluation*. (Ed. G. A. Stewart.) (Macmillan: Melbourne.)

COWAN, I. R. (1965). Transport of water in the soil-plant-atmosphere system. *J. appl. Ecol.* **2**, 221.

COWAN, I. R. (1968). Mass, heat and momentum transfer between plant stands and their atmospheric environment. *Q. Jl R. met. Soc.* (in press.)

DEACON, E. L., and SWINBANK, W. C. (1958). Comparison between momentum and water vapour transfer. Climatol. and Microclimatol. Proc. Canberra Symposium *UNESCO Arid Zone Res* **11**, 38.

DYER, A. J. (1961). Measurements of evaporation and heat transfer in the lower atmosphere by an automatic eddy-correlation technique. *Q. Jl R. met. Soc.* **87**, 401.

DYER, A. J. (1963). The adjustment of profiles and eddy fluxes. *Q. Jl R. met. Soc.* **89**, 276.

DYER, A. J. (1967). The turbulent transport of heat and water vapour in an unstable atmosphere. *Q. Jl R. met. Soc.* **93**, 501.

DYER, A. J., and CRAWFORD, T. V. (1965). Observations of the modification of the microclimate at a leading edge. *Q. Jl R. met. Soc.* **91**, 345.

DYER, A. J., and MAHER, F. L. (1965). Automatic eddy-flux measurement with the Evapotron. *J. appl. Met.* **4**, 622.

GARDNER, W. R. (1964). Relation of root distribution to water uptake and availability. *Agron. J.* **56**, 41.

INOUE, E. (1963). The environment of plant surfaces. In *Environmental Control of Plant Growth*. (Ed. L. T. Evans) (Academic Press: New York.)

MCILROY, I. C., and ANGUS, D. (1964). Grass, water and soil evaporation at Aspendale. *J. agric. Met.* **1**, 201.

MONIN, A. S., and OBHUKOV, A. M. (1954). Basic relationships of turbulent mixing in the surface layer of the atmosphere. *Works of Geophys. Inst. Acad. Sci. U.S.S.R.* **24**, 163.

MONTEITH, J. L. (1963). Gas exchange in plant communities. In *Environmental Control of Plant Growth*. (Ed. L. T. Evans) p. 95. (Academic Press: New York.)

PENMAN, H. L. (1948). Natural evaporation from open water, bare soil and grass. *Proc. R. Soc. A.* **193**, 120.

PENMAN, H. L. (1953). The physical bases of irrigation control. *Rept. 13th int. Hort. Congr.* **2**, 913.

PHILIP, J. R. (1957). The theory of local advection: I. *J. Met.* **16**, 535.

PRIESTLEY, C. H. B. (1959). *Turbulent Transfer in the Lower Atmosphere*. (The University of Chicago Press: Chicago.)

PRUITT, W. D., and LOURENCE, F. J. (1966). Tests of aerodynamic, energy balance and other equations over a grass surface. In *Investigation of Energy, Momentum and Mass Transfer near the Ground*. Final report under grant number DA-AHC-28-043-65-G12, p. 65. (University of California: Davis.)

RIDER, N. E., PHILIP, J. R., and BRADLEY, E. F. (1963). The horizontal transport of heat and moisture—a micrometeorological study. *Q. Jl R. met. Soc.* **89**, 507.

ROSE, C. W., and THOMAS, D. A. (1968). Remote sensing of land surface temperature and some applications in land evaluation. In *Land Evaluation*. (Ed. G. A. Stewart.) (Macmillan: Melbourne.)

SLATYER, R. O., and MCILROY, I. C. (1961). *Practical Microclimatology*. (CSIRO: Melbourne.)

SWINBANK, W. C. (1951). The measurement of vertical transfer of heat and water vapour by eddies in the lower atmosphere. *J. Met.* **8**, 135.

SWINBANK, W. C. (1964). The exponential wind profile. *Q. Jl R. met. Soc.* **90**, 119.

SWINBANK, W. C., and DYER, A. J. (1967). An experimental study in micrometeorology. *Q. Jl R. met. Soc.* **93**, 494.

TANNER, C. B. (1963). Basic instrumentation and measurements for plant environment and micrometeorology. *Soils Bull.* 6, Department of Soil Science, College of Agriculture, University of Wisconsin.

TANNER, C. B., and PELTON, W. L. (1960). Potential evapotranspiration estimates by the approximate energy balance method of Penman. *J. geophys. Res.* **65**, 3391.

THORNTHWAITE, C. W., and HOLZMAN, B. (1942). Measurement of evaporation from land and water surfaces. *U.S. Dept. Agric. Tech. Bull.* No. 817.

VAN BAVEL, C. H. M. (1966). Potential evaporation: the combination concept and its experimental verification. *Water Resources Res.* **3**, 455.

VAN BAVEL, C. H. M. (1967). Changes in canopy resistance to water loss from alfalfa induced by soil water depletion. *J. agric. Met.* **4**, 165.

VRIES, D. A. DE (1959). The influence of irrigation on the energy and the climate near the ground. *J. Met.* **16**, 256.

WEBB, E. K. (1965). Aerial microclimate. *Met. Monogr.* **6**, 27.

Catchment Parameters for a Deterministic Rainfall-Runoff Model

T. G. Chapman

Division of Land Research,
CSIRO, Canberra, Australia

A deterministic model for catchment hydrology should be a realistic approximation of the physical rainfall-runoff process on a catchment. The closeness of fit of the model output to recorded stream flow depends on the mathematical and logical structure of the model, which defines the catchment parameters, and the numerical values of these parameters. In this application, two types of catchment parameter can be distinguished.

A basis for model development can be achieved by grouping individual processes into mainly vertical and mainly lateral water transport. A deterministic model has been developed for the vertical transport processes, and the parameters of this model can be estimated or measured at various levels of detail. Only statistical models have yet been developed for the lateral transport processes.

MODELS, INPUTS, AND PARAMETERS

Hydrologic Models

A hydrologic model can be regarded as a symbolic representation of known or assumed relations between components of the hydrologic cycle and features of the land surface and subsurface (Snyder and Stall 1965). The use of mathematical symbolism can achieve more precision than word communication of complex logical relationships, and is necessary for computation and quantitative evaluation.

There are two main approaches to model development: deterministic and statistical. A deterministic model seeks to express relationships based on known physical laws or empirical inferences, with no randomly varying components. Statistical models are expressed in terms of random or probabilistic components, and the numerical results are stated in terms of statistics such as return period, frequency, expected value, or probability of exceedance.

Apart from personal bias, the choice between these two approaches is influenced by the data available, the complexity of the hydrologic process under study, the available computational facilities, and the aims of the study. A deterministic model normally requires simultaneous data for at least two components of the hydrologic cycle, while statistical models can operate with time sequences of a single variable. The element of empiricism (with consequent predictive shortfall) in a deterministic model tends to increase with the complexity of the process, even when relations between individual components can be expressed in terms of known physical laws, and this can be attributed to the very large computational requirements for rational treatment of complex natural situations. Computational requirements for the statistical approach are less obviously connected to the scale of the study. Finally, referring to the aims of the study, the statistical approach may be regarded as most suitable for prediction within the range of statistics of the observed data, while the deterministic approach can lead to increased understanding of hydrologic processes, and can ultimately be applied to prediction of the hydrologic effects of changes in the nature of the land surface.

This paper describes a deterministic rainfall-runoff model, developed for the initial analysis of the hydrology of a wide range of Australian catchments. The aim of the analysis is to obtain increased understanding of the hydrologic processes in these catchments, with the ultimate objects of synthesizing long-term runoff records, extrapolating to ungauged catchments, and forecasting the possible hydrologic effects of changes in land management. While there are some similarities with other deterministic models (Bell 1966), emphasis in this model has been placed on identifying and measuring hydrologically significant features of the land surface and subsurface.

Inputs and Outputs

A deterministic rainfall-runoff model uses an input of recorded time sequences of rainfall and potential evaporation to derive an output time sequence of simulated stream flow. A concurrent time sequence of recorded stream flow is necessary for validation of the structure of the model and for optimising the output.

While recorded time sequences of soil moisture at various depths and locations in the catchment may be used to validate the structure of the model, these are not regarded here as input data, as a mandatory requirement for recorded soil moisture data would seriously limit the general application of the model. Similar considerations hold for recorded groundwater levels, although the situation is more flexible in this case, due to possible lack of coincidence between the surface and subsurface catchments. Where this condition is acute, extrapolation to other surface catchments may require separate (though linked) models of the surface and groundwater runoff, and recorded groundwater levels could then be an input to the model.

The usual approach in mathematical models of hydrologic processes is to assume uniform rates of input and output over fixed time intervals. If this interval is too long, information will be lost and the analysis will lack discrimination. If it is too short, unnecessary computation is involved, with no gain in information. The appropriate time interval depends on the response time of the catchment (Eagleson and Shack 1966), and will vary with catchment area and other catchment characteristics. Suitable trial values might be $0 \cdot 1$ hour for a 1 sq kilometer catchment, ranging to one hour for 100 sq km. For periods of base flow or no flow, calculations at daily intervals should be adequate.

The shortest time interval for the model sets a lower limit for the frequency of recording of the input rainfall and stream flow data. Adequate spatial sampling of rainfall is necessary, and a typical network might consist of 4 daily-read rain gauges and one rainfall recorder centred in the catchment (Eagleson 1967). Data from these instruments would be combined to derive a bulked catchment rainfall input to the model. In larger catchments, where typically only part of the catchment contributes to stream flow in a given storm, the approach could be to develop parallel models for subcatchments, but for the present discussion it will be assumed that a bulked rainfall input is adequate for model development and testing.

The input time sequence of potential evaporation is usually derived from climatic data. The features of the land surface, which influence evapotranspiration under conditions of low moisture stress, are the subject of another paper in this Symposium (Cowan 1968), and the present discussion will therefore assume that calculated values of potential evaporation are available as an input to the model.

Precipitation falling as snow is not considered here. Appropriate techniques and relevant parameters for snowfall and snowmelt are used in the Stanford watershed model (Crawford and Linsley 1966).

The Nature of Catchment Parameters

The closeness of fit of the simulated flows, predicted by the model, to recorded stream flows depends on the mathematical structure of the model, which defines the type of catchment parameters used, and the numerical values of these parameters.

In this application, catchment parameters are of two kinds, fitted and measured. The numerical values of fitted parameters are selected to obtain the best fit of the model to observed data (Boughton 1967a). Measured parameters are catchment characteristics that vary little with time, such as drainage density, root depth of vegetative cover, soil moisture capacity, or permeability of underlying rock (Boughton 1967b). Confidence in the utility of the model as a predictive tool depends largely on reducing the number of fitted parameters and increasing the number of measured parameters, as far as is practicable. This can only be achieved if the mathematical and logical structure of the model is a realistic approximation of the physical rainfall-runoff process on the catchment. To the extent that the model depends on fitted parameters, it is subject to the limitations of the statistical approach.

The distinction between a fitted and measured parameter requires some modification to allow for errors in measurement and spatial variability of measured parameters. The numerical value of such a parameter is therefore best expressed as a confidence range. A parameter which is not measured, but can be defined in terms of the physical characteristics of the catchment, can usually be assigned a conceptual range within which its numerical value can be expected to lie. In either case, use of these ranges as a further constraint on the parameter in optimisation of the model will avoid simulations which are unrealistic or physically impossible. Further, if the optimised values of several parameters are found to be at one or other of their prescribed limits, there are strong grounds for doubting the validity of the model.

The point emphasized here is that the logical structure of the model should exclude as far as possible the use of parameters which can not be defined in physical terms, or which have been introduced solely to improve the fit of the model to observed data.

DEVELOPMENT OF THE MODEL STRUCTURE

The model is required to simulate the whole catchment process in which a rainfall input is successively modified as it moves through the land phases of the hydrological cycle (Linsley, Kohler, and Paulhus 1949), such as interception by vegetation, evapotranspiration, gain and loss of soil water, surface detention, overland flow, stream channel flow, and groundwater recharge and discharge. Most of these processes are sufficiently understood to permit their local description in mathematical terms. It is the areal extent and variability of a natural catchment which makes it unrealistic to develop a complete model structure in terms of the differential equations describing the individual processes.

The basis for model development proposed here is the grouping of individual processes into mainly vertical water transport (interface processes) and mainly lateral transport (overland flow, channel flow, and groundwater flow). The "interface" is conceived as extending from the top of the vegetative cover to the water-table. The output of the interface processes (rainfall excess and through drainage) may then be regarded as inputs to the lateral transport processes.

This approach implies that catchment parameters for the interface process are uniform over the catchment, in the same way that the rainfall-climate inputs are assumed to be uniformly distributed. The numerical effect is to widen the confidence range for parameter values, above that which would hold if the systematic variation of these parameters over the catchment could be explicitly expressed in the model.

A more serious shortcoming of the approach is that it assumes negligible lateral soil-water movement above the water-table (implying that interflow is negligible), and it ignores interactions between the interface process and the overland flow process. A development of the model, aimed at eliminating these features, is described in a later section, and it becomes apparent that this would increase the volume of computation by at least one order of magnitude.

MODELLING THE INTERFACE PROCESSES

The flow diagram for the model processes described in this section is shown in Figure 1. The symbols are defined in the text and listed in Table 1.

TABLE 1
List of symbols for interface processes

Symbol	Meaning
Model catchment parameters	
ISC	Capacity of interception storage
DSC	Capacity of depression storage
USC	Storage capacity of upper soil zone
LSC	Storage capacity of lower soil zone
ER	Proportion of evapotranspiration from upper soil zone
UH	Maximum evapotranspiration from upper soil zone
LH	Maximum evapotranspiration from lower soil zone
SO	Sorptivity of dry soil in upper zone
A	Infiltration constant for upper soil zone
A_0, A_1, A_2, A_3	Soil water redistribution constants
LDR	Lower soil zone drainage rate
Other model variables	
IS	Current value of interception storage
DS	Current value of depression storage
US	Current water storage in upper soil zone
LS	Current water storage in lower soil zone
GS	Current value of groundwater storage
P	Rainfall input
PE	Potential evaporation
UE	Evaporation from upper soil zone
LE	Evaporation from lower soil zone
RD	Redistribution between upper and lower soil zones
S	Upper soil sorptivity at beginning of infiltration process
INF	Infiltration in current time interval
T	Time since current infiltration process began
TI	Time interval of model
RE	Rainfall excess

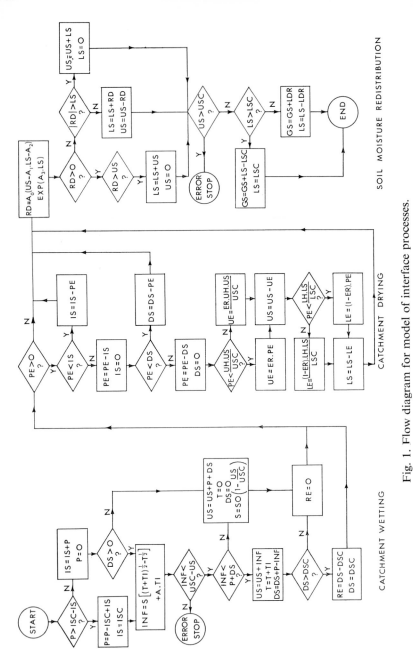

Fig. 1. Flow diagram for model of interface processes.

Simulation of Catchment Wetting

Interception—Interception (IS) by vegetation will be the first deduction from incoming rainfall (P) and is modelled as a simple storage of capacity ISC. This parameter may be determined by experiment, or a suitable range may be estimated by reference to published values (e.g., Penman 1963; Helvey and Patric 1965). A more sophisticated treatment would involve estimating the proportion of rainfall which can reach the ground without interception, and allowing for experimentally observed slow increases in interception storage during prolonged rain.

Depression Storage—Water held in local depressions (DS) is modelled as a simple storage of capacity DSC. It begins to fill as soon as the rainfall rate, after deduction of interception losses, exceeds the infiltration rate of the upper soil zone. When DSC is exceeded, the surplus becomes rainfall excess (RE), one output of the interface process model. On cessation of rainfall, water in depression storage continues to infiltrate into the surface soil.

The parameter DSC may be estimated from runoff plot measurements with controlled rainfall rates (Kidder and Holtan 1943), but there appears to be scope for a more direct approach based on measurements of the microtopography of the ground surface (Burwell, Allmaras, and Amemaya 1963). This parameter is dependent on surface slope, and can be considerably modified by many soil conservation and land management practices (Burwell, Allmaras, and Sloneker 1966).

Infiltration—The aim of the approach is to model the infiltration process in terms of the potential and unsaturated conductivity characteristics of the upper soil zone (to be defined later), without numerical solution of the appropriate differential equations. The method proposed is the adaptation to variable input conditions of Philip's (1964) infiltration equation:

$$i = St^{-\frac{1}{2}} + A, \qquad (1)$$

where i is the infiltration rate at time t from the beginning of the infiltration process, and S (the sorptivity) and A are functions of the initial water content and the soil potential-conductivity characteristics.

Infiltration is assumed to occur at the rate given by equation (1) as long as it can be maintained from rainfall and depression storage. As soon as this supply is insufficient, the infiltration is taken as equal to the supply and the water content in the upper soil zone is regarded as uniformly distributed for calculation of a new value of S.

The parameters S and A are preferably calculated from soil water characteristics measured in the laboratory on samples from the upper soil zone. In the absence of measurements S may be taken as a linear function of soil water content, and A as independent of water content (Philip 1957), and appropriate ranges of values may be estimated from published data for the appropriate soil texture.

Simulation of Catchment Drying

Interception and Depression Storages—Evaporation is assumed to occur at the potential rate while there is water in the interception and depression stores. When these are exhausted the potential evaporation is regarded as a demand on the upper and lower soil zones.

Soil Water—The model assumes two soil water zones, in each of which the water content distribution is taken as uniform. The boundaries of these zones should be related to hydrologically significant zones in the catchment soil. Thus, the upper soil zone could be identified with the A horizon in texture-contrast soils, or with the typical rooting depth of grasses in uniform soils. The lower boundary of the lower soil zone could be taken as the rooting depth of typical shrubs and trees (Douglass 1965), provided these do not penetrate to the water-table.

When the boundaries of the zones are defined, appropriate ranges can be specified for the water capacity parameters USC and LSC, either by estimation from soil texture (e.g. Reeve, Isbell, and Hubble 1963; Salter and Williams 1965) or preferably by calculation from laboratory tests on field samples.

In the catchment drying phase, the distribution of potential water loss rates between the upper and lower soil zones is defined by the ratio of evaporation rates when all the vegetation is freely transpiring. The best estimator for this ratio would appear to be the proportion ER of the catchment not covered by deep-rooted vegetation.

The maximum rate of water loss (UH or LH) from each soil zone is assumed to be a linear function of its water content (Boughton 1966), and either this loss or the potential evaporation, whichever is lower, is taken as the actual evaporation.

The parameters UH and LH can again be determined by experiment, or estimated (with a wider confidence range) from soil texture.

Redistribution of Soil Water

Upper and Lower Soil Zones—It is difficult to define a rational approach to an approximate solution of soil water redistribution, owing to the complexity of the real situation, which includes hysteresis effects between the wetting and the drying phases. Given bulked water contents in the upper and lower soil zones, and neglecting hysteresis, the rate of water movement between the zones is assumed to be proportional to, and in the direction determined by, the difference in soil-water potential in the zones. The rate is also assumed to be proportional to the unsaturated conductivity in one of the zones, and the lower zone is arbitrarily selected, as being more stable. Assuming further that the conductivity and potential functions are simple forms, which are reasonable approximations over certain ranges of potential (Philip 1967), the following semi-empirical equation can be developed for redistribution (assumed positive downwards):

$$RD = A_0 (US - A_1.LS - A_2) \exp (A_3.LS), \tag{2}$$

where US and LS are the current water contents in the upper and lower soil zones, and the coefficients A_0, A_1, A_2, A_3 can be approximately related to the experimentally determined potential and conductivity functions of the two soil zones.

It should be recognized that equation (2) is a first approach, which may require modification in the light of experience.

Lower Soil Zone and Groundwater—Any excess of water in the lower soil zone, above its capacity LSC, is assumed to drain directly to groundwater. When the storage in the lower soil zone is below its capacity, drainage to groundwater is assumed to occur at a rate LDR proportional to the unsaturated conductivity of the lower soil zone. The functional relation between LDR and moisture content LS may be assumed from texture or determined by experiment.

MODELLING THE TRANSPORT PROCESS

Groundwater Runoff

The contribution of groundwater to stream flow can be inferred from an analysis of stream flow recession curves, taking the groundwater runoff as proportional to some power (usually in the range 1 to 2) of the groundwater storage (Chapman 1964). This can be expressed as:

$$\begin{aligned} GR &= KG.(GS)^{GN} & GS > 0 \\ &= 0 & GS \leqslant 0 \end{aligned} \tag{3}$$

$$GS \leftarrow GS\text{--}GR \tag{4}$$

where GR is the groundwater runoff and KG and GN are the routing constants derived from base flow recession curves.

This approach takes no account of the spatial distribution of the groundwater or of the hydraulics of its flow, and has assumed that all groundwater storage becomes stream flow within the catchment. Invalidity of this assumption will be demonstrated by cumulative increases or decreases in GS which result in unrealistic values of groundwater runoff GR. In these circumstances it would be most desirable to estimate groundwater leakage from the catchment by measurements on observation bores.

Overland and Stream Flow

There is no rational method, in terms of the physical principles of hydraulics, yet available for routing rainfall excess to the catchment outlet. The kinematic-wave approach of Wooding (1965) represents an advance in this direction, and avoids the assumption that the process is linear, but it requires considerable development to take better account of the geometric properties of the drainage net (Wooding 1966).

Many conceptual models are based on assumed relations between storage (in overland flow or stream channels) and discharge. Laurenson's (1965) catchment storage model is a non-linear model which requires some detailed measurements of catchment parameters. Unfortunately, representational models of this type have not developed to the stage where they always give superior results to models which take little account of catchment parameters (Laurenson 1962). This may be due to lack of general validity for the basic assumptions of the approach.

As the quantitative effect of the non-linearities is often small in natural catchments, description of the transport process as a linear system (the unit hydrograph approach) is usually justified as a first approximation. The instantaneous unit hydrograph can be readily computed from the rainfall excess, given by the interface process model, and the recorded stream flow, by a linear programming method (Eagleson, Mejia, and March 1966). The degree of non-linearity can be determined by the variation in the unit hydrograph for storms with different rates of rainfall excess. As data accumulate, it should be possible to determine whether linearity is associated with a catchment parameter, such as geometric similarity as defined by Eagleson (unpublished data, 1967).

The defining parameters of the instantaneous unit hydrograph may be taken as the peak discharge and the time to peak, or may be expressed in terms of conceptual models of the runoff process as various combinations of linear channels with linear reservoirs (Chow 1964). Statistical models have been developed to relate unit hydrograph parameters to simple catchment parameters (Nash 1960; Gray 1961; Cordery 1967), for limited ranges of catchment types.

There is little rational basis for selecting hydrologically significant parameters of the drainage net from the many inter-related catchment parameters that have been proposed (Strahler 1964). Those that have demonstrated relevance to stream flow are area, drainage density (Carleston 1963), mean basin slope (Bigwood and Thomas 1957), length of main stream, distance to centroid of the catchment, and the Manning roughness coefficient for the stream (Cordery 1967). The statistical nature of these relations precludes any extrapolation outside the range of available catchment data.

FURTHER DEVELOPMENT OF THE INTERFACE–OVERLAND FLOW MODEL

Overland Flow

Computer solutions of the differential equations for one-dimensional overland flow on a uniform slope have been developed and verified by experimental data (Morgali and Linsley 1965; Chen and Hansen 1966). The equations require modification for a real catchment, to allow for lateral convergence of the stream lines. In terms of the symbols illustrated in Figure 2, the continuity equation becomes

$$V\frac{\partial z}{\partial x} + z\frac{\partial V}{\partial x} + \frac{Vz}{g}\frac{\partial y}{\partial x} + \frac{\partial y}{\partial t} = RE \tag{5}$$

and the momentum equation for friction slope S_f is

$$\frac{\partial V}{\partial t} + \frac{\partial V}{\partial x} + g\left\{ \frac{\partial z}{\partial x} + \frac{z}{2y}\frac{\partial y}{\partial x} \right\} = g(S_0 - S_f) \tag{6}$$

subject to the general assumptions quoted by Morgali and Linsley.

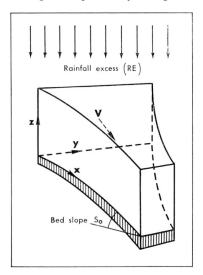

Fig. 2. Definition diagram for converging overland flow.

For a given field situation in overland flow, the relation between y and x is given by the convergence of orthogonals to contour lines (Speight 1968), and the forward integration method of Morgali and Linsley can be used to determine the outflow hydrograph at the downstream end of the overland flow path. Gradual measured variation in bed slope S_0 can also be incorporated in the solution.

The finite difference step limits for the problem studied by Morgali and Linsley were found to be not more than 5 seconds for t and one-sixth of the total flow depth for x. The incorporation in the main model of the step solutions of equations (5) and (6), for a typical overland flow path would therefore increase the volume of computation by a considerable factor (500 steps of the overland flow model for each 0·1 hour step of the main model in the case cited above).

On any real catchment there is usually a wide range of distances of overland flow to a first-order stream, dependent on the local contour pattern. It can be expected that there will be a much smaller range in the predicted outflow hydrograph for these situations, and research in this field may lead to useful generalisations for this part of the catchment runoff process, which then can be incorporated in the general catchment model.

Soil Moisture

The equation for unsaturated flow of soil moisture in the liquid phase can be written (Philip 1964)

$$\frac{\partial \theta}{\partial t} = \nabla(D \nabla \theta) + \frac{dK}{d\theta}\frac{\partial \theta}{\partial z}, \qquad (7)$$

where θ is the volumetric moisture content, and D and K are the diffusivity and capillary conductivity respectively, both of which are dependent on moisture content.

If soil water movements are predominantly vertical, equation (7) becomes

$$\frac{\partial \theta}{\partial t} = \frac{\partial}{\partial z}(D\frac{\partial \theta}{\partial z}) + \frac{\partial K}{\partial z} \qquad (8)$$

which has been solved by Philip for the case of infiltration with initial uniform moisture content and water available in excess at the soil surface.

Computer techniques for the solution of the finite difference form of equation (8) have been developed (Remson *et al.* 1965) for various boundary conditions, including water supply or evaporation at the soil surface and a water-table at the lower boundary. While hysteresis was ignored and uniform soil was assumed, these restrictions can be readily overcome if appropriate experimental data are available. A more serious difficulty is the modification of the finite difference form of equation (8) to allow for removal of soil moisture by roots of vegetation, and it may therefore be more realistic to increase the number of zones of uniform moisture content in the original model, rather than to attempt a solution of the one-dimensional diffusion equation with distributed sinks.

Lateral movement of soil moisture may be an important factor in the rainfall-runoff relation, particularly in deep soil on steep slopes (Hewlett and Hibbert 1963). Development of computer solutions for the finite difference form of equation (7) would not appear justified for the typical case of slopes with vegetative cover, and the work of Hewlett and Hibbert suggests that the storage-discharge approach used for modelling the groundwater runoff would also be appropriate in this situation.

CONCLUSIONS

Spatial variations in land characteristics are the major difficulty in developing a deterministic rainfall-runoff model for a natural catchment. This difficulty can be reduced to a sampling problem for the hydrologic processes involving mainly vertical water transport, and modelling these processes as a group should lead to effective prediction of total runoff. Lateral water transport has been related to the morphometric properties of the drainage net by statistical models only, and effective prediction of these processes is therefore limited to the range of catchment types under study.

The deterministic model developed for interface processes has led to the definition of measurable catchment parameters which are expected to be hydrologically significant. Experience in using the model with data for a wide range of catchments may show that some of these parameters have little effect on the rainfall-runoff relation, while new parameters may be required for better definition of particular phases of the process.

REFERENCES

BELL, F. C. (1966). A survey of recent developments in rainfall-runoff estimation. *J. Instn Engrs Aust.* **38**, 37.

BIGWOOD, B. L., and THOMAS, M. P. (1957). Connecticut flood planning: Session I — Basic magnitude and frequency relationship. *73rd Annual Report Conn. Soc. Civil Engrs*, p. 76.

BOUGHTON, W. C. (1966). A mathematical model for relating runoff to rainfall with daily data. *Instn Engrs Aust. civ. Engng Trans.* **CE3**, 83.

BOUGHTON, W. C. (1967a). Evaluating the variables in a mathematical catchment model. Paper presented at Institution of Engineers, Australia, Hydrology Symposium, Brisbane, November 27–28, 1967.

BOUGHTON, W. C. (1967b). Hydrologic characteristics of catchments. Paper presented at Symposium on Stream flow and Catchment Characteristics, Wellington, New Zealand, November 21–22, 1967.

BURWELL, R. E., ALLMARAS, R. R., and AMEMIYA, M. (1963). A field measurement of total porosity and surface micro-relief of soils. *Proc. Soil Sci. Soc. Am.* **20**, 697.

BURWELL, R. E., ALLMARAS, R. R., and SLONEKER, L. L. (1966). Structural alteration of soil surfaces by tillage and rainfall. *J. Soil Wat. Conserv.* **21**, 61.

CARLESTON, C. W. (1963). Drainage density and stream flow. *U.S. Geol. Survey Prof. Paper* 422-C.

CHAPMAN, T. G. (1964). Effects of ground-water storage and flow on the water balance. In *Water Resources, Use and Management.* pp. 290–301. (Melbourne University Press.)

CHEN, C., and HANSEN, V. E. (1966). Theory and characteristics of overland flow. *Trans. Am. Soc. agric. Engrs* **9**, 20.

CHOW, V. T. (1964). Runoff. In *Handbook of Applied Hydrology.* Section 14–34. (McGraw-Hill: New York.)

CORDERY, I. (1967). Synthetic unitgraphs for small catchments in Eastern New South Wales. Paper presented at Institution of Engineers, Australia, Hydrology Symposium, Brisbane, November 27–28, 1967.

COWAN, I. R. (1968). Estimation of evaporation using meteorological data. In *Land In Land Evaluation.* (Ed. G. A. Stewart.) Macmillan: Melbourne.)

CRAWFORD, N. H., and LINSLEY, R. K. (1966). *Digital simulation in hydrology: Stanford Watershed Model IV.* Tech. Report No. 12, Dept. Civ. Engng, Stanford University, U.S.A.

DOUGLASS, N. E. (1965). *Effects of species and arrangements of forests on evapotranspiration.* Coweeta Hydrologic Lab., Asheville N.C., U.S.A.

EAGLESON, P. S. (1967). Optimum density of rainfall networks. *Wat. Resour. Res.* **3**, 1021.

EAGLESON, P. S., MEJIA, R. R., and MARCH, F. (1966). Computation of optimum realizable unit hydrographs. *Wat. Resour. Res.* **2**, 755.

EAGLESON, P. S., and SHACK, W. J. (1966). Some criteria for the measurement of rainfall and runoff. *Wat. Resour. Res.* **2**, 427.

GRAY, D. M. (1961). Synthetic unitgraphs for small watersheds. *J. Hydraul. Div. Am. Soc. civ. Engrs* **87** (HY4), 33.

HELVEY, J. D., and PATRIC, J. H. (1965). Canopy and litter interception of rainfall by hardwoods. *Wat. Resour. Res.* **1**, 193.

HEWLETT, J. D., and HIBBERT, A. R. (1963). Moisture and energy conditions within a sloping soil mass during drainage. *J. geophys. Res.* **68**, 1081.

KIDDER, E. H., and HOLTAN, H. N. (1943). Application of a graphic method of analysis to hydrographs of runoff-plots of various lengths. *Trans. Am. geophys. Un.* **24**, 487.

LAURENSON, E. M. (1962). *Hydrograph synthesis by runoff routing.* Report No. 66, Water Res. Lab., University of New South Wales.

LAURENSON, E. M. (1965). Storage routing methods of flood estimation. *Instn Engrs Aust. civ. Engng Trans.* **CE7**, 39.

LINSLEY, R. K., KOHLER, M. A., and PAULHUS, J. L. H. (1949). *Applied Hydrology.* (McGraw-Hill: New York.)

MORGALI, J. R., and LINSLEY, R. K. (1965). Computer analysis of overland flow. *J. Hydraul. Div. Am. Soc. civ. Engrs* **87** (HY3), 81.

NASH, J. E. (1960). A unit hydrograph study, with particular reference to British catchments. *Proc. Instn civ. Engrs* **17**, 249.

PENMAN, H. L. (1963). Vegetation and hydrology. *Tech. Commun. Commonw. Bur. Soils* No. 53.

PHILIP, J. R. (1957). The theory of infiltration: 5. The influence of the initial moisture content. *Soil Sci.* **84**, 329.

PHILIP, J. R. (1964). The gain, transfer and loss of soil–water. In *Water Resources, Use and Management.* pp. 257–75. (Melbourne University Press.)

PHILIP, J. R. (1967). Sorption and infiltration in heterogeneous media. *Aust. J. Soils Res.* **5**, 1.

REEVE, R., ISBELL, R. F., and HUBBLE, G. D. (1963). Soil and climatic data for the brigalow lands, eastern Australia. *CSIRO Aust. Div. Soils divl Rep.* No. 7/61.

REMSON, I., DRAKE, R. L., MCNEARY, S. S., and WALLO, E. M. (1965). Vertical drainage of an unsaturated soil. *J. Hydraul. Div. Am. Soc. civ. Engrs* **91** (HY1), 55.

SALTER, P. J., and WILLIAMS, J. B. (1965). The influence of texture on the moisture characteristics of soils. II. Available-water capacity and moisture release characteristics. *J. Soil Sci.* **16**, 310.

SNYDER, W. B., and STALL, J. B. (1965). Men, models, methods, and machines in hydrologic analysis. *J. Hydraul. Div. Am. Soc. civ. Engrs* **91** (HY2), 85.

SPEIGHT, J. G. (1968). Parametric description of land form for land resource surveys. In *Land Evaluation.* (Ed. G. A. Stewart). (Macmillan: Melbourne.)

STRAHLER, A. N. (1964). Quantitative geomorphology of drainage basins and channel networks. In *Handbook of Applied Hydrology* (Ed. V. T. Chow). Section 4–11. (McGraw-Hill: New York.)

WOODING, R. A. (1965). A hydraulic model for the catchment-stream problem. I. Kinematic-wave theory. *J. Hydrol.* **3**, 254.

WOODING, R. A. (1966). A hydraulic model for the catchment-stream problem. III. Comparison with runoff observations. *J. Hydrol.* **4**, 21.

Aerial and Space Photographs as Aids to Land Evaluation

Robert N. Colwell

*School of Forestry,
University of California, U.S.A.*

If an accurate evaluation of land is to be made, an accurate inventory of its resources must first be obtained. Photography of the land surface, when taken from aircraft and spacecraft, and used in conjunction with small amounts of direct on-the-ground observation, usually provides the best means of making such an inventory. However, to be of maximum usefulness, this photography must have been taken to proper specifications in terms of photographic film, filter, scale, resolution, time of day, and season of year. In some instances more than one kind of photography is needed in order to make an adequate inventory of the land's many resources as quickly and economically as possible. Once each type of resource has been inventoried, the process of land evaluation can be further facilitated if an integrated picture of the total resource is available. Aerial or space photography, suitably annotated and supported with only a limited amount of tabular and textual data, commonly provides the best means for presenting such an integrated picture to the land evaluator.

INTRODUCTION

As the world's population increases, man's demand for wise use of the land and its resources also increases. The making of accurate land evaluations constitutes an important first step toward satisfying that demand. The present paper seeks to update our knowledge of how photographs taken from air or space can be used as aids to land evaluation.

A decade ago, when discussing how we might be able to acquire information about the land from aerial photographs, Dill (1958) stated: 'The face of our land looks to the sky. To see its many features, we must get above it and look down. The airphoto is our best chance to get this bird's eye view'. He then gave an excellent appraisal of what was at that time the true state of the art.

Rapid progress has been made since Dill wrote his appraisal. Symptomatic of this progress, we now hear words similar to his being used to extol the merits of 'space photography' as a means of getting the 'God's eye view' of this land we seek to manage.

Historically speaking, the fields of photogrammetry and photo interpretation have been plagued by enthusiastic statements that maximize the advantages and minimize the limitations of photography. This has been especially true in articles that have addressed themselves to problems of land evaluation. Such overselling has led to numerous misguided efforts by land classifiers. Their consequent failures and disillusionments have been publicized sufficiently to deter others from attempting similar uses of photography, even in situations where it clearly could have been of great value to them. In the interest of helping to prevent recurrences of such misfortunes, the present paper will attempt to set forth some of the basic considerations which should be kept in mind by potential users of air and space photography in land evaluation work, and to provide a summary of the major uses and limitations of such photography for land evaluation purposes.

BASIC CONSIDERATIONS

When obtaining aerial or space photography of the landscape, we are recording energy that travels with a wave-like motion. If we are to interpret this photography correctly, we should know something about such energy.

Anyone who has observed ocean waves surely has been impressed by their ability to transmit energy from one part of the ocean to another. He also will have developed the correct concept of wavelength—the distance from one wave crest to the next. If he has observed carefully he will have noted that, at a given time, there are not only the primary waves, but various secondary waves also, of differing wavelengths. In fact, there can be an entire 'spectrum' of wavelengths, ranging from very short ones to very long ones. These same concepts are useful in considering characteristics of another spectrum—the electromagnetic spectrum—which classifies according to wavelength all energy that moves with the constant velocity of light in an harmonic wave pattern. (Harmonic implies that the waves are equally and repetitively spaced in time). It is with this spectrum that we are primarily concerned when we record the landscape by means of aerial photography, space photography, and related kinds of imagery. In fact, the amount of information potentially derivable from the sensing of *electromagnetic* energy is so great that it pales to insignificance that obtainable from sound waves, force fields or any of the other energy spectra.

This paper deals only with that portion of the electromagnetic spectrum in which photographic emulsions can be used directly to obtain the images (i.e., it deals with wavelengths ranging from about 0·3 to 1·2 microns). A companion paper by Simonett deals with imagery obtained at longer wavelengths, in the thermal infrared and microwave regions. The acquiring of information throughout *all* of the electromagnetic spectrum through the use of remotely situated cameras or other sensing devices is collectively termed 'remote sensing'.

In considering how information useful to the land classifier can be obtained from photography and other forms of remote sensing, we must understand something about the minimum unit of electromagnetic energy, the 'photon'. Electromagnetic waves can differ not only in wavelength, but also in energy content. When a photon of any specific energy strikes the boundary of solid matter, a number of interactions are possible. Mass and energy are conserved in accordance with basic physical principles, and the photon can either be

1. *transmitted*, that is, propogated through the solid matter,
2. *reflected*, that is, returned unchanged to the medium in which it was travelling,
3. *absorbed*, giving up its energy largely into heating the matter,
4. *emitted* (or commonly re-emitted) by the matter as a function of temperature and structure, at the same or different wavelength, or
5. *scattered*, that is, deflected to one side and lost ultimately due to absorption or further scatter.

Transmission, reflection, absorption, emission, and scattering of electromagnetic energy by any particular kind of matter are selective with regard to wavelength, and are specific for that particular kind of matter, depending primarily upon its atomic and molecular structure. In view of this fact we can, in principle, identify the material comprising a target (e.g., a natural resource feature on the earth's surface) from any record which is sufficiently detailed to show the target's spectral transmission, reflectance, absorption, emission, and/or scattering properties. One such possibility is exploited through a process known as 'multiband photographic reconnaissance'. By this process, several photographic film-filter combinations, each specially suited to sensing in its own spectral band, are used in concert to obtain information that could not have been obtained from any single band.

Despite the great potential importance of this concept, something of practical value to the land classifier will result from it only when he has a clear understanding of his informational requirements. What kinds of information then does he seek to obtain through photographic reconnaissance? The answer to that question often depends upon the discipline within which the land classifier is working. For example:

Geologists seek, by remote sensing, to locate important mineral and petroleum deposits, to improve their knowledge of the genesis and world-wide distribution of geomorphic features, and to better understand the energy exchanges associated with earthquakes, volcanic eruptions, and other crustal disturbances. Soil scientists, with the aid of remote sensing, seek to inventory the important physical and chemical characteristics of soils, area by area, and to relate these to the associated geologic, geomorphic, climatic, and vegetational factors. Foresters and agriculturists attempt to use remote sensing to determine the species composition of vegetation in each area studied, and to estimate crop vigor and eventual crop yield. Information of a similar nature also is sought with respect to the livestock, wildlife, and fish populations which come under their purview. Hydrologists seek to locate developable aquifers and to estimate the volume of surface and sub-surface flow from watershed units. They also seek quantitative data on factors involved in the hydrologic cycle including evaporation, precipitation, percolation, and transpiration. Geographers find remote sensing of value in making global, regional, and sub-regional analyses of land use patterns and in studying the interplay of climate, topography, plant life, animal life, and human inhabitants in specific areas.

PHOTOGRAPHIC EQUIPMENT

For more than a century man has been taking aerial photographs. To be sure, the first of these photos were taken from rather uncertain platforms, including kites, balloons, and even homing pigeons to which miniature cameras were strapped. But since those early days, both the platforms and the cameras mounted on them have been greatly improved. Modern remote sensing platforms range from the hovering helicopter, through a variety of smoothly performing fixed-wing aircraft, to the earth-orbital reconnaissance satellite. Camera mounts have been gyro-stabilized against roll, pitch, and yaw motions of the platform and have been effectively insulated against aircraft vibrations that might otherwise cause image blur. Camera lens aberrations have been greatly reduced to ensure sharp images at the focal plane. Roll film of very high dimensional stability has almost entirely replaced the old emulsion-coated glass plates. Furthermore, panchromatic and infrared-sensitive black-and-white films are being augmented or replaced by various color films.

Cameras

Many types of aerial cameras have been developed since the first aerial photographs were taken near the middle of the nineteenth century. Of these camera types, three which presently show greatest promise for obtaining imagery needed for land classification purposes are the conventional aerial camera, the panoramic camera, and the multiband camera.

The Conventional Aerial Camera—The basic components of a modern aerial camera are the magazine, drive mechanism, cone and lens. These components are fully described in many photogrammetric textbooks and no further description of them is needed here.

The Panoramic Camera—The impetus for developing this camera was provided by one salient fact: among long focal-length lenses (the kind needed to provide imagery of large scale, even when flown at high altitudes), only those having a narrow angular field can provide both high spatial and high spectral resolution. However, in order to photograph a suitably wide swath with such narrow angle optics, it is necessary for the optical train of the camera to 'pan' from side to side as the plane flies along. An opaque partition near the focal plane of the camera is equipped with a narrow slit parallel to the line of flight. Only light passing through this slit can strike the photographic film. To maintain uniformly high focus in a panoramic camera it is necessary to hold the frame of film in an arcuate position, while it is being exposed, rather than in a flat plane as in conventional cameras. This feature causes the photographic scale to become progressively smaller toward the left and right edges of the frame because of an increasing distance from the camera lens to the area photographed. As compared with conventional cameras, the resulting photogrammetric problems sometimes (but by no means always) outweigh the advantages resulting from improved resolution.

The Multiband Camera—Reference previously was made to a concept known as multiband spectral reconnaissance. The implementation of this form of remote sensing is of great potential benefit to those seeking to inventory the earth's resources. In most of the cameras that have been developed for the taking of simultaneous photographs in each of several spectral bands (an example is given in Figure 1) each film-filter combination employs its own 'collecting optics'. Such a camera permits exploitation of the concept of multiband spectral reconnaissance throughout the visible and very near infrared parts of the electromagnetic spectrum (roughly $0 \cdot 4$ to $0 \cdot 9$ microns). With this camera one can take simultaneous exposures of exactly the same area, using several spectral zones. By proper choice of photographic film and filter, the limits of each spectral zone can be controlled, as necessary, to obtain the maximum amount of the desired information from that zone. From photo interpretation of the multiband imagery obtainable through the use of such equipment, the land evaluation expert can identify many of the terrain features and conditions that are of interest to him. He does this primarily by comparing tonal values, object-by-object, on several of the frames with corresponding tonal values previously derived for each type of object and condition (i.e., he compares the observed tonal values with a master set of 'tone signatures').

For both conventional cameras and multiband cameras, film transport mechanisms have been significantly improved. Through employment of a principle known as 'forward motion compensation', the film can be made to travel, even during the instant of exposure, at a rate commensurate with the rate of travel of images at the focal plane, caused by the camera's forward motion as the aircraft flies along. By this means, sharper images can be obtained since the image of any particular feature is in effect 'frozen' to the same spot on the film during the entire time that the exposure is being made. Such a refinement is necessary to minimize 'image blur' when taking aerial photos of the earth's surface from high speed aircraft at low altitudes.

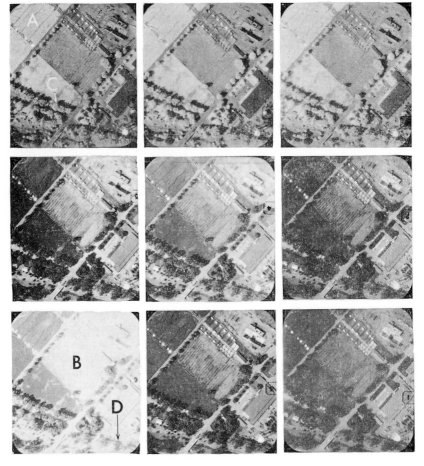

Fig. 1. An example of multiband photography. Vegetated areas such as 'A' appear
        lighter in tone on the top three (infrared) photos than on any of the others;
        exactly the opposite is true for bare soil areas such as 'B'. Similarly, hard-
        wood trees such as the row at 'C' exhibit a much different tone signature
        on these 9 photos than do conifers such as those at 'D'.

Films

In the discussion which follows, consideration is given first to representative
black-and-white panchromatic films currently being used to photograph areas
for land evaluation purposes. That discussion is followed by similar treatments
of black-and-white infrared-sensitive films and of various color films.

Several panchromatic, black-and-white, aerial films that have been developed
by Eastman Kodak are compared in Table 1. From this table it is apparent that
photographic scientists continue to struggle with the inherent 'trade-off' that
exists between film speed and film definition.

On the one hand it is desirable, especially when taking aerial or space photography from unstable, fast-moving platforms, to use films of high speed. With
such films one can obtain an adequate photographic exposure in a very short
time interval, thereby minimizing blur effects due to various kinds of image
motion. But to achieve this high speed we must use a film that has large silver
grains in the emulsion, so that only a few photons of energy will be needed to

TABLE 1

Characteristics of some commonly used panchromatic aerial films

Film designation and Type	Resolution in line pairs per mm	Speed relative to film type 3404	Wratten 12 filter factor
High definition aerial Type 3404	550	1	1·5
High definition aerial Type SO-243	440	1·2	1·6
Special fine grain aerial Type SO-190	180	3·7	1·5
Panchromatic X aerial Type 3400	150	9·0	1·9
Plus X aerial Type 3401	100	33·0	1·7
Super XX aerial Type 5425	75	41·0	2·0

form the picture. These few photons, upon striking a given silver halide crystal, even if it is a large crystal, will produce sufficient 'latent image nuclei' to raise the crystal's energy level above a critical point. Thereby, the crystal will become able to accept additional electrons when later placed in contact with a suitable developing agent. Consequently, during the film-developing process, the entire silver halide crystal can be reduced to opaque metallic silver. Because of its large size, each reduced crystal of this fast, coarse-grained film can contribute substantially to the production of a negative of proper density in terms of image quality.

On the other hand it is equally desirable when taking aerial or space photography (i.e., photography which is necessarily of small scale because of the great distance from camera to ground) to use films of high definition. With such films one can obtain very sharp edge gradients and perceive important photographic detail by viewing the image under suitably high magnification. To achieve this high definition we must use a film that has very small silver grains in the emulsion, so that important details will not be blurred from view as indeed they are in a coarse-grained film. But the smaller the crystal size the larger the number of crystals required per unit area of emulsion. It is at this point that we must pay the price in terms of film speed, because as the crystal size decreases the number of photons required to activate the crystal does not decrease proportionately. Consequently, the finer the film grain, the larger the total number of photons required to produce a negative of suitably high density. In order that this larger number of photons can be captured, the film must be given a longer exposure, i.e., the film is 'slower'. Because of this longer exposure, the resulting photograph is likely to suffer from blur effects caused by various kinds of image motion.

The following conclusions are indicated by Table 1: (1) there is an inverse correlation between film resolution and film speed, and (2) as evidenced by the column of filter factors for a Wratten 12 minus-blue filter, the high definition films are less sensitive to light from the blue end of the spectrum. This fact partly accounts for their lower speeds, although a compensating factor is their extended red sensitivity.

As the term 'panchromatic' implies, these films are about equally sensitive to all parts of the visible spectrum, although with some modification as indicated in the preceding paragraph. The human eye also is 'panchromatic' in the same sense. Consequently, the relative tones or brightness values of objects are essentially the same on panchromatic photography as those seen directly by the human eye. The resulting natural appearance of features may greatly facilitate their photo identification. Herein lies one of the primary advantages to the land evaluator of panchromatic photography.

Infrared black-and-white aerial film is produced in the United States by only one company, Eastman Kodak. The spectral sensitivity of this film is from 0·36 to 0·90 microns. Consequently, to obtain pure infrared effects with it, the ultraviolet and visible wavelengths to which it is sensitive should be screened out by use of a Wratten 89B filter, or equivalent.

The resolution of Kodak aerial infrared film (Type 8433) is only 55 line pairs per mm. However, when aerial photographs must be taken on hazy days, or even on clear days but from very high altitudes, the superior haze penetration obtainable with this film may enable it to produce sharper images than could be obtained with a nominally high-resolution panchromatic film.

Healthy broad-leaved vegetation has very high infrared reflectance and therefore photographs very light in tone on this film. When such vegetation becomes unhealthy (e.g., due to damage done by diseases, insects, drought, fire, mineral deficiency, or mineral toxicity) it is likely to undergo a loss in its ability to reflect infrared light, even before any other change in its spectral behavior occurs. Consequently, it is of more than passing interest to the land evaluator that infrared photography may provide him with 'previsual symptoms' of unhealthy conditions that are developing on the broad-leaved vegetation within certain parts of a landscape that he seeks to evaluate. Conversely, if the broad-leaved vegetation registers only in light tones on infrared photography, the land evaluator can be reasonably sure that it is not suffering from any of these maladies.

Aerial color films are of three types: color positive films, color negative films, and false color films. Each is potentially useful to the land evaluator for specific purposes. However, the cost of obtaining color photography, when compared with black-and-white photography, is not always justified by the additional information which it provides.

Color positive films are sensitized to three primary colors, blue, green, and red, and when exposed and processed produce transparencies which appear similar to the original scene when viewed by white light. (During development color dyes are introduced into the three layers to produce full color images). Two such films that currently are in common use are Kodak Ektachrome aero film (E-3 process) and Anscochrome D/200. The former has an ASA film speed of 160, and the latter of 200; both are capable of resolving approximately 100 line pairs per mm. Since the land evaluator is accustomed to seeing and identifying objects, not only by their size, shape, and association, but also by their color, such films give him one more important dimension for use in making his aerial photo identifications. For example, Heller et al. (1964) reported that the accuracies with which tree species could be identified averaged 17% higher on large-scale color transparencies than on the same scale of panchromatic prints. According to Evans (1948) the human eye can separate over 100 times as many color combinations (based on hue, brightness, and saturation) as grey scale values, although color films cannot discriminate as many colors as the human eye can see.

Color negative films have the dye coupler components incorporated in the emulsion layers at the time of manufacture. After the film has been developed and bleached, dye images remain that are not only negative to the tone gradations of the subject, but also complementary to colors of the scene photographed. From such negatives it is possible to make color prints and transparencies as well as black-and-white prints and transparencies, the latter of which are almost indistinguishable from those made using panchromatic negatives.

Cooper and Smith (1966) report that color prints made from a negative color film are somewhat lacking in color balance and have considerably poorer resolution than color transparencies. The color balance was found to be most deficient for blue and green objects, including vegetation. Aerial negative films are approximately 3-fold slower than aerial positive films, a factor which sometimes further limits the resolution obtainable with them.

The most recent development in color photography is the Kodak aero-neg color system. The heart of this system is Kodak Ektachrome MS aerographic film (estar base), Type SO-151. Although this film is more commonly known as a reversal color film that can be processed to a positive transparency, it is now possible to process the film to a negative. The aerial exposure index for this film, when processed to a color negative is only 8, and this relatively slow speed may constitute the greatest limitation on its use from aircraft and spacecraft. However, it reportedly has higher resolution than other negative color films. The most thorough testing of this film to date has been done by various groups of Australian scientists, notably those of the Forest Research Institute, Commonwealth Forestry and Timber Bureau (Sims and Benson 1967a, 1967b). They find that it has an unusually wide latitude of acceptable exposure and that, by employing proper filtering techniques at the time of printing, one can eliminate most of the adverse bluish cast and related haze effects that usually plague high-altitude color photography.

False color films are those on which objects purposely are imaged with different colors than they exhibit in nature. The purpose of the false color is to accentuate certain features and facilitate the making of certain distinctions, even at the expense of making features of lesser importance less interpretable. One such film is Kodak infrared aero film (E-3 process); since the film is normally exposed through a Wratten 12 filter, blue light does not contribute to formation of the image. As indicated in Table 2, where the spectral characteristics of this film are compared with those of a normal color film, its three dyes respond to green, red, and infrared wavelengths, respectively, with the net result that green objects (except healthy vegetation which is also highly infrared reflective) appear blue; red objects appear green; and infrared-reflective objects (such as healthy vegetation) appear red. One effect is that the infrared energy of highest intensity produces the brightest reds in the photograph. The predecessor of this film was known as 'camouflage detection film' and was used as early as World War II, primarily to differentiate healthy green (and highly infrared-reflective) foliage from green camouflage paint and green, recently-cut foliage, both of which have low infrared reflectance. From a distance all of these features of the landscape looked the same to the naked eye, and on panchromatic or conventional color films, but conspicuously different on the camouflage detection film—hence its name. Tarkington and Sorem (1963) report that the new emulsion, released in 1962, provides better resolution and is three times as fast as the old one. Because of its sensitivity to long wavelengths and the exclusion of short ones through use of a Wratten 12 filter, this film has the ability to penetrate haze exceptionally well.

A false color film containing only two dyes and known as 'SN-2 spectrozonal film' is produced by Russian film makers (Mikhailhov 1960). One layer of the emulsion responds to visible wavelengths of energy; the other to infrared wavelengths in the 0.7 to 0.9 micron region. During film development, color dyes are introduced into both layers to produce images in various colors.

Both of the above-mentioned false color films are of great potential interest

TABLE 2

Spectral characteristics of a normal color film(Ektachrome Type 8442) and an infrared-sensitive color film (infrared Ektachrome Type 8443)

Film Type	Spectral Region			
	Blue	*Green*	*Red*	*Infrared*
Ektachrome				
Sensitivity bands	Blue	Green	Red	
Corresponding colors of dye layers	Yellow	Magenta	Cyan	
Resulting colors on photographs	Blue	Green	Red	
Infrared Ektachrome				
Sensitivity bands with Wratten 12 filter		Green	Red	Infrared
Corresponding colors of dye layers		Yellow	Magenta	Cyan
Resulting colors on photographs		Blue	Green	Red

to the land evaluator. Some features of interest to him can be distinguished on photography taken in the visible part of the spectrum, but not on that taken in the infrared part; exactly the reverse is true for other features. These false color films combine in a single composite color image the possibility of distinguishing both types of features.

Platforms

The photography dealt with in this paper can be obtained from a variety of platforms ranging from hovering helicopters and balloons through the various types of fixed-wing photo reconnaissance aircraft, some of which are equipped with a large assortment of aerial cameras and related sensing devices, to earth-orbiting spacecraft.

If the spacecraft is unmanned, either the photographic images must be televised back to earth, as in EROS—the Earth Resources Observation Satellite —or the rolls of exposed film must be housed in a capsule that can be ejected from the remainder of the earth-orbiting vehicle and retrieved by means of an 'air snatch'. However, if the spacecraft is manned, the astronauts who have served as photographers are able to bring the exposed film back to earth with them, as in the 'Gemini' and 'Apollo' types.

One reason why this paper deals with both aerial and space photography is that the two types, when properly used by the land evaluator, provide excellent opportunities for the effective use of double, triple, or even quadruple sampling techniques as described later.

EQUIPMENT FOR DATA ANALYSIS

Broadly speaking, the equipment which a land evaluator needs as he seeks to extract information from aerial or space photography falls into three categories: viewing, measuring, and plotting. The full gamut of these devices is covered in the *Manual of Photographic Interpretation* (American Society of Photogram-metry 1960). Consequently, no further detail relative to such equipment need be given here. However, with the recently-developed capability for acquiring imagery simultaneously in several parts of the spectrum there has arisen a need to develop new kinds of equipment, as described below, that will facilitate the extraction of information from such multiband imagery.

In considering multiband data analysis systems, it is helpful to paraphrase an important point made earlier in this paper: reflection and emission of electromagnetic energy by a particular kind of natural terrain feature are selective with regard to wavelength and specific for that particular kind of feature. Exploitation of this principle, through multiband reconnaissance and multiband data analysis, theoretically should lead to positive identification of every feature with which we are concerned as we seek to inventory the earth's natural resources and evaluate the lands containing them.

As the number of spectral bands used in multiband remote sensing is increased, the tone signature for each natural resource feature becomes more complete and more reliable. However, with this increase of spectral bands the task of data analysis can become astronomic unless the image analyst is provided with some kind of image-correlating equipment. Three methods of accomplishing the required image correlation will be described presently.

In order to use any of these methods successfully, it first is necessary to 'calibrate' the multiband tone signature (response) for each type of object or condition that is to be identified. This is best done if a suitable 'ground truth' test site has been included in the multiband reconnaissance flight. Within such a test site (if it has been properly selected), each type of object and condition that is to be identified operationally is exhibited in each of several accurately known localities. It is from a preliminary study of the multiband images for these test sites that the identifying tone signatures are derived. The task of image correlation is greatly facilitated if all of the multiband frames of imagery covering a given area of terrain have the same geometry. This is a standard attribute of multiband cameras and ordinarily poses no serious problem. Uniform image geometry is not only useful in the calibration phase—it is essential in the subsequent operational phase if one of the following three methods is to be used.

Method No. 1—The multiband imagery of a given portion of the terrain is reconstituted as a single color composite. Each type of feature is then identified merely through visual perception of the color exhibited by it on the composite color imagery. When this method is employed, it is common practice to project simultaneously onto a viewing screen several or all of the black-and-white images of a given portion of the terrain that have been obtained with the multiband reconnaissance system. The color rendition is achieved by the use of colored filters. Each black-and-white frame is projected, usually in lantern slide form, through a filter of suitable hue. For any feature, the intensity of that particular hue, as seen on the color composite, is governed by the grey scale value (tone) exhibited by the feature on the corresponding black-and-white lantern slide.

Method No. 2—A battery of photo-electric (brightness sensitive) scanners is used to scan all of the multiband black-and-white images simultaneously. For each of the multiband images of a given area of terrain a scanner is assigned. The scanners, operating in unison, scan the black-and-white multiband images, line-by-line, progressing from the top of the frame to the bottom. Because all of the multiband images have identical geometry, all of the scanners simultaneously view conjugate images. Consequently, a multiband tone signature automatically is read out by the battery of scanners for each 'x' and 'y' coordinate position that is scanned. Theoretically, each spot scanned is in this way found to have a tone signature identical with that of some particular object or condition that was studied in the calibration phase. In its ultimate form this method results in an encoded automatic print-out on tape, indicating the objects and conditions encountered at every 'x–y' coordinate position appearing in the multiband imagery. At present such a method has not been perfected, but even with its present limitation, it is able to provide an amount of automatic image analysis that can greatly reduce the amount of work to be done by the image analyst, himself. An example of the encoded print-out from one member of a multiband series of images is shown in Figure 2.

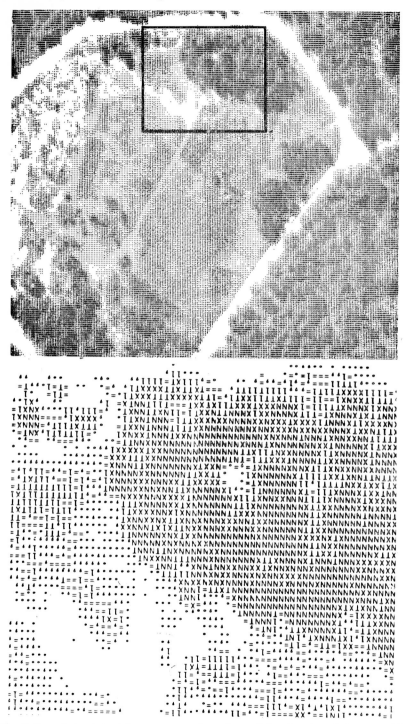

Fig. 2. Encoded printout from one member of a multiband series of photographic images.

Method No. 3—When this method is employed, the multiband reconnaissance system records on magnetic tape, rather than on photographic film, the signal strength from each object in each spectral band. From that point forward the procedure is the same as that described in Method 2. The essential difference is that Method 3 does not even require that photographic images be formed since it permits an analysis of the signal strengths (commonly called 'responses')

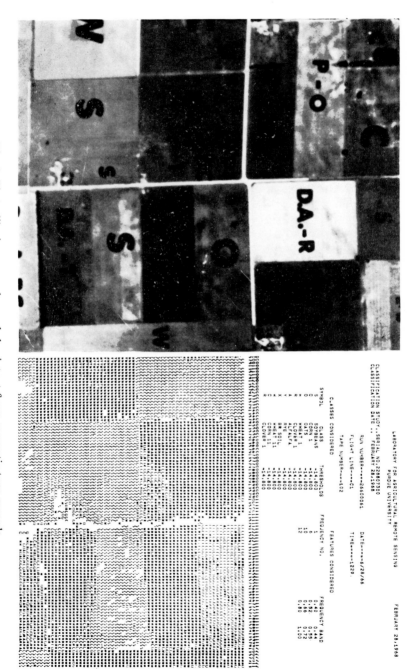

Fig. 3. Photo-like images and encoded printout from magnetic tape records.

emanating *directly* from the objects. In Method 2, however, only the tones of the multiband images of the objects can be analysed. An example of the print-out obtained by this means is illustrated in Figure 3. If, in Method 3, photo-like images also are desired, these can be produced from the original tape records. Furthermore, the resulting imagery can be presented either as individual black-and-white frames or as multiband color composites.

PRESENT APPLICATIONS

The usefulness of any tool is enhanced if the user clearly recognizes, at the outset, both the advantages and the limitations of that tool.

The advantages and limitations of aerial and space photography are discussed in some detail in an article by Colwell (1963) and need only be summarized here. The principal advantages include (1) reliability; (2) favorable vantage point; (3) discernible detail; (4) completeness of coverage; (5) three-dimensional presentation; (6) ease of interpretation; (7) opportunity to extend limited ground observations; (8) ease of measurement; (9) ease of checking for sources of error; (10) opportunity for study of the area throughout the year; (11) rapidity of obtaining inventory data; (12) suitability for comparative studies; (13) suitability for filing; and (14) economy.

The principal limitations which aerial and space photographs impose on the land evaluator include those that are a consequence of the following facts: (1) aerial photographs do not entirely eliminate field work; (2) prolonged training and careful supervision of personnel may be required before they can consistently extract data from the photography to an acceptably high order of accuracy; (3) scale usually varies throughout a photograph due to tilt and relief displacements; (4) photographs may emphasize the wrong features; (5) photographs may rapidly become outdated; and (6) a single photograph rarely shows all of the area of interest.

Various of the advantages and limitations referred to above are discussed much more fully in articles by Avery and Meyer 1962, Badgley *et al.* 1967, Burnham 1966, Colwell *et al.* 1960, Moessner 1957, Stone 1961, and Wilson *et al.* 1962.

In view of the foregoing, the land evaluator should not regard photography as a tool which will completely substitute armchair inventory for field work. Neither should he regard photographs as map substitutes which can be used in lieu of maps for the direct measurement of areas, distances, and directions. Rather, he should consider photographs as valuable aids which, if intelligently used in conjunction with a limited amount of field work, can lead to a more accurate evaluation of the land at an appreciable saving in time and money.

Turning now to examples of the specific procedures that have been found useful for evaluating the land and its resources, these likewise have been discussed in several important articles (Avery 1962; Dudzinski and Arnold 1967; Nysonnen 1961; Pope, MacLean, and Bernstein 1961; Sayn-Wittgenstein 1961; Wilson 1948; U.S. Geological Survey 1944). Perhaps it will suffice here to discuss two examples which illustrate many of these procedures. The first deals with an evaluation of the vegetational resources (timber, forage, etc.) and the second with an evaluation of the soils resources. In each instance the methods presented have been found applicable in a wide variety of situations and, with only slight modification, might be employed in most of the parts of the world where land evaluations are to be made.

In estimating timber volumes of a large forest area with the aid of photography, the following steps are commonly followed: (a) the total allowable expenditure ascertained; (b) the most suitable photography of the area, consistent with cost limitations, is procured; (c) the timber-volume classes which are to be recognized on the photos are defined, typically in terms of the stand-height range and crown-closure range to be embraced by each class. Some field checking usually must be done concurrently, to establish 'ground truth'. Care must be taken at this point to be sure that enough classes are recognized to make the classification useful, while avoiding the establishment of more classes than can be consistently identified on the photos, lest this lead to inaccuracies which will negate the value of the whole classification procedure; furthermore, the classes should roughly conform to the expected range of heights and densities to be encountered in the area to be classified; otherwise, most of the plots might fall into one or two classes and nullify the primary objectives of the classification; (d) from preliminary time-cost analyses, the average cost per field plot and per photo plot are determined since it will be highly desirable to field-check several of the photo plots; (e) also from preliminary analyses a measure of the standard deviation within photo volume classes and of the variance between photo volume classes is obtained; (f) from the information obtained in these preliminary steps a determination is made of the number of ground plots and photo plots that should be taken (Wilson et al. 1960); (g) the required photo plots are pinpointed on the photos in such a way as to achieve either a systematic or a random distribution of these plots throughout the area; (h) each photo plot is studied stereoscopically, measurements of its stand height and crown closure are made, and these figures are entered in the aerial-photo, stand-volume table to compute the stand-volume of the plot; (i) distribution is made of the previously calculated number of ground plots so that the appropriate number will be obtained in each photo-volume class; in this step a sampling interval is calculated and is used to decide which photo plots in each class will also become ground plots; the interval is computed for each class by dividing the number of photo plots in that class by the number of ground plots to be taken in the class; (j) field measurements of the timber of each ground plot are made, and from these measurements the timber volumes on the ground plot are computed; these volumes are then applied to the photo plots also, class-by-class; (k) the forest area within each volume class is determined, either by using a separate dot-grid count or by using the proportion of the interpreted plots occurring in each class to determine the proportion of the total area which should be allocated to that class; (l) the average timber-volume per unit area in that class and the total timber-stand volume for the entire property is computed from the sums of the volumes in various classes.

Numerous modifications of the foregoing procedure can be made, to better meet the needs in any specific timber-inventory problem, as described, for example, in articles by Boon (1962), Hildebrandt (1962), and Loetsch (1962).

In analyzing the non-timber vegetation resources of an area, basically the same procedures can be followed.

An evaluation of the soils resources of an area entails some close similarities of procedure to those just discussed for a vegetational survey. Most of the differences are in the photo-recognition features. For example, drainage patterns, by suggesting geologic structure to the soil scientist as he examines the aerial photos, may point to the origin and composition of underlying rocks and hence to important soil properties. The sequence of events which formed a particular soil can often be reconstructed by the trained soil scientist through skilful photo interpretation of pattern and associated features, and in this way additional soil properties of significance to the soil survey can be inferred. Tone also is important to the soil scientist, just as to the vegetation analyst, but in a somewhat different light. In general, coarse-textured and well-drained soils have light photographic tones, while fine-textured and poorly drained soils have dark tones. In attempting to use such relationships, however, the photo interpreter must consider the nature of the parent rock, and the mode of soil deposition, and the climatic, biotic, and physiographic factors of the environment. For example, in humid regions clay soils, as seen on panchromatic photography, generally have dark photographic tones, while silts and sands have light tones; but in arid regions the tones of sand and clay may be indistinguishable (Frost et al. 1960). In many of the less developed areas of the world there is a dense cover of native vegetation; consequently, the soil itself is rarely imaged on aerial photographs in such areas. It frequently is possible, however, to establish a high correlation between vegetation type and soil type and in this way use aerial photos to great advantage in soil surveys, even in heavily vegetated areas (U.S. Navy 1945). Buringh (1960) lists, under 20 separate headings, the analytical elements discernible on aerial photographs, which are valuable for soil-mapping purposes. He also discusses eight basic procedures for mapping soils with photos and provides an excellent comparative analysis of five commonly used methods of soil survey, indicating situations in which each method might appropriately be used.

POTENTIAL FUTURE APPLICATIONS

Many of the applications of aerial photography to land evaluation that have been discussed in this paper have become standard practice during the past two or three decades. For example, in the United States for at least 30 years, aerial photos have been used effectively both in the making of timber inventories and in soil mapping. As early as 1948 that government's Range Management Manual specified that 'aerial photos will be used as a base for all range resource inventories made on national forests' (U.S. Forest Service 1948). However, many applications suggested in this paper are yet to be realized in practice on any extensive scale. This is, of course, especially true of applications that might employ space photography. The achievement of new applications will depend heavily on further research and upon the exercise of due care that the usefulness and limitations of such applications are objectively reported.

In considering potential future applications one can foresee the possibility that certain kinds of land evaluation will be automatically made by means of earth-orbiting multiband sensors and computers as indicated in Figure 4.

In this configuration part of the space vehicle's optical system would consist of a rotating mirror assembly which has only a small 'instantaneous field of view'. By means of this mirror system and supporting optical elements, the full spectrum of electromagnetic energy emanating from only a small portion of the land surface is, at one particular time, directed to the multiband sensors. Rotation of the mirror system is synchronized to the forward motion of the vehicle (towards the left in Fig. 4) so that contiguous 'line scans' of the terrain are obtained. The sensing elements convert the multiband energy strengths emanating from the terrain into corresponding electrical signal strengths which eventually are transmitted to the 'inventory computer'. There, each multiband signal is compared with the characteristic multiband signals previously derived for various terrain features and conditions (e.g., dry clay soil, rust-infested wheat). By a process known as 'spectral matching', the computer thus identifies predominant terrain features and conditions within each instantaneous field of view and produces an 'inventory printout'.

EARTH   ORBITING   NATURAL   RESOURCES   SATELLITE

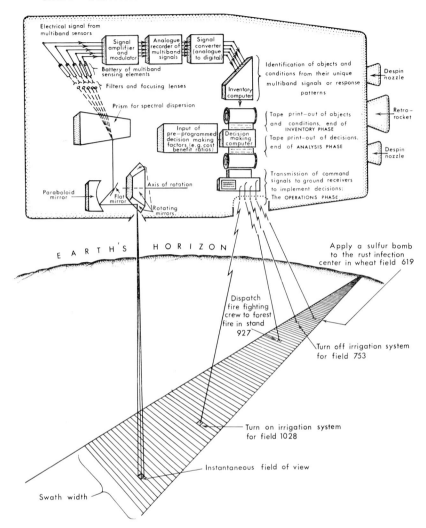

Fig. 4. Schematic diagram indicating the possible future for multiband space reconnaissance as an aid to land evaluation and land management.

Thus equipped, a satellite might be able to take inventory of the land's resources, area-by-area, and produce a printout that would amount to a resource map. The computer could then use the inventory data in conjunction with various pre-programmed factors (such as what ratio of benefits to costs would likely result from the implementation of various land management practices) and could reach a decision for the optimum management of the land and its resources. The decision could then be telemetered to the ground for whatever action seemed appropriate.

As a simple example, the satellite's sensors might spot a fire in a large forest. Its computer might then derive information as to the location and extent of the fire, the type and relative value of the timber, the trafficability of surrounding terrain, the best means of access to the fire, and the best spots in which to build firelines to control the blaze. On the basis of the assessment, the computer would send to the ground a recommendation for combating the fire. Capabilities of this kind need not be limited to emergencies. There are many routine 'housekeeping' chores that now must be done through the mental and physical efforts of land evaluators and land managers as they engage in the sequential process of inventory, analysis, and operation. It is conceivable that a computer-equipped satellite might perform not only the inventory and analysis, but also bring about the action (operation) dictated by the analysis. For example, by means of electronic command signals from a satellite, the proper irrigation valve might be turned on when multiband reconnaissance showed that an agricultural field was becoming too dry. Similarly it might be turned off when, a few orbits later, the field appeared to have been sufficiently watered.

A satellite of such capabilities may seem now to be a rather distant prospect. After a few more years of research and development, however, the prospect might well become a reality.

REFERENCES

AMERICAN SOCIETY OF PHOTOGRAMMETRY (1968). *Manual of Color Aerial Photography.* (In press).
AVERY, T. E. (1962). *Interpretation of Aerial Photographs.* (Burgess Publishing Co.: Minneapolis, Minn.).
AVERY, T. E., and MEYER, M. P. (1962). Contracting for forest aerial photography in the United States. *Lake States Forest Exp. Sta. Paper.*
BADGLEY, P. C., COLVOCORESSES, A. P., and CENTERS, C. D. (1967). *NASA earth sensing space flight experiments.* Special Publication of the NASA Earth Resources Survey Program.
BOON, D. A. (1962). Use of aerial photographs for mapping tropical forests. (In German.) *Allg. Forstz.* **17**, (1/2), 7–9.
BURINGH, P. (1960). The applications of aerial photographs in soil surveys. In *Manual of Photographic Interpretation.* pp. 633–66. (American Society of Photogrammetry: Washington, D.C.)
BURNHAM, J. M. (1966). *Aerial color photography bibliography.* Aero-Neg Notes No. 2 of Kodak (Australasia) Pty. Ltd.
COLWELL, R. N. (1963). Aerial photo interpretation for the evaluation of vegetation and soil resources. In *Proceedings of U.N. Cartographic Conference for Africa.* 20 pp.
COLWELL, R. N. et al. (1960). Procurement of photography. In *Manual of Photographic Interpretation.* pp. 19–98. (American Society of Photogrammetry: Washington, D.C.)
COOPER, C. F., and SMITH, F. M. (1966). Color aerial photography: Toy or tool. *J. For.* **64**, 373–88.
DILL, H. W. (1958). Information on land from airphotos. In *Land, Yearbook of Agriculture.* (U.S. Dept. of Agriculture: Washington, D.C.)
DUDZINSKI, M. L., and ARNOLD, G. W. (1967). Aerial photography and statistical analysis for studying behavior patterns of grazing animals. *J. Range Mgmt* **22**, 77–83.
EVANS, R. N. (1948). *An Introduction to Color.* (John Wiley and Sons: New York.)
FROST, R. E. et al. (1960). Photo interpretation of soils. In *Manual of Photographic Interpretation.* (American Society of Photogrammetry: Washington, D.C.)
HELLER, R. C., DOVERSPIKE, G. E., and ALDRICH, R. C. (1964). Identification of tree species on large scale color and panchromatic photographs. *U.S. Dep. Agric. Handb.* 261.
HILDEBRANDT, G. (1962). Use of aerial photographs in forest inventories of temperate deciduous and coniferous forests. (In German.) *Allg. Forstz.* **17**, (1/2), 20–22, 25–26.
LOETSCH, F. (1962). The importance of aerial photographs in forest inventories of the tropics. (In German.) *Allg. Forstz.* **17**, (1/2), 9–17.
MIKHAILHOV, V. Y. (1960). The use of color sensitive films in aerial photography in U.S.S.R. Transl. Canadian National Research Council, Ottawa.
MOESSNER, K. E. (1957). How important is relief in area estimates? *Res. Paper* 42, *Intermountain Forest and Range Exp. Sta, Ogden, Utah.*
NYYSSONEN, A. (1961). *Survey Methods of Tropical Forests.* (FAO: Rome.)
POPE, R. B., MACLEAN, C. D., and BERNSTEIN, D. A. (1961). *Forestry uses of aerial photographs.* Pacific Northwest For. and Range Exp. Sta., Portland, Ore.

SAYN-WITTGENSTEIN, L. (1961). Phenological aids to species identification on air photographs. *Dep. For. Canada, Tech. Note* No. 104.

SIMS, W. G., and BENSON, M. L. (1967a). Zoom viewing of stereo pairs. *Forest Res. Inst., Canberra, Aust. Special publication.*

SIMS, W. G., and BENSON, M. L. (1967b). Atmospheric haze penetration in color air photography. *Forest Res. Inst. Canberra, Aust. Special publication.*

STONE, K. H. (1961). World air photo coverage. *Photogramm. Engng* **27**, 605–10.

U.S. FOREST SERVICE (1948). *Instructions for Range Resource Inventories on National Forests.* (Washington, D.C.)

U.S. GEOLOGICAL SURVEY (1944). *Photo Interpretation of Vegetation in the Tropical Pacific Area and its Use as an Indication of Kind of Ground.* (Army Map Service, U.S. Army: Washington, D.C.) No. 201550.

U.S. NAVY PHOTO INTERPRETATION CENTER (1945). Pacific landforms and vegetation. *PIC Report* No. 7, NavAer 10-35-560.

WILSON, R. C. (1948). Photo interpretation aids for timber surveys. *J. For.* **46**, 41–4.

WILSON, R. C., et al. (1960). Photo interpretation in forestry. In *Manual of Photographic Interpretation.* pp. 457–520. (American Society of Photogrammetry: Washington, D.C.)

WILSON, R. C., et al. (1962). Aerial photographs in forest inventories — Applications and research stidies. Unpublished report of IUFRO advising group cn aerial photo applications to forestry.

Spectral Luminance of Sand Deposits as a Tool in Land Evaluation

Mariya A. Romanova

Laboratory of Mathematical Geology,
Mathematical Institute of Academy of Sciences,
Leningrad, USSR

A method of determining the composition of desert sands from the air was developed, using a spectrometer and barite paper standard.

Spectral luminance of the sands was measured at different wavelengths, and gave a bimodal frequency distribution for λ = 900 μ, the mixture of two normal distributions. Regions of accumulation and of deflation were distinguished, by the fitting of trend surfaces, and correlation with geological data. These methods can indicate recent tectonic movement, and provide a tool for rapid and relatively cheap land evaluation, for oil and water search, and agricultural research in desert areas.

INTRODUCTION

The investigation of large desert regions presents numerous difficulties. These difficulties can be overcome by the use of aircraft with remote sensing apparatus for measuring properties of the desert terrain. Thus, recently there have been important studies with remote sensors of rocks, surface roughness, soils, and vegetation, using their reflectance properties to assist in land evaluation (Hobson 1967).

The author's experience indicates that numerous features of deserts important for land evaluation can be investigated by measurement and treatment of spectral luminance of sands with special devices. This problem was outlined in the author's book and permits us to avoid technical details (Romanova 1964a). The book describes basic photometry concepts, instruments for measuring spectral luminance, conditions for spectro-photometry of geological objects, the evaluation of spectral luminance curves and their geological interpretation, and an aeropetrographic study of modern sand deposits. We recall only that spectral luminance is a property connected with scattering of radiant energy by reflection from the surface of an object, that this reflection is related to properties of the object, and that the results of measurement can be expressed as a curve for wavelength (λ) plotted against spectral luminance factor (ρ_λ) expressed as a percentage relative to the standard sample.

Desert sands are suited to this method because their diffuse reflection of light gives similar luminance values over a range of angles of illumination. In this study the luminance was measured further into the infrared than in earlier studies and in the evaluation of the data, luminance at a specific wavelength is used rather than polynomial coefficients of luminance curves. For quantitative comparison of geologic models trend surface analysis has been used.

The following is an illustration of the use of spectral luminance for land evaluation in the Karakum desert (Turkemia, USSR) made by the author some years ago.

PROBLEMS OF LAND EVALUATION IN KARAKUM DESERT

The Karakum desert is a sand desert with enormous areas covered with bark-hans. The central part of the desert has been an area of great activity during recent years, connected with boring of petroliferous uplifts, civil engineering, building of roads, and organization of agriculture. All these activities require a good knowledge of the origin of the desert sands because these sands can be the result of two processes – aeolian accumulation, or deflation of sands of local rocks which are composed, in the Karakum desert, of pure sands (Karakum and Zaunguz suites).

The purpose of our work was to separate regions with accumulated sands from regions with sands formed by erosion of local rocks and the generation of deflation surfaces. The general model in such a case can be the following: 1. Accumulated sands are composed of mixed material. The pattern of the properties of these sands can be related to modern morphology, relief of the region, and meteorological conditions.

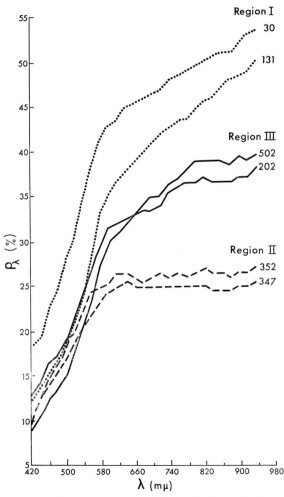

Fig. 1. Types of spectral luminance curves of the sandy deposits. Zaunguz Karakum (I), Low Karakum (II), and Intermediate region (III). Number by the curve is the number of the sample.

2. Sands of remnants of local deposits on a deflation surface should have properties related to those of the original local rocks (Karakum and Zaunguz suites).

Study of these properties permits us to separate regions of accumulation from the regions of deflation. The region investigated is rectangular in shape, with a size of 160×300 km, and is located in the central part of the Karakum region around the village of Darvaza.

The northern part of this rectangle is the Zaunguz plateau and it is composed of desert on Tertiary deposits of the Zaunguz suite.

The southern part is called Low Karakum and is composed of desert on Quarternary Karakum suite. The boundary between the Zaunguz plateau and Low Karakum is the dry valley called Unguz.

The study area was covered by a sampling net with size of cell about 10 km. The number of sampling points was 513. All sampling points were similarly located on the flat top of barkhans.

The spectral luminance of sand was measured at each point; all samples were examined petrographically. We used the field photoelectric spectrometer constructed by Voronkova et al. (1960). The resolution of this spectrometer was 10 mμ, the viewing angle was 2°, and the absolute mean square error of one measurement was 1%. The spectral width of the slit was about 8 mμ. The measurement of ρ for one sand sample was made at 20 mμ intervals in the wavelength range 400–1000 mμ. The standard was a barite paper.

Some typical shapes of luminance curves are shown in Figure 1. The greatest difference in the curves is at the longest wavelengths, and the percentage reflectance at $\lambda = 900$ mμ was chosen for evaluation.

A frequency distribution of ρ_{900} for all 513 samples is plotted on Figure 2, which indicates that there is a bimodal distribution of ρ_λ. This distribution can be explained as a mixture of two normal distributions (Romanova 1964b). The separated normal distributions permit us to find values of ρ_{900} between modes of normal distributions on a distance more than two standards from the modes of these distributions. This part of the frequency distribution envelops the values of ρ_{900} in the interval $31 < \rho_\lambda < 36$%. Thus, investigation of spectral luminance of sands revealed that all samples can be divided into two groups: sands with $\rho_{900} < 31$% and sands with $\rho_{900} > 36$%.

Figure 3 shows the location of points of observation and isopleths of $\rho_{900} < 31$. The isopleth for $\rho_{900} = 36$ is located to the south of the geological boundary of Zaunguz Karakum. This is a result of aeolian processes, and we chose the morphological feature — the Unguz valley — as a boundary of the sands with high values for ρ_λ.

Three regions were separated I: northern — Zaunguz Karakum where the sands have high value spectral luminance; II — southern — Low Karakum, where the sands have $\rho_{900} < 31$%; and III — intermediate. Generalized patterns of $\bar\rho_{900}$ within regions I, II, and III can be interpreted separately in land evaluation terms. This generalization was made by computing trend surfaces (Vistelius and Romanova 1964).

$$\bar\rho_{900} = \exp P_n (\psi, \lambda),$$

where exp indicates that it is the exponential function, $P_n (\psi, \lambda)$ is a polynomial of geographical co-ordinates ψ and λ, and n is a power of the polynomial.

Experiments with $n = 1$, 2, and 3 have indicated that in our case the most convenient is $n = 3$. The approximation was made to $\psi n \rho_{900}$ by the least squares procedure with checking of the stability of the normal system with the Todd number (Lanczos 1957).

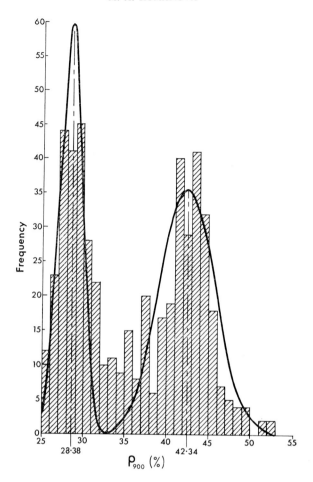

Fig. 2. Frequency distribution of values of coefficients of ρ_{900} for all 513 samples of the sandy deposits.

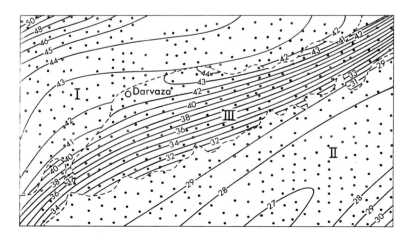

Fig. 3. The isopleths of ρ_{900} for trend surfaces of sand deposits of regions I, II, and III. Black dots are the sampling points.

The pattern of isopleths for each region is plotted on Figure 3. It is clear that there are three different patterns.

The pattern of region I is very clear. The spectral luminance increases rapidly to the north, with increasing gradient.

The pattern of region II indicates that, in the axial part of this region, there are sands with the smallest $\bar{\rho}_{900}$ and with a very small gradient of $\bar{\rho}_{900}$ from the central part to both north and south.

The pattern of region III is quite different from the other regions. The isopleths of $\bar{\rho}_{900}$ are closely spaced and are parallel to the northern boundary of the region and to one another. The gradient is very steep.

Thus, all three regions have quite different patterns for generalized $\bar{\rho}_{900}$.

The interpretation of the origin of the patterns of $\bar{\rho}_{900}$ was obtained by petrographic analysis of samples, comparison with geological data, and mathematical processing of data.

GEOLOGICAL INTERPRETATION OF THE SPECTRAL LUMINANCE OF KARAKUMS SANDY DEPOSITS

Geological data and observations on relief and drainage pattern indicate that the composition of sands of region I is close to the composition of the Kyzilkum region located to the north of the investigated region.

The composition of sands of region II is similar to that of the sands of Tedjun River and to the composition of rocks and deposits in northern Iran.

The petrographic analysis of sands gave the results summarized in Table 1 and it can be seen that the composition of sand of region III is intermediate between that of regions I and II.

TABLE 1

Petrographic characteristics of sands

	Content (% vy volume)					
	Region I (196 samples)		Region II (245 samples)		Region III (68 samples)	
	Mean	S.D.	Mean	S.D.	Mean	S.D.
Quartz	50·1	12·9	24·8	7·2	36·0	8·9
Feldspars	16·6	6·6	16·0	5·3	16·8	5·1
Dark coloured minerals	3·6	2·7	10·2	3·8	8·0	3·1
Intrusive and volcanic rocks	16·5	8·5	32·1	7·6	25·9	6·7
Ore's minerals	2·7	2·3	3·9	2·5	3·1	1·5
Limestones	10·0	6·9	12·9	4·2	10·5	4·4
Heavy fraction	1·9	0·9	9·2	2·5	4·8	1·4
ρ_{900}	42·34	3·22	28·38	1·15		

A comparison of the composition of the sands with composition of Zaunguz and Karakum suites deposits shows their similarity.

The geological interpretation of the sedimentation of Zaunguz and Karakum suites coincides with the generalized pattern of ρ_{900}.

Thus, the generalized pattern of ρ_{900} of regions I and II should be interpreted as reflection of the petrographic patterns of Zaunguz and Karakum sites. In other words, it is evident that regions I and II are deflated surfaces and their sands are remnant deposits.

Correlation coefficients for quartz content are $+0\cdot5$ for region I, and $+0\cdot4$ for region II; and for the heavy fraction $-0\cdot7$ for both regions.

The generalized pattern of ρ_{900} for region III indicates a linear decrease from values typical for sands of region I to values typical for sands of region II. This pattern is impossible to explain in paleogeographic terms.

The relief of region III is dominated by the vertical precipice of the Zaunguz plateau to the north. It is known that there are very strong winds from north to south during summer and from the opposite direction during winter; the winter winds being weaker than the summer winds. During winter the desert is wet.

Comparison of the generalized pattern of $\bar{\rho}_{900}$, specific features of the relief and characteristics of wind and moisture action on sands in different seasons indicate that an aeolian accumulative origin of sand for region III is likely.

A check was made on the aeolian origin of the sands of this region. The most characteristic properties of sands determining the behaviour of their particles are the density of particles and their shape. If the size of particles is the same, the density is determined by the specific density of the component minerals. Accordingly, trend surfaces were computed for all minerals over region III. The gradient value for each surface and the influence of the specific density and shape of grains on the gradient values was investigated, using a method of linear hypotheses (Lehmann 1956).

The result of checking indicates that the pattern of concentration of mineral grains in region III is determined by the specific density and the shape of grains. This is additional proof of the aeolian origin of these sands. Thus, the sands of region III are the result of accumulation.

The measured values of ρ_λ of the sandy deposits in a desert can give indications of recent tectonic movement and can help in prospecting for petroleum and gas, and in the search for water.

CONCLUSIONS

An investigation was made to determine if the spectral luminance of sands in Karakum desert could be registered by remote sensing apparatus, and it was shown that the spectral luminance of the sands does indeed reflect the origin of the deposits.

The area can be divided into three parts; regions I and II are deflation surfaces; region III is an area of aeolian accumulation of sands.

Regions I and II are suitable for oil search in petroliferous uplifts by investigation of the surface (natural outcrops). Building of roads and civil building requires precautions because of possible deflation of the area. Agriculture is difficult because deflation of the ground is severe.

Region III is not suitable for search for petroliferous uplifts by field geology methods because the bed-rock is buried under recent aeolian sands which are accumulating all the time. Roads and civil buildings in this region require precautions against burying by sand. There are similar difficulties in agriculture as pastures and wells become covered under accumulating sands.

All these conclusions may be drawn by using only the spectral luminance property of the sand deposits. The spectral luminance factors can be measured by means of special tools from the air. The replacement of ground methods of geological mapping of sand deserts by aerial investigation would very considerably reduce the cost of the investigation.

The author wishes to express her appreciation to Professor A. B. Vistelius for his advice during the development of this project.

REFERENCES

HOBSON, R. D. (1967). Fortran IV programs to determine surface roughness in typography for CDC 3400 computer. *Computer contribution* **14**. The University of Kansas. Lawrence.

LANCZOS, C. (1957). *Applied analysis.* (Prentice Hall: Englewood Cliffs.)

LEHMANN, E. L. (1956). Testing statistical hypotheses (in Russian, retranslated from English.)

MILLER, R. L. (1956). Trend surfaces: their application to analysis and description of environments of sedimentation. *The Journal of Geology* **64**, No. 5, 425.

ROMANOVA, M. A. (1964a). *Air survey of sand deposits by spectral luminance.* Consultants Bureau, New York.

ROMANOVA, M. A. (1964b). Region stability of sand deposits of central Karakums by spectral luminance. *Doklady Akad. Nauk SSSR* **156**, No. 5, 1095.

ROMANOVA, M. A. (1964c). Recent sand deposits of Central Karakum and Search-problem of hidden structures. *Sov. Geol.* **12**,70 (in Russian).

VISTELIUS, A. B., ROMANOVA, M. A. (1964). On the distribution of heavy fraction in the sand deposits of Central Karakum. *Doklady Akad. Nauk SSSR* **158**, No. 5, 860.

VORONKOVA, N. M., MELESHKO, K. E., SEMENCHENKO, I. V., SNYTKIN, A. V., and SHISHKINA, T. A. (1960). A study of the spectral luminance of natural formations. *Geodezia i Kartografia.* No. 11.

Land Evaluation Studies with Remote Sensors in the Infrared and Radar Regions

David S. Simonett

Department of Geography, University of Kansas, U.S.A.

This paper reviews the literature, especially of the last two years, dealing with remote sensor evaluation of surface and shallow sub-surface characteristics, employing remote sensors in the infrared ($1 \cdot 5\mu$–14μ) and radar ($0 \cdot 5$ cm–100 cm) regions. Imaging and non-imaging sensors are examined to assess their current status and possible value in 1) assisting in the mapping of natural plant communities, 2) deriving hydrologic parameters, 3) discriminating among broad land use, crop type and, to a lesser degree, crop state, 4) delineating soil and geomorphic units, and 5) estimating soil moisture. Possible applications of these remote sensors in reconnaissance-scale evaluation of natural resources are considered. The paper leans heavily on unpublished and limited-circulation studies sponsored by the National Aeronautics and Space Administration, U.S.A.

INTRODUCTION

During the last few years the tempo of research and publication in remote sensing has picked up rapidly as the National Aeronautics and Space Administration, U.S.A., has funded a great variety of sensor studies for earth resources evaluation. These studies are, of course, intended to support possible spacecraft sensing, but they have also had the immediate effect of defining more clearly than before both the potentials and practical difficulties, as well as the research frontiers of remote sensing. In this paper two areas where NASA-sponsored research has been substantial – the infrared and radar regions – have been chosen for review.

In the sections which follow the infrared area is treated first and then the radar. For each area a brief sketch of energy-matter interactions is given. Imaging and non-imaging sensors are described, their advantages and disadvantages noted, and the technical state of the art is discussed. Then follows an account of the present status of interpretation in studying natural plant communities, hydrology, land use, geomorphology, soil types, and soil moisture.

In order to make the most effective use of space I have not used infrared and radar images in the report. At the Symposium a number of false colour combination and black and white images will be discussed. Well-illustrated articles to which the reader may refer are those by Colwell (1966, 1968), and Moore and Simonett (1967a).

REMOTE SENSING IN THE INFRARED

In the visible and near infrared-regions of the electromagnetic spectrum (respectively $0 \cdot 4$–$0 \cdot 7\mu$ and $0 \cdot 7$–$1 \cdot 3\mu$) conventional framing cameras and photographic techniques may be used if desired in land evaluation studies. However, in the middle infrared ($1 \cdot 5$–$5 \cdot 5\mu$) and the far infrared ($5 \cdot 5$–$14 \cdot 0\mu$), which are the areas considered here, such methods cannot be used for a number of reasons including the high level of background radiation which would arise from the camera and film itself at ambient temperatures. Consequently, other recording devices are used, of which the most usual is an aircraft-borne optical-mechanical scanner. In such a system the forward motion of the aircraft provides the along-track co-ordinates and across-track dimension is provided by a scanning rotating prism. The instantaneous field of view of the scanner is normally a few milliradians. Successive scans are swept out across-track through the rotation of the prism as the aircraft moves forward, and each scan in a properly functioning system is contiguous or slightly overlaps its neighbour. The energy incident on the prism mirror at various angles from the aircraft sub-point is focussed onto a sensitive detector element and the photon energy is transformed to an electric analog signal which in turn is recorded on magnetic tape, or is used to modulate a glow-tube or cathode-ray tube for direct film recording. One, two, or three channel systems are relatively common and normally direct film record. Multi-channel scanners employing up to about 20 channels also have been developed to cover the region between $0·32\mu$ to 14μ. The incoming energy is beam-split, filtered and directed onto detectors sensitive to each wavelength and the resulting electrical signal is recorded on magnetic tape for direct computer studies of the reflectances and emissions.

In land evaluation studies, aircraft-borne short wavelength ($0·4-2·5\mu$) and long wavelength ($8-14\mu$) radiometer-spectrometers have been virtually unused and unavailable to date. They will, however, be used more extensively in future research in order that better quantitative data may be obtained on the radiometric and spectral quality of different elements of the landscapes, for it is infeasible in a single instrument to optimize spectral, spatial, and radiometric resolution. Imaging systems tend to optimize for spatial and to a lesser degree radiometric resolution and sacrifice spectral resolution. Non-imaging line trace spectrometers and radiometers sacrifice spatial resolution to obtain the spectral and radiometric resolution.

Both reflection and emission are important in the infrared region. Solar reflection on the skirts of the solar radiation curve is important in daylight to about $3·5\mu$, and is negligible beyond. Between $3·5-5·5\mu$ earth glow also is modest, hence this is a useful region for forest fire detection. The peak of the earth-glow emission lies near 10μ. Atmospheric water vapour absorption blanks out the region between 14μ and 1 mm for terrestrial remote sensing.

Many fundamental vibrational resonances occur in the infrared region such as those for water vapour ($2·66$, $2·74$, and $6·3\mu$) and the SI-O bond of the silicate minerals near 10μ. Information related to the composition of some substances is thus potentially available in the infrared region through emission spectroscopy. The most active worker in this region is R. J. P. Lyon (Lyon 1967; Vickers and Lyon 1967) who has studied the emission spectra of a wide variety of rocks. Further research is needed in the practical application of this technique to land evaluation.

Since there are substantial differences in the thermal inertia of substances, this property also lends itself to remote sensing use in the infrared. The daily cycle of thermal response provides information which is related to composition (such as bulk density and contained moisture content) and several flights through the course of a day may enable these qualities to be estimated.

The relatively high energy levels, the spatial, spectral, and radiometric (thermal) resolutions available, and the vibrational, rotational, and thermal interactions available in the infrared region give reason for believing this will be a most attractive area for remote sensing applications. It is, however, at present a complex area, for unambiguous quantitative answers are few – being restricted to the simplest cases such as forest fire surveillance in the $4 \cdot 5$–$5 \cdot 5 \mu$ band, which is now operational (Wilson 1966) – and much research lies ahead before operational infrared systems can be used in tackling earth resource problems. As Buettner, Kern, and Cronin (1964) note, the effects of actual temperature differences, of variations in emissivity, and of atmospheric inter- ferences are of about equal orders of magnitude in influencing the energies recorded in the infrared. They could well have added that the natural variances of plants, soils, and water both in space and time through different days, weeks, seasons, and years are at least equal in order of magnitude to the other variables. The extremely variable state of the atmosphere both vertically and horizontally makes infrared imagery difficult to use for quantitative purposes. Pertinent observations may be found in Menon and Ragotzkie (1967) and Blythe and Kurath (1967).

Far-infrared imaging systems currently available and declassified in the United States have resolutions of about 3 milliradians. When used at the normal photographic mapping altitudes of 10, 20, and 30 thousand ft a 3 milliradian system would have respective spatial resolutions of 30, 60, and 90 ft. These resolutions are notably inferior to those obtained with 6 in. focal length cameras at the same altitudes and many objects of both natural and cultural interest simply cannot be effectively resolved. While there is no theoretical reason why these resolutions cannot be improved, probably one milliradian resolution is about all that we ought to look forward to for some time. Unlike framing camera systems from which all data can be brought to equivalent planimetry, infrared line-scan imagery has geometric distortions which make multiple images taken at different time and in different directions exceedingly difficult to bring to a compatible planimetric format (Derenyi and Konecny 1964), yet diurnal imagery is needed for full use of infrared.

To the degree that multiple wavelengths obtained at the same time can substitute for the temporal information available from a single wavelength used several times in the course of a day or a season, a multiple-wavelength scanning system such as that developed at the University of Michigan (Donald Lowe, personal communication) and which records all channels on tape in compatible geometry may overcome in part this geometric problem. The University of Michigan 18-channel scanner is interesting in a number of respects: 13 of the channels lie in the visible, near ultraviolet, and near infrared regions, while the remaining 5 lie in the infrared regions in the wavelength bands $1 \cdot 5$–$1 \cdot 7 \mu$, 2–$2 \cdot 6 \mu$, 3–$4 \cdot 1 \mu$, $4 \cdot 5$–$5 \cdot 5 \mu$, and $8 \cdot 2$–14μ. In addition, unlike most infrared imagery, there are provisions for some calibration of the radiometric quantities involved in the analogue signal.

Practical resolutions from spacecraft are likely to lie in the range of several hundred feet at least for the next decade. Consequently infrared imagery from spacecraft will properly be addressed to problems of large spatial dimensions and it is not appropriate to look to it for a solution of problems requiring detailed resolution. The key technical reference for this area is Wolfe (1965).

Studies of Natural Plant Communities and Their State

Surprisingly little work has been done with infrared in studies of natural vegetation. Part of this arises from the fact that a good deal of infrared imagery has been flown at night and, as Blythe and Kurath (1967) note, since leaf temperatures at night tend to be close to local air temperature, trees in leaf look brighter than shorter plants irrespective of whether the tree is a conifer or deciduous or of the type of lower plants. They do however note that in 'summer-time images of adjacent stands of conifers and deciduous trees during the daytime, conifers appear to be brighter than adjacent deciduous trees'. They also note that, while boundaries between plant communities are commonly visible in midday thermal infrared imagery, differences between tree types within these communities is not easily detectable on the infrared images. This was true despite the fact that considerable ground information was available for the images they studied. It is fair to say that tree species cannot be dif-ferentiated at present with the thermal infrared line scanner because of inadequate spatial resolution and inadequate reflectance and emittance data.

Most spectral reflectance measurements in the literature are laboratory data with single leaves. While such data may accurately predict the response by several species when imaged there is no guarantee that this will be the case, for as Myers et al. (1966b) have demonstrated, this could lead to misleading interpretations, especially in the longer wavelengths, where layers of leaves have a very different response to a single leaf. C. E. Olson (personal com-munication) has also found that there are substantial differences between species in this regard, leathery leaves such as some oaks or rhododendrons giving a much higher percent reflectance from a single leaf than, say, a cotton leaf. There is a pressing need for spectral measurements obtained from aircraft using short and long wavelength radiometer-spectrometers of the type developed by R. J. P. Lyon of Stanford University (Lyon 1967).

Spectral reflectance studies by Olson (1964) in late August, 1963, showed that in the near infrared region and portions of the middle infrared region the leaves of white ash (*Fraxinus americana*), black oak (*Quercus velutina*), black cherry (*Prunus seratina*), shag bark hickory (*Carya ovata*), Norway spruce (*Picea excelsa*), and Austrian pine (*Pinus nigra*) all show the same pattern of reflectance and only Norway spruce of this group is sufficiently less reflective to have a chance of being discriminated from the other species. The results of aircraft flights at the same time agreed with the laboratory studies.

Colwell and Shay (1965) report an analysis of multispectral tone signatures given of 10 vegetation trafficability types, in and near Mud Lake Bog, Michigan, at 11 a.m., June 26, 1963. A six-channel scanner with 3 channels in the $2-2 \cdot 6$, $4 \cdot 5 - 5 \cdot 5$, and $8 - 14\mu$ bands was used. They found much the same results were obtained in the $4 \cdot 5 - 5 \cdot 5$ as in the $8 - 14\mu$ band, and that there was a tendency for different vegetation types to group their response in pairs or triplets. How-ever, in the $2 - 2 \cdot 6\mu$ band there was a wide spread in tone signatures between various swamp types.

Carneggie, Poulton, and Roberts (1967) found considerable redundancy between the 18 channels of the University of Michigan scanner when used to detect soil and natural vegetation boundaries. The most useful information lay in the following bands: $0 \cdot 32 - 0 \cdot 38$, $0 \cdot 62 - 0 \cdot 68$, $0 \cdot 8 - 1 \cdot 0$, $1 \cdot 5 - 1 \cdot 8$, and $8 - 14\mu$. More soil-vegetation boundaries were distinguished in the $0 \cdot 62 - 0 \cdot 68\mu$ band than in any other; moist meadow sites were best distinguished in the $0 \cdot 8 - 1 \cdot 0\mu$ band; and wet soils, marsh, and narrow streams obscured by vegeta-tion were best determined in the $8 - 14\mu$ band. Many areas of wet soils observed in the latter could not be seen on any other band. Finally, they found that occasional vegetation and soil boundaries were seen in the $0 \cdot 32 - 0 \cdot 38$ and $1 \cdot 5 - 1 \cdot 8\mu$ band.

Early work by C. E. Olson (personal communication) in the $8 - 14\mu$ band suggested that imagery of trees taken during the maximum thermal and trans-piration load in the early afternoon should produce different responses from healthy trees with an abundance of water for transpiration, and those which are under moisture stress caused by insect attack, plant pathogens, or drought. Continued tests of this possibility are being made by Heller *et al.* (1967) and Weber and Olson (1967). Working with poisoned red pine Weber (1965) found that elevation of leaf temperatures from 3 to 5°C occurred under the high radiation load in the middle of the afternoon. The practical application of this information is at present hindered because of poor scanner spatial resolution, and Heller *et al.* (1967) found that tree crowns within a forest canopy could not be distinguished on thermal imagery as to whether they were healthy or dying. They found that (in mid-June) in South Dakota, 'the foliage temperatures of dying trees were 6° to 8°C higher than healthy trees at 1000 hours; the difference was slightly less at 1400 hours (4° to 6°C)'. Detectors in optical-mechanical scanners are capable of discriminating temperature differences this small; however, the resolution cell at safe aircraft operating altitudes in hilly regions is usually larger in area than the dying tree crowns which are surrounded by cooler healthy trees. They also found in this study of Black Hills beetle (*Dendroctonus ponderosae* Hopk.) infestation of *Pinus ponderosa* that radiometer readings showed consistently higher temperature readings from those infested trees which subsequently died than from those which did not.

Thus, while it is still not possible to predict the location of low vigour trees from previsual thermal symptoms with airborne imagery, there seems to be good grounds for believing that it may be feasible with infrared scanners with better spatial resolution.

Myers *et al.* (1967) found that, when plant leaves slowly dried in plants under severe moisture stress, reflectances increased at all wavelengths, probably as a response to shrinking and increased density of leaf and to changes in refractive index discontinuities. However, leaves dried in the laboratory or on a forest floor may respond differently (V. I. Myers, personal communication; Olson 1967a). In his study of fine forest fuels Olson found that not all bands respond equally. At $1\cdot55\mu$ and at $2\cdot05\mu$ he recorded a slight but steady increase in reflectance with drying in the moisture range 330%–20% (oven-dry basis). At $2\cdot5\mu$ the reflectance curve is flat from 330 to 250% contained moisture and then increases rapidly. Since the $2\cdot5\mu$ band lies near the fundamental vibration frequency for water vapour ($2\cdot66\mu$), this is probably a response to reduced absorption.

In a study of sycamore and yellow poplar seedlings Weber and Olson (1967) discovered that 'in all cases the level of water stress at the time of leaf formation and development appeared to exert a greater influence on foliar reflectance (in the near and mid IR region) than did the level of water stress at the time the reflectance measurements were made'. The implications of this research are many for remote sensing and this study must be extended and repeated with other species, situations, and ages of plants.

Land Use, Crop Discrimination, and Crop State Studies

Important remote sensing studies are being made at the Laboratory for Agricultural Remote Sensing at Purdue University, and at the U.S.D.A. Weslaco Agricultural Experiment Station, Texas. Those by Myers and his colleagues at Weslaco on plants under stress will be discussed first. Myers *et al.* (1967) note that reflectance from plants affected by drought, salinity, disease, and other factors is complex. This arises because not all parts of the plant react in the same manner. Russian studies quoted by Myers and his co-workers indicate that the upper leaves of the plant, which are the ones detected by aerial sensors, keep in good shape the longest by drawing water from leaves positioned lower, as a result of which, the latter are the first to wilt or dry up during a drought. In orchard crops the upper leaves also draw water from the fruit rudiment as well as from the lower leaves. Thus, drought may cause failure of the fruit crop while the upper leaves are perhaps still not registering stress in thermal imagery.

Myers *et al.* (1966a, 1966b) measured plant leaf temperatures as a method for studying the energy budgets of agricultural areas, for estimating soil moisture, and for detecting the occurrence and extent of soil salinity. They found that leaves from cotton plants affected and unaffected by salinity have contrasting reflectances in the range from $0 \cdot 5$–$2 \cdot 5\mu$. These contrasts may provide the means for remote prediction and differentiation of moisture and salinity stress.

C. L. Wiegand and L. N. Nanken presented data at the American Society of Agronomy meetings in Columbus, Ohio, in 1965 on the range of temperatures in cotton leaves under moisture stress. These were evaluated through variations in relative turgidity between 1430 and 1500 CST, the time of maximum daily plant moisture stress. Under the conditions of the experiment they found that cotton leaves exhibited symptoms of wilt at 70–72% relative turgidity. With a relative turgidity of 82% a leaf temperature of $36 \cdot 5°C$ was obtained and with a relative turgidity of 58% a leaf temperature of 40°C was obtained. The slope of the best fit regression line was $-0 \cdot 15°C$ per percent relative turgidity.

In a valuable recent study of crops on the Purdue University Agricultural Experiment fields, Hoffer (1967) discusses the variations in multispectral response patterns of different crops and soils at various times during the growing season. Numerous examples are given of different responses in each wavelength for the various crops, including striking differences in response between, for example, corn and soybeans in the $1 \cdot 5$–$1 \cdot 7$, $2 \cdot 0$–$2 \cdot 6$, and $3 \cdot 0$–$4 \cdot 1\mu$ bands at a time of the year — July 29, 1964 — when the photographic and thermal infrared portions of the spectrum showed little, if any, differentiation.

Other significant observations by Hoffer include the following:

1. There is not necessarily a direct correspondence between ground-measured temperatures of crops and thermal infrared scanner response.

2. 'Analysis of many pieces of multispectral imagery in many wavelength bands indicates that a capability exists to differentiate and perhaps identify various crops species or crop categories by remote sensing. The key is to obtain multispectral data at the proper period of crop development and at intervals throughout the growing season.'

3. A major variable in response patterns is the proportion of soil covered by the crop canopy — that is, the relationship between crop cover and bare soil as observed from above. 'From a limited number of situations studied, it would appear that very early in the growing season radar and thermal infrared imagery may be more useful than visible or infrared photography in differentiating between field crops in early developing stages, and fields of bare soil.'

4. Stage of maturity causes considerable variation in reflectance within a crop species.

5. During the period of active growth of crops it is difficult to discriminate between crops because the reflectance curves — from $0 \cdot 32\mu$ to $2 \cdot 6\mu$ — for green leaves 'had about the same shape and differences among the species were small'.

6. A number of researchers have found the photographic infrared portion of the spectrum very useful in detecting certain crop diseases, because of the common reduction in reflectance in the near infrared regions as a result of

plant stress. The Purdue studies, however, have shown virtually no difference in reflectance between diseased and non-diseased crops. Rather, the difference in response arises because the diseased plants were severely dwarfed and allowed more soil to be exposed causing a lower response in the diseased plots.

7. Moiré patterns in row crops obtained with a line scan infrared image flown at modest altitudes above the crop can be used to obtain information on row direction, row width, and general crop category. However, moiré patterns severely affect the spectral response determination of an area.

8. 'Multispectral reflectances may not be the same on a given date from year to year, even for the same geographic region'. This was the case for corn and soybean imagery near the end of August, 1964 and 1965.

The key comment in Hoffer's paper is the variation on a year-to-year basis in the multispectral response pattern for various crops. This clearly implies a need to build up an empirical catalogue of seasonal response patterns so that these annual and seasonal variations may be taken into account in a probability model for crop identification.

Another useful report by the Purdue group is that by Shay et al. (1967). Detailed work with the University of Michigan 18-channel scanner is reported, including quantitative analysis of the 1964 multispectral imagery using statistical pattern recognition techniques. They report a range of correct recognitions of oats, wheat, alfalfa, various soil types, soybeans, corn, wheat stubble, etc. For various groups of crops, identifications ranged between 99% correct recognition to a low of 87% correct recognition. These exceedingly encouraging results for multispectral identification of crops required the use of the wavelength bands in the middle and far infrared as well as those in the visible and photographic near infrared regions to ensure discrimination.

Another useful part of this report is a series of cross tabulation plots of responses from crops for one wavelength against another. As might be expected adjacent wavelengths in the visible region had very high correlation with one another. For example, that between $0 \cdot 53$–$0 \cdot 57\mu$ and $0 \cdot 62$–$0 \cdot 68\mu$ are very closely correlated, as are those between $1 \cdot 4$–$1 \cdot 9\mu$ and $1 \cdot 6$–$1 \cdot 8\mu$. However, the cross tabulation plot of the wavelengths $0 \cdot 53$–$0 \cdot 57\mu$ versus $1 \cdot 2$–$1 \cdot 25\mu$ showed very little correlation indicating that with sufficient wavelength separation truly orthogonal parameters are being evaluated.

Lyon (1967) has obtained detailed field spectra of a number of crops at the Davis test farm of the University of California, employing a short wavelength spectrometer in the region $0 \cdot 75$–$2 \cdot 1\mu$. Stepwise discriminant analysis of these data indicated that one single wavelength ($1 \cdot 05\mu$) was all that was necessary with 99 spectra to make a 97% decision out of 5 crop possibilities including wheat.

Broader land use evaluations with $4 \cdot 5$–$5 \cdot 5\mu$ imagery of a type of interest in reconnaissance surveys may be found in Olson (1967b).

Hydrology and Soil Moisture

Studies in California by Draeger (1967), in Indiana by Hoffer (1967), and by Myers and Heilman (in press) in Texas have demonstrated conclusively that variations in the moisture content of bare soils notably affects the daily cycle of their response in the 8–14μ band.

In the Weslaco, Texas studies, even though soils were equally dry on the immediate surface, variations in water content (Myers and Heilman, in press) in the shallow sub-surface and to depths as much as 50 cm were detectable with diurnal imagery. As would be expected, moist soils having a large thermal inertia show a damped response throughout the day.

Myers and Heilman believe that the daily temperature oscillations can be a good indicator of gross soil moisture conditions of significance to farm management in irrigated and dry farming regions. They found that soils at Weslaco, which were relatively dry, had an oscillation between 45 and 51°C and adjacent moister fields had oscillations between 40 and 42°C. They also suggested that negative heat exchange during the cooling phase of the daily cycle and in the fall months would be helpful not only in giving information on subsurface moisture content, but on the variations in physical properties of the soils at depth.

While much additional work will be needed to bring infrared sensing of bare soils to the stage of semi-quantitative estimation of soil moisture, the results obtained to date are sufficiently encouraging that we may reasonably hope that operational systems for this purpose will eventually be developed.

Estes (1966) and others have reported detection of buried stream channels on infrared imagery. Wallace and Moxham (1966) found that infrared imagery of the San Andreas Fault showed moisture held back along the fault zone in a semi-arid to arid environment. Flights at several times a day over potential irrigation areas may aid in the detection of water-bearing channels and thereby improve irrigation prospects substantially. However, much experimentation will be needed before such a water divining tool is perfected.

A potentially important application of spacecraft in semi-arid areas is monitoring the path of heavy rain storms during the break of the monsoon season. To some degree almost any sensor, be it photography, infrared, micro-wave, or radar, will sense major storm boundaries after the fact. The well-known Gemini photograph of the high plains of Texas analyzed by Hope (1966), for example, shows the path of heavy rainfall photographed from space. A Nimbus high-resolution infrared scanning system should be able to do equally as well scanning in the 8–14μ band. At the same time preliminary studies by Cato et al. (1967) and Moore and Simonett (1967a) suggest that spacecraft-borne passive microwave and radar systems may perhaps detect rain falling over land.

The ultimate possibility also arises of using a number (perhaps three) of sun synchronous Nimbus infrared or passive microwave satellites of modest resolution following one another in orbit, but separated by eight hours (2 p.m., 10 p.m., 6 a.m.). Such space vehicles following the same path could well be used to monitor the state of moisture changes in semi-arid irrigated or pasture lands. While quantitative detection and identification using thermal infrared is fraught with many difficulties, the ability to detect *change* and to derive valuable qualitative and semi-quantitative data from short-term changes is both feasible and reasonable.

Additional hydrologic roles which infrared imagery may fulfill include: (1) seeking sites of ground water discharge into marine coastal waters as documented in Hawaii by Fischer et al. (1964), and Fischer, Davis, and Sousa (1966) who mapped 219 springs along the shoreline with infrared images; (2) in studying effluence both natural and artificial (Moxham 1967); and (3) in studying flood, tide, and salt damage along inundated coastlines.

REMOTE SENSING IN THE RADAR REGION

Imaging radars with characteristics suitable for land evaluation surveys have been developed in the past two decades. Because most of the images produced in the past by these radars have not been available to the scientific community, their potential in resource surveys is not recognized widely.

The kind of radar which has the greater application in such surveys is side-looking airborne radar. Such radar produces a continuous-strip image that looks much like a continuous strip photograph taken from a very high altitude. Unlike a photograph or an infrared scan image, however, the area imaged is not below the aircraft, but rather extends from a short distance out to the side to a considerably larger distance away from the aircraft.

Figure 1 and the following description after Moore and Simonett (1967a) shows the operation of a side-looking airborne radar. The antenna directs its energy at right angles to the flight path. A short pulse is transmitted. The signal

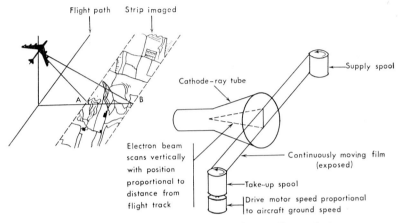

Fig. 1. Side-looking airborne radar and recording technique.

first returns from a region at the inner edge of the illuminated area. The strength of the signal determines the brightness of a dot on a cathode ray tube. As time goes on, the return signals come from further and further away. During this time, the position of the spot on the cathode ray tube is changed in synchronism with the time delay or with the ground range until, at the time the signal is returning from the farthest point illuminated, the spot on the cathode ray tube has moved from the bottom to the top of the tube. Since the spot brightness is determined by the strength of the signal received from the different portions of the ground, the density of film exposed to this spot is also proportional to the signal intensity. Hence, a line on the film has been exposed whose density is proportional to the 'brightness' of the radar signal from the different points to the side of the aircraft. By the time the next pulse is transmitted the film has advanced slightly and so has the aircraft. Hence, a new line on the film is exposed and the film density is proportional to the 'brightness' of the area to the side of the new position of the aircraft. Thus, as the aircraft advances the film advances and a continuous picture is produced. As is true in the infrared region this information could be recorded on tape, though film recording is much the most usual technique.

Because radar is an active remote sensor, it is not limited to the resolutions imposed at first sight by its long wavelengths. Side-looking radar systems by a variety of methods, including use of short pulses, can readily achieve across-track or range resolutions of 50 ft. Short wavelength (say 1 cm) diffraction-limited systems usually have about $0 \cdot 1°$ to $0 \cdot 2°$ angular azimuth or long-track resolution. Thus, when such systems are flown at modest altitudes and look only a short distance to the side of the aircraft they also may obtain along-track resolutions of 50 ft. However, with higher altitudes, longer path lengths, longer wavelengths, and short antennas, resolutions of from 300 to 600 ft in azimuth are common.

To obviate this difficulty and to enable the use of much longer wavelengths, and also to reduce the size of antennas so as not to affect the stability of aircraft, synthetic aperture radar systems have been developed. In synthetic aperture systems the phase as well as the amplitude of the returning pulse are stored and are later put together in a computer as if they were produced by an antenna a great deal larger than the aircraft. By this means finer resolution is achieved along-track than can be obtained with a 'brute force' or 'real aperture' diffraction-limited system.

The radar echo intensity that determines the brightness of an image is proportional to four basic factors: the geometry of the material imaged; its dielectric properties; the radar wavelength employed; and the polarization of the transmitted and received energy. Materials having large flat surfaces cause strong signals when the radar beam is perpendicular to the surface and weak signals at other angles. Very rough surfaces – roughness, say, equal to or greater than the wavelength employed – give signals more nearly independent of the angle at which radiation strikes them.

The dielectric properties determine both the strength of the signal produced by a given material and the amount of absorption experienced by this signal in passing through the material. The absorption is primarily influenced by the conductivity, and the signal returned by the permittivity. The latter is most influenced by water which has the highest permittivity commonly found in nature. Thus, the moisture content of plants and soils can be an important factor in the strength of the signal and hence the brightness of the image, although the roughness of the vegetation mantle is normally much the most important single factor with short wavelength radar.

The wavelengths used range from 0·5 cm to 60 cm or longer. Those shorter than 3 cm may be used for real aperture systems, while synthetic apertures may cover the whole range. In this wavelength range radar signals penetrate slightly moist to dry substances a distance of perhaps the order of the wavelength employed. Consequently the information in the return signal is not exclusively surficial as is the case in the visible region. Thus, different information is to be expected from different radar wavelengths both from this penetration effect and the differential effect of various roughnesses.

Polarization of radar waves has turned out to be a useful discriminent in crop and land use studies. The radar wave is said to be polarized in the direction of its electric field vector. An object permitting current to flow in the direction of the electric field vector will give a stronger return than one for which such current flow is difficult. Thus vertical polarization may be expected to emphasize trees with straight trunks and few secondary limbs better than horizontal polarization and so on. Most surfaces also tend to depolarize the wave to some extent but not all to the same extent; that is, an incident horizontally polarized wave is returned with both horizontal and vertical components, of varying intensity. Thus, there is merit in employing radar systems with the capacity to transmit alternate horizontal or vertical polarization pulses and to receive both polarizations. In this article the convention is followed that the transmitted polarization and received polarization are given as abbreviations in that order, i.e., HV is horizontal transmit, vertical receive.

There are several major advantages to be noted with radar systems. First, they are unaffected by clouds and by all except the heaviest of storms, but, even more importantly, the atmosphere makes virtually no contributions to the radar return signals. Since, in addition, the quantity of energy transmitted is known, radar has a unique opportunity for quantitatively handling terrain reflectances which is not available in any other portion of the spectrum or in passive systems. The radar back scattered return from terrain targets which are areally extensive and which do not contain point high reflectors such as metal objects, corners of buildings and so on, unambiguously represent the back scattering properties unaffected by the atmosphere.

The necessity for retaining accurate phase as well as amplitude information with synthetic aperture radar systems has led to the development of very accurate inertial control devices so that it is possible to construct almost planimetric quality synthetic aperture radar imagery over areas of slight relief. Finally, the side-looking illumination mode emphasizes relatively minor terrain features and has therefore proven useful in certain geologic and geo-morphic studies.

The disadvantages of imaging radar systems are several. First, the side-looking nature of these systems means that the data cannot be obtained at the same instant or in the same geometric format as that of either optical-mechanical scanners or framing cameras. The point-by-point pattern recognition approach that becomes feasible with the Michigan multi-band scanning system between $0 \cdot 32 \mu$ and 14μ cannot be made compatible with the point-by-point output of imaging radar systems. Second, relief displacements are opposite to those in the optical region. There is, consequently, an inevitable tendency to regard radar systems as being set apart from the other systems. Multiple-frequency and multiple-polarization radars are, however, as a group capable of being made mutually compatible and multi-spectral pattern recognition is quite feasible with multiple radar systems carried on the same aircraft. Finally, since the long wavelengths make for much specular reflection, cultural objects tend to show severe scintillation, target breakup, and a general graininess to the image not found with broad band, i.e., panchromatic, images in which there is much frequency averaging. Studies are underway at the University of Kansas employing broad band, non-imaging, and imaging systems to help overcome this problem.

Studies of Natural Plant Communities and their State

A number of studies on the effect of natural vegetation on radar returns have been made with two-polarization K-band imagery in various environments in the United States, and in all areas some influence of vegetation on radar returns was observed.

The methods which my colleagues and I are using in our vegetation studies include the familiar analysis of tone and texture together with more sophisticated analysis using a multiple Image Discrimination Enhancement Combination and Sampling System (IDECS) developed at the University of Kansas. Operations presently possible with the IDECS system include tri-colour image combinations, gray-scale level selection, automatic texture discrimination, signature selection, generation of probability density functions, and various differentiation and other enhancement techniques. The IDECS system is naturally more applicable to area-extensive flat or gently sloping uniform targets such as the fields in an agricultural area and is difficult to employ in studies of natural vegetation.

Our studies to date indicate that multiple-polarization K-band radar is sufficiently crude both in resolution and discrimination between natural plant communities that it is suited best for gross-scale reconnaissance studies. This is not to say, however, that broad band radar, and additional frequencies and polarizations will not contain additional information. It is quite feasible, for example, that long wavelength radar systems may well contain information relating to the spatial periodicities and densities of trees in plant communities and might thus usefully supplement other methods for estimating timber volumes. I hasten to add that this is at the moment nothing more than a possibility and it needs much thorough analysis.

In summary form, radar appears to have a possible role in:

1. Preparation of small-scale regional or reconnaissance maps of vegetation type, especially when there are pronounced structural differences between plant communities.

2. Delimiting vegetation zones that vary with elevation.

3. Tracing burn patterns of previous forest fires.

4. Delimiting the altitudinal timber line.

5. Identification of species by inference in areas characterized by monospecific stands.

6. Possible discrimination of structural sub-types in cutover, burned, and regrowth forests.

7. Deriving estimates of vegetation density in sparsely vegetated areas.

8. Supplementing very high altitude low-resolution photography in which textural differences related to vegetation are weakly expressed.

Some of these are likely to be more successful than others, but all are worthy of further study. Details will be found in Simonett and Morain (1965), Morain and Simonett (1966), Morain (1967), and Morain and Simonett (1967).

A number of general comments should be made about the use of radar imagery in studying plant communities. Because the radar return is markedly influenced by major variations in topography, radar imagery is not suited for use in mountainous regions. R. N. Colwell and associates have found it of quite limited use, for example, in their studies at Buck's Lake in California. We have also found that logged and cutover areas on the Oregon coast simply cannot be distinguished from high forest because of the slope of the terrain and the radar look-angles involved. For this reason those environments where radar is likely to be most sensitive to vegetation differences are regions which have pronounced seasonal contrasts and are relatively flat, such as the great sweeps of the tropical savannas or the arctic plain of North America, and in which notably disjunct lithology and ground moisture states are juxtaposed. However, to date no such imagery has been obtained or interpreted.

Land Use, Crop Discrimination, and Crop State Studies

Because different crop types and varieties are planted at various times, are subjected to diverse life experiences and mature at different dates, there is considerable natural variance in reflectance and emission in all parts of the electromagnetic spectrum. For these reasons it will be necessary to obtain remote sensor imagery at several times throughout the agricultural cycle in a given region. Given multiple-frequency, multiple-polarization radar images at several times throughout a growing season, I am reasonably sanguine that radar will prove to be a useful tool in the mapping of broad land use categories, in statistical pattern recognition studies, in crop discrimination including semi-automation, and even to some degree ultimately in perhaps discriminating crop state. While in effect expressing my faith in long-term potential of radar for such studies in the future it is necessary to emphasize that very little work has been done to date. The most detailed studies are those with a K-band multiple-polarization flown twice (1965 and 1966) in a single test area near Garden City, Kansas. Despite the paucity of available data the results of the Garden City studies (Simonett *et al.* 1967; D. E. Schwarz and F. C. Caspall, unpublished manuscript; and F. Caspall, R. Haralick, R. K. Moore and D. S. Simonett, unpublished manuscript) are very encouraging.

Seven types of agricultural information gathering ranging from simple to very complex are of potential interest for remote sensing application. These involve:
1. Delineation of field boundaries.
2. Detecting the presence of different crops.
3. Determining the acreage of different crops.
4. Determining which crops are actually present.
5. Determining the vigour of crops.
6. Determining the agent responsible for any loss of crop vigour.
7. Predicting yields.

Research to date with radar has dealt with items 1, 2, and 3 and a fair amount of success is indicated. In the Western Kansas test site, 85% of the fields were detected as being separate using flights in August and September of 1965. Quite possibly flights at a different time of year would have distinguished many more fields since in September (and even to some extent in August) many fields had been harvested and look much alike to radar or photography. The results of this study are:

Total Number of Fields in Test Area: 419	Number of Fields Identified	% of Fields Differentiated or Added	Total % Fields Separated on Imagery
September – HH imagery	267	64	64
Added by Sept. HV imagery	16	4	68
Added by Aug. HH imagery	38	9	77
Adjacent fields – same crop	34	8	85

No comparative study has been made to differentiate these fields on photographs.

The K-band radar used was able to distinguish sugar beets from corn with a 97% probability, and corn from all other crops with a probability of 87% during September. Bare or essentially bare ground could be distinguished with a probability of 93%. Hoffer (1967) also found bare ground appeared to be distinguishable at Purdue. Grain sorghum, wheat, and alfalfa however are hard to distinguish at that time of year.

Further study of various parameters influencing the return showed the following results:
1. Percent ground cover strongly influences the return.
2. Crop height makes a substantial contribution to the return, particularly after cover is nearly 100%.
3. Crop moisture may add to the variations in return, the difference being a function of crop type.
4. Soil moisture may also influence the radar return, although in general, because soils moistened through irrigation tend to be smoother than dry-farmed fields, the relation is masked by the effects of differential surface roughness.

Statistical pattern recognition studies on radar images of crops are also under way at the University of Kansas. Electronic circuits have been built to perform a number of algorithms in adaptive signature recognition (Haralick

1967) and Bayesian decision theory techniques (Dalke 1966) for use with the IDECS system.

Drainage Nets

Little work has yet been done in application of radar images to hydrologic problems. Preliminary study by McCoy (1967) of radar as a tool for drainage basin analysis shows considerable promise. The large areal coverage and abundance of land form detail available on radar images make them especially suitable for such studies. Twenty-eight basins were analyzed by McCoy and the results of the radar analysis were compared with hydrologic data obtained from a 1 : 24,000 scale map. The same methods of stream ordering, counting, measuring, and data handling were applied to map and radar drainage displays. The radar imagery shows a substantial number but not all first-order streams. Correlation and regression analysis therefore was used to determine the actual relationship between the radar data and topographic map data. As a result it was found that drainage area, basin perimeter, bifurcation ratio, average length ratio, and circularity ratio can be measured from radar and map-derived values. Correlation between lengths of streams or drainage basin areas as determined on 1 : 24,000 scale topographic maps and the radar imagery was very high (r = 0·98).

Though monoscopic radar images were used in McCoy's study, observation of terrain slope angles was possible using two different radar views on the same slope. The regional slope was the same using map data or radar data on 35 sample slopes (r = 0·99, 1 S.E.E. = 2·9°). Automatic interpretation techniques were applied to the imagery by means of edge enhancement and line-scanner counter systems. The experiments show a promising correlation between the total enhanced line length of a drainage basin and the total stream length measured from a topographic map. These relationships may provide a useful means for rapid analysis of large drainage areas. The results are sufficiently promising that further testing is under way.

Reconnaissance Geology, Geomorphology, and Soil Mapping
with Radar Imagery

Fracture trace and lineament maps obtained from air photos have proven valuable in many phases of hydrogeologic and mining exploration.

In some cases, in the identification of faults and lineaments, radar has proven to be superior to conventional aerial photography (Dellwig, Kirk, and Walters 1966; MacDonald, Brennan, and Dellwig 1967). Gross resolution, X-band, radar imagery of the southern Boston Mountains in Arkansas, for example, shows a series of pronounced, north-trending linear features which exert a marked control on the topography. These linear features were not detected on either air photos or in detailed geologic mapping. Kover (in press) reports on unpublished studies by the U.S. Geological Survey that major lineaments and other structures not previously known to exist even in well-mapped areas were found with radar imagery. Many unmapped lineaments have been located on radar images of the Ouachita Mountains in Arkansas and Oklahoma (J. N. Kirk, personal communication). These have been noted on images from five different radar systems, obtained at different times and with different flight paths. The reality of the lineaments thus appears well established. In areas of very low relief it has been noted by Rydstrom (1967) that minor topographic expression of deep-seated faults and other structures not normally detected on air photographs, may be observed on radar images when the illumination angle is near grazing. A close correlation has been found between lineaments detected on aerial photographs and radar near Lawrence, Kansas (H. C. MacDonald, personal communication). However, more lineaments were noted on the radar imagery than on the photographs and certain long lineaments seen on the radar appeared as small segments only in the photographs. The detection by radar of lineaments is not uniformly so successful, however, as observed in a study in Pennsylvania by Wise (1967).

Thin sand veneers have been detected with radar imagery which were not evident on air photographs, and this has been confirmed in an unpublished USGS study referenced by Kover (in press). Differences between alluvial drainages in a complex bajada at Pisgah Crater, California, were better detected on radar than on photographs and cross-polarization added significantly to the detection of some lava-alluvial contacts (Dellwig and Moore 1966). Radar imagery has also been shown to be very sensitive to micro and meso surface roughness in flat playa lakes as a function both of the wavelength of the radar and the penetrating capabilities of the radar system (Ellermeier, Simonett, and Dellwig 1967). In Arizona radar and photographs each contained information the other lacked: a major fault and certain soil texture differences were better expressed on the radar image than on the photo (MacDonald, Brennan, and Dellwig 1967). Several geologists have noted a number of areas where cross-polarized radar images emphasize certain volcanic rocks. No single explanation appears to account for this feature and further studies are under way (Gillerman 1967).

Numerous additional references to geologic and other studies are to be found in a radar bibliography for geoscientists prepared by Walters (1967).

In regard to the use of radar in soil reconnaissance mapping, Simonett (in press) found in northern Oklahoma that 'the information obtainable from . . . radar imagery for soil mapping is distinctly uneven in both distribution and quality for, while it is sometimes possible to make clear distinctions between adjacent soils even at the series level, and more usually at the association level, there are many instances when neither is feasible. Separation of soil groups at the association level is more likely in untilled and sub-humid to arid regions, than in cultivated or densely forested humid lands. To put these conclusions in another way, where extreme differences occur in adjoining plant structures, in soil or plant moisture content, in soil texture, in topography and – in areas of scanty vegetation – small-scale surface roughness, then discrimination on the radar image of soil units closely tied to these differences will usually be possible. Lesser differences will not be so easily detected, especially in cultivated areas, and careful timing of aircraft flights to coincide with the greatest seasonal vegetation contrasts will be necessary.',

I wish to acknowledge with gratitude the open-handed generosity with which a number of active workers in remote sensing have made their ideas, and unpublished and limited circulation papers available to me in preparing this review, in particular R. N. Colwell and colleagues at the University of California, Berkeley; C. E. Olson and colleagues at the University of Michigan; V. Myers and associates at the U.S.D.A. Agriculture Experiment Station, Weslaco, Texas; and R. J. P. Lyon, Stanford University.
This review was supported by U.S. Geological Survey Contract No. 14-08-0001-10848.

REFERENCES

BLYTHE, R., and KURATH, E. (1967). Infrared and water vapor. *Photogramm. Engng* **33**, 772–7.

BUETTNER, K. J., KERN, C. D., and CRONIN, J. F. (1964). The consequences of terrestrial surface infrared emissivity. *Third Symposium on Remote Sensing of Environment*, Institute of Science and Technology, University of Michigan, pp. 549–62.

CARNEGGIE, D. M., POULTON, C. E., and ROBERTS, E. H. (1967). The evaluation of rangeland resources by means of multispectral imagery. *Annual Progress Report*, 30 Sept., Forestry Remote Sensing Laboratory, University of California, Berkeley, Calif.

CATOE, C., NORDBERG, W., THADDEUS, P., and LING, G. (1967). *Preliminary results from aircraft flight tests of an electrically scanning microwave radiometer*. Report No. X-622-67-352, Goddard Space Flight Center, Green Belt, Maryland.

COLWELL, R. N. (1966). Aerial photography of the earth's surface, its procurement and use. *Appl. Optics* **5**, 883–92.

COLWELL, R. N. (1966). Aerial photography of the earth's surface, its procurement and

COLWELL, R. N., and SHAY, J. R. (1965). Applications of remote sensing in agriculture and forestry. *American Astronautical Society, Science and Technology Series*, vol. 4, *Scientific Experiments for Manned Orbital Flight*, pp. 35–70.

DALKE, G. W. (1966). Automatic processing of multispectral images. *CRES Technical Report* 61–16, University of Kansas, Lawrence, Kansas.

DELLWIG, L. F., KIRK, J. N., and WALTERS, R. L. (1966). The potential of low-resolution radar imagery in regional geologic studies. *J. geophys. Res.* **71**, 4995–8.

DELLWIG, L. F., and MOORE, R. K. (1966). The geological value of simultaneously produced like- and cross-polarized radar imagery. *J. geophys. Res.* **71**, 3597–601.

DERENYI, E., and KONECNY, G. (1964). Geometry of infrared imagery. *Can. Surveyor* **28**, 279–90.

DRAEGER, W. C. (1967). The interpretability of high altitude multi-spectral imagery for the evaluation of wildland resources. *Annual Progress Report*, Sept. 30, Forestry Remote Sensing Laboratory, Berkeley, Calif.

ELLERMEIER, R. D., SIMONETT, D. S., and DELLWIG, L. F. (1967). The use of multi-parameter radar imagery for the discrimination of terrain characteristics. *IEEE Int. Conv. Rec.* **15**, 127–35.

ESTES, J. (1966). Some applications of aerial infrared imagery. *Ann. Ass. Am. Geogr.* **56**, 673–82.

FISCHER, W. A., DAVIS, D. A., and SOUSA, T. M. (1966). Freshwater springs of Hawaii from infrared images. *U.S. Geol. Survey, Hydrol. Inv. Atlas* MA-218.

FISCHER, W. A., MOXHAM, R. M., POLCYN, F. C., and LANDIS, G. H. (1964). Infrared surveys of Hawaiian volcanoes. *Science, N.Y.* **146**, 733–42.

GILLERMAN, E. (1967). Investigation of cross-polarized radar on volcanic rocks. *CRES Report* 61–25, University of Kansas, Lawrence, Kansas.

HARALICK, R. M. (1967). Pattern recognition using likelihood functions. Unpublished M.S. Thesis, University of Kansas, Lawrence, Kansas.

HELLER, R. C., ALDRICH, R. C., MCCAMBRIDGE, W. F., and WEBER, F. P. (1967). The use of multispectral sensing techniques to detect ponderosa pine trees under stress from insect or pathogenic organisms. *Annual Progress Report*, Sept. 30, Forestry Remote Sensing Laboratory, University of California, Berkeley, Calif.

HOFFER, R. M. (1967). Interpretation of remote multispectral imagery of agricultural crops. *Research bulletin* No. 831, *Laboratory for Agricultural Remote Sensing*, vol. 1. Purdue Univ., Agricultural Exp. Sta., Lafayette, Indiana.

HOPE, J. R. (1966). Path of heavy rainfall photographed from space. *Bull. Am. met. Soc.* **47**, 371–3.

KOVER, A. N. (in press). Radar imagery as an aid in geologic mapping. Paper presented to 1967 ASP-ACSM Conv., Hilton Hotel, Washington, D.C., March.

LYON, R. J. P. (1967). *Field infrared analysis of terrain*. Semi-annual report NGR-05-020-115. Remote Sensing Laboratory Geophysics Department, Stanford University.

MACDONALD, H. C., BRENNAN, P. A., and DELLWIG, L. F. (1967). Geologic evaluation by radar of NASA sedimentary test site. *IEEE Trans. Geosci. Electronics* GE-5, 72–78.

MCCOY, R. M. (1967). An evaluation of radar imagery as a tool for drainage basin analysis. Unpublished Ph.D. dissertation, University of Kansas, Lawrence, Kansas.

MENON, V. K., and RAGOTZKIE, R. A. (1967). *Remote sensing by infrared and microwave radiometry*. Technical Report No. 31, ONR Contract No. 1202(07), University of Wisconsin, Dept. Meterology, Madison, Wis.

MOORE, R. K., and SIMONETT, D. S. (1967a). Radar remote sensing in biology. *Bioscience* 17, 384–90.
MOORE, R. K., and SIMONETT, D. S. (1967b). Potential research and earth resource studies with orbiting radars: results of recent studies. *American Institute of Aeronautics and Astronautics, 4th Annual Meeting*, Paper No. 67-767, pp. 1–22.
MORAIN, S. A. (1967). Field studies on vegetation at Horsefly Mountain, Oregon and its relation to radar imagery. *CRES Report* 61–11, University of Kansas, Lawrence, Kansas.
MORAIN, S. A., and SIMONETT, D. S. (1966). Vegetation analysis with radar imagery. *Proc. 4th Symp. on Remote Sensing of Environment*, University of Michigan, pp. 605–622.
MORAIN, S. A., and SIMONETT, D. S. (1967). K-band radar in vegetation mapping. *Photogramm. Engng* 33, 730–40.
MOXHAM, R. M. (1967). Aerial infrared surveys in water resources study. *USGS Technical Letter*, NASA-74, Contract R-146-09-020-006.
MYERS, V. I., CARTER, D. L., and RIPPERT, W. J. (1966a). Remote sensing for estimating soil salinity. *J. Irrig. Drain., Div. Am. Soc. civ. Engrs* 94, IR4, Proc. Paper 5040, 59–68.
MYERS, V. I., WIEGAND, C. L., HEILMAN, M. D., and THOMAS, J. R. (1966b). Remote sensing in soil and water conservation research. *Proc. 4th Symp. on Remote Sensing of Environment*, University of Michigan, pp. 801–13.
MYERS, V. I. et al. (1967). *Spectral sensing in agriculture.* Annual Report NASA Contract R-09-038-002, Fruit, Vegetable, Soil and Water Research Laboratory, ARS, for U.S. Dept. of Agriculture.
MYERS, V. I., and HEILMAN, M. D. (in press). Thermal infrared detection of soil characteristics in an area of alluvial floodplain soils. *Photogramm. Engng.*
OLSON, C. E. JR. (1964). *Spectral reflectance measurements compared with panchromatic and infrared aerial photographs.* Technical Report No. 7, Project NONR 1224(44), Geography Branch, Office of Naval Research, Washington, D.C.
OLSON, C. E. JR. (1967a). *Optical sensing of the moisture content in fine forest fuels.* Report No. 8036-1-F, Infrared and Optical Sensor Laboratory, University of Michigan.
OLSON, C. E. JR. (1967b). Accuracy of landuse interpretation from infrared imagery in the 4·5 to 5·5 micron band. *Ann. Ass. Am. Geogr.* 67, 382–8.
RYDSTROM, H. O. (1967). Interpreting local geology from radar imagery. *Bull. geol. Soc. Am.* 78, 429–36.
SHAY, J. F., et al. (1967). Remote multispectral sensing in agriculture. *Research Bulletin* No. 832, *Laboratory for Agricultural Remote Sensing*, vol. 2 (Annual Report). Purdue Univ., Agricultural Lab. Sta., Lafayette, Indiana.
SIMONETT, D. S. (in press). Potential of radar remote sensors as tools in reconnaissance geomorphic, vegetation and soil mapping. *Proc. 9th Int. Soil Science Congress*, Adelaide, Australia.
SIMONETT, D. S., EAGLEMAN, J. R., ERHART, A. B., RHODES, D. C., and SCHWARZ, D. E. (1967). The potential of radar as a remote sensor in agriculture: 1. A study with K-band imagery in Western Kansas. *CRES Report* 61–21, University of Kansas, Lawrence, Kansas.
SIMONETT, D. S., and MORAIN, S. A. (1965). Remote sensing from spacecraft as a tool for investigating arctic environments. *CRES Report* 61–5, University of Kansas, Lawrence, Kansas.
VICKERS, R. S., and LYON, R. J. P. (1967). Infrared sensing from spacecraft—a geological interpretation. *American Institute of Aeronautics and Astronautics. Thermophysics Specialist Conference*, New Orleans, La., April 17–20. AIAA paper No. 67–284.
WALLACE, R. W., and MOXHAM, R. M. (1966). Use of infrared imagery in a study of the San Andreas Fault system, California. *USGS Technical Letter*, NASA-42, Contract No. R-09-020-015.
WALTERS, R. L. (1967). Radar bibliography for geoscientists. *CRES Report* 61–29, University of Kansas, Lawrence, Kansas.
WEBER, F. P. (1965). Explanation of changes in reflected and emitted radiation properties for early remote detection of tree vigor decline. M.F. Thesis, School of Natural Resources, The University of Michigan, Ann Arbor, Michigan.
WEBER, F. P., and OLSON, C. E. JR. (1967). Remote sensing implications of changes in physiologic structure and function of tree seedlings under moisture stress. *Remote Sensing Applications in Forestry, Annual Progress Report*. Remote Sensing Lab., University of California, Berkeley, California.

WILSON, R. A. (1966). The remote surveillance of forest fires. *Appl. Optics* **5**, 899–904.
WISE, D. U. (1967). Radar geology and pseudo-geology on an Appalachian piedmont cross section. *Photogramm. Engng* **33**, 752–61.
WOLFE, W. L. (1965). *Handbook of Military Infrared Technology.* Office of Naval Research, Dept. of the Navy, Washington, D.C.

Remote Sensing of Land Surface Temperature and Some Applications in Land Evaluation

C. W. Rose and D. A. Thomas

Division of Land Research, CSIRO, Canberra, Australia

The problems involved in measuring land surface temperature from remote radiometric measurements, made in the 8–13 micrometre atmospheric 'window' are discussed. Two possible applications of using land surface temperature in land evaluation are examined.

1. The assessment of the extent and density of vegetation over large areas.
2. The relative assessment of water storage in bare soil.

Quantitative information is obtainable with respect to soil moisture status by measuring the relative diurnal amplitude and phase in surface temperature.

INTRODUCTION

Continued developments are being made in the design and sensitivity of sensors measuring the radiance and spectral distribution of radiation in the electromagnetic spectrum. The increased sensitivity of these sensors has made possible the measurement of radiation from remote sources. Balloons, aircraft, and earth-orbiting satellites can be used to carry sensors that remotely measure the radiation emitted and reflected from the earth. The use of such remote sensing can quickly cover large areas, when atmospheric absorption does not obscure surface emission, and can provide an accurate and more efficient alternative to spatially replicated ground-based measurement.

In this paper we discuss remote sensing of the infrared or thermal radiation from which surface temperatures can be calculated. All objects at temperatures above absolute zero emit thermal radiation whose spectral composition is related to absolute surface temperature by Planck's distribution law. The development of accurate portable radiometers for the measurement of surface temperature is recent, and such measurement was infrequent prior to satellite observations. Hence the applications of this measurement have not been fully explored.

Surface temperature is an important factor controlling the fluxes of sensible heat and water transfer from the earth's surface (Sutton 1953; Rose 1966).

This paper deals with the use of remotely determined land surface temperature in assessing the type of ground cover and soil water status.

EARTH SURFACE TEMPERATURE MEASUREMENT BY REMOTE SENSORS

From the vantage point of a satellite or aircraft passing over the sunlit side of the earth, the thermal radiation stream includes both 'short-wave' (< 3–4 micrometre, μm) radiation in the form of reflected and back-scattered sunlight, and 'long-wave' flux (> 3–4 μm) emitted by clouds, atmosphere, or ground. However, we shall consider here only the long-wave flux, which may be separated from short-wave radiation by suitable filters, and which is the only thermal radiation observable on the dark side of the earth. The terms 'long-wave' and 'infrared' may be regarded as synonomous for purposes of this paper, though the lower wavelength limit of infrared radiation is customarily taken at the upper limit of human vision (about $0 \cdot 78$ μm).

The radiance N (defined as the radiant power per unit area per unit solid angle emitted from a surface or layer) is given by:

$$N = \varepsilon(\sigma/\pi) \, T_s^4 \qquad (\text{W cm}^{-2} \text{ ster}^{-1}) \tag{1}$$

where ε is emissivity, the ratio of radiance to blackbody radiance at the same temperature, σ is the Stefan-Boltzmann constant ($5 \cdot 67 \times 10^{-12}$ W cm^{-2} deg^{-4} K). T_s is temperature of the emitting surface ($^{\circ}$K).

Even in the absence of clouds, the atmospheric gases CO_2, O_3, and water vapour are strongly absorbent in a complex variety of wavebands (Sutton 1953; Kellogg, Buettner, and May 1964) of particular relevance to the measurement of long-wave emission at terrestrial temperatures (which has a maximum in the region of 10 μm wavelength). In the transmission 'window' between 8 and 13 μm radiation absorption is generally weak for all atmospheric gases except O_3, and, in what follows, measurement will be restricted to this waveband. The radiance $N_{8,13}$ in this infrared waveband measured by a remote sensor may be separated into two terms representing radiation of the atmosphere and that originating from the earth's surface. These are given by the first and second terms respectively on the right hand side of equation (2):

$$N_{8,13} = \int_{\lambda = 8}^{\lambda = 13} \int_{o}^{H} (\partial B_{a,\lambda}/\partial \tau_{a,\lambda})(\partial \tau_{a,\lambda}/\partial h) \, dh \, d\lambda$$

$$+ \varepsilon_s \int_{\lambda = 8}^{\lambda = 13} B_{s,\lambda} \int_{o}^{H} (\partial \tau_{a,\lambda}/\partial h) \, dh \, d\lambda$$

$$= N_a + N_s \qquad (\text{W cm}^{-2} \text{ ster}^{-1}) \tag{2}$$

where B_λ is spectral blackbody radiance, and the prior subscripts a and s refer to the atmosphere and earth surface (W cm^{-2} ster^{-1} μm^{-1}), λ is wavelength of radiation (μm), h is height above the earth surface (m), H is height at which radiation is measured (m), $\tau_{a,\lambda}$ is spectral transmissivity of the atmosphere for wavelength λ at height h, N_a, N_s are atmospheric and surface radiances in the waveband 8–13 μm (W cm^{-2} ster^{-1}), and ε_s is emissivity of the earth surface in the 8–13 μm waveband.

Equation (2) neglects the radiance contributed by reflection of radiation incident to the earth surface from its surrounding atmosphere. Radiation from cloudless sky in the 8–13 μm waveband is low, being $0 \cdot 2$ W cm^{-2} at maximum (Fuchs and Tanner 1966), and reflection back to space is approximately 5% of this (or $0 \cdot 01$ W cm^{-2} maximum). The error introduced through the neglect of this term is less than that due to uncertainties in ε_s, as will be discussed.

When clouds are absent N_a is small compared with N_s, though possibly not negligible at satellite altitudes. Craig (1965) has described methods used in calculating N_a at infrared wavelengths.

Considering the earth surface radiance Ns, Wark, Yamamoto, and Liensch (1962) have described the methods used in evaluating $\int_{o}^{H}(\partial \tau_{a,\lambda}/\partial h) \, dh$ in equation (2), and in correcting TIROS II measurements for the presence of both water vapour and ozone in the atmosphere to yield corrected surface temperature under clear sky conditions. Corrections to T_s for absorption by either ozone or water vapour are comparable in magnitude, and can be of the order of $5°K$.

The spectral blackbody radiance $B_{s,\lambda}$ in equation (2) is given by Plancks' equation:

$$B_\lambda = C_1\lambda^{-5}[\exp(C_2/\lambda T_s) - 1]^{-1} \qquad (\text{W cm}^{-2}\text{ ster}^{-1}\,\mu\text{m}^{-1}) \qquad (3)$$

where C_1 and C_2 are known constants. Therefore, T_s can be derived from $N_{8,13}$ using equation (2) provided ε_s can be determined.

It follows from equation (1) that the magnitude of the possible error (δT_s) in T_s at terrestrial temperatures because of an uncertainty $(\delta\varepsilon_s)$ in ε_s is approximately given by:

$$\delta T_s = \frac{\delta\varepsilon_s\, T_s}{4\varepsilon_s} \qquad (°K) \qquad (4)$$

Substituting in equation (4) $T_s = 300°K$ (a typical figure for terrestrial temperatures), $\delta\varepsilon_s = 0\cdot01$, and $\varepsilon_s = 1$ (ε_s is $>0\cdot9$ for most land surfaces) gives $\delta T_s = 0\cdot75°K$ for this 1% uncertainty in ε_s. A reasonable estimate, based on published data, of the uncertainty in ε_s for most land surfaces, excluding uncommonly low values, would be $\pm0\cdot05$, leading to an uncertainty of $\pm3\cdot8°K$ in T_s. The corresponding uncertainty in T_s would be only approximately $\pm1\cdot5°K$ if the surface were known to be water, snow, or ice (assuming near vertical viewing), or $\pm1\cdot1°K$ if dense vegetation was the covering (Kellogg, Buettner, and May 1964). These estimates appear more realistic than the lower figures of Gates (1963) and Monteith and Sziecz (1962).

These considerations show that a knowledge of ε_s is of some importance if surface temperatures are to be correctly inferred from radiometric measurements, especially if the surface is effectively bare soil, as in arid or desert regions where values of ε_s considerably less than unity are common. Such low values in many surface materials are caused by a quasi-metallic behaviour of ions bound in the crystal lattice structure of minerals. The particulate and irregular character of natural surfaces leads to multiple reflection within surface structures and to diffractive scattering which practically removes the wavelength dependence of ε_s typical of polished mineral surfaces (Lyon 1964). Similarly, with a vegetal cover, multiple internal reflections result in stand emissivities greater than those of single leaves from the same stand (Fuchs and Tanner 1966). This means that the emissivities of natural surfaces must be measured *in situ*.

One way in which ε_s could be determined from remote sensor observations is to have a contemporary ground-based observation of radiant surface temperature (Buettner and Kern 1965). For ocean surfaces, standard thermometric techniques may be adequate for this measurement of surface temperature (Kellogg, Buettner, and May 1964). On land, however, surface temperature would in general have to be measured radiometrically, and this requires the knowledge of ε_s in any case (Fuchs and Tanner 1966).

Land-based techniques for the *in situ* measurement of ε_s have been developed (Buettner and Kern 1965; Fuchs and Tanner 1966) which provide mean values only over a scale of metres. However, the field of view of satellite-born radiometers has been of the order of a kilometre, though this depends on both the altitude of the sensor and its solid angle of radiation acceptance. A radiometer measures the radiance of the incident radiation integrated over the solid angle of acceptance of the instrument.

It may be shown that, if a radiometer sees a surface where large proportions of the field of view differ in emissivity, mean surface temperature cannot be accurately calculated. To improve accuracy, a radiometer therefore should see a surface of effectively uniform emissivity, and choice of a suitable field of view would assist in this aim. Spatial uniformity of emissivity and application of the data are other factors affecting this choice. The principle of a possible method will now be outlined whereby a simultaneous measure of T_s and effective ε_s could be obtained. The method is related to a discussion of radiation pyrometry by Conn and Avery (1960, p. 189).

Suppose measurements of radiance were made over two non-adjacent wavebands, λ_1 to λ_2 and λ_3 to λ_4 chosen for low atmospheric absorption and adequate levels of radiance for emission at terrestrial temperatures. It is assumed that atmospheric absorption and emission has been corrected for as described earlier. Let:

$$N_{1,2} = \varepsilon_s \int_{\lambda_1}^{\lambda_2} B_\lambda \, d\lambda = \varepsilon_s f_1 \, (T_s) \tag{5}$$

and

$$N_{3,4} = \varepsilon_s \int_{\lambda_3}^{\lambda_4} B_\lambda \, d\lambda = \varepsilon_s f_2 \, (T_s) \tag{6}$$

where $N_{1,2}$ in equation (5) is the measured radiance over the waveband λ_1 to λ_2, f_1 (T) a function of temperature derived from equation (3), with similar definitions for the terms in equation (6). Emissivities have been assumed equal over both wavebands. The three equations (3), (5) and (6) enable solution of the three unknowns ε_s, f_1 (T_s), and f_2 (T_s), hence also yielding T_s.

At least for satellite measurements, we have been assuming clear-sky conditions. There is the further implicit assumption, also made by Wark, Yamamoto, and Lienesch (1962) that clear-sky conditions are not uncommon. However, Lienesch and Wark (1967) have stated that much of the earth has been found to have some degree of cloudiness when viewed from satellite altitudes, including partly cloudy skies, or thin cirrus. Either radiometers operating in the 10–11 μm waveband, where absorption due to water vapour, O_3, and CO_2 are a minimum, or flight at aircraft altitudes could significantly extend effectively clear-sky conditions. Hodgin (1962) has given evidence of a somewhat greater flexibility in measuring surface temperature at millimetre and centimetre wavelengths.

Infrared radiation measurements have been made from 'NIMBUS' and most 'TIROS' satellites (e.g. Nordberg *et al.* 1962), and a close correlation has been found between thermal emission and cloud cover (e.g. Weinstein and Suomi 1961). Whilst cloud cover is routinely measured with satellites using their very high reflection coefficient in the visible spectrum, long-wave radiation measurement alone may provide an adequate indication of opaque cloud cover because of the relatively cold cloud tops compared with that of the earth's surface. With low, relatively warm cloud, partly cloudy skies, or thin cirrus, supplementary evidence of cloud cover at visible wavelengths would be necessary.

SOME POSSIBLE APPLICATIONS OF REMOTE MEASUREMENT OF EARTH SURFACE TEMPERATURE

There have been two main applications of the satellite measurement of long-wave radiation from the earth or its atmosphere. One application is in connection with studies of the radiant energy balance of the earth and atmosphere, and the second is in the measurement of earth surface and atmospheric temperatures. For reasons given in the last section measurements are restricted to the 8–13 μm wavelength atmospheric 'window'.

The temperature difference across a 1 mm thick layer of soil can be as great as 2–3°C. The accurate non-radiometric measurement of surface temperature T_s is therefore difficult, which is probably why T_s has received limited attention in standard meteorological texts. Kellogg, Buettner, and May (1964) have shown that in quartz sand radiometric measurement gives the temperature in about the top 7 μm layer, across which the temperature difference cannot exceed 0·02°C.

Assessment of Type of Land Cover

Recording and telemetering photographic-type information is very much more complex than with the output of radiometers because of the much greater information content in a photograph. Furthermore, there are applications where the single spatially-integrated radiometer output has the advantage of immediately providing the required information, thus removing the necessity of a detailed analysis of scanned or photographically recorded information. Two examples of such applications will be given.

In rangeland and arid zone research generally, ground-based assessment of the seasonal variation in forage or vegetative ground cover can be expensive in relation to the value of the land for adequate sampling of extensive areas. Whilst not eliminating the need for sampling and other ground-based observations, satellite-born radiometer measurements over large areas could provide a quantitative basis for the extrapolation of such observations, both in space and time.

By the relative coolness of wet compared with dry areas, the extent of rainfall in arid regions can also be assessed from remote radiometry. This information could be used in the studies on vegetation dynamics mentioned above, and as a basis for weighting rain-gauge catches in investigating the hydrology of catchments.

Satellite observations can provide a sufficient number of measurements during 24 hours to yield the daily amplitude in radiation in the measured waveband for particular cloud-free locations. Sufficient is known concerning the daily swing in surface temperature, and thus in emitted radiation, to suggest with some confidence that an estimate of its daily amplitude would provide an adequate basis for the applications described above. Especially if this daily amplitude can be compared with the known surface cover in either aerially photographed or surveyed areas, this application of satellite radiometry could provide a useful tool in extrapolating such information as surface cover into unsurveyed areas, as well as providing a key to the likely range of values of ε_s to be used in calculating T_s.

Rose (1968) measured a daily amplitude in T_s of the order of 40°C for a slightly moist bare sandy soil at Alice Springs (133°50′E, 23°45′S) in the month of October, and this amplitude can certainly be exceeded. With living vegetation in a similar environment the diurnal amplitude of T_s was only approximately 15°C. Whilst these figures are from a region of high daily radiation ($\doteq 2590$ J cm^{-2}) measurable amplitude differences between such surfaces would be expected in a wide variety of environments. However, there may well be surfaces where more than a simple comparison of amplitudes in T_s is necessary for discrimination between dry vegetated and non-vegetated areas. For example, under clear-sky conditions the night minimum in T_s for dead or dry vegetation would usually be less than for bare soil under the same conditions, whereas the daytime maximum for such vegetation would be less than for bare soil, so that despite these differences, diurnal amplitudes in T_s might be equal for these two surfaces.

Relative Assessment of Water Storage in Bare Soils

Were it feasible to assess the amount of water stored in bare soils, even in a relative manner, there is a variety of ways in which this information could be used.

Radar is a remote sensor whose potential in the measurement of soil water content is currently being examined (Moore 1966). However, interpretational difficulties are at present sufficiently great that it is pertinent to examine the possibilities and likely limitations of earth surface temperature measurements.

The change in emissivity of quartz sand from dry ($0 \cdot 914$) to near saturation with water ($0 \cdot 936$) (Kellogg, Buettner, and May 1964) introduces an apparent change in T_s of only $1 \cdot 7°C$, which is not large compared with diurnal amplitude in T_s. The idea of using the diurnal amplitude in T_s in bare soil as computed from satellite-born radiometer measurements will therefore be quantitatively explored for the two model situations depicted as cases 1 and 2 of Figure 1. The aim is to distinguish between case 1 with a moist layer at depth d' and case 2 with no moist layer, using differences in the diurnal amplitude of T_s. The two cases are assumed situated in similar macroenvironments, and on soils with comparable relationships between water content and thermal conductivity.

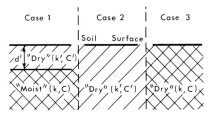

Fig. 1. Three idealized soil profiles of uniform layers of 'dry' and 'moist' soil, with differing thermal conductivity (k) and heat capacity (C). Product (k'C') is less than (kC).

Such a distinction, if quantitatively adequate, could be useful in investigations on the productivity of arid zones for example, by providing information on the aerial extent and duration of a moist layer at some depth below the soil surface.

An agricultural application might be in providing information on relative water storage to assist in the decision on whether or not to provide an annual fallow in marginal rainfall areas.

Whilst in reality the change in water content will not be as abrupt as assumed in case 1 of Figure 1, nor will thermal properties be constant with depth as assumed within the layers of Figure 1, such idealizations are adequate for the stated purposes of this section.

It will be assumed that for all the cases depicted in Figure 1, the diurnal history of surface temperature T_s is well represented by a sinuosoidal function of time, which is a reasonable approximation (West 1952; Rose 1968). Thus:

$$T_s = \overline{T} + A \sin (\omega t + \varphi) \quad (°C) \tag{7}$$

where $\overline{T}$ is mean surface temperature (°C), A is diurnal amplitude in T_s (°C), ω is daily angular frequency of the diurnal temperature wave at the surface (rad sec^{-1}), t is time (sec), and φ is phase angle of the surface temperature (rad).

With this assumption the theory developed by van Duin (1954) for predicting the daily course of temperature in the soil in the presence of a surface layer of different thermal properties may be applied to this problem. A simplifying assumption made by van Duin (1954) is that the amplitude of the heat flux density into the soil surface is independent of the thermal properties of soil and air. As van Duin has indicated, the effect of this assumption is to over-estimate the temperature amplitude A in equation (7) in case 1 relative to case 2 (Fig. 1).

The 'dry' soil in case 3 (Fig. 1), with thermal properties equal to those of the 'moist' soil in the lower layer of case 1 is introduced solely to facilitate the employment of van Duin's (1954) analysis.

Define the surface temperature amplitude ratios F, between the various cases of Figure 1 by:

$$F_{12} = A_1/A_2, \qquad F_{13} = A_1/A_3, \tag{8}$$

where the numerical subscripts refer to the case numbers of Figure 1, so that A_1 is the amplitude of surface temperature in case 1 etc. It follows from van Duin (1954) that:

$$F_{12} = (A_1/A_3) \quad (A_3/A_2)$$
$$= F_{13} (k'C')^{\frac{1}{2}} (kC)^{-\frac{1}{2}} \tag{9}$$

where the symbols are defined in Figure 1. Van Duin (1954) has derived an analytical expression for F_{13} (denoted p_0 in his notation), and for the difference in phase angle φ between case 1 and cases 2 and 3.

The implications of equation (9) for the ratio of surface temperature amplitudes between cases 1 and 2 in Figure 1 will be illustrated for the particular set of soil thermal properties given in Table 1. The volumetric water contents (X_w) in Table 1 correspond to the field capacity for each layer, and the ratio $(k'C')^{\frac{1}{2}}(kC)^{-\frac{1}{2}}$ in equation (9) comes to $0 \cdot 60$. This figure for the square root of the ratio of thermal properties in the dry and moist layers corresponds to a distinct but by no means extreme change in such properties.

TABLE 1

Properties of two-layered sandy soil. X_s and X_w are the volume fractions of solid material and water respectively

Layer	X_s (cm^{3}cm^{-3})	X_w (cm^{3}cm^{-3})	k (cal cm^{-1}sec^{-1} deg^{-1}C) $\times 10^{-3}$	C (cal cm^{-3})
Upper	$0 \cdot 40$	$0 \cdot 125$	$1 \cdot 70$	$0 \cdot 31$
Lower	$0 \cdot 57$	$0 \cdot 175$	$3 \cdot 40$	$0 \cdot 44$

Computations of F_{12} using van Duin's (1954) data for F_{13} are shown plotted against the depth to the lower moister layer (d^1) in Figure 2. The ratio F_{12} becomes unity at $d^1 = 9 \cdot 7$ cm (Fig. 2), and, after a slight overswing tends to unity (as it must) as d^1 increases.

Assume for example that the temperature amplitude A_2 is 20°C, and that a *change* in surface temperature of ± 2°C can be detected (even though accuracy in absolute surface temperature may be poorer than this). These particular assumptions imply that the presence of a moist lower layer in this particular example could be detected only if F_{12} was less than $0 \cdot 9$, so that d^1 could not exceed approximately 6 cm (Fig. 2).

The dependence of F_{13} and hence F_{12} on thermal properties is most complex, and it is emphasised that Figure 2 applies *only* to the particular case detailed in Table 1. West (1932), for example, observed a difference of approximately

6°C between the daily amplitudes in surface temperature for a soil with loose upper layer 13 cm deep, and the original soil. The depth at which a layer with thermal properties different from the soil above it may be detected, will increase both with the precision of temperature measurement and the degree of contrast in thermal diffusivity between the layers.

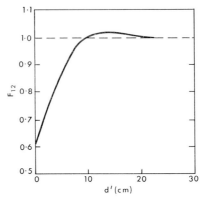

Fig. 2. The temperature amplitude ratio (F_{12}) for the particular example of the layered sandy soil with properties given in Table 1, plotted against depth to the lower layer (d^1).

It follows from equation (9) and the nature of the problem that unambiguous deductions concerning either d^1 or $(k'C')^{\frac{1}{2}}(kC)^{-\frac{1}{2}}$ (and hence possibly of relative water content in the lower layer) cannot be made from the remote measurement of amplitudes A_1 and A_2 alone. In principle, the difference in phase angle (φ in equation (7)) between cases 1 and 2 could be used to remove this ambiguity, though determining this difference with adequate accuracy may present practical difficulties.

The higher amplitude in T_s for case 2 (dry) compared with case 1 (moist at depth) will result in higher heat exchanges between soil and atmosphere, which will tend to reduce the amplitude A_2 expected on the above theory by approximately 1 to 2°C if A_2 was 20°C (van Duin 1964). Van Duin's (1954) theory (and the particular example given above) therefore slightly over-estimates the relative magnitude of differences in A.

CONCLUSIONS

Some interpretational problems and applications in land evaluation of remote radiometry in the 8–13 μm atmospheric 'window' have been examined. To obtain land-surface temperature using this technique important corrections must be made for:
1. Thermal emission by the atmosphere between the earth and radiometer.
2. Atmospheric absorption of ground surface emission.
3. The emissivity of the ground surface in the radiometer's field of view. The method suggested for the remote measurement of this quantity requires careful experimental investigation. There are other important applications in land evaluation of remotely-measured earth surface temperature besides those discussed in the previous section, and it is clearly a key factor in large-scale investigations of energy and water exchanges at the earth's surface. Of the applications considered in this paper, there should be little technical difficulty in assessing the degree of vegetal cover, or in distinguishing between dry and wet soil surfaces.

The application of surface temperature measurements in the assessment of relative water storage in effectively bare soil has been shown to be feasible. However, determinations based solely on the relative diurnal amplitudes in surface temperature do not give unambiguous indications of the absolute quantity of water stored in a soil profile.

REFERENCES

BUETTNER, K. J. K., and KERN, C. D. (1965). The determination of infrared emissivities of terrestrial surfaces. *J. geophys. Res.* **70**, 1320.

CONN, G. K. T., and AVERY, D. G. (1960). *Infrared Methods.* (Academic Press: New York.)

CRAIG, R. A. (1965). *The Upper Atmosphere, Meteorology and Physics.* (Academic Press: New York.)

FUCHS, M., and TANNER, C. B. (1966). Infrared thermometry of vegetation. *Agron J.* **58**, 597.

GATES, D. M. (1963). Leaf temperature and energy exchange. *Arch. Met. Geophys. Bioklim.* **B12**, 321.

HODGIN, D. M. (1962). The characteristics of microwave radiometry in remote sensing of the environment. *Proc. 2nd Symp. Remote Sensing of Environment*, Ann Arbour, Michigan. 127.

KELLOGG, W. W., BUETTNER, K. J. K., and MAY, E. C. (1964). *Meteorological satellite observation on thermal emission* (Part 2 of an examination of the application to satellite meteorology of various segments of the electromagnetic spectrum). The Rand Corporation, R.M.-4392-NASA, Santa Monica.

LIENESCH, J. H., and WARK, D. Q. (1967). Infrared limb darkening of the earth from statistical analysis of TIROS data. *J. appl. Met.* **6**, 674.

LYON, R. J. P. (1964). *Evaluation of infrared spectroscopy for compositional analysis of lunar and planetary soils: rough and powdered surfaces.* Final Report, Part II, Project PSV-3943, Stanford Research Institute.

MONTEITH, J. L., and SZEICZ, G. (1962). Radiative temperature in the heat balance of natural surfaces. *Q. Jl. R. met. Soc.* **88**, 496.

MOORE, R. K. (1966). Radar as a sensor. *CRES Report* No. 61–7, University of Kansas.

NORDBERG, W., BANDEEN, W. R., CONRATH, B. J., KUNDE, V., and PERSANO, I. (1962). Preliminary results of radiation measurements from the TIROS III meteorological satellite. *J. atmos. Sci.* **19**, 20.

ROSE, C. W. (1966). *Agricultural Physics.* (Pergamon Press: Oxford.)

ROSE, C. W. (1968). Evaporation from bare soil under high radiation conditions. *Proc. 9th Int. Soil Science Congress* (in press).

SUTTON, O. G. (1953). *Micrometeorology.* (McGraw-Hill: New York.)

VAN DUIN, R. H. A. (1954). Influence of tilth on soil and air temperature. *Neth. J. agric. Sci.* **2**, 229.

VAN DUIN, R. H. A. (1964). On the influence of tillage on conduction of heat, diffusion of air and infiltration of water in soil. *Reports on Agricultural Investigation* No. 627, Ministry of Agriculture, Fisheries and Food Supply of the Netherlands.

WARK, D. Q., YAMAMOTO, G., and LIENESCH, J. H. (1962). Methods of estimating infrared flux and surface temperature from meteorological satellites. *J. atmos. Sci.* **19**, 369.

WEINSTEIN, M., and SUOMI, V. E. (1961). Analysis of satellite infrared radiation measurements on a synoptic scale. *Mon. Weath. Rev. U.S. Dep. Agric.* **89**, 419.

WEST, E. S. (1932). The effect of a soil mulch on soil temperature. *J. Coun. scient. ind. Res. Aust.* **5**, 236.

WEST, E. S. (1952). A study of the annual soil temperature. *Aust. J. scient. Res.* Series A **5**, 303.

The Potential of Large-Scale Air Photographs and Radar Altimetry in Land Evaluation

R. L. Westby,[1] A. H. Aldred,[2] and L. Sayn-Wittgenstein[2]

[1] Radar technician, Defence Section, Radio and Electrical Engineering Division, National Research Council, Ottawa, Canada.

[2] Research Scientists, Research Section, Forest Management Institute, Department of Forestry and Rural Development, Ottawa, Canada.

The potential in forest and land inventory for large-scale aerial photographs (1 : 1000 to 1 : 1500) with accurate height determination is demonstrated. Accurate height is achieved by a radar altimeter specifically designed for this purpose, attached to the aerial camera. Detailed interpretation of these photographs is possible and precise determination of altitude allows accurate measurements. Use of the above information in specific application of forest inventory is discussed.

The combination of large-scale air photographs and accurate radar altimetry as tools in forest and land inventory is now emerging from the experimental stages. It has great potential value in all resource surveys, and opens the door to a challenging new series of research tasks to improve its efficiency and to explore its full potential.

The system relies to a large extent on obtaining accurate, detailed information from aerial photographs at scales in the approximate range of 1 : 1000 to 1 : 1500. The idea of obtaining detailed information from large-scale photographs must surely have occurred to the first person who ever saw such photographs. What is new, is that an efficient, practical system of exploiting the potential of large-scale photographs has now been developed. This was accomplished by coupling the aerial camera to a radar altimeter that was developed especially for this task. The precise determination of flying height makes reliable measurements on these photographs possible.

INFORMATION OBTAINABLE FROM LARGE-SCALE PHOTOGRAPHS

Qualitative Information

On large-scale photographs information that could not be obtained from smaller scales suddenly becomes available. For example, in a typical North American forest, almost every tree photographed can be examined individually in great detail; small branches, and often individual leaves, are visible. Sometimes even the shrubs and herbs of the ground vegetation can be identified. Figure 1 is an example of such a photograph; it was taken with a 70 mm reconnaissance camera, which proved very promising for work at low altitudes because of its fast shutter and film cycling speeds.

Thus, at least in North American forests, tree species can usually be identified with little difficulty. An example of a typical characteristic used to identify species on large-scale photographs is as follows: white birch (*Betula papyrifera* Marsh.), and trembling aspen (*Populus tremuloides* Michx.) in the northern parts of its range, both have very light-coloured barks which usually assume the same whitish grey tone in panchromatic photographs. But, whereas the small branches and twigs of birch are slender and russet brown, the twigs of aspen are light in tone and coarser. Figure 2 demonstrates how this characteristic can be observed on a large-scale photograph. The existence of such a characteristic provides an absolutely reliable method for separating the two species during those seasons when the trees are leafless.

Fig. 1. Stereogram of a white spruce–aspen stand made from low-altitude, 15 degree oblique 70 mm photographs enlarged 2 times.

Typical of the accuracy achieved in species identification are the following results from a mixedwood forest in Ontario; panchromatic winter photographs at a scale of 1 : 1200 were used.

When trees were separated into three species groupings (pines, spruce and fir, and hardwoods), 97·7% were placed in the correct category. When an attempt was made to identify individual tree species, 72·7% of all trees were correctly identified. This is highly satisfactory because the errors made were of little consequence. The greatest difficulty was caused by small trees; 33·3% of the errors were made in attempting to separate small balsam fir (*Abies balsamea* (L.) Mill.) and small white spruce (*Picea glauca* (Moench) Voss). Another 27·5% of the errors were due to the confusion of small maples (*Acer*) with small hornbeam (*Ostrya virginiana* (Mill.) K. Koch). Tall coniferous trees, on the other hand, were identified with a high degree of accuracy. This test, and others with similar results, have been described by Kippen and Sayn-Witt-genstein (1964) and Aldred and Kippen (1967).

Fig. 2. Identification of birch and aspen on 4X enlargement of a 70 mm photograph (contact scale about 1 : 1200).

The accuracy of tree counts made on large-scale photographs is equally encouraging. Very few important trees were missed by the interpreter. For example, in the test described above, an enumeration in the field proved that the interpreter had missed only 7·9% of the trees on the area. In one experiment (Aldred and Kippen 1967) the trees missed contained only 1·2% of the stand's total volume. Again, the errors were of little consequence; well over half of the trees missed were in the 4-inch d.b.h. class, and most errors were made in stands that contained a dense understorey of balsam fir, spruce, and tolerant hardwoods—all of which were overtopped by tall pines. Large trees were counted with great accuracy; for example, no errors were made in counting numbers of mature white pine (*Pinus strobus* L.).

There is also ample evidence that large-scale photographs are useful in the appraisal of insect and disease damage. Dead or diseased trees can often be easily distinguished from healthy ones, particularly when colour films are used; among the many supporting references are Heller, Aldrich, and Bailey (1959) and Wear, Pope, and Orr (1966).

Large-scale photographs also have a great and largely unexploited potential use in soil and site surveys. Ground vegetation can often be accurately examined to yield evidence of site quality. Colour photography can provide further evidence of soil characteristics and geology. Promising possibilities also exist for surveys of forest regeneration, ecology, wildlife, and land use in general.

Measurement :

Precise, reliable measurements of trees and stands are required for a forest inventory and such measurements demand not only sharp, high-quality photographs but also an efficient system of determining flying height accurately to obtain the photographic scale.

A few years ago, when a fully satisfactory method of obtaining flying height was not available, research was directed to determining the accuracy with which trees and stands could be appraised if photographic scale was known. This research often had to rely upon slow and expensive methods of scale determination, for example, radial line plotting. The following are examples of such experiments: Avery (1959); Seely (1962); Kippen and Sayn-Wittgenstein (1964); Bonnor (1964).

This research proved that accurate measurements could be made and that these measurements provided useful estimates of the volume and diameter of individual trees. The selection of variables for estimating volume and diameter has been described by Sayn-Wittgenstein and Aldred (1967). Generally, the chosen functions included at least one of the following measurements:

1. H   = The height (in feet) of the tree measured on the photograph.
2. CA = The crown area (in square feet), measured with a fine dot-grid overlay.
3. Some measure of the relationship between the subject tree and its neighbours, to express the degree of the tree's dominance or crowding in its vicinity. Such variables influence the relationship between crown shape, height, volume, and diameter. Examples are:

NH = The number of trees growing in a circular area surrounding the subject tree, with the radius of this circle equal to the tree's height.

N6   = The number of the six nearest neighbouring trees that are taller than the tree under consideration.

Functions derived by this approach have appeared in the following form:

$$D = 1 \cdot 5272 + 0 \cdot 1661H - 0 \cdot 3426 \, N6 \qquad (R^2 = 0 \cdot 720)$$

where, D = diameter (inches, b.h.) for white spruce in the Mackenzie River delta.

$$V = e^{0 \cdot 0611H - 0 \cdot 9836} \qquad (R^2 = 0 \cdot 874)$$

where, V = volume (cubic feet) for white spruce in the Mackenzie River delta.

These two equations are merely examples of a large number of functions for different species and regions, which are still being evaluated in the Forest Management Institute in Ottawa. But, as previously stated, these developments are of little practical value without an efficient system of determining flying height and photographic scale.

DETERMINATION OF FLYING HEIGHT AND SCALE

To rectify this situation, the Department of Forestry and Rural Development approached the National Research Council for advice on the feasibility of developing an instrument for determining flying height, to the following minimum specifications:

1. The altitude must be measured to an accuracy of at least $\pm 2\%$.
2. Altitude should be measured to the ground surface and should be unaffected by intervening tree canopy.

3. The instrument must be compact and should be readily transferable from one type of aircraft to another; it must function properly on aircraft equipped with floats.
4. The instrument must operate at least in the flying height range of 600 ft to 2500 ft.
5. The altitude at the instant of exposure should appear on each photograph.
6. The cost[1] should be as low as possible, and preferably below $10,000.

Various approaches, including a system of two cameras separated by a fixed boom, a laser altimeter, and a radar altimeter were considered. A laser altimeter appeared too expensive, and did not have the ability to penetrate leaves and wood. A two-camera system was deemed too inflexible: a given installation is at its best in a relatively narrow range of flying heights, and it is awkward to estimate altitude from photogrammetric measurements on two photographs. The method, however, is feasible, as has been proven by the work of Lyons (1966) in British Columbia.

All these alternatives were considered, but radar was chosen as the most practical. The Radio and Electrical Engineering Division of N.R.C. then-developed a radar altimeter that met or surpassed the above specifications in all respects, except in cost, which is not yet firmly established. Commercial manufacture has begun.

The instrument itself is compact and weighs about 45 lb, although its antenna is rather large (diameter 36 in.), at least for flying heights above approximately 500 ft. It can, however, be readily mounted below the cargo-hatch of a de Havilland Beaver or Otter.

Various possibilities for mounting the camera exist. On the successful prototype, a Vinten 70 mm reconnaissance camera is mounted to sight through

Fig. 3. Altimeter antenna and camera mounted beneath an aircraft.

---

[1] Costs are given in Canadian currency.

the dish of the antenna (Fig. 3). The altimeter is connected to the camera through an optical system and the altitude appears in the corner of each photograph.

The instrument is exceedingly accurate; in a preliminary test it measured altitudes within ± 5 ft when flying over level terrain at 1200 ft. The instrument's signal succeeds in penetrating the canopy of North American forests at any altitude above 200 ft; it has not yet been tested under tropical conditions. Penetration of tree cover is one of the most important characteristics of the altimeter and is achieved by careful selection of wavelengths and by use of the following circuit design.

The altimeters readings are based on the time a radar pulse takes to travel from the aircraft to the ground and back. The pulse returned from the ground and trees is amplified and divided into two paths: in one path the pulse is further amplified and stretched over a 15 microsecond period; in the other, the pulse is inverted and delayed $0\cdot5$ microseconds. The signals are mixed and inverted in a field effect transistor, to appear as in Figure 4.

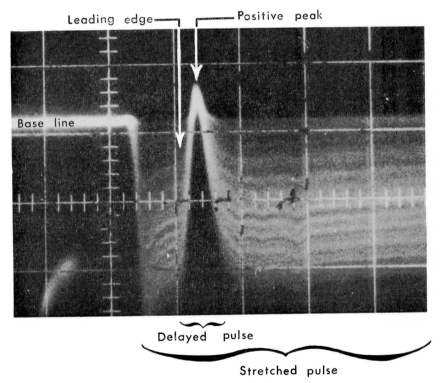

Fig. 4. The output of the field effect transistor.

The signal returned from the tree canopy is smaller in amplitude because of the selected wavelength, and occurs before the signal returned from the ground; therefore, it appears on the leading edge of the pulse and below the base line. The stretched pulse and the delayed signal below the base line are then removed to leave only the positive peak, i.e., the signal returned from the ground surface. Timing is started by the out-going pulse and is stopped by the received clipped pulse; time is converted to distance.

A FOREST INVENTORY BY LARGE-SCALE PHOTOGRAPHY

To illustrate the potential of large-scale photography in forest inventory we will now briefly describe a practical task that was recently performed. The problem was to obtain a preliminary estimate of the timber volume and the tree size distribution in the spruce forests on a 1200 sq mile area in the Mackenzie River delta north of the Arctic Circle. Access on the ground is difficult, except near navigable rivers and channels.

This inventory was completed by relying almost entirely on large-scale photography. The sampling procedure was as follows: the area was divided into seven large, rectangular blocks; two strips of large-scale photography, with random starting points, were flown across each block (Fig. 5). The pilot had little difficulty in completing this mission, since points along these random lines were tied to conspicuous landmarks along the river channels.

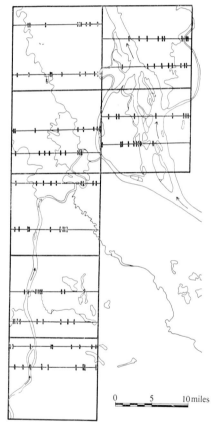

Fig. 5. Sampling design of forest inventory using large-scale 70 mm photographs.

Since the radar altimeter was not yet completed, scale was determined by radial line plotting, relying on ground control from topographic maps. The altimeter would have performed the same task more efficiently even though special circumstances – the area contained little topographic relief – minimized the usual difficulties with radial line plotting.

Nine rectangular sample plots (equivalent to 10 × 70m on the ground) were established on photographs at random locations along each flight line. The diameter and volume of each tree on these plots was estimated using the functions mentioned above. Measurements were made on about 100 trees to derive these functions, but this was the only field work necessary to complete the project.

This is a particularly simple design and, since strips and plots were chosen at random, the desired block averages (e.g., mean timber volume per acre, number and size of trees) were compiled by simply averaging the relevant plot values. The precision of this inventory can also be calculated; it follows a well-known design whose analysis is described by Schumacher and Chapman (1954, p. 94). A detailed report on the results and procedures is under preparation.

This design is but one of a large number of possible approaches to forest inventory; the potential of the method is great. There appear to be even greater possibilities for the combined system, or for the altimeter alone, in topographic mapping and magnetometer surveys. Let us hope that research will keep up with the practical applications that have evolved, so that the full potential of the system can be exploited.

REFERENCES

ALDRED, A. H., and KIPPEN, F. W. (1967). Plot volume from large-scale, 70 mm air photographs. *Forest Sci.* **13**, 419.

AVERY, G. (1959). Photographing forests from helicopters. *J. For.* **57**, 339.

BONNOR, G. M. (1964). A tree volume table for red pine by crown width and height. *For. Chron.* **40**, 339.

HELLER, R. C., ALDRICH, R. C., and BAILEY, W. F. (1959). Evaluation of several camera systems for sampling forest insect damage at low altitude. *Photogramm. Engng* **25**, 137.

KIPPEN, F. W., and SAYN-WITTGENSTEIN, L. (1964). Tree measurements on large-scale vertical 70 mm air photographs. *Canada, Department of Forestry Publication* No. 1053.

LYONS, E. H. (1966). Fixed air-base 70 mm photography, a new tool for forest sampling. *For. Chron.* **42**, 420.

SAYN-WITTGENSTEIN, L., and ALDRED, A. H. (1967). Tree volumes from large-scale photos. *Photogramm. Engng* **33**, 69.

SCHUMACHER, F. X., and CHAPMAN, R. A. (1954). *Sampling Methods in Forestry and Range Management.* (Duke University Press: Durham, N.C.)

SEELY, H. E. (1962). The value of 70 mm air cameras for winter air photography. *Woodld Rev.* WR-218.

WEAR, J. F., POPE, R. B., and ORR, P. W. (1966). *Aerial photographic techniques for estimating damage by insects in western forests.* Pacific Northwest Forest and Range Experiment Station, U.S. Department of Agriculture Forest Service.

Remote Determination of Soil and Weather Variables

Carlton E. Molineux

Terrestrial Sciences Laboratory, Air Force Cambridge Research Laboratories, L. G. Hanscom Field Bedford, Massachusetts, U.S.A.

An automated sensing system is described which can obtain and telemeter data on soil moisture, soil strength, and local weather variables from a remote site to a monitoring headquarters. Moisture measurements are by electrical resistance or neutron meter sensors and soil strength is determined by response of a hydraulic-loaded penetrometer. Variables of wind, temperature, and rainfall are reported through digitized sensors. The system can be implanted at a site or deployed on a small, self-propelled tracked vehicle. A thermal generator maintains battery power for operations and telemetry is by teletype or radio link. On-call or programmed operation can be provided and the telemetered data are both printed out and punched on tape.

INTRODUCTION

The Air Force Cambridge Research Laboratories is one of the main research and development centers of the Office of Aerospace Research and conducts geophysical and environmental research in response to operational problems of the U.S. Air Force. The Terrestrial Sciences Laboratory of AFCRL conducts basic and applied research on the composition and properties of the land forms and materials of the earth's surface and develops instrumentation and interpretative techniques to determine their nature. One of our present responsibilities is to develop methods for remotely monitoring the conditions of selected natural terrain sites which might be affected by seasonal or climatic variations and hence might have varying trafficability situations for vehicle and aircraft operations.

SOIL PROPERTY CONSIDERATIONS

The main factor in trafficability determination of a suitably flat and smooth area is, obviously, soil strength. The strength is derived from interrelations of soil composition and moisture content. The latter in turn is dependent largely on precipitation, evaporation, and percolation, with subsurface lateral moisture movement of much lesser effect. Localized random slipperiness and stickiness of the surface is generally insignificant for modern vehicles or aircraft.

The problem of remote site evaluation thus becomes one of monitoring the strength and/or moisture content to the desired depth of a selected area, and the weather conditions which might add to or subtract from these variables. Any remote area monitoring system must be simple, portable, accurate, and reliable.

It must be protected from extreme temperatures of the environment, and be capable of operating on limited internal power with no human attention for extended periods of time after emplacement. It must have a means for obtaining its data either on call or on a programmed basis, and for transmitting these data to a central headquarters for immediate analysis or storage.

SOIL MOISTURE MEASUREMENTS

With the above considerations, a system was first developed in conjunction with the U.S. Army Engineer Waterways Experiment Station (WES) for the measurement and telemetry of soil moisture and weather variables at a remote site (Hanes and Womack 1965).

The system monitors wind direction, wind velocity, air temperature, and soil moisture and temperature, is battery operated, and records the data on a teletype machine located several miles away. Unique features of the system include extended range a.c. ohmmeter circuits for low moisture measurements, a loop charging circuit to maintain the battery in a charged condition, and teletype transmission of the data.

The system was designed around a teletype reporting weather station manufactured by Berkeley Instruments Corporation (BI), Oakland, California, consisting of a portable mast; digitizers for wind velocity, wind direction, and air temperature; and a control unit containing the logic and teletype conversation equipment as well as the battery. Measuring characteristics of the weather part of the system are:

Wind direction—0 to 360 degrees in 10 degree increments (measurement is in degrees east of north).

Wind velocity—0 to 99 miles per hour.

Air temperature—0 to 135 degrees Fahrenheit.

Wind direction measurement accuracy is $\pm5°$ and wind velocity $\pm2\%$ with printout resolution of 1 mile per hour. Air temperature accuracy is $\pm1\%$ with printout resolution of 1°F. If a BI rain gauge is incorporated into the system, reading from 0 to 10 in. of precipitation, its accuracy is $0\cdot01$ in. with equal printout resolution.

SYSTEM DETAILS

The soil moisture measuring circuit designed by WES consists of an especially designed a.c. ohmmeter with three overlapping measuring ranges. Also, soil temperature is measured by means of a thermistor located in each moisture unit. The measuring circuit is transistorized and ranges are automatically and remotely selected by logic circuits in the control unit. The moisture sensors used were the standard Colman fibreglas units. Measuring characteristics of the soil moisture–temperature part of the circuit are:

Soil temperature—25°F to 125°F.

Soil moisture—2% to 25%.

All currently available soil moisture sensors operating on the electrical resistance principle are particularly sensitive to soil type and soil temperature. Also, since it is necessary to use an a.c. ohmmeter to avoid polarization, cable reactance presents a limitation on the distance between a moisture unit and its measuring circuit. In this work, it was desired to measure in the low moisture content region even beyond the range of a conventional portable soil moisture bridge. Each moisture-measuring circuit was therefore mounted in a watertight aluminum box about 10 ft from the soil moisture sensor. The test installation consisted of two measuring locations each with two moisture sensors located at 3 in. and 6 in. depths. Four 500-ft cables were run from the measuring circuits to the control box located at the base of the weather station mast.

A microammeter (0–300μA) with optical digitizer is located in the control box and is used to read all moisture-measuring circuits. This digital micro-ammeter is constructed around a General Electric switchboard-type meter with 270° of pointer travel. The optical digitizer seeks a mirror on the pointer and gates out pulses to the control and logic circuits from a fixed zero reference until the pointer is found. The printed output from this part of the system consists of digits in the range of 00 to 99.

The moisture-measuring circuits are adjusted to give overlapping ranges by means of 1% resistance decade boxes. Resistance calibration was made for the three ranges of each measuring circuit. The thermistor is always read on the low resistance scale so that the first switching function changes the measuring circuit from the thermistor to the moisture unit. Additional switching functions switch the electronic circuitry to change the range in two successive steps. With three ranges for moisture, an appropriate reading will occur on one of the ranges over the moisture content range from 2% to 25%. From the typical readings obtained, it was determined that the numbers 00 and 99 are not to be considered as data. The digitizer construction is such that an overrange reading will produce a reading of 99. The intentional meter overranging does not damage the meter since the worst case is a 50% overload. To conserve power, the measuring circuits are energized for a period of about 2 seconds only when actually making measurements.

In order that a permanent record can be maintained without manual operations, a time accumulator was installed at the teletype machine location. The digital clock accumulates days (0 to 999) and hours (to nearest 0·1 hr) on a 24 hr basis. Commercial power is used to operate the digital clock and the teletype machine. In addition to page-printing the data, the teletype machine

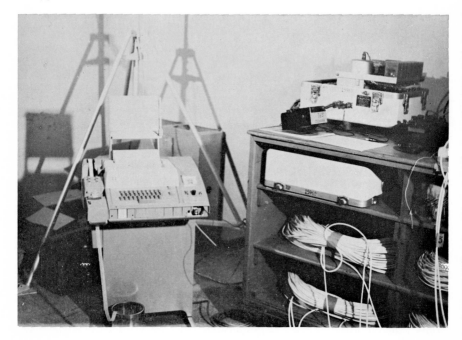

Fig. 1. Teletype receiving station for telemetered data.

stores the information in punched paper tape. This tape also has day and hour information so that computer operations can be performed on the data if desired. Additionally, the information can be retransmitted between conventional teletype machines. Figure 1 shows the soil moisture-weather sensors and receiving station equipment grouped to indicate their size and simplicity.

Each cell to be used in the field installation was individually calibrated in the laboratory. Soil samples obtained from the area where the cells were to be installed were processed to six different moisture contents ranging from approximately 2% to 22% by weight of dry soil. Plastic frozen food containers were used to contain the soil and moisture cells during calibration at soil temperatures from 40°F to 110°F, estimated to be the minimum and maximum values which would be encountered at the depths of installation. Twelve hours were allowed at each stage for stabilization prior to the calibration readings. Moisture calibration curves for any given temperature were thus developed and used for the four cells installed for test.

TEST AND APPLICATION

The soil-moisture and weather telemetry station was installed for preliminary field testing at Rogers Dry Lake, Edwards Air Force Base, California. The dry lake occupies about 30,000 acres and is composed chiefly of clays deposited during the Pleistocene age. Areas along the edge of the lake bed have accumulated appreciable quantities of windblown sand. Natural surface drainage of the surrounding area is toward the Dry Lake; however, most of the surface flow is absorbed, and it is only after heavy rains that surface drainage reaches the lake bed. This site was selected because of its frequent use for both planned and emergency aircraft operations and also its representation of many dry lake beds prevalent in arid regions throughout the world.

Even though situated in the northern Mojave Desert, the Edwards Air Force Base area is subject to distinct seasonal changes. The summers are hot and dry, the mean maximum temperature for the six summer months being 90°F. The mean low for the six winter months is 36°F. Record high is 112°F and record low is 9°F. The relative humidity ranges from 5% to 12% during the summer afternoons, and from 40% to 60% between midnight and dawn. The average annual precipitation is 4·3 in. The entire annual precipitation usually occurs during from one to six rainstorms each winter season. The measurable precipitation totals for each of these storms vary from 0·25 in. to more than 4 in. Winds vary from moderately high during the winter to a somewhat lesser velocity during summer afternoons.

The system recorded and telemetered data at this site for a period of $2\frac{1}{2}$ months satisfactorily. Figure 2 shows the system as installed at the test site. The telemetered data of wind direction, speed, and air temperature checked closely with that recorded at the Base Weather Station, indicating that the system is dependable and its data can be telemetered satisfactorily to a central location. A radio link could have been easily substituted for the teletype transmission to cover longer ranges.

The various sensors print out on the teletype in the format illustrated in Figure 3. There appear to be no difficulties in sequential sampling of the sensors nor in their page printout interpretation.

Fig. 2. Soil moisture and weather sensing station installed at the test site.

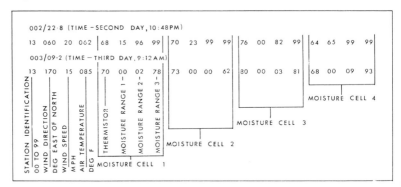

Fig. 3. Output format of printout of soil moisture and weather variables. Note: moisture range 1 is low resistance, high moisture content; moisture range 2 is medium resistance, medium moisture content; moisture range 3 is high resistance, low moisture content.

Moisture contents recorded by the four cells were generally reliable, with hourly differences between moisture contents of 0·2% to 0·5% in most of the readings. Erratic readings of moisture are generally attributable to erratic thermistor data, which bear directly on moisture determination. Erratic response of the moisture sensor may also be due to the alkalinity of the soil. As the moisture content of the soil increases, soluble salts are transported to the moisture sensor, thus changing the resistivity of the cell. Through a process of wetting and drying, it is possible that an accumulation of salts can be deposited.

It is again emphasized that all soil moisture sensors operating on the electrical resistance principle are sensitive to the chemical composition and temperature of the soil. They may thus become erratic over extended periods of wetting and drying. Therefore, to enhance the long-term operational capability, a commercial neutron soil moisture meter was obtained and added to the system during the final stages of the initial program. This sensor operated successfully over a several months later period and should be considered preferable in any future design of a soil moisture measurement system.

The Troxler neutron moisture meter was modified to reduce its maximum counting rate to about 25 per second. The counts were accumulated for several seconds, stacked in the unipulse function of the control unit, and read out on-call as a total of average counts per minute. The accuracy is estimated to be within 5% except for the extremely wet or dry ends of the moisture curve. The neutron meter obtains its output from a soil volume extending about 8 in. in diameter rather than a point source such as the fibreglas unit. It has advantages in needing no calibration for differing soil types, having an integrated output from a soil volume, and its insensitivity to salts or chemical action.

Cost[1] of the initial soil-weather variable measuring system is estimated at $12,000. The weather sensors are the BI TELADVISOR Digital Transducer costing about $400 each. The BI control unit costs about $2000 and their digital rain gauge suitable for incorporation into the system, if desired, sells for about $1000. The receiving teletype machine with page printer is available from the Teletype Corporation, Skokie, Illinois for about $800. Neutron soil moisture meters are commercially available from a number of manufacturers for approximately $5000.

SOIL STRENGTH CONSIDERATIONS

Since the relationship between soil moisture and soil strength varies with soil type and great inhomogenieties may exist in soil composition over any large area, it is often difficult to estimate with confidence the strength of a given site from moisture data alone. Lag times in strength response to wetting or drying are also variable, especially at the depths to which an aircraft or vehicle tire might penetrate. The necessity for having reliable families of curves for a variety of soil types to relate strength to moisture also handicaps the planner who may not have prior adequate knowledge of the area in which operations are required. In view of these factors, the most effective way of monitoring, forecasting, or estimating soil trafficability is to measure the soil strength directly.

The airfield cone penetrometer has been used by engineers for two decades to determine directly the shear strength or penetration resistance of a soil and its data are not dependent on soil chemical composition or temperatures. Direct correlation between cone penetrometer readings and other standard soil engineering strength units such as the California Bearing Ratio have also been established. Consideration was therefore given to the use of an automated power-operated cone penetrometer with provision for telemetry to transmit the force required and hence the resultant shear strength of the soil.

---

[1] Costs are given in U.S. currency.

SOIL STRENGTH MEASUREMENTS

The second system was also designed and fabricated for AFCRL by the Waterways Experiment Station and utilizes a small track-laying self-propelled vehicle, shown in Figure 4. Soil strength measurements are made by a hydraulic cylinder

Fig. 4. Track-lying vehicle for soil strength measurement system.

which forces the conical point of a penetrometer into the ground. A sliding collar stops at the surface of the ground, providing a reference for depth of penetration. At predetermined positions of the cone shaft relative to the collar, the hydraulic pressure in the cylinder is accurately measured by a TELADVISOR digital pressure gauge calibrated to read out in standard penetrometer force units. Measurements are made in up to 8 increments over a 2-ft depth at a constant penetration rate adjustable from 0·3 to 1·2 in. per second. The force data are telemetered and can be recorded as a X–Y plot of force versus depth at the receiving station. Four sets of penetration recordings will be made at each time in a programmed sequence. A control unit on the vehicle progams the operation of the penetrometer and movement of the vehicle. The measurement and reporting program can be initiated at regular intervals by a local clock or on demand from the central monitoring station. Provision is made at the central station to initiate another sequence if the data reported lie outside certain limits, as might be the case where a rock would be encountered.

Power for the entire system is provided by a propane-burning thermopile with 2 watts continuous output. Energy is stored in lead-acid or nickel-cadmium batteries maintained on charge by the propane generator. Temperature inside the generator is also telemetered to indicate proper operation. With the station on a programmed/on-call basis about 100 gallons of propane would be required for one year operation. Recent consideration has been for incorporation of a gross moisture sensor into the system to signal a change in soil moisture and trigger the strength measurement cycle. This feature will remove the need for soil strength measurements under conditions where no moisture change occurs or the site is not affected by rainfall, and therefore will conserve system power.

The track-laying vehicle provides for automatic leveling of its platform before initiation of a strength measurement cycle. It is guided with a cable attached to the center control mast installed in the ground, about which it revolves in a spiral interval pattern so as to have an undisturbed location for each penetrometer measurement. The cable also transmits the strength information to the control and telemetry station located at the base of the mast. The mast also holds the weather station equipment previously cited, the thermal generator and propane tank, and the telemetry system. If a radio link is used for the data transmission over large distances the mast would also provide for the antenna.

All equipment is housed in weather-tight enclosures and is designed for operation under extremes of environmental conditions. Weight and dimensions are such that the entire system can be readily transported by truck and set up at a remote site without special equipment. The receiving station at a central monitoring headquarters consists of a teletype page printer and tape punch together with manual/automatic programming and radio equipment or land line termination as appropriate. Development cost of the automated penetrometer and vehicle was $18,000. The 2-watt thermoelectric generator manufactured by Minnesota Mining and Manufacturing Corporation costs about $300.

CONCLUSIONS

The systems described above have satisfactorily demonstrated that such techniques can be used to determine and monitor the soil and weather conditions of remote areas. The components may require inspection and maintenance following initial installation but should be subsequently capable of long-term unattended operation. The telemetry of such information presents no problem; if telephone circuits are not available, radio can be used or a combined radio-telephone circuit system can be established. Although developed to gather information by which the trafficability of a remote site can be estimated, such a system can be used for monitoring of hydrologic conditions, subsurface drainage, watershed runoff, rainfall occurrence, or similar information required for land evaluation.

The intensity of sampling the soil moisture conditions would depend, naturally, on how frequently or by what magnitude the prevailing conditions would change. For the system test purposes, soil moisture readings were made twice daily (morning and evening) to establish any diurnal variations. For remote area evaluation purposes, unless rapid or large changes occur, a daily sampling should suffice to establish trends or gradients. As indicated previously, strength measurements need not be made unless significant weather changes occur, leading to the desirability of monitoring any subsequent effect on the remote area.

Satisfactory operation of the various sensors would be indicated by the consistency of their measurements as indicated at the central monitoring headquarters. Obvious discrepancies could be checked against available weather data for the remote site to verify their occurrence.

The majority of the sensors are commercially manufactured and have been used over many years in various meteorologic, hydrologic, and forestry data gathering systems.

REFERENCE

HANES, F. P., and WOMACK, L. M. (1965). *Telemetry of soil-moisture and weather variables.* U.S. Army Corps Engrs, Waterways Exp. Stn, Vicksburg, Miss. Micell. Paper No. 5–711.